GEOLOGICAL SURVEY
PAPER 80-10

THE COASTLINE
OF CANADA

Littoral processes and shore morphology

edited by
S.B. McCann

Proceedings of a conference held in
Halifax, Nova Scotia, May 1 - 3, 1978

1980

Scientific and Technical Editing

R.G. Blackadar
P.J. Griffin
Val Donnelly

Design and Layout

M.J. Kiel
L.A. Firth

Word Processing

C.M. Whittaker & Assoc. Ltd.
Judy Côté, GSC

FOREWORD

This volume is a record of papers presented at the conference on "The Coastline of Canada – Its Littoral Processes and Shore Morphology" held May 1-3, 1978 at Halifax, Nova Scotia. The conference, sponsored by the Geological Survey of Canada, and ably organized under the chairmanship of Brian McCann, presented the first review of the state of knowledge of the Canadian coastline. It was particularly timely because the need for a description and understanding of Canada's coasts and of the processes by which they were formed and that currently affect them is greater than ever before. Much of this increased need results from oil and gas developments in the frontier regions of the Canadian and Alaskan Arctic. We must be able to provide suitable remedial measures in case of oil spills, whose likelihood will increase with increased offshore drilling and tanker traffic; onshore landings of pipelines that will cross inter-island channels in the Arctic Islands and remain unaffected by ice scour must be properly designed and safely constructed; and the new harbours needed to stage frontier development will need careful planning.

Coastline knowledge is also essential for the more inhabited regions, for example, estuaries are favoured sites for our coastal cities and towns. In southern Canada, information concerning coastlines is needed for harbour design and maintenance, beach preservation for recreation and parks, planning of set-back allowances for construction of shoreline communities, evaluation of sand and gravel resources for constructional materials, environmental impact statements to assess the effects of proposed engineering developments, and for the dumping of wastes offshore. Quantitative data on the rates of coastal processes and of the amounts of materials moved are especially important for the design of engineering works and for countermeasures to remedy deleterious man-induced or natural events affecting the coastline.

Accordingly, as proposed a few years ago within the Geological Survey of Canada, one major task to be completed is the description and classification of the coastline of Canada. Stretches of coast will be cartographically represented by suitable symbols and explanatory legend according to a classification of coastal types. These will be the basis of an atlas and a national thematic map similar to other thematic compilations such as those of bedrock geology, glacial geology, and physiographic provinces for which Canada has an enviable reputation. The map and atlas will be accompanied by an appropriate description of the coastline and inferences about the processes by which it evolved.

The description of the coastline should not be regarded as a routine task but rather it should be undertaken creatively. If approached with this attitude, it will result in the generation of ideas to be tested and will permit the anticipation of problems and methods of study for the succeeding more detailed process studies. Such detailed studies, of course, are essential to explain the coastal evolution and predict future change.

AVANT-PROPOS

Cet ouvrage constitue un compte-rendu des documents présentés lors de la conférence sur le littoral du Canada, ses processus littoraux et la morphologie des côtes, qui a eu lieu du 1er au 3 mai 1978 à Halifax (Nouvelle-Écosse). Cette conférence, sous l'égide de la Commission géologique du Canada et très bien organisée par le président Brian McCann, a présenté le premier état des connaissances sur le littoral canadien. Le moment de cette conférence était particulièrement bien choisi parce que le besoin de décrire et de comprendre les côtes du Canada et les processus qui ont contribué à leur formation et qui les affectent aujourd'hui est plus grand que jamais. Une bonne partie de ce grand besoin provient de l'exploitation du pétrole et du gaz dans les régions pionnières de l'Arctique canadien et de l'Alaska. Nous devons être en position de remédier aux fuites de pétrole, qui risquent de plus en plus de se produire à mesure qu'augmentent les forages au large des côtes et la circulation des pétroliers; les points d'arrivée à terre des pipelines qui traverseront les chenaux entre les îles de l'Arctique et qui ne seront pas touchés par le décapage des glaces doivent être conçus convenablement et construit de manière sécuritaire; il faudra de plus planifier soigneusement les nouveaux havres nécessaires à l'exploitation des région pionnières.

Les connaissances du littoral sont également essentielles dans les régions habitées, par exemple, les estuaires constituent des endroits de prédilection pour les cités et les villes. Dans le sud du Canada, nous avons besoin de renseignements sur le littoral pour la conception et l'entretien des havres, sur la conservation des plages, pour les loisirs et les parcs, sur la planification de la création de marges en ce qui concerne la construction de collectivités en bordure des côtes, et sur l'évaluation des ressources en sable et en gravier pouvant servir de matériaux de construction, sur les répercussions environnementales, afin d'évaluer les effets des travaux de génie proposés et pour les déversements d'ordures au large des côtes. Les données quantitatives relatives au taux d'évolution des littoraux et aux quantités de matériaux déplacées sont particulièrement importantes pour la conception des travaux de génie et pour la prise de contre-mesures afin de remédier aux phénomènes nuisibles artificiels ou naturels qui touche le littoral.

C'est pourquoi, comme le proposait il y a plusieurs années la Commission géologique du Canada, la description et la classification des littoraux du Canada constitue une entreprise majeure devant être menée à bonne fin. Des bandes de côtes seront représentées cartographiquement au moyen de symboles convenables et de légendes explicatives selon la classification des types de littoraux. Ces symboles constitueront le fondement d'un atlas et d'une carte nationale thématique semblables aux autres ouvrages thématiques tels que ceux qui portent sur la géologie de la roche en place, de la géologie glaciaire et des provinces physiographiques qui ont créé une réputation enviable pour le Canada. La carte et l'atlas seront accompagnés de descriptions appropriées du littoral et d'hypothèses quant à leur évolution.

On ne devrait pas considérer la description du littoral comme une tâche ordinaire, mais on devrait plutôt l'effectuer d'une façon créative. De cette façon des idées naîtront qui devront être mises à l'épreuve et qui permettront d'anticiper les problèmes et les méthodes d'études relatives aux études plus détaillées qui ne manqueront pas d'être effectuées par la suite. De telles études, naturellement, sont essentielles pour expliquer l'évolution du littoral et en prédire les modifications futures.

A perceptive coastal description, therefore, will allow suitable areas to be selected for more detailed study and will permit the range, magnitude and priorities of problems to be tackled and the human and financial resources required to be established. Considering the magnitude of the task, in which only 3 per cent of the nearly 250 000 km of Canada's coastline has been investigated, it will clearly require the pooling of all Canada's coastal research resources.

This then raises questions concerning the state-of-the-art in coastal research and what kind of person should carry it out. The coastal zone involves the land-air-ocean interface and accordingly requires input by scientists from many disciplines. In fact, the "complete" coastal scientist would have to be part physicist, part engineer, part sedimentologist, part geomorphologist with a good knowledge of Quaternary events and biology thrown in. Consequently, future coastal workers will require a broadly based background.

Several groups of "incomplete" coastal scientists have made significant advances over the last 10 to 15 years in the study of the nearshore currents, longshore transport of sediment, and of coastal sedimentology in general. Important basic problems, however, remain to be solved both at the theoretical and empirical levels. Water motion due to waves taxes the theoreticians and likewise the empiricists who wish to monitor it. Its effect in moving and arranging coastal sediments is critical in studies of erosion and deposition of contemporary shoreline development as well as in the interpretation of ancient sediments. For example, much of the work on barrier islands in the United States was done to provide modern analogs of ancient shelf and nearshore sandy facies and to demonstrate their relationship to hydrocarbon reservoirs in "shoestring sands".

Even though scientists recognize that the coastal zone is a fertile area for research and one of growing concern to society, information on the coastal zone is not easily attained. From a physical and logistical standpoint it is a difficult zone in which to work as it involves shallow, turbulent water that is highly dynamic and continually changing. Furthermore, as routine deep-water technology and ships are not suitable in the coastal zone, specialized equipment such as amphibious vehicles, divers to take cores and samples, and installation of a new generation of current meters with a rapid response time are required. Finally, studies of Canadian coasts must commonly deal with ice-covered and ice-infested waters.

Ainsi, les descriptions attentives du littoral permettront d'étudier plus en détail certaines zones et permettront également d'aborder la question de la portée, de la grandeur et des priorités des problèmes et d'établir les ressources humaines et financières requises. Compte tenu de l'ampleur de la tâche, c'est-à-dire que seulement 3% des 250 000 km de côtes du Canada ont fait l'objet d'études, ce travail nécessitera clairement la mise en commun de toutes les ressources de recherches côtières du Canada.

Cela soulève des questions relatives à l'état présent de la recherche sur le littoral et sur le type de personne qui devrait l'effectuer. La zone côtière comprend le point de rencontre terre-air-océan et c'est pourquoi cette étude fait appel à des scientifiques de plusieurs disciplines. En fait, le spécialiste du littoral global devrait être en partie physicien, en partie ingénieur, en partie sédimentologue, en partie géomorphologue et posséder une bonne connaissance des évènements du Quaternaire et de la biologie. En conséquence les futurs travailleurs du littoral devront posséder des connaissances très vastes.

Plusieurs groupes de spécialistes du littoral ont effectuée des progrès importants au cours des 10 à 15 dernières années dans l'étude des courants près des côtes, des déplacements des sédiments le long des côtes et de la sédimentologie côtière en général. Il reste cependant à résoudre d'importants problèmes fondamentaux tant au niveau théorique qu'au niveau empirique. Le mouvement de l'eau dû aux vagues met les théoriciens à l'épreuve ainsi que les praticiens qui souhaitent en faire l'étude. Les effets des mouvements de l'eau sur les déplacements et l'organisation des sédiments côtiers sont très importants dans les études portant sur l'érosion et le dépôt littoral contemporain de même que pour l'interprétation des anciens sédiments. Par exemple, une bonne partie des travaux sur les îles de corail aux États-Unis a été effectuée afin de trouver des correspondances modernes aux anciens faciès sablonneux du plateau continental ou en bordure des côtes et de démontrer leurs rapports avec les réservoirs d'hydrocarbures situés dans les "cordons sableux".

Même si les scientifiques admettent que la zone côtière est un domaine fertile de recherche et une région qui préoccupe de plus en plus la société, il n'est pas nécéssairement facile d'obtenir des informations sur cette zone. D'un point de vue physique et logistique, c'est une zone difficile où les eaux peu profondes et turbulentes constituent une zone hautement dynamique et en modification constante. De plus, étant donné que ni la technique ni les navires d'études en eaux profondes ne conviennent généralement aux études de la zone côtière, il faut disposer d'équipement spécialisé tel que véhicules amphibies, l'utilisation de plongeurs pour retirer des carottes et des échantillons et l'installation d'une nouvelle série d'appareils de mesure des courants, à réaction rapide. Finalement, les études du littoral canadien doivent généralement s'effectuer dans des eaux couvertes ou infestées de glace.

A start on a description of the coastline of Canada has already been made. Already described and classified are: much of the sandy shore of the Gulf of St. Lawrence, Bay of Fundy, part of the Atlantic Coast of Nova Scotia, parts of the Arctic Islands, the northern Yukon coast, Mackenzie and Fraser deltas, and the shores of Lake Ontario and Lake Erie. Nevertheless, it remains a gigantic task to physically describe and classify the rest of the coastline – a task that also has a significant intellectual challenge to deal with the wide variety of environmental conditions that influence the nature of the Canadian coastline. These include a variety of sediment types and sources governed, in many cases, by the elevation of formerly submerged coasts and locally, as in Nova Scotia, by recently submerged coastlines. The Canadian coastline is subject to tidal ranges that are the highest in the world in the Bay of Fundy and Hudson Strait, very low in the Western Arctic, and nil in the Great Lakes. The coastline is exposed also to a range of wave energies which are particularly frequent and intense on the Pacific Coast, infrequent in our numerous enclosed seas and estuaries, and virtually absent from the ice-bound polar coasts. It is noteworthy that ice has played an important role in coastal processes and on the morphology of the beach and nearshore zones on all parts of Canada's coasts except in Western Canada. Finally, all the coasts have undergone a common series of events related to the direct and indirect effects of the Wisconsin glaciation, in particular the isostatic recovery that followed the retreat of the ice.

Although attention has been drawn to the importance of coastline description, Canadian coastal studies must also have a strong component of process-oriented studies, which, building on the environmental description of the coastline, focus on mechanisms and patterns of sediment transport. Some areas of emphasis include:

- the rates of coastal erosion, sediment transport and deposition along characteristic stretches of coast (coastal zonals), each representing distinct coastal process-oriented regimes;
- the relationship of onshore-offshore sediment motion to that in the longshore domain to assess the sediment balance between the shore zone and inner shelf;
- sediment budget of some typical estuary mouths and adjacent shelf systems;
- sediment rates and patterns of accumulation and erosion on the Continental Shelf;
- process-oriented studies of coasts featured by rocky cliffs, characteristic of at least half the Canadian coastline; and
- continuing study of the widespread role of ice.

Although analogous shores have been studied elsewhere in the world, it is fair to say that good Canadian studies have provided new perceptions on coastal processes and not just added descriptive knowledge. New insights have been provided on the formation and change of bed forms in sand bars the in Bay of Fundy and a novel approach has been taken to sediment budgets in Minas Basin. Perceptive

Des travaux préliminaires de description du littoral du Canada ont déjà été effectués. Une bonne partie des rives sablonneuses du golfe du Saint-Laurent et de la baie de Fundy, certaines parties du littoral de l'Atlantique et de la Nouvelle-Écosse, certaines parties des îles de l'Arctique, du littoral nord du Yukon, les deltas du McKenzie et du Fraser de même que les rives du lac Ontario et du lac Érié ont déjà été décrits et classifiés. Néanmoins, la description physique et la classification du reste des autres littoraux n'en demeure pas moins une tâche gigantesque et qui présente également des défis intellectuels importants en ce qu'il s'agit de traiter d'une très grande variété de conditions environnementales qui influencent la nature du littoral canadien. Celles-ci comprennent un assortiment de types de sédiments et de sources régies, dans plusieurs cas, par l'élévation de côtes autrefois submergées et localement, comme en Nouvelle-Écosse, par des côtes récemment submergées. Le littoral canadien connaît des marnages parmi les plus importants du monde dans la baie de Fundy et dans le détroit d'Hudson, et très bas dans l'Arctique de l'Ouest et inexistants dans les Grands Lacs. De plus, le littoral est exposé à une gamme d'énergies provenant des vagues, particulièrement fréquentes et intenses sur la côte du Pacifique, moins fréquentes dans nos nombreuses mers intérieures et estuaires et presque absentes sur les côtes polaires prises par les glaces. Il est à remarquer que la glace a joué un rôle important dans les processus littoraux et sur la morphologie des plages et des zones près du rivage dans toutes les parties du littoral canadien sauf dans l'Ouest. Enfin, toutes les côtes ont eu à subir les répercussions d'une série d'événements se rapportant aux effets directs et indirects de la période glaciaire du Wisconsin, en particulier la récupération isostatique qui a suivi le retrait des glaces.

Quoiqu'on ait attiré l'attention sur l'importance de la description du littoral, les études canadiennes sur le littoral doivent également porter en grande partie sur des études axées sur les phénomènes qui portent surtout sur les mécanismes et les modes de transport des sédiments, à partir de descriptions environnementales du littoral. On remarque parmi les domaines les plus importants:

- le rythme de l'érosion du littoral, du transport et du dépôt des sédiments, sur certaines parties caractéristiques de la côte (zone côtière), dont chacune représente des régimes distincts axés sur les phénomènes;
- le rapport entre les mouvements des sédiments en bordure et au large des côtes et le domaine du littoral afin d'évaluer l'équilibre des sédiments entre la zone littorale et le plateau continental côtier
- le bilan de sédimentation de certaines bouches d'estuaires typiques et des systèmes adjacents du plateau continental;
- le taux et les modalités de sédimentation de l'accumulation et de l'érosion du plateau continental;
- les études axées sur les phénomènes des côtes constituées de falaises rocheuses, caractéristiques d'au moins la moitié du littoral canadien; et
- l'étude constante du rôle très important de la glace.

Quoique des littoraux analogues aient fait l'objet d'études ailleurs dans le monde, il est juste de dire que de bonnes études canadiennes ont donné lieu à de nouveaux points de vue sur les processus côtiers et n'ont pas fait qu'ajouter des connaissances descriptives. De nouveaux points de vue ont été obtenus sur la formation et la modification des lits des bancs de sable dans la baie de Fundy

reconnaissance studies in the Arctic Islands have recognized the variable roles of permafrost, widespread cover of sea ice and the degree of wave action dependent on availability of large areas of open waters. Canada's two principal deltas, Mackenzie and Fraser, its Arctic shores and its barrier islands, are sufficiently different from other world analogs to provide additional information for the development of general models of shoreline development. A textbook, written 5 or 10 years from now, should include reference to, and discussion of, Canadian work on these topics, and also on macrotidal sediment dynamics of the Bay of Fundy system.

If coastal research in Canada continues to provide perceptive descriptions of shore morphology and well conceived process studies, which do not neglect rates and budgets, then good science will be done as well as providing information essential to planners and engineers concerned with what might be called "coastal husbandry". This is a large task. However, as a member of the Geological Survey of Canada concerned with the national interest, I am equally concerned that the task be done. As stated earlier, the pooled talents of coastal researchers from government, university and industry are required to make significant progress. In the years ahead, although the number of coastal researchers may increase, it will likely still be a relatively small "band of brothers" that will carry the load. I am sure that coastal researchers will respond to the challenge of describing and understanding our coastline by "putting on the map", literally and figuratively, a heretofore neglected area of Canadian research.

et on a utilisé une nouvelle méthode pour établir le bilan de sédimentation dans le bassin Minas. Des études approfondies de reconnaissance effectuées dans les îles de l'Arctique ont reconnu les rôles variables du pergélisol, de la couverture étendue des eaux par la glace et du degré de mouvement des vagues selon la présence de vastes zones d'eau libre. Les deux principaux deltas du Canada, soit celui du Mackenzie et du Fraser, le littoral arctique et celui des îles barrières s'y attachant sont suffisamment différents de modelés analogues dans le monde et ainsi donnent des informations additionnelles pour l'élaboration de modèles généraux de formation du littoral. Un manuel écrit d'ici 5 ou 10 ans devrait faire référence aux travaux canadiens sur ces sujets, il devrait en discuter et porter sur la dynamique des sédiments macrotidaux du système de la baie de Fundy.

Si la recherche sur le littoral au Canada continue à fournir des descriptions rigoureuses de la morphologie du rivage et des études de procédés bien conçues qui ne négligent pas les taux et les bilans, alors de bons travaux scientifiques seront effectués et des informations essentielles seront à la disposition des planificateurs et des ingénieurs qui se préoccupent de ce qu'on peut appeler "la gestion du littoral". Il s'agit là d'une tâche d'envergure. Toutefois, à titre de membre de la Commission géologique du Canada, je me préoccupe de l'intérêt national et aussi de la tâche qui reste à accomplir. Comme je l'ai dit plus haut, les talents commun des chercheurs dans le domaine du littoral qu'ils soient à l'emploi des gouvernements, des universités ou de l'industrie, doivent accomplir des progrès importants. Dans les années à venir, quoique le nombre de chercheurs puisse augmenter, il constituera probablement toujours un groupe relativement restreint pour porter le fardeau. Je suis sûr que ces chercheurs pourront relever le défi de décrire et de comprendre notre littoral en "mettant sur la carte" au propre et au figuré, un domaine jusqu'ici négligé de la recherche canadienne.

J.O. Wheeler
Deputy Director General
Geological Survey of Canada

April 6, 1979

Le directeur général adjoint
Commission géologique du Canada
J.O. Wheeler

6 avril 1979

Contents

INTRODUCTION

The coastline of Canada fronts on three oceans – the North Atlantic, the Arctic and the North Pacific – and includes also the northern shorelines of four of the five Great Lakes. It extends over 40° of latitude and covers a wide range of oceanographic environments and geologic provinces. Not surprisingly, therefore, most major shoreline types, except those associated with subtropical or tropical climates such as coral or mangrove, are present somewhere around the coastline of Canada. Until recently there had been few scientific and technical studies of this long and varied coastline and our knowledge of the physical characteristics and processes of the coast was very limited. In the last five to ten years, however, there has been a phase of active research by a small but diverse group of scientists, from a number of disciplines, working at different institutions across the country.

The Coastline of Canada Conference, which was the first national meeting to focus attention on the landforms, sediments and processes of the coastal zone in Canada, succeeded in bringing together most of the people undertaking research in this area, and many others with a related interest in coastal zone management and planning. The papers in this volume, with one exception, were presented at the conference, and, together, cover some aspects, at least, of each of the four coasts of Canada – Atlantic, Pacific, Northern and Great Lakes. Some of the papers are very specific, either by topic or geographic location, others provide a regional view of coastal characteristics. They are arranged here on a regional basis, with the exception of two, more general papers, which are presented first. The disparity in the number of papers in each regional section, and the differences in the types of study reported for each region, are fair reflections of the disparity in research effort on the different coasts. Half of the papers in the volume deal with the Atlantic coast, south of Labrador, where two contrasting environments have received considerable attention in the last ten years, namely, the microtidal barrier shorelines of the southern Gulf of St. Lawrence and the macrotidal sedimentary regime of the Minas Basin, Bay of Fundy. These two particular environments are the concern of six and four papers, respectively, within the Atlantic coast section. There are seven papers on northern coasts, of which five are reconnaissance descriptions of coastal segments about which very little, if anything, has been written previously. The northern coasts extend as far south as 52°N in southern James Bay and southern Labrador. Generally, sea ice is present for six months and more each year, but there is a wide range of tidal and wave energy environments. The two papers on the Pacific coast are both reviews, the first providing a very thoroughly documented introduction to the coast as a whole, and the second a commentary on some aspects of sedimentation on the Fraser Delta. The four papers on the Great Lakes each cover a different topic and together provide a good indication of the shoreline types present, and the problems encountered.

INTRODUCTION

La zone littorale du Canada donne sur trois océans, soit l'Atlantique nord, l'Arctique et le Pacifique nord, et inclut les littoraux nord de quatre des cinq Grands Lacs. Elle s'étend sur plus de 40° de latitude et comprend une grande variété de milieux océanographiques et de provinces géologiques. Il n'est donc pas étonnant que les principaux types de littoraux, exception faite de ceux associés aux climats tropicaux et subtropicaux tels les coraux et les mangroves, soient représentés au Canada. Jusqu'à tout récemment, peu d'études scientifiques et techniques avaient été faites sur ce littoral long et diversifié. Nos connaissances des phénomènes et des processus physiques de la côte canadienne étaient donc très limitées. Cependant, au cours des cinq ou dix dernières années, un petit groupe de chercheurs versés dans des disciplines différentes ont entrepris des recherches actives dans diverses institutions à travers le pays.

La Conférence sur le littoral canadien, première réunion nationale sur le relief, les sédiments et les processus physiques de la zone côtière du Canada, a permis de réunir la majorité des chercheurs dans ces domaines de même que plusieurs autres personnes intéressées à la gestion et à l'aménagement de la zone littorale. Tous les documents qui composent cet ouvrage, sauf un, ont été présentés à la conférence et traitent ensemble d'au moins quelques aspects de chacune des zones littorales du Canada, soit celles de l'Atlantique, du Pacifique, de l'Arctique et des Grands Lacs. Certains de ces documents abordent expressément un sujet ou un emplacement géographique déterminé, tandis que d'autres donnent une vision régionale des caractéristiques côtières. Dans ce volume, ils sont classés par région, à l'exception de deux documents plus généraux qui sont présentés au début. La différence entre chaque région quant au nombre de documents et la diversité des études propres à chaque région démontrent bien la disparité des recherches effectuées sur les différentes zones côtières. La moitié traitent du littoral atlantique, au sud du Labrador, où, au cours des six dernières années, deux milieux totalement différents, notamment les barrières microtidales du littoral sud du golfe Saint-Laurent et le régime de sédimentation macrotidal du bassin Minas, dans la baie de Fundy, ont été amplement étudiés. Ces mêmes milieux font respectivement l'objet de six et de quatre articles dans la section de la zone de l'Atlantique. La zone de l'Arctique est étudiée dans sept articles, dont cinq descriptions de reconnaissance de segments côtiers sur lesquels il n'existait jusqu'ici que peu ou pas de documentation. Le littoral arctique s'étend jusqu'au 52° de latitude nord dans le sud de la baie James et du Labrador. En général, des glaces de mer le recouvrent six mois par année ou plus, mais il s'y trouve une grande variété de milieux propices à l'énergie de la marée et des vagues. Les deux études sur la zone du Pacifique sont l'une, une introduction très bien documentée sur l'ensemble de la zone littorale et l'autre, un exposé sur quelques aspects de la sédimentation du delta du Fraser. Les quatre documents sur les Grands Lacs traitent chacun d'un sujet différent et donnent, ensemble, une bonne indication sur les types de littoral présents dans cette zone et des problèmes rencontrés.

In editing the volume, I was conscious of the wide range of approaches and different levels of scientific endeavour represented by the papers. However, this did not concern me unduly, as my intention from the outset was to assemble a comprehensive collection of papers which would indicate the state of knowledge about, and the sophistication of our approaches to the study of, the Canadian coastline, at this time. I included, after taking the advice of a number of critical readers, all the papers that were submitted, though several were considerably revised. This policy, and the fact that the Geological Survey's sponsorship of the conference extended to the publication of the proceedings in the present format, has meant that several longer papers could be included and that authors could include good illustrations and in some cases extended bibliographies.

It would be remiss to conclude this short introduction without acknowledging the advice, help and encouragement of the following people. In planning the conference I was fortunate to be able to draw on the advice of a program committee consisting of C.F.M. Lewis Geological Survey of Canada, G.V. Middleton (Department of Geology, McMaster University) and N.A. Rukavina (Hydraulics Research Division, Canada Centre for Inland Waters), and in the day to day organization of the meeting, I had the ready assistance of my former colleagues of the coastal geodynamics group at the Atlantic Geoscience Centre. The positive response of my more senior colleagues at the Centre, B.D. Loncarevic and D.E. Buckley, in the fall of 1976, when I proposed that the Survey sponsor a coastal conference, was an important factor in encouraging me to proceed. Subsequently, I have received encouragement from J.O. Wheeler and editorial advice from R.G. Blackadar.

En préparant cet ouvrage, je savais que ces documents exprimaient une grande diversité de points de vue et représentaient différents niveaux d'efforts scientifiques. Cependant, cela ne m'inquiètait pas outre mesure, car mon but était de rassembler une collection complète de documents qui feraient le bilan de nos connaissances et démontreraient le degré de perfectionnement que nous avons atteint dans l'étude du littoral canadien. Sur les conseils d'un bon nombre de réviseurs, j'ai inclu tous les documents qui ont été présentés, bien que plusieurs aient été largement révisés. Cette façon de procéder et le fait qu'en plus de la conférence, la Commission géologique a aussi subventionné la publication des délibérations dans le format actuel, ont permis d'inclure plusieurs documents plus longs. De plus, les auteurs ont pu ajouter de bonnes illustrations et, dans certains cas, des bibliographies détaillées.

Je ne peux conclure cette courte introduction sans remercier les personnes suivantes de leur encouragement et de leurs conseils. En ce qui a trait à la planification de la conférence, j'ai pu compter sur les conseils du comité des programmes formé de C.F.M. Lewis (Commission géologique du Canada), de G.V. Middleton (Département de géologie, université McMaster), et de N.A. Rukavina (Division de la recherche en hydraulique, Centre canadien des eaux intérieures). Mes anciens collègues du Groupe de la géodynamique du Centre géoscientifique de l'Atlantique m'ont beaucoup aidé dans l'organisation au jour le jour des réunions. L'encouragement des collègues plus anciens du Centre, B.D. Loncarevic et D.E. Buckley, lorsqu'à l'automne 1976, j'ai proposé que la Commission géologique subventionne la conférence, m'a fortement incité à aller de l'avant. Par la suite, je voudrais aussi remercier J.O. Wheeler qui m'a accordé son appui et R.G. Blackadar ses conseils pour la mise au point finale.

S.B. McCann

SIMPLE MODELS OF NEARSHORE SEDIMENTATION; BEACH PROFILES AND LONGSHORE BARS

A.J. Bowen

Department of Oceanography, Dalhousie University, Halifax, Nova Scotia

Bowen, A.J., Simple models of nearshore sedimentation; beach profiles and longshore bars; in The Coastline of Canada, S.B. McCann, editor; Geological Survey of Canada, Paper 80-10, p. 1-11, 1980.

Abstract

Starting from a basic model of sediment transport, an expression for on/offshore movement of sediment on a beach is developed. Equilibrium profiles are determined by requiring that the time-averaged transport is zero everywhere on the profile. The results obtained from this particular model are in much better, general agreement with field observations than is the classical, null-point theory. The formation of longshore bars, due either to the reflection of incoming waves or the existence of low frequency, standing waves, is found to be an explicit prediction of the model.

Résumé

Les auteurs se sont appuyés sur un modèle élémentaire de transport des sédiments en suspension pour formuler une expression du mouvement de va-et-vient littoral des matériaux sur une plage. Des profils d'équilibre ont été déterminés en supposant que la durée moyenne du transport est nulle à tout endroit le long du profil. Les résultats obtenus à partir de ce modèle particulier correspondent, dans l'ensemble, de beaucoup plus près aux observations sur le terrain que la théorie classique du point nul. La formation de cordons littoraux, due soit à la réflexion des vagues déferlantes ou à l'existence de vagues stationnaires et à basse fréquence est considérée comme une prédiction explicite du modèle.

INTRODUCTION

Any understanding of the relationship between the incident waves and the topography of a beach is greatly complicated by the beach being rarely, if ever, in equilibrium with the existing wave field. The morphology depends on some complex integral of past wave conditions, an integral apparently heavily weighted towards periods of high waves. In principle, one can approach the problem of monitoring the beach topography as a function of the changing wave climate (for example, Shepard and LaFond (1940), Shepard (1950), Bascom (1954) and many, more recent studies); this approach has indeed led to some new insights, some phenomenology and new problems, but not generally to the development of new, quantitative theories. The real situation is perhaps too complex for parameters to be developed without some guidance as to the relative importance of various possible processes.

Simple theoretical models are particularly useful in defining these possibilities. However, as the models are generally idealized to some very simple, equilibrium situation, their relevance to the real world is certainly questionable. In this context, it is very unfortunate that the most widely quoted, simple model, the null-point hypothesis for beach equilibrium due originally to Cornaglia, provides theoretical predictions seriously at odds with reality. The null-point concept as developed by Ippen and Eagleson (1955) and Eagleson and Dean (1961) suggests that if a sediment sample with a wide distribution of grain sizes is placed on the seabed seaward of the surf zone, only one grain size can be a null-point position; coarser material should move offshore, finer onshore. However, field observations using marked sand of different sizes (Zenkovitch, 1946; Murray, 1967) generally show the coarsest particles moving onshore and the fine ones moving offshore.

Despite this direct conflict with field measurements, the null-point hypothesis is still a central point of discussion in any paper on beach equilibrium. Perhaps this illustrates most strongly the need to express ideas in terms of a simple model. The null-point may require very convoluted discussion, but a doubtful model is clearly preferable to no model.

The purpose of the present paper is to develop a consistent model for onshore-offshore sediment transport under the influence of waves, currents and gravity. One of the end products is a new null-point model much more in line with actual observations. This model is, however, neither unique nor necessarily correct. The most important aspect of the present approach is the rigorous development of a theory, starting from any given model of sediment transport.

The first step is to look at the general concepts involved in applying any sediment transport model to a wave-dominated environment. Interest is then centred on the particular model of Bagnold (1963, 1966), which is used to illustrate the development of an expression for onshore-offshore transport. As for the classical null-point model, equilibrium profiles can be determined by insisting that the net transport, the transport averaged over wave periods, should be zero everywhere. The resulting equilibrium between the beach and the incoming waves may be perturbed by the existence of further wave modes. The effect of the standing waves formed by the reflection of the incoming waves and low-frequency waves in the surf beat range is of particular interest. Bars may tend to form in either case, but bars associated with the frequencies of normal incoming waves tend to be rather small in shallow water, of the order of tens of metres in wave length. Large-scale sedimentary features, with wave lengths of hundreds of metres, appear to be associated with low-frequency wave activity (Bowen and Inman, 1971; Short, 1975).

THE TRANSPORT MODEL

If a beach were exposed to waves having an exactly symmetrical, orbital velocity, all the sediment would slide down the slope and out to sea. The existence of the beach depends on small departures from symmetry in the velocity field balancing this tendency for gravity to move material offshore. A primary requirement for an adequate model of sediment transport is therefore the explicit inclusion of the gravitational effect of a sloping bed. An empirical or semiempirical model developed for transport over a flat bed can not be simply adapted by the addition of a gravitational term; it is usually not possible to assess how gravity will modify the formulation (Madsen and Grant, 1977). Given a reasonable representation of the effects of bottom slope, the adequacy of any transport model may be assessed by how well a rigorous application of the theory to the nearshore environment reproduces the expected behaviour of the system.

Clearly it is desirable to minimize the number of assumptions that must be introduced after the basic transport model is specified. The development of the theory assumes as a basic hypothesis that orbital velocity of the incoming waves is the dominant motion. The velocity u consists of two components, the symmetrical orbital velocity U_0 and a perturbation U_1 where

$$u = U_0 + U_1, \quad U_0 \gg U_1 \quad \text{generally} \tag{1}$$

To illustrate the development of a theoretical model for onshore-offshore transport from a basic sediment transport model, the equations suggested by Bagnold (1963, 1966) will be used. These contain many of the fundamental requirements of such a model, particularly the explicit inclusion of terms due to gravity. In this model, the possibility of autosuspension (Bagnold, 1962) or avalanching provides a much more complete description of possible physical processes than most of the alternatives.

If u is defined as positive seawards, the direction of x positive, then the results derived by Bagnold are:

for suspended transport i_s on a slope β

$$i_s = \frac{\varepsilon_s \cdot C_D \cdot \rho u^3 \, |u|}{w - u \cdot \beta} \tag{2}$$

and for bed load transport i_b

$$i_b = \frac{\varepsilon_b \cdot C_D \cdot \rho \cdot u^3}{\tan\phi - u \cdot \beta / |u|} \tag{3}$$

where ε_s, ε_b are efficiencies, C_D is the drag coefficient, ρ the water density, w the settling velocity and $\tan\phi$ the friction angle of the sediment. The modulus signs are necessary to properly account for the direction of transport in terms of velocity and slope. For seaward transport, u positive, the denominators in Equations 2 and 3 are reduced; material is therefore transported more easily downslope. In addition there are limits as:

$$\beta \to \tan\phi \qquad \text{giving avalanching or slumping}$$
$$\text{and } \beta \to w/u \qquad \text{the autosuspension condition}$$

Although Equations 2 and 3 do contain many of the essential qualities needed for an adequate model, and although Bagnold's approach has been applied fairly successfully in a much wider variety of sedimentological problems than any alternative model, a more complete model may be necessary to produce useful, quantitative predictions of onshore-offshore transport.

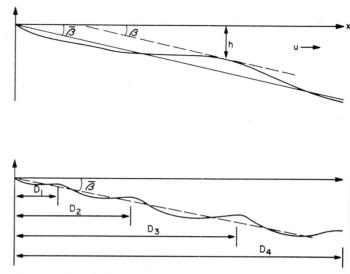

Figure 1.1. *Definition diagram for the nearshore region.*

There are at least two obvious problems. First, and perhaps most serious, the transport in this model depends only on the immediate flow conditions, adjusting instantaneously to changes without any time lag. Second, the theory applies to fully developed flow and does not describe initiation of movement; it does not apply to large particles that may move only intermittently at peak flows.

However, one of the purposes of this procedure is to investigate the adequacy of the model as originally formulated, and if possible to identify areas in which improvement is clearly required.

To expand Equations 2 and 3 using Equation 1, one needs the general result that, if U_0 is very much larger than U_1,

$$u^n |u| = U_0^n |U_0| + (n+1) U_1 U_0^{n-1} |U_0| + \tag{4}$$
$$\frac{n(n+1)}{2} U_1^2 U_0^{n-2} |U_0| + \ldots$$

In practice, U_0 is the wave orbital velocity

$$U_0 = u_0 \cos \sigma t$$

which vanishes during the orbital cycle, and the assumption that U_1 is small compared to U_0 can not really be satisfied. The approximation is really that $U_1 \ll u_0$, the maximum orbital velocity, and that the significant periods for transport are when U_0 is large. This is probably a reasonable assumption as the transport goes as the third or fourth power of the total velocity; however the validity of the approximation can be checked numerically for specific examples, if required.

The perturbation U_1 can take many forms. The cases of particular interest are:

(i) $U_1 = u_1$, a constant, a steady current;
(ii) $U_1 = u_m \cos (m\sigma t + \theta_m)$, the velocity field associated with a higher harmonic of the incoming wave, $m = 2,3,4 \ldots$; and
(iii) $U_1 = u_t \cos \sigma_t t$, a perturbation due to a wave with frequency σ_t unrelated to σ.

It is convenient to keep the algebra fairly simple at first by looking at the development of a model for the suspended load alone.

SUSPENDED LOAD

From Equation 2, the suspended load transport can be expressed as

$$i_s = \frac{\varepsilon_s \cdot C_D \cdot \rho}{w} \cdot u^3 |u| \cdot [1 - \gamma u]^{-1}, \quad \gamma = \frac{\beta}{w} \tag{5}$$

where $\gamma u < 1$ for normal transport. If $\gamma u \to 1$ autosuspension effects totally dominate the transport. The possibility of autosuspension, one of the key predictions of this particular transport model, is an obvious target for critical observations and experiments.

Expanding Equation 5, substituting Equation 1 and taking a time average (denoted by an overbar), the net transport over a number of wave periods is

$$\overline{i}_s = \frac{\varepsilon_s \cdot C_D \cdot \rho}{w} \left[\overline{U_0^3 |U_0|} + \overline{4U_1 U_0^2 |U_0|} + \overline{6U_1^2 U_0 |U_0|} + \right.$$

$$\overline{4U_1^3 |U_0|} + \gamma \left(\overline{U_0^4 |U_0|} + \overline{5U_1 U_0^3 |U_0|} + \cdots \right) +$$

$$\gamma^2 \left(\overline{U_0^5 |U_0|} + \overline{6U_1 U_0^4 |U_0|} + \cdots \right) +$$

$$\left. \gamma^3 \left(\overline{U_0^6 |U_0|} + \cdots \right) \right] \tag{6}$$

Terms of the form $U_0^n |U_0|$ vanish if n is odd when U_0 is oscillatory. The first three of the remaining terms describe the transport, onshore or offshore, due to a perturbation in the flow field U_1. All the other terms involve the slope β and are generally positive, representing the tendency for downslope transport; the sum of this expansion in γU_0 must become infinitely large when $\gamma U_0 \to 1$. The transport relations for various forms of U_1 can now be investigated by substituting for U_1 in Equation 6 and taking the appropriate time averages. Three examples follow.

1. $U_0 = u_0 \cos \sigma t$, $U_1 = u_1$ *a constant in time*

$$\overline{i}_s = \frac{\varepsilon_s \cdot C_D \cdot \rho}{w} \left[\frac{16}{3\pi} \cdot u_1 u_0 + \frac{8}{\pi} u_1^3 u_0 + \right.$$

$$\frac{16}{15\pi} \gamma u_0^5 \left(1 + \frac{25}{2} \left(\frac{u_1}{u_0} \right)^2 + \cdots \right) +$$

$$\left. \frac{32}{3\pi} \gamma^2 u_1 u_0^5 + \frac{32}{35\pi} \gamma^3 u_0^7 + \cdots \right] \tag{7}$$

This expansion involves the two small quantities u_1/u_0 and γu_0. Therefore, to first order,

$$\overline{i}_s = \frac{\varepsilon_s \cdot C_D \cdot \rho}{w} \left[\frac{16}{3\pi} \cdot u_1 u_0^3 + \gamma u_0^5 \cdot \frac{16}{15\pi} \right] \tag{8}$$

where the neglected terms are of size $(u_1/u_0)^2$, $(\gamma u_0)^2$ or γu_1 square terms in these small parameters. Equation 8 is a general result for any distribution of steady flow u_1 (x). The most commonly considered values for u_1 are the drift velocities at the top of the bottom boundary layer (Longuet-Higgins, 1953; Hunt and Johns, 1963) but one could consider other effects, for example, upwelling or downwelling due to steady winds as in the experiment of King (1959).

An equilibrium profile, purely in suspended load, exists if the gravitational effects balance the influence of the steady currents everywhere and i_s vanishes everywhere. The profile is determined by the locus of all the null-points. From Equation 8, when $\overline{i}_s = 0$,

$$\gamma = \frac{\beta}{w} = - \frac{5u_1}{u_0^2} \tag{9}$$

a relationship which contains essentially no free parameters. This lack of adjustable constants is an attractive feature of Bagnold's model. In theory Equation 9 should provide a critical test of the model; in practice it is not easy to determine u_1 very precisely. The second-order, Eulerian mean velocity due to the incoming waves is theoretically of order $-u_0^2/C$ (Longuet-Higgins, 1953), where C is the phase velocity. Then

$$\beta \simeq \frac{5w}{C} = \frac{5w\sigma}{g \tanh kh} \tag{10}$$

where k is the local wave number, h the water depth. This gives an expression for the equilibrium slope in terms of $w\sigma/g$, a dimensionless parameter also used by Dean (1973).

If sediment of a given grain size is in equilibrium with the local slope so that i_s vanishes for this grain size, any coarser sediment with a larger settling velocity has a smaller value of γ. The term involving gravity is reduced, the onshore term remains constant, coarser material therefore moves *onshore*; similarly, finer material should move *offshore* as observed (Zenkovitch, 1946; Murray, 1967). As can be seen in Equation 10, beaches of coarser material are steeper; any material that finds itself on a beach that is 'too steep' moves seawards. This leads to a new null-point hypothesis which is in far better agreement with observations than the classical model developed by Eagleson and Dean (1961).

In shallow water C tends to $(gh)^{1/2}$ and Equation 10 is readily integrated

$$\beta = \frac{dh}{dx} \simeq 5w \, (gh)^{-\frac{1}{2}} \tag{11}$$

so $h^3 \simeq (7.5 \, wx)^2/g$

Intriguingly, Dean (1977) has shown that a surprisingly large number of beach profiles on the United States east and Gulf coasts give a depth profile which increases as $x^{2/3}$ out to three or four hundred metres from the shore (Fig. 1.2). As the grain size of the sand is unknown and probably somewhat variable with distance from shore, a quantitative match between the profiles and Equation 11 is not really expected. In fact the numerical values are the right order of magnitude. However, Equation 9 is only the first approximation to a much more complicated situation. The effects of wave asymmetry must be significant in some depth range and the role of bedload has not yet been discussed.

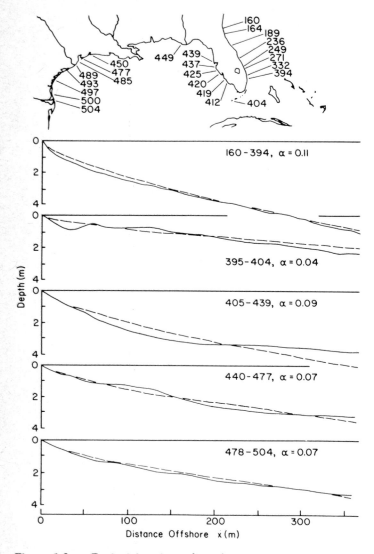

Figure 1.2.   *Typical beach profiles for the U.S. East Coast obtained by averaging a large number of profiles from each area (after Dean, 1977). A reasonable fit to the data of the form $h = \alpha x^{2/3}$ is shown by the dashed lines.*

2.   *Wave asymmetry, the role of the higher harmonics associated with the incoming wave field*

$$U_0 = U_0 \cos\sigma t, \quad U_1 = u_m \cos(m\sigma_m t + \sigma_m)$$

The effect of the wave asymmetry in moving material is again derived from the first three terms in Equation 6. The first order term $4U_1 \, U_0^2 \, |U_0|$ vanishes if n is odd, and the term $6U_1^2 \, U_0 \, |U_0|$ vanishes for all n. The most significant terms therefore arise from the even harmonics n = 2, 4, 6..., the most important being from n = 2 for which

$$\overline{4U_1 |U_0^2| U_0} = -\frac{16}{5\pi} U_0^3 U_2 \; \cos\theta^2 \qquad (12)$$

Now the second term in the Stokes solution provides a reasonable estimate of u_2 provided the Ursell Number $ak/(kh)^3$ is small (Flick, 1978), a being the wave amplitude. The complete, second order, Stokes solution for the orbital velocity being

$$u = \frac{a\sigma}{\sinh kh} \cdot \sin(kx - \sigma t) + \frac{3}{4} \cdot \frac{a^2\sigma k}{\sinh^4 kh} \qquad (13)$$
$$\cdot \cos 2(kx - \sigma t)$$

in this case $\theta_2 = 0$, $\cos\theta_2 = 1$, so the asymmetry reinforces the maximum onshore flow of the orbital velocity, providing the maximum possible onshore forcing.

The term arising from Equation 12 is not an alternative to the drift velocity term used in 7 and 8 but an additional factor. Then, from Equation 8, to first order

$$i_S = \frac{\varepsilon_S \cdot C_D \cdot \rho}{w} \cdot \frac{16}{15\pi} \cdot u_0^3 \left[5u_1 - 3u_2\cos\theta_2 + \gamma u_0^2 \right] \quad (14)$$

so that, for an equilibrium profile (for suspended load)

$$\gamma = \frac{\beta}{w} = -\frac{5u_1}{u_0^2} + \frac{3u_2 \, \cos\theta_2}{u_0^2} \qquad (15)$$

or, substituting for u_0, u_1, and u_2, for $\theta_2 = 0$

$$\beta \simeq \frac{9}{4} \cdot \frac{w}{C} \left[2 + (\sinh kh)^{-2} \right] \qquad (16)$$

In deep water, the effect of the wave asymmetry is, therefore, negligible compared to that of the drift velocity. However, as the wave shoals, the wave harmonics become increasingly important. The expressions used for u_1 and u_2 are both theoretical results of a somewhat questionable range of validity but should certainly be sufficient to provide a first, rough indication of the relative importance of the two terms. Equation 16 suggests that wave asymmetry becomes as important as drift when

$$\sinh kh \sim 2^{-\frac{1}{2}} \qquad (17)$$
$$\text{or} \qquad h \sim 0.01 \; g \cdot T^2$$

where T is the wave period $(2\pi/\sigma)$. In shallow depths the effect of asymmetry becomes increasingly dominant (Fig. 1.3). However, in very shallow water, the Stokes solution is not necessarily a good approximation; the trend is therefore indicated in Figure 1.3 by a dashed line. At some point, the waves break and the form of u_2 is then known only from very limited empirical data (Flick, 1978).

Equation 17 suggests that the extent of the nearshore area in which wave asymmetry is the dominant effect is strongly dependent on the frequency of the incoming waves. On the west coast of North America, which is generally exposed to waves of much longer periods, wave asymmetry should have a much more significant effect than on the east coast. As kh becomes small, then an expression for the equilibrium profile due to asymmetry, corresponding to Equation 11 is then

$$h^5 \sim \left(\frac{5.7 \; wx}{\sigma^2} \right)^2 \cdot g \qquad (18)$$

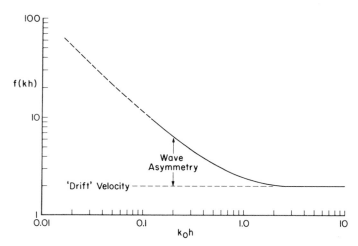

Figure 1.3. *The term, $2 + (\sinh kh)^{-2}$, plotted as a function of the nondimensional depth $k_o h$ where $k_o = \sigma^2/g$ is the deep water wave-number.*

3. *The effect of disturbances unrelated to σ.* Suppose there is a disturbance $u = u_t \cos(\sigma_t t + \theta_t)$. In general this does not contribute to the forcing if σ_t is not related to σ as the orthogonality conditions ensure that the time averages in the forcing terms vanish. However, any wave has an influence at a higher order through its drift velocity; if the perturbing wave is small $u_t \ll u_0$ and the drift velocity will be small compared to that of the incoming wave.

The discussion is somewhat artificial in that only a single incoming wave has been considered in the basic forcing. Further interactions may be possible in a true spectrum; such contributions arise primarily when the condition that there is one, dominant wave characterized by velocity u_0, frequency σ, is no longer really applicable.

BED LOAD

The whole approach used for suspended load can be repeated, starting from Equation 3. This procedure is analogous to the approach used by Inman and Bagnold (1963) in their discussion of beach equilibrium due to bed load transport. The expression corresponding to Equation 14 is then

$$\bar{i}_b = \frac{\varepsilon_b \cdot \rho \cdot C_D}{\tan\phi(1-\nu^2)} \cdot \frac{u_0^2}{4}\left[6u_1 - 3u_2 \cos\theta_2 + \nu \frac{16}{3\pi} \cdot u_0 + \cdots\right] \quad (19)$$

where $\nu = \beta/\tan\phi$ and an equilibrium profile under purely bed load motion is given by

$$\beta \frac{9\pi}{16} \tan\phi \left[-\frac{2u_1}{u_0} + \frac{u_2 \cos\theta_2}{u_0}\right] \quad (20)$$

So, substituting for u_0, u_1, u_2, $\cos\theta_2 = 1$

$$\beta = \frac{27\pi}{64} \tan\phi \cdot \frac{ak}{\sinh kh}\left[2 + (\sinh kh)^{-2}\right] \quad (21)$$

Interestingly, the ratio between the contributions due to drift and asymmetry is similar to that for suspended load (Fig. 1.3). In shallow water, as the waves begin to break

$$\frac{ak}{\sinh kh} \rightarrow \frac{a}{h} \rightarrow 0.4$$

and β becomes the order $\tan\phi$. If this were real, there would be a trend towards avalanching during the downslope phase of transport, arising from the term $(\tan\phi - \tan\beta)$ in the denominator of Equation 3. However, for this to be important the beach slope must be of the order of 30°. This solution is clearly not applicable to sand beaches but may be relevant to very coarse cobble beaches. However, for all systems, an onshore trend due to bed load motion is very strong. The suspended load solution suggested that coarser material, still transported in suspension, moves shoreward over the equilibrium profile of a finer size. Similarly, coarse sediment, transported primarily as bed load, will generally move shorewards as it will find itself on a beach which is not steep enough for the third term in Equation 19 to balance the first two.

To look at the equilibrium conditions on most sandy beaches it is probably necessary to consider the combined effects of bed load and suspended load. From Equations 14 and 19, the total transport $\bar{i}$ is

$$\bar{i} = C_D \rho u_0^2 \left[\frac{16}{15\pi} \frac{\varepsilon_s u_0}{w}(5u_1 - 3u_2 \cos\theta_2 + \frac{\beta}{w} \cdot u_0^2) + \frac{3\varepsilon_b}{4\tan\phi}\left(2u_1 - u_2 \cos\theta_2 + \frac{16}{9\pi} \cdot \frac{\beta u_0}{\tan\phi}\right)\right] \quad (22)$$

The relative importance of these terms is given by ratios involving ε_s, ε_b, $\tan\phi$, u_0 and w. Bagnold (1966) has suggested that $\varepsilon_s \sim 0.01$, $\varepsilon_b/\tan\phi \sim 0.15$. The ratio between the drift terms, suspended and divided by bed load is

$$\frac{32}{9\pi} \frac{\varepsilon_s u_0}{w} \frac{\tan\phi}{\varepsilon_b} \simeq \frac{1}{15} \frac{u_0}{w} \quad (23)$$

The terms arising from wave asymmetry, must similarly give

$$\frac{64}{15\pi} \frac{\varepsilon_s u_0}{w} \frac{\tan\phi}{\varepsilon_b} \simeq \frac{1}{15} \frac{u_0}{w} \quad (24)$$

but, for the gravitational terms, the ratio is

$$\frac{4}{5} \frac{\varepsilon_s u_0^2}{w} \frac{\tan^2\phi}{\varepsilon_b} \simeq \frac{1}{15} \tan\phi \left(\frac{u_0}{w}\right)^2 \quad (25)$$

where $\tan\phi \sim 0.6$. For there to be a well developed suspended load, $w < u_*$ where u_* is the friction velocity (Bagnold, 1966). The maximum value u_* during the wave period is given by

$$u_*^2 = C_D u_0^2$$

so, for suspension $\quad \dfrac{u_0}{w} \leq C_D^{-\frac{1}{2}} \quad (26)$

The value of C_D is probably in the range 10^{-2} to 10^{-3} so u_0/w must exceed something like 10 for a reasonably developed suspension. Now for $u_0/w \sim 15$, the suspended and bed load contribute equally to the onshore movement, Equations 23 and 24. The tendency for downslope transport due to gravity is, however, some 10 times greater for the suspended load; offshore movement due to bed load is negligible. The ineffectiveness of the slope for moving bed load results in the very steep slopes predicted for an equilibrium profile under bed load alone.

A perfectly sensible local equilibrium may, however, exist where the onshore movement is due to both bed load and suspended load but the compensating seaward transport arises primarily from the effects of gravity on the suspended fraction. If this result is correct (and it depends on the relevance of Bagnold's basic formulation) it helps to explain the total confusion which exists in the literature on the relative importance of suspended load and bed load in the nearshore region. Equations 22 to 25 suggest that this balance changes with distance from shore and changing wave conditions, the important parameter being

$$\frac{u_0}{w} = \frac{a\sigma}{w \sinh kh} \qquad (27)$$

If a typical value for u_0 is, say, 1 m/s for sediment with a settling velocity of 5 cm/s (medium sand), the onshore movement due to bed load will be significant. For settling velocity of 1 cm/s, Equations 23 and 24 suggest that bed load effects will be small.

The total expression for the equilibrium slope for which the net transport vanishes is, from Equation 22,

$$\beta \left[\frac{4}{5} \cdot \varepsilon_s \left(\frac{u_0}{w}\right)^2 + \frac{\varepsilon_b}{\tan^2\phi} \right] = \frac{u_0}{C} \left[2 + (\sinh kh)^{-2} \right] \cdot$$
$$\left[\frac{9}{5} \varepsilon_s \frac{u_0}{w} + \frac{27\pi}{64} \frac{\varepsilon_b}{\tan\phi} \right] \qquad (28)$$

β is then a function of three parameters:

$$\beta = f\left(\frac{w\sigma}{g}, ak_0, k_0h\right), \quad k_0 = \sigma^2/g \qquad (29)$$

a can be expressed in terms of the deep water amplitude a_0 but this is not really necessary to the present order of the approximation. The amplitude of interest is that of the fundamental frequency; the increase in amplitude of this component due to shoaling is balanced by the loss of energy to higher harmonics. In fact, this amplitude may actually decrease slightly during wave shoaling (Flick, 1978). For a particular beach, a and σ are given functions of the wave field. In an idealized case, w is constant but the calculation can obviously be extended to cases in which w is a known function of depth. For constant w, Equation 29 can be expressed a little more simply as

$$\frac{\beta}{ak_0} = f\left(\frac{a\sigma}{w}, k_0h\right) \qquad (30)$$

so that Figure 1.4 β/ak_0 is plotted as a function of depth k_0h for various values of $a\sigma/w$. As $a\sigma/w \to 0$, the equilibrium slope is a function of bed load only. For any particular value of $a\sigma/w$ there is a transition region from bed load dominance which is shown by the dashed lines in Figure 1.4, as in this region u_0/w is less than 10 and the orbital velocities are not sufficiently strong to ensure a fully developed suspension.

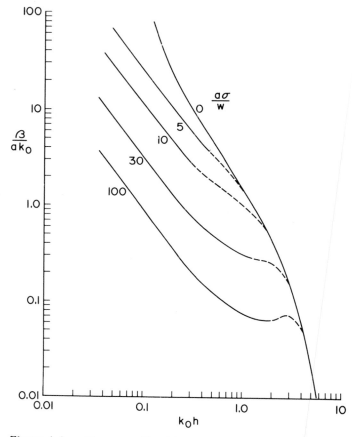

Figure 1.4. *The normalized beach slope β/ak_0 as a function of the nondimensional depth k_0h for various values of the suspension parameter $a\sigma/w$. The case $a\sigma/w = 0$ is pure bed load motion.*

Bed load would continue to be important and the beach may become rather steep before the offshore transport component of the suspension becomes important and reduces the slope. This suggests a perturbation, a minor bar, in the region where suspended load becomes significant. Dalrymple and Thompson (1977) have used $a\sigma/w$ as a direct indicator of foreshore slope and showed that the criteria of Dean (1973) for the existence of an offshore bar can be re-expressed in terms of $a\sigma/w$. Clearly the present development can be made even more sophisticated and the expressions 14 and 18 expanded to include higher order terms. These are likely to become important in shallow water where u_1 and u_2 become larger relative to u_0 and the beach is generally steeper so that terms such as γu_0 also increase. However, the theoretical expressions for u_1 and u_2 have a limited range of application and this restricts the relevance of any complex expansion. This leads into a whole range of problems above and beyond the present expansion. The questions raised are, however, fundamental in evaluating whether the basic formulation of the sediment transport is adequate. In addition the data used, for example, by Dalrymple and Thompson (1977) are primarily from laboratory experiments in which scale effects may seriously alter the basic physics of the problem. Neither the wave effects, particularly the distribution of drift velocity, nor the sediment dynamics are likely to be reproduced very exactly in small-scale experiments. The adequacy of a detailed model for onshore-offshore transport can not really be critically evaluated using laboratory results.

WAVE REFLECTION

So far the dicussion has concentrated on the effects of progressive waves approaching the shore. In practice some reflection takes place at the shoreline, producing a small, standing wave component at the frequency of the incoming waves.

Carter et al. (1973) showed in a series of laboratory experiments that over a flat bed the drift velocity associated with a standing wave tends to rework sediment into a series of bars (Fig. 1.5). Theoretically, zeroes in the drift velocity occur under both nodes and antinodes of the standing wave: material should converge at either nodes or antinodes, depending on the direction of sediment movement. The situation is complicated because the theoretical drift velocity changes sign in the bottom boundary layer. There is substantial disagreement in the literature as to where deposition tends to take place, at antinodes, nodes or both (Short, 1975). Looking at Figure 1.5 a reasonable guess is that bed load tends to accumulate at nodes, suspended load under antinodes.

To obtain reasonable bars on a flat bed, Carter et al. (1973) required relatively high reflection coefficients, $R > 0.4$. When Lau and Travis (1973) applied this concept to beaches they reiterated this requirement for high reflectivity, greatly weakening the apparent applicability of their suggestion, since such high reflection coefficients are rarely found in practice. However, it can be seen from Equation 22 that if the basic beach equilibrium consists of a balance between the incoming, progressive waves and gravitational effects, any new perturbation will create a small readjustment; the slope changes to balance the new local value of the total drift velocity. Small standing waves will have relatively little effect as the drift velocity is proportional to the square of the wave amplitude (Longuet-Higgins, 1953) but any standing wave component will perturb the profile; larger reflection coefficients result in larger bars.

To investigate the effect of standing waves on a beach it is convenient to consider the wave solutions for a beach with a mean slope $\bar{\beta}$ (Fig. 1.1). An incoming progressive wave is described in terms of the surface elevation η by

$$\eta = a(J_0(\chi)\ \sin\sigma t + Y_0(\chi)\ \cos\sigma t) \qquad (31)$$

and an outgoing wave reflected from the beach by

$$\eta = b(J_0(\chi)\ \sin\sigma t - Y_0(\chi)\ \cos\sigma t) \qquad (32)$$

where $\chi^2 = 4\sigma^2 x/g\bar{\beta}$, J_0 and Y_0 are Bessel Functions.

Using Hunt and Johns (1963), the drift velocity at the top of the bottom boundary is

$$u_1 = \frac{g}{4\bar{\beta}\sigma x^2}\left[-\frac{5}{\pi}\cdot(a^2-b^2)+\right.$$
$$\left. 3(a^2+b^2)\ E(\chi)+6abP(\chi)\right] \qquad (33)$$

$$\text{where}\quad E(\chi)=\frac{\chi}{2}\cdot\left[J_1(\chi)\cdot J_2(\chi)+Y_1(\chi)\cdot Y_2(\chi)\right]$$

$$\text{and}\quad P(\chi)=\frac{\chi}{2}\cdot\left[J_1(\chi)\cdot J_2(\chi)-Y_1(\chi)\cdot Y_2(\chi)\right]$$

are shown in Figure 1.6a. $E(\chi)$ is an offshore-directed component of the drift velocity arising from the increase in wave height towards the shore, probably not very important in practice. The mean onshore drift is reduced by the reflection but this is not significant unless the reflection coefficient R, which is equal to b/a, is large. The term which gives a pattern of maxima and minima in the drift velocity is $P(\chi)$. For a pure standing wave ($a=b$) the drift reduces to

$$u_1 = \frac{3gb^2}{4\bar{\beta}\sigma x^2}\ \chi J_1(\chi) J_2(\chi) \qquad (34)$$

where $\chi J_1(\chi)J_2(\chi)$ is shown in Figure 1.6b in comparison with the standing wave, amplitude variation $j_0(\chi)$. The offshore variation and the positions of the zeroes is virtually the same for $P(\chi)$ as it is for $\chi J_0(\chi)J_1(\chi)$, both having zeroes close to the nodes and antinodes of $j_0(\chi)$. The position of

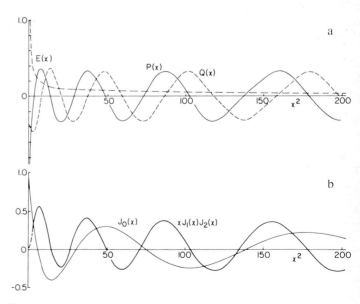

Figure 1.6a. *The function $E(\chi)$, $P(\chi)$ plotted against non-dimensional distance χ^2.*

Figure 1.6b. *$\chi J_1(\chi)J_2(\chi)$ and the basic wave form $J_0(\chi)$ as functions of the non-dimensional distance χ^2.*

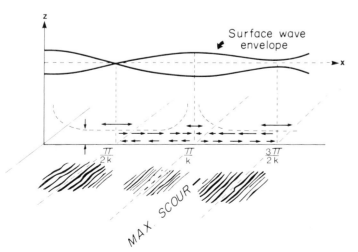

Figure 1.5. *The movement of sediment on a flat bed due to a standing wave (after Carter et al., 1973).*

these zeroes is therefore not critically dependent on the existence of the progressive component of the wave motion. As before, bars are expected at either nodes or antinodes; Short (1975) suggested antinodes.

In Figure 1.6b bars might be expected either at zeroes of $J_1(\chi)$ defined as $Z_n^{(1)}$ or at zeroes of $J_1(\chi)$, $Z_n^{(2)}$, the distances to the bars from the shoreline being given by

$$x_n^{(r)} = \frac{g\bar{\beta}}{4\sigma^2} \cdot Z_n^{(r)}, \quad r = 1,2 \qquad (35)$$

The values of Z_n are readily obtained from any handbook of functions; for $J_1(\chi)$ they occur at $\chi^2 = 13.9, 49.2, 103, 178, 271 \ldots$ and for $J_2(\chi)$ at $\chi^2 = 26.3, 70.2, 135, 219, 322 \ldots$ (Fig. 1.6b). It appears from Equation 35 that the scale lengths for bars at incoming wave frequency are small, particularly if beach slope is small. For $\bar{\beta} \sim .03, T = 8 s$ the inshore bars are less than 10 m apart, much more the size of ridge and runnel systems than major bars. As a quick check on the validity of these estimates, a typical wave length in shallow water is

$$L = T \cdot (gh)^{\frac{1}{2}} \qquad (36)$$

Bars will occur at spacing $L/2$ so that even in 2 m of water, for $T = 8 s$ bars would be less than 20 m apart. However, Equation 35 does provide an explicit prediction for relative spacing of multiple bars: bars become farther apart as the water depth increases.

LARGE-SCALE BAR SYSTEMS

Bowen and Inman (1971) suggested that large, crescentic bar systems might be formed by the drift velocities associated with low-frequency, standing edge waves. Short (1975) identified low-frequency, infragravity waves as a possible cause for the parallel bars observed off Alaska. Equation 35 provides a prediction for the relative spacing of a series of bars, the distance between bars increasing seawards. Figures 1.7 and 1.8 show some examples of profiles taken across multiple bar systems. The spacing between successive bars does tend to increase as the depth increases; Figure 1.8, a bar system on an extremely gentle slope, indicates a very slow increase in spacing.

If the scales are normalized by dividing by the distance to the third bar D_3 (Fig. 1.6) then a direct comparison can be made with the theoretical predictions of Equation 35. Table 1.1 shows the general form of the ratios between the bar spacing. Even without any theory, the constancy of the ratio D_2/D_3 is notable. The ratio D_1/D_3 is less stable but the inshore bar is much more likely to be perturbed by the effects of wave breaking, the energy levels are highest here and the bar contains relatively little sediment.

The theoretical results, bars at antinodes, $J_1(\chi) = 0$, or nodes, $J_2(\chi) = 0$, are shown at the foot of the table. Either provides reasonable agreement with the observations. Having determined the relative spacing and knowing $\bar{\beta}$, the wave period associated with this scale can be calculated. Slightly different results are obtained using zeroes of $J_1(\chi)$ as opposed to $J_2(\chi)$. The resulting periods are very similar to those obtained by Bowen and Inman (1971) for crescentic bars, that is, periods typical of the surf beat frequencies.

It appears that these large-scale nearshore features are associated with low-frequency waves, either edge waves or free waves. Crescentic bars require standing edge waves to produce their particular shape. Linear bars may be related to free waves, either coming in from deep water or

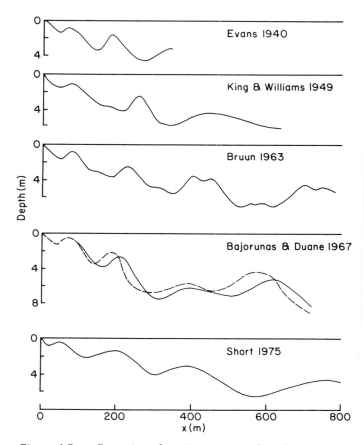

Figure 1.7. *Examples of multiple bar profiles from a range of different environments (see Table 1.1).*

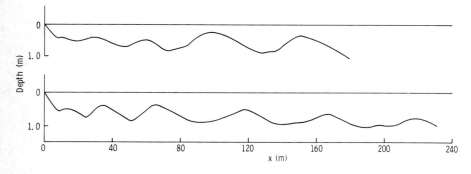

Figure 1.8

Profiles from the south coast of Prince Edward Island, a large number of closely spaced bars on a beach of very gentle slope (E.H. Owens, personal communication).

Table 1.1.   Multiple bars —— profile measurements.

Author	Location	$D_3(m)$	D_1/D_3	D_2/D_3	D_4/D_3	D_5/D_3	$\bar{\beta}$	T(sec.)
Evans (1940)	Lake Michigan	342	.18	.54			.012	55 (65)
		345	.19	.55				
		354	.25	.54				
		359	.22	.54				
		382	.23	.53				
		271	.16	.45				
		285	.17	.51				
King and Williams (1949)	S. France Blackpool	442	.17	.56			.011	68 (80)
		244	.16	.44	1.68			
Bruun (1963)	Denmark	410	.20	.54	1.71		.010	70 (80)
Bajorunas and Duane (1967)	Lake Superior	385 (1964)	.17	.47	1.61		.010)	65 (80)
		499 (1966)	.18	.50	1.56		.010)	
Saylor and Hands (1970)	Lake Michigan	345	.17	.48				
Short (1975)	Alaska	393	.14	.49	1.93	3.13	.0075)	90 (105)
		367	.19	.56		2.66	.0073)	
		521	.13	.46			.0086)	95 (110)
		445	.11	.48			.0073)	
Owens (pers. com.)	Prince Edward Island	61	.18	.52	1.57	2.52	.0022)	55 (65)
		65	.18	.52	1.80	2.55	.0025)	
Theory	$J_1(x) = 0$		.14	.48	1.73	2.63	J_1	
	$J_2(x) = 0$		.19	.52	1.62	2.38	(J_2)	

generated by nonlinear interaction near the shore, or by progressive edge waves. Low-mode, edge waves have only a limited number of nodes and antinodes in the offshore direction and the number of possible bars would depend on the modal number (Fig. 1.9).

The drift velocity Equation 34 dies away seawards as x^{-2} and appears to lessen. However, the influence of the drift velocity has to be seen in comparison with other effects. The results of Table 1.1 do not distinguish between the possibility of bars occurring at nodes or antinodes. However, it has generally been found that the sediment on the bar is finer and better sorted than that in the troughs (e.g., Bajorunas and Duane, 1967). This suggests that suspended load is significant and that bars are more likely to be formed under antinodes.

The equation for the perturbation of the equilibrium slope β' by a low-frequency standing wave

$$\eta = 2a_t J_0(\chi t)\cos\sigma_t \cdot t, \quad \chi_t^2 = \frac{4\sigma_t^2 x}{g\bar{\beta}} \quad (37)$$

is simply (Equation 9)

$$\beta^1 \simeq -\frac{5wh_1}{u_0^2} \quad (38)$$

where u_1 is given from Equation 34 and u_0 can be derived from 31. The expression is rather complicated because of the Bessel Functions and it is convenient to look at large values of χ, χ_t where

$$J_n(\chi) \rightarrow \left(\frac{2}{\pi\chi}\right)^{\frac{1}{2}} \cos\left(\chi - \frac{n\pi}{2} - \frac{\pi}{4}\right) \quad (39)$$

then

$$u_1 = \frac{3ga_t^2}{8\pi\sigma_t \cdot \bar{\beta}x^2} \cdot \cos 2\chi_t \quad (40)$$

and

$$u_0 = \frac{ga}{\sqrt{\pi\sigma}}\left[\frac{\sigma^2}{g\bar{\beta}x^3}\right]^{\frac{1}{4}} \quad (41)$$

then substituting Equations 40 and 41 in 38,

$$\beta' \simeq -\frac{15}{8} \cdot \frac{w}{(g\bar{\beta}x)^{\frac{1}{2}}} \cdot \frac{\sigma}{\sigma_t}\left(\frac{a_t}{a}\right)^2 \cos 2\chi_t \quad (42)$$

Now $\bar{\beta}x$ is the mean depth, so that the solution is of the same order, as far as the offshore dependence is concerned, as the basic solution for the mean equilibrium profile, Equation 10. The size of the perturbation β' depends on the ratio between the frequencies of the incoming and low-frequency waves, where σ/σ_t may be a large quantity, and

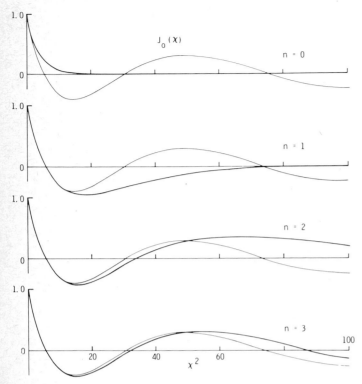

Figure 1.9. *The offshore structure of the surface elevation of low mode edge waves in comparison with $J_0(\chi)$.*

the ratio of the wave amplitudes a_t/a, which may of course be small. However, unless a_t/a is very small the drift velocity associated with low-frequency waves is likely to be significant over the whole profile.

For the particular case of reflection of the incoming wave Equation 42 reduces to

$$\beta' \simeq -\frac{15}{8} \cdot \frac{w}{(g\bar{\beta}x)^{\frac{1}{2}}} \cdot \frac{b}{a} \cos 2\chi \qquad (43)$$

illustrating the linear relationship between the perturbation of the beach slope and the reflection coefficient b/a. The effect of wave reflection on the sediment is therefore more likely to be noticeable on steep beaches where the reflection coefficient tends to be larger (Miche, 1951; Guza and Bowen, 1977). However, even on shallower beaches it may be interesting to look at small scales such as ridge and runnel systems in terms of the possible effect of reflection from the shoreline.

CONCLUSIONS

The initial motivation for this paper was to show that, starting from any simple model for sediment transport, a model for wave-induced, onshore-offshore transport on a beach could be derived. All such models result in an expression for the time-averaged transport $\bar{i}$ as a function of local wave and current conditions and beach slope. A null-point model should then always be obtainable from the condition that $\bar{i}$ vanishes everywhere if the beach is truly in equilibrium.

The model used as an example, that due to Bagnold (1963, 1966), provides results which seem to be more in line with observations than the existing, classical null-point results. The qualitative trend of the results suggests that Bagnold's model contains much of the essentiel physics required in an adequate description of nearshore transport. The comparison between the effects of bed load and suspended load may help to explain why the existing literature is so confused on this subject. The predictions of the effect of reflected or standing waves in perturbing the beach profile to form longshore bars show that the drift velocity can play an important role. The prediction of the spacing of the bars, and inference that low-frequency waves are responsible, arises primarily from the drift velocity distribution and should not be particularly sensitive to the form of the transport model. It does require a model in which the beach slope is related, quite simply, to the drift velocity, but this is probably a condition that any sensible model would meet.

More critical predictions arising from Bagnold's model are the possible importance of autosuspension and the obvious importance of the effect of slope on the suspended fraction of the transport. For bed load, avalanching is similarly important as the slope becomes steep. As a rule bed load equilibrium requires very steep slopes, slopes not typical of sand beaches. However, the degree to which the quantitative predictions of the present model can be taken seriously is unclear. Many of the data that have been used in the discussion of beach equilibrium are from laboratory experiments. As in the case of longshore transport of sediment, laboratory data provide a very poor indication of the prototype trends (Komar and Inman, 1970).

In general, the beach slopes predicted for suspended transport or for combined bed and suspended load are of the right order. However, uncertainties as to the appropriate values of the perturbation velocities u_1 and u_2 are substantial, particularly when u_1 is a drift velocity. These 'purely hydrodynamic' unknowns create difficulties for any sediment transport model.

One of the prime purposes for generating simple expressions (or, at least, fairly simple expressions) is to suggest hypotheses which may be tested by field or laboratory data. Several of these equations could be examined critically if the offshore distribution of the settling velocity w of the sediment was known.

Acknowledgment

This research was supported by a grant from the National Research Council of Canada.

References

Bagnold, R.A.
    1962: Autosuspension of transported sediment; turbidity currents; Proceedings of the Royal Society of London, Series A, v. 265, p. 315 - 319.
    1963: Mechanics of marine sedimentation; in The Sea, M.N. Hill, ed.; Interscience, v.3, p. 507 - 528.
    1966: An approach to the sediment transport problem from general physcis; U.S. Geological Survey, Professional Paper 422-I, 37 p.

Bajorunas, L. and Duane, D.B.
    1967: Shifting offshore bars and harbor shoaling; Journal of Geophysical Research, v. 72, p. 6195 - 6205.

Bascom, W.H.
  1954: Characteristics of natural beaches; American Society of Civil Engineers, Proceedings of the 4th Conference on Coastal Engineering p. 163-180.

Bowen, A.J. and Inman, D.L.
  1971: Edge waves and crescentic bars; Journal of Geophysical Research, v. 76, p. 8662-8671.

Bruun, P.
  1963: Longshore currents in one and multi-bar profiles in relation to littoral drift; American Society of Civil Engineers, Proceedings of the 8th Conference on Coastal Engineering, p. 211-247.

Carter, T.G., Liu, P.L.-F., and Mei, C.C.
  1973: Mass transport by waves and offshore sand bedforms; American Society of Civil Engineers, Journal of Waterways, Harbors, and Coastal Engineering Division, WW2, p.165-184.

Dalrymple, R.A. and Thompson, W.W.
  1977: Study of equilibrium beach profiles; American Society of Civil Engineers, Proceedings of the 15th Conference on Coastal Engineering, p. 1277-1296.

Dean, R.G.
  1973: Heuristic models of sand transport in the surf zone; Conference on Engineering Dynamics in the Surf Zone, Sydney, Australia, 7 p.
  1977: Equilibrium beach profiles: U.S. Atlantic and Gulf Coasts; Ocean Engineering Report 12, Department of Civil Engineering, University of Delaware, 45 p.

Eagleson, P.S. and Dean, R.G.
  1961: Wave-induced motion of bottom sediment particles; American Society of Civil Engineering, Transactions, v. 126, p. 1162-1189.

Evans, O.F.
  1940: The low and ball of the east shore of Lake Michigan; Journal of Geology, v. 48, p. 476-511.

Flick, R.E.
  1978: Study of shoaling waves in the laboratory; unpublished Ph.D. thesis, University of California, San Diego, 159 p.

Guza, R.T. and Bowen, A.J.
  1977: Resonant interactions for waves breaking on a beach; American Society of Civil Engineers, Proceedings of the 15th Conference on Coastal Engineering, p. 560-579.

Hunt, J.N. and Johns, B.
  1963: Currents induced by tides and gravity waves; Tellus, v. 15, p. 343-351.

Inman, D.L. and Bagnold, R.A.
  1963: Littoral processes; in The Sea, M.N. Hill, ed.; Interscience, v. 3 p. 529-543.

Ippen, A.T. and Eagleson, P.S.
  1955: A study of sediment sorting by waves shoaling on a plane beach; U.S. Army Corps of Engineers, Beach Erosion Board Technical Memorandum 63, 83 p.

King, C.A.M.
  1959: Beaches and Coasts; Edward Arnold, London, 403 p.

King, C.A.M. and Williams, W.W.
  1949: The formation and movement of sand bars by wave action; Geographical Journal, v. 113, p. 70-85.

Komar, P.D. and Inman, D.L.
  1970: Longshore sand transport on beaches; Journal of Geophysical Research, v. 75, p. 5914-5927.

Lau, J. and Travis, B.
  1973: Slowly varying Stokes waves and submarine longshore bars; Journal of Geophysical Research, v. 78, p. 4489-4497.

Longuet-Higgins, M.S.
  1953: Mass transport in water waves; Royal Society of London, Philosophical Transactions, Series A, v. 245, p. 535-581.

Madsen, O.S. and Grant, W.D.
  1977: Quantitative description of sediment transport by waves; American Society of Civil Engineers, Proceeding of the 15th Conference on Coastal Engineering, p. 1093-1112.

Miche, M.
  1951: Le pouvoir réfléchissant des ouvrages maritimes exposés à l'action de la houle; Annales des ponts et chaussées v. 121, p. 285-319.

Murray, M.
  1967: Control of grain dispersion by particle size and wave state; Journal of Geology, v. 75, p. 612-634.

Saylor, J.H. and Hands, E.B.
  1970: Properties of longshore bars in the Great Lakes; American Society of Civil Engineers, Proceedings of the 12th Conference on Coastal Engineering, p. 839-853.

Shepard, F.P.
  1950: Beach cycles in Southern California; U.S. Army Corps of Engineers, Beach Erosion Board Technical Memorandum 20, 26 p.

Shepard, F.P. and LaFond, E.C.
  1940: Sand movement near the beach in relation to tides and waves; American Journal of Science, v. 238, p. 272-85.

Short, A.D.
  1975: Multiple offshore bars and standing waves; Journal of Geophysical Research, v. 80, p. 3838-3840.

Zenkovitch, V.P.
  1946: On the study of shore dynamics; Akademiya nauk S.S.S.R., Institut Okeandogi, Trudy, v. 1, p. 99-112.

2

REMOTE SENSING FOR COASTAL STUDIES IN CANADA

P.J. Howarth and A.E. Lucas
Department of Geography, McMaster University, Hamilton, Ontario

Howarth, P.J. and Lucas, A.E., Remote sensing for coastal studies in Canada; in The Coastline of Canada, S.B. McCann, editor; Geological Survey of Canada, Paper 80-10, p. 13-22, 1980.

Abstract

The use of remote sensing for both land and water studies in the Canadian coastal environment is reviewed. A three-fold chronological division forms the framework for discussion, the emphasis being on the current capabilities of remote sensing systems. Several studies have demonstrated the capabilities of panchromatic photography and Landsat imagery and consideration should be given to the use of colour infrared photography and thermal imagery in Canadian investigations. Two types of study are identified, static and dynamic. Current research efforts are directed towards dynamic studies using microwave sensing from aircraft and spacecraft for monitoring and surveillance.

Résumé

Les auteurs passent en revue les différentes méthodes de télédétection permettant d'étudier à la fois le milieu masin et le milieu terrestre des côtes canadiennes. Une division chronologique en trois phases forme le cadre de la discussion, l'accent étant mis sur les possibilités actuelles des appareils de télédétection. Plusieurs études ont démontré les possibilités de la photographie panchromatique et de l'imagerie Landsat; c'est pourquoi il faudrait accorder plus d'attention à l'emploi de la photographie couleur à infrarouge et à l'imagerie thermique dans ces études au Canada. Deux types d'étude ont été décrits, le mode statique et le mode dynamique. Les efforts actuels de recherche portent sur les études dynamiques faisant appel à la détection à micro-onde à partir d'aéronefs et de navires spatiaux pour le contrôle et la surveillance.

INTRODUCTION

Three major factors make remote sensing important in studies of the Canadian coastline. The first is the length of the coastline. Gathering data over great distances is frequently not feasible and therefore aerial photography or other remotely sensed data are often required to extrapolate between ground observation points. The second factor is the dynamic nature of processes and events that occur in the nearshore zone. To be able to record and monitor changes in this zone, it is valuable to use some form of imaging system. Data from earlier periods must be archived for subsequent detection and measurement of change over both long and short time periods. The third factor is the need for surveillance within our 200-mile (320 km) zone of jurisdiction. A remote sensing approach using repetitive data is seen as an important element in any monitoring or surveillance system.

In this paper, the emphasis is on the current capabilities of remote sensing systems for studying the coastal zone. A chronological approach has been adopted based on the various periods when different remote sensing systems became available in Canada. The important characteristics of the data recorded by each of these systems are identified and their use in coastal zone studies is discussed. A synthesis of the different types of studies in which remote sensing is important is also presented.

In April 1978 the computer-based bibliographic referencing system (RESORS) at the Canada Centre for Remote Sensing (CCRS) indicated that the library held 270 articles with 'coastal region' as a primary keyword. For this reason, the work discussed in this paper is generally restricted to Canadian studies. A second restriction is that the discussion of sea ice studies has been purposely limited. Although this is a major area of emphasis in remote sensing work, it has been considered in detail elsewhere. It formed part of a Symposium on Remote Sensing in Glaciology held in 1974. Several papers in a special issue of the *Journal of Glaciology* (v. 15, no.73, 1975), in particular a review article by Campbell et al. (1975), give a good indication of the current state of the art. Finally, much of the remote sensing literature is to be found in government reports and documents that have limited circulation. In this paper, therefore, references are drawn whenever appropriate from articles in journals and symposium proceedings.

EARLY DEVELOPMENTS AND APPLICATIONS

The use of panchromatic aerial photography to provide an overview of an area of study is a standard procedure that requires little comment. Nine-inch format (230 mm by 230 mm) mapping photography still provides the major source of remote sensing data for studies in the coastal zone and will no doubt continue to do so for some time.

Two types of study can be identified. First, the most recent photography available is used to provide information on physical and vegetative features in the coastal zone, frequently but not exclusively for mapping purposes. In certain circumstances, the photography can show additional features such as patterns of surface waves and the nearshore bottom topography. The second type of study involves the use of aerial photography from two or more moments in time to detect change in the coastal zone. Care is required in the interpretation of change since the photography shows the environment only at individual moments. Different states of tide, seasonal changes and the fact that a coastal zone may undergo several major erosional and depositional events between dates of photography must be taken into account in interpretation.

At the National Air Photo Library (NAPL), Canada has one of the best collections of aerial photography in the world, with panchromatic photography readily available for the whole of the country. Although for northern areas there is frequently only single coverage at a small scale (1:60 000), for the more inhabited parts of the country there are usually a number of dates of coverage at a variety of scales. In some cases photography dates back to the late 1920s or early 1930s, giving 50 years of record. NAPL coverage plus provincial photography permit mapping and the study of temporal changes in many coastal areas. From an annotated bibliography of remote sensing in the coastal zone (Stafford et al., 1973), it is readily apparent that the work of Cameron (1950, 1952, 1962, 1965a, b and c) stands out among Canadian investigators using aerial photography in the early years. His work involved mapping of nearshore seaweed, the measurement of current velocities and the investigation of coastal changes.

More recent coastal studies have also taken advantage of sequential aerial photography, particularly in areas where spits and barrier islands occur. Bryant and McCann (1973), for example, used four sets of photographs, taken from 1930 to 1965, as part of their study documenting changes in the barrier island system of Kouchibouguac Bay, New Brunswick. In practice, mapping of shoreline changes is frequently a difficult task. To minimize possible errors, Armon and McCann (1979) describe a mapping procedure using extensive networks of control points. These consist of ground locations identifiable on all three sets of photographs used in their study. In addition, plots of both duneline position and waterline position are used to determine shoreline change in the barrier islands of Malpeque Bay, Prince Edward Island. The changes are averaged over 250 m segments to minimize the influence of local variations. Data derived from this type of study can be used further; for example, in estimating sediment exchanges in budget studies (Armon and McCann, 1977).

RECENT DEVELOPMENTS AND APPLICATIONS

A variety of remote sensing systems have been available in Canada since the early 1970s. The Canada Centre for Remote Sensing was established in 1971. Through its airborne sensing program 70 mm format multispectral photography and both 70 mm and 230 mm format colour and colour infrared photography have been provided for investigators. Much of the early photography was acquired at a very small scale (1:100 000 or smaller) as simulation imagery for the Earth Resources Technology Satellite program. Subsequently special-purpose photography over selected test sites at a variety of scales was obtained for investigators. About 1974, good quality thermal imagery became available and currently several specialized sensors for use in the coastal zone are under development by CCRS. The aircraft are now operated by industry.

Since 1972 LANDSAT (formerly ERTS) satellite data have been received in Canada. With LANDSAT 3 currently operating, large amounts of data have already been recorded and processed into images. As a result most areas of the country have reasonably cloud-free imagery recorded under a variety of seasonal conditions. Finally, the amount of weather satellite data being recorded has increased significantly, particulary from geostationary satellites (SMS-GOES) located above the equator. Although the resolution of the imagery recorded by such systems is comparatively low, this drawback is counteracted by the capability for data acquisition every half hour.

The use of data from these remote sensing systems in studies of the Canadian coastal zone is discussed below.

Specialized photography

The difficulties of using panchromatic photography for studying vegetation types and their distribution in the coastal zone are well known. In such studies colour and colour infrared photography are particularly valuable. For example, in colour infrared photography the red of healthy vegetation is clearly separated from the blue of bare surfaces. Both types of photography can be used to study patterns produced by variations in suspended sediment concentrations, while for differentiating land and water both colour infrared and black-and-white infrared photography provide good contrasts. The types of differentiation described above may also be obtained using appropriate bands of multispectral photography in 70 mm format. In this case maximum differentiation may not always be easy unless a multispectral viewing system is used.

Although CCRS has provided specialized photographic flights at both high and low altitudes in the coastal zone, there are few detailed reports of the use of this photography. The types of information that can be obtained are summarized, for example, in papers describing high-altitude photography of the Oregon and Texas coasts (Keene and Pearcy, 1973; Tuyahov and Holz, 1973), but there are no similar descriptions for Canadian coastal environments. On the west coast, however, colour and colour infrared photographs have been used in waterline definition and to determine depths in shallow water (Gower, 1973). Gower (1975) also discussed the use of small-scale colour photography to map the plume of the Fraser River, to determine water movement in Burrard Inlet and to study the upwelling of mine tailings in Rupert Inlet.

For studies of land areas in the coastal zone, the literature exhibits a lack of Canadian reports on the use of specialized photography. The photography would be of particular benefit in the study of coastal vegetation. This is confirmed by Paul (1974), who used colour and colour infrared photography to study dune and marshland vegetation on Les Îles-de-la-Madeleine. As part of a remote sensing study of the subarctic environment, Kozlovic (1977) showed that 1:60 000-scale colour infrared photography could be used to differentiate three zones of coastal marsh. It was suggested that these zones represented different vegetation types resulting from varying degrees of inundation by salt water.

In contrast to Canada, mapping of coastal wetlands in the United States has received considerable attention. There are many papers that discuss the way in which different types of remote sensing data may be used for this task, but colour and colour infrared photography appear to be preferred. In a review article Carter (1977) indicated that in 23 states wetland inventories have been undertaken using various scales of panchromatic, colour and colour infrared photography. Depending upon their purpose, maps ranging from scales of 1:2400 to 1:500 000 have been produced for this type of inventory.

It is important to emphasize that a remote sensing approach does not always require vertically oriented photogrammetric or 70 mm cameras. Hand-held 35 mm photography can be extremely valuable, not only for inventory purposes, but also for giving specialized information such as quick estimates of water-covered areas (Gower, 1975). When a sequence of photographs at short time intervals is required, 35 mm photography from a light aircraft is the most feasible method of data acquisition. Such an approach minimizes the constraints of weather and reduces cost. Gower (1975) used such a system in studies of the Fraser River plume and Burrard Inlet, his 35 mm camera being fitted with a fish-eye lens to give broad coverage and to aid in location. For the Rupert Inlet area, a 35 mm camera attached to a tethered balloon was used.

If care is taken in handling the film, excellent quality colour infrared photography can be acquired from hand-held 35 mm cameras. As a supplement to the interpretation of vegetation on existing panchromatic aerial photography, small samples of colour infrared photography greatly increase the amount of information that can be extracted (Lucas, in prep.). In addition, the 35 mm photography can be used to record changes since the panchromatic photography was flown.

Thermal sensing

Apparent temperature data for water surfaces may be obtained from aircraft with an infrared radiation thermometer or with an infrared line scanner. In the first case a trace on a chart records the surface temperature directly beneath the aircraft. As an example, Irbe (1972) has described the use of airborne radiation thermometer surveys from light aircraft to provide temperature data for selected traverses in the Great Lakes and St. Lawrence Seaway over several years. From tests it is estimated that temperature data can be obtained to 1°C absolute and 0.5°C relative accuracy.

The second instrument, the infrared line scanner, records emitted radiation from the surface. Usually operating in the 8 - 14 μm region of the spectrum, data recorded on magnetic tape are later converted into strips of imagery to show apparent surface temperatures. As surface temperatures are constantly changing, it is obviously an advantage to obtain data at more than one time to study dynamic events.

Complications in data acquisition arise, however, if more than one strip of imagery is required to cover the area of interest. Even with a short time lag between recording adjacent strips, there will be changes in water conditions. In addition, matching strips where there is no land detail for reference is difficult (Thomson, 1972).

There are two obvious areas in which thermal imagery can be of particular value in studies of the coastal zone. First, it has been used in the investigation of temperature patterns over water surfaces. Thomson (1972), for example, was able to show the thermal bar and the effects of upwelling and surface winds near the shoreline of Lake Ontario on two successive days. On the west coast Gower (1975) recorded surface temperatures during both ebb and flood tides in Burrard Inlet. The information aided in the study of water movement within the inlet.

The second type of study where thermal imagery may be of particular value is in determining temperature variations over sea ice. Recent work by Cihlar and Thomson (1977) over an area in the Beaufort Sea used imagery recorded during the day and at sunset, to study diurnal surface temperature changes and determine whether this information would aid in mapping sea ice. It was found that although certain ice types could be differentiated using either day- or nighttime imagery, temperature differences between the two sets of data did not assist the identification and mapping of sea ice.

Bajzak (1974) used a similar sensing system to study icebergs. Relative surface temperatures of meltwaters and their surface mixing patterns could be clearly identified on the thermal imagery.

It can be appreciated that it is practically impossible to obtain detailed spatial patterns of surface temperature, except with thermal infrared imagery. Given this fact, it is perhaps surprising that more use has not been made of this sensing device in Canadian coastal studies.

LANDSAT

To a large extent, LANDSAT is an abused remote sensing system. It was initially an experimental satellite scheduled to last for one year. Subsequently it was expected to function as part of an operational remote sensing program providing data that would lead to considerable cost savings. The first satellite lasted five and one half years and has clearly provided valuable information for a variety of environmental studies.

In a discussion of the applications of LANDSAT imagery, it is important to remember what is being recorded, as this sets the limits for how the data can be handled and for what can reasonably be expected from the system. Basically, the scanning and sensing system of the spacecraft (multispectral scanner) records reflected radiation in four parts or bands of the visible and near-infrared spectrum (Band 4, 0.5 - 0.6 μm; Band 5, 0.6 - 0.7 μm; Band 6, 0.7 - 0.8 μm; and Band 7, 0.8 - 1.1 μm). Individual picture elements (pixels) for which data are recorded represent areas on the ground measuring 57 m by 79 m (NASA, 1976). On any one scan line, perpendicular to the direction of orbit of the spacecraft, there are approximately 3200 pixels. In the forward direction, the strip being recorded is subdivided into scenes containing approximately 2400 lines of data. Each scene covers a ground area of 185 km by 185 km (Fig. 2.1). From the point of view of all later manipulations, it can be considered that each pixel has four values. Each value is on a scale from 0 to 63 and represents the amount of reflected radiation in one of the four bands recorded by the scanner. This is all the specialist has to work with, a set of four numbers for each pixel. Analysis can be undertaken using an image recorded on a transparency or photographic print, or using the original digital data in a computer.

Visual analysis

For visual analysis, the original digital data must be transformed into a photographic image, the standard scale being 1:1 000 000. This inevitably leads to loss of information and resolution through the photographic process. Given the initial size of the pixel and the loss of detail in image production, it is obvious that LANDSAT imagery is most suited to studies of large areas where identification of fine detail is not important.

Apart from its almost universal application to show 'the location of my area of study', LANDSAT imagery in its visual format has been applied in several ways to the study of Canadian coastal environments. One of the most effective uses of the imagery is the near-real-time transmission of data to ships operating during the summer in the high Arctic (Shaw, 1975). Data received at the Prince Albert Satellite Station are transmitted to facsimile recorders on ships. The images are then used to assist in route selection through ice-infested waters. The problem, of course, is that cloud-free conditions are required for the areas of interest and daily coverage of all areas is not possible with the orbits of LANDSAT.

Water and sea ice provide excellent contrasts on LANDSAT imagery and several different types of ice can be identified. When sequential data are available, deformation of the pack ice, the velocity of ice movement and strain rates can readily be calculated (Campbell et al., 1975; Nye, 1975). It has also been demonstrated that, using LANDSAT imagery and surface weather charts over a period of three days, it is possible to predict the motions of drifting ice floes (Feldman, 1978).

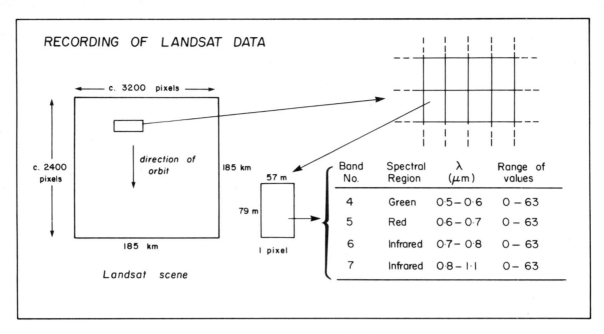

Figure 2.1. *Schematic diagram of the recording of reflectance values by the Landsat multispectral scanner.*

In Canadian coastal waters off Labrador, LANDSAT imagery has aided in locating uncharted hydrographic features (Fleming and Lelievre, 1977). Although slight geometric distortions may occur in the LANDSAT imagery, it has been calculated that errors in positioning are no more than 150 m in comparison with standard survey procedures.

Standard LANDSAT images are rarely processed to emphasize water detail. Thus information which could be available in the image is lost. Falconer et al. (1975) have clearly demonstrated that a photo-optical procedure to increase the contrast over water could provide better products for the interpreter. Enhancements are also produced with digital methods, as discussed in the next section, and described in Sabins (1978).

The size of the objects being studied and their distinction from surrounding features are obviously important criteria when analyzing LANDSAT imagery. In all the above cases, it can be seen that the features being studied are comparatively large and distinct. Thus resolution of the imagery is not a critical factor in the applications that have been described. Over land areas, however, the environment is more complex and variable. To a certain extent, this explains why visual analysis of satellite data in land areas of the coastal zone has received little attention in the literature.

Digital analysis

The main research emphasis in Canadian remote sensing during the 1970s has probably been digital analysis of LANDSAT data. This statement holds true for the coastal zone where studies have been undertaken for both land and water environments. Various approaches to digital analysis are possible.

Enhancement. With this approach, the original data are manipulated before an image is produced. The aim is to provide maximum contrasts between the environmental features being studied, which greatly assists the subsequent visual interpretation of the image. Several enhancement procedures have been suggested but one of the most effective is principal components enhancement developed by Taylor (1974). This has been used in the study of sedimentation and flow patterns within lac St.-Jean, and it results in the display of patterns which cannot be seen on a standard LANDSAT image (Taylor and Langham, 1975; Jones et al., 1977). As far as is known, however, this procedure has not been applied to coastal waters.

Correlation. As shown in Figure 2.2, field measurements can sometimes be correlated with reflectance values recorded on individual bands of the satellite data. This approach has been demonstrated by Bukata et al. (1974, 1975) in water quality studies of the Great Lakes. They found a linear correlation between surface chlorophyll *a* concentration and Band 6 and Band 7 data, while Band 4 was related to water depth in nonturbid water. With the correlations established, it was possible to suggest explanations for the patterns observed in Lake Ontario which were produced by mapping the reflectance values for each band (Bukata and Bruton, 1974). Correlations between turbidity and Band 5 reflectance values have also been identified by Rochon (1977) and by Jones et al. (1977); in the latter paper a correlation between surface chlorophyll *a* and Band 6 values is also displayed.

Classification. In the study of LANDSAT data, classification (Fig. 2.2) involves grouping of pixels that have similar reflectance values. Whether the classification is carried out using supervised procedures (Goodenough, 1976) or unsupervised methods (Goldberg and Shlien, 1976), the basic concepts are the same. The aim is to produce an image or map, derived from the reflectance values, which corresponds to a logical classification of features in the environment. In Figure 2.2 the groupings are shown based on two reflectance values, but in practice the classification is carried out using all four values for each pixel.

A simple classification (e.g., land versus water) is a relatively easy task that can be done with a high degree of accuracy. This is because the range of the reflectance values for the two types of surface are very different. More difficult, however, is separating or mapping two or more vegetation types that have very similar ranges of reflectance values. The accuracy with which such a classification can be achieved is correspondingly much lower.

A particular problem of mapping in the coastal zone is that features such as beaches and dune systems can have great length, but are rarely very wide. Mapping of narrow, linear features is difficult because the approximately 60 m by 80 m resolution of the LANDSAT pixel may cover more than one environmental feature. This leads to errors or unclassified pixels.

Alföldi and Beanlands (1975) and Alföldi (1975) have looked at the possibilities of mapping the coastal zone using both visual and digital data. Using a test site near Port Mouton, Nova Scotia, they showed that not only can several land categories (e.g., grasses, softwood, hardwood and mixed wood) be differentiated, but also features in the shore zone such as clear water, shallow water with sand bottom, dry beach sand and rock, mud, and littoral vegetation. Comparing the satellite analysis results with ground information, they found a 25 per cent error in land classes, but only a 3 per cent error in the shore zone. Alföldi (1975, p.13) concluded that "resource mapping of the coastal environment in Atlantic Canada is practical from LANDSAT imagery." He emphasizes, however, that ground data and colour or colour infrared photography are necessary for verification and that the analyst undertaking the task must have familiarity with the environmental conditions. A study of the Nova Scotia coastal zone is at present being undertaken with LANDSAT digital data as a major source of information (Prout, 1979).

Kozlovic and Howarth (1977) were able to obtain similar levels of environmental information for the coastal environment of northwestern Ontario. By using both visual and digital data, the tidal flats and three zonations of marsh vegetation could be mapped. Inland, differentiation of vegetation on the LANDSAT data picked out the drier relict beach ridges from the surrounding fens and bogs.

Classification procedures have not generally been used in mapping water surfaces. The reason is that boundaries of water characteristics (e.g., suspended sediment concentra-tions) normally are gradual. Thus placing a boundary is rather artificial, especially as surface information is usually inadequate to justify the boundary.

Chromaticity. One of the most promising techniques to be developed for the study of water bodies recorded on LANDSAT data is chromaticity analysis. The technique, which originates from methods of colour measurement, was initially applied to LANDSAT data by Munday (1974a, b). Subsequently a procedure to measure suspended sediment concentrations from LANDSAT data was developed by Alföldi and Munday (1977, 1978). As shown in Figure 2.2, the data used in the analysis are the normalized reflectance values for Bands 4 and 5. The several steps involved in the procedure are outlined in detail by Alföldi and Munday (1977).

A problem with the correlation approach to measuring suspended sediment concentrations is that the results are only applicable to the specific LANDSAT pass when the regression was established. Variations in atmospheric conditions between satellite overpasses cause this problem, but Alföldi and Munday (1977) have been able to apply atmospheric corrections in their analysis.

Chromaticity analysis has been tested in the Minas Basin, Nova Scotia, using measurements of suspended sediment concentration from samples acquired by the Bedford Institute (Amos, 1976). The surface sampling was carried out simultaneously with several passes of LANDSAT over the Minas Basin. The results indicate "a very high correlation (r = 0.96) between suspended sediment concentration and chromaticity-transformed satellite data after atmospheric adjustments" (Alföldi and Munday, 1977, p. 328).

With the correlation established, calculations of suspended sediment concentrations in the Minas Basin are being made from the satellite data. With LANDSAT data from several passes, the patterns which the suspended sediment measurements display are being analyzed (Stewart, in prep.). The extent to which the regression equation (established in the chromaticity analysis for the Minas Basin) can be universally applied is being further investigated (Alföldi, pers. com.).

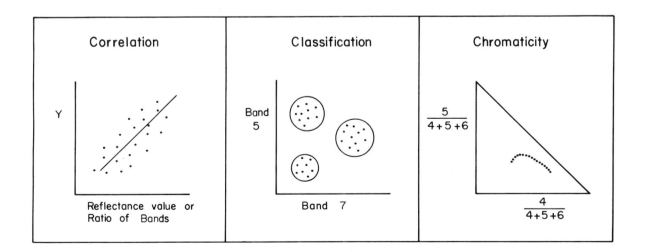

Figure 2.2 *Diagrammatic presentation of several ways in which Landsat digital data may be used for analysis. Note that in classification, values for four bands are usually used at the same time. In the chromaticity diagram, the set of points represents a typical locus for values acquired over water.*

FUTURE DEVELOPMENTS

Several current developments in remote sensing are relevant to studies of the coastal zone.

SEASAT-1

With the launch of SEASAT-1 on June 24, 1978, microwave data from space will soon become available for selected areas on an experimental basis. As the name of the satellite indicates, the sensors are primarily designed to provide information about the oceans. Of particular interest is a synthetic aperture radar system that in virtually all weather will provide imagery of the earth's surface over a 100 km wide swath. Although SEASAT failed in October 10, 1978, sufficient synthetic aperture radar imagery was obtained to demonstrate the capability of recording such data from space. Details of the sensors, their area of coverage, resolution, accuracy and probable applications are shown in Table 2.1. Further discussion of the sensors is to be found in McCandless (1975) and Sherman (1977), and some possible Canadian studies using SEASAT data are listed in the Oceanography Report of CCRS (1978).

Nimbus G

This satellite, launched on October 24, 1978 and now known as Nimbus 7, carries a variety of sensors, two of which are of interest to coastal specialists. First is a Scanning Multi-channel Microwave Radiometer, similar to the one being carried on SEASAT-1. As indicated in Table 2.1, it will provide data on sea surface temperatures, ice distribution, and surface wind magnitude under all weather conditions. The second instrument is a Coastal Zone Colour Scanner which records data in six narrow (0.02 μ m) bands of the spectrum. Five bands are centred in the visible spectrum (0.443, 0.520, 0.550, 0.670 and 0.750 μ m) and one in the emitted infrared at 11.5 μ m. Selection of the bands is particularly designed for the measurement of chlorophyll in the ocean (Sherman, 1977).

SURSAT Project

A study has been initiated by the federal government with the aim of "determining the feasibility of using satellites to assist in meeting forecast surveillance requirements associated with the management of Canada's offshore and Arctic areas" (SURSAT Project Office, 1977, p. 1). As part of this program, the Surveillance Satellite (SURSAT) Project is co-ordinating the acquisition and analysis of microwave data. The microwave data will come from two sources: from SEASAT-1, and from an airborne Synthetic Aperture Radar system. This second system is on lease for one year from a company in the United States and will be used to provide data for a variety of experiments. Several proposed experiments on aspects of oceans, floating ice and renewable resources will be of direct interest to those studying the coastal zone. To date, data acquisition has only just started.

Table 2.1. SEASAT-1 sensors: some characteristics and applications

Sensor	Swath width	Resolution/ accuracy	Anticipated applications
	(km)		
Radar altimeter	2 - 12	*wave height* ± 0.5 m or 10% over range 1 - 2 m *geodesy* 10 cm RMS	wave height, geodesy, currents, storm surge analyses
SEASAT-A scatterometer system	1000	*wind magnitude* ± 2 m s^{-1} or 10% over range 3 - 25 m s^{-1} *wind direction* ± 20°	estimates of surface wind magnitude and direction
Synthetic aperture radar	100	25 m	wave and current patterns, mapping of ice and open water (plus some land coverage)
Scanning multichannel microwave radiometer (5 frequencies)	600	*resolution* varies with frequency 22 - 100 km *temperature* ± 2°K *wind magnitude* ± 2 m s^{-1} or 10% over range 3 - 25 m s^{-1}	sea surface temperature, ice mapping, surface wind magnitude
Visible and infrared radiometer	1800	*visible* 3 km *infrared* 5 km	cloud and surface features

Based on McCandless (1975) and Sherman (1977).

Two recent studies undertaken by Canadian investigators indicate the type of result that will be obtained. As part of their experiments, Lowry et al. (1977) looked at ocean wave and ship imagery using different wavelengths, polarizations and resolutions. Suitable combinations of radar characteristics were identified to provide the best imagery of these features. Gower (1977), working off the British Columbia coast used L-band radar imagery in a simulation of SEASAT data. He detected surface markings due to internal waves and concluded that SEASAT imagery would be suitable for studying such features. Considerable work evidently will be required to understand and explain some of the radar imagery characteristics. At the same time the results will no doubt raise interesting questions about environmental interactions.

Sensors

Two projects at present being undertaken at CCRS will aid investigations in the coastal zone. In the first, an airborne hydrographic system is being developed (O'Neill, 1978). A modified inertial navigation system will provide locational and attitude information for the aircraft, and a lidar bathymeter will record depth profiles in shallow coastal waters.

A second instrument under development is a laser fluorosensor for the detection of oil on water. According to a recent report (CCRS, 1978), it is planned to use the sensor along with others in an experimental Arctic Marine Oil Spills Program. The program is designed to determine the conditions in which remote sensing devices can detect oil spills in ice-infested waters.

The above listing of future developments is by no means exhaustive but represents some of the main activities that will take place in the period 1978 - 1980. Satellite programs have to be planned well in advance, so many decisions have already been made for the 1980s. For example, LANDSAT D is scheduled to be launched in 1981. The multispectral scanner on this satellite will record in 7 bands, as opposed to the present 4 bands, and the system will have an increased resolution of approximately 30 m. It is anticipated that the increased resolution will greatly assist thematic mapping. The Space Shuttle Program taking place during the 1980s will carry a variety of sensors into orbit. Use of film in space will increase as data can be brought back to earth. There are even proposals for a satellite to be instrumented for the coastal zone and to be known as COASTSAT. Such future developments, however, are beyond the scope of this paper.

DISCUSSION

In reviewing the way remote sensing data are used in studies of the coastal zone, two main approaches may be identified. First, some studies may be designated as producing 'static' information. Although they are important, there is little or no change over time. Much of the basic mapping or inventory of the coastal zone can be placed in this category. Once the information is obtained, there is little need to update it, except over long periods.

In the second group of studies, termed 'dynamic', change is constantly occurring. Detection, recording, measuring and understanding the change are frequently required. Types and rates of change will vary depending upon what is

Table 2.2. Summary of remote sensing activities in the coastal zone

Type of study	Past (pre-1970)	Present (1970s)		Future (1978 on)	
	Airborne	Airborne	Satellite	Airborne	Satellite
Static	Mapping from panchromatic aerial photography	Panchromatic mapping continued. Better quality photography. Some colour and colour IR for easier mapping	Experiments on small-scale mapping (1:250 000) in the coastal zone	Continuation of present practice. Perhaps use of thermal and radar imagery in special projects	Better resolution from LANDSAT D and Space Shuttle leading to larger scale and more detailed mapping
Dynamic (monitoring of change)	Coastal change with sequential panchromatic aerial photography	Continued use of panchromatic photography with some colour and colour IR. Use of light aircraft photography for special projects	Experimental work on monitoring of change: suspended sediment concentration, chlorophyll a, ice breakup and movement	Continuation of present practice. Increased use of thermal, radar and special purpose sensors for detecting and recording change	LANDSAT - monitoring of water quality parameters - suspended sediment concentration, chlorophyll a, temperature patterns. Radar-monitoring of ice breakup and movement, study of ocean characteristics
Dynamic (surveillance)	---	Experiments on oil spill detection	---	Use of satellites and airborne sensing systems as part of a program of surveillance in the coastal zone	

being studied. Some changes may take place over a tidal or seasonal cycle. In other cases, a general trend may be observed over a period of years.

However, a subdivision of 'dynamic' into 'monitoring' and 'surveillance' has been suggested. The term 'monitoring' is meant to indicate that known changes are occurring but information is required on the details of these events. A good example would be the monitoring of ice breakup in the spring. In the case of 'surveillance', an element of the unknown is implied and a need for protection against possible dangers. Thus detection of oil spills, illegal incursions of fishing vessels into coastal waters or simply the guiding of vessels would be placed in this category.

The above subdivisions have been used as a basis to summarize the observed trends in remote sensing (Table 2.2). The types of activities described under the heading static are really self explanatory. Increased use of satellites for mapping is anticipated for the future as the resolutions of the sensing systems are increased.

It is really in the dynamic category that a remote sensing approach becomes of increased importance, particularly in the realm of satellite sensing. Three situations are suggested where remote sensing from satellites should be adopted. First, when the information cannot be obtained by any other practical means. An example of this would be the simultaneous measurement of suspended sediment concentration at numerous points over a large area. The second situation is when repetitive data are required. A satellite system is the only practical way to provide data for regular monitoring over a large area. In some types of study where data in the visible part of the spectrum are required, the constraints of weather would have to be anticipated. The third case is when information about the earth's surface is required without interruption by weather. In this situation, a microwave sensing system is necessary. The technology now exists to monitor some of the changes indicated in Table 2.2 and serious thought should be given to implementing some of these programs.

The potential uses of remote sensing in a surveillance system for ocean and nearshore activities have been outlined by Morley et al. (1977). They suggest that surveillance satellites will be increasingly used in the future as they "observe environmental factors on a global scale with unparalleled economies of coverage" (Morley et al., 1977, p. 121). Although satellites would reduce the need for aircraft, airborne sensing would still be essential for more detailed or frequent coverage and in situations where human observers are required. They suggest that satellites and aircraft would be valuable components of a series of different surveillance platforms, including coastal stations, ships and buoys.

CONCLUSIONS

It has been demonstrated that there is a considerable range of studies in the coastal zone for which remote sensing can be of assistance. Research into the ways in which the different sensors can be used in the coastal zone is generally progressing well in Canada, although slowly. Colour and colour infrared photography for the study of coastal wetlands and thermal imagery for investigating water temperatures and circulation in the coastal zone have, however, received little attention in Canadian coastal studies.

Several applications of remote sensing that could be used to provide data for the coastal zone on a regular basis have been described. To apply these, however, might require an initial investment of funds and personnel, as well as a change in the operating procedure of an organization. Because of the current fiscal restraints, this is not always possible, but is certainly worth consideration.

A final point is that remote sensing specialists can demonstrate the capabilities of a particular sensing system or indicate the type of features that can be identified during analysis. The need, however, is for an emphasis on using the data in the solution of specific problems, the identification of which can only come from the coastal specialist. Continued discussion and collaboration between the two groups of scientists is thus important for future developments of remote sensing in the coastal zone.

References

Alföldi, T.T.
  1975:   The use of satellite imagery for an inventory of coastal resources in the Atlantic Provinces; Canada Centre for Remote Sensing, Research Report 75-5.

Alföldi, T.T. and Beanlands, G.E.
  1975:   Towards an operational inventory of coastal regions; Proceedings of the 3rd Canadian Symposium on Remote Sensing, p. 323 - 329.

Alföldi, T.T. and Munday, J.C., Jr.
  1977:   Progress toward a Landsat water quality monitoring system; Proceedings of the 4th Canadian Symposium on Remote Sensing, p. 325 - 340.
  1978:   Water quality analysis by digital chromaticity mapping of Landsat data; Canadian Journal of Remote Sensing, v. 4, no. 2, p. 108 - 126.

Amos, C.L.
  1976:   Suspended sediment analysis of seawater using Landsat imagery, Minas Basin, Nova Scotia, in Report of Activities, Part C; Geological Survey of Canada, Paper 76-1C, p. 55 - 60.

Armon, J.W. and McCann, S.B.
  1977:   Longshore sediment transport and a sediment budget for the Malpeque barrier system, southern Gulf of St. Lawrence; Canadian Journal of Earth Sciences, v. 14, no. 2, p. 2429 - 2439.
  1979:   Longshore variations in shoreline erosion, Malpeque barrier system, Prince Edward Island; Canadian Geographer, v. 23, no. 1, p. 18 - 31.

Bajzak, D.
  1974:   Thermal mapping of water envelopes surrounding icebergs; Proceedings of the 2nd Canadian Symposium on Remote Sensing, p. 573 - 579.

Bryant, E.A. and McCann, S.B.
  1973:   Long and short term changes in the barrier islands of Kouchibouguac Bay, southern Gulf of St. Lawrence; Canadian Journal of Earth Sciences, v. 10, no. 10, p. 1582 - 1590.

Bukata, R.P. and Bruton, J.E.
  1974:   ERTS-1 digital classifications of water regimes comprising Lake Ontario; Proceedings of the 2nd Canadian Symposium on Remote Sensing, p. 628 - 634.

Bukata, R.P., Bruton, J.E., Jerome, J.H. and Bobba, A.G.
  1975:   The application of Landsat-1 digital data to a study of coastal hydrography; Proceedings of the 3rd Canadian Symposium on Remote Sensing, p. 331 - 348.

Bukata, R.P., Harris, G.P. and Bruton, J.E.
1974: The detection of suspended solids and chlorophyll *a* utilizing digital multispectral ERTS-1 data; Proceedings of the 2nd Canadian Symposium on Remote Sensing, p. 551 - 564.

Cameron, H.L.
1950: The use of aerial photography in seaweed surveys; Photogrammetric Engineering, v. 16, no. 4, p. 493 - 501.

1952: The measurement of water current velocities by parallax methods; Photogrammetric Engineering, v. 18, no. 1, p. 99 - 104.

1962: Water current and movement measurement by the time-lapse air photography - an evaluation; Photogrammetric Engineering, v. 28, no. 1, p. 158 - 163.

1965a: Sequential air photo interpretation in coastal change studies; Maritime Sediments, v. 1, no. 2, p. 8 - 13.

1965b: Coastal studies by sequential air photography; Canadian Surveyor, v. 19, no. 4, p. 372 - 381.

1965c: The shifting sands of Sable Island, Geographical Review, v. 55, no. 4, p. 463 - 477.

Campbell, W.J., Weeks, W.F., Ramseier, R.O. and Gloersen, P.
1975: Geophysical studies of floating ice by remote sensing; Journal of Glaciology, v. 15, no. 73, p. 305 - 328.

Canada Centre for Remote Sensing
1978: The Canadian Advisory Committee on Remote Sensing: 1977 Report.

Carter, V.
1977: Coastal wetlands: the present and future role of remote sensing; Proceedings of the 11th International Symposium on Remote Sensing of Environment, p. 301 - 323.

Cihlar, J. and Thomson, K.P.B.
1977: Diurnal temperature variations and their usefulness in mapping sea ice from thermal infrared imagery; Proceedings of the 4th Canadian Symposium on Remote Sensing, p. 208 - 219.

Falconer, A., Deutsch, M., Myers, L.C. and Anderson, R.
1975: Photo-optical contrast stretching of Landsat data for multidisciplinary analyses of the Lake Ontario basin: Proceedings of the 3rd Canadian Symposium on Remote Sensing, p. 173 - 193.

Feldman, U.
1978: Predicting the motions of detached ice floes; unpubl. Ph.D. thesis, McMaster University, Hamilton.

Fleming, E.A. and Lelievre, D.D.
1977: The use of Landsat imagery to locate uncharted coastal features on the Labrador coast; Proceedings of the 11th International Symposium on Remote Sensing of Environment, p. 775 - 781.

Goldberg, M. and Shlien, S.
1976: A four-dimensional Histogram approach to the clustering of Landsat data; Canadian Journal of Remote Sensing, v. 2, no. 1, p. 1 - 11.

Goodenough, D.
1976: IMAGE 100 classification methods for ERTS scanner data; Canadian Journal of Remote Sensing, v. 2, no. 1, p. 18 - 29.

Gower, J.F.R.
1973: Remote sensing at the Marine Sciences Directorate (Pacific Region); Canadian Aeronautics and Space Journal, v. 19, no. 10, p. 507 - 510.

1975: Uses of aircraft and balloon photography in studying coastal areas; unpubl. MS., Pacific Marine Science Report 75-78.

1977: Microwave sensing of sea surface wave patterns; Proceedings of the 4th Canadian Symposium on Remote Sensing, p. 395 - 406.

Irbe, J.G.
1972: An operational program for measuring surface water temperature by airborne radiation thermometer (ART) survey; Proceedings of the 1st Canadian Symposium on Remote Sensing, p. 183 - 200.

Jones, G., Sochanska, W., Fortin, J.-P. and Langham, E.J.
1977: Étude de la dynamique des eaux du lac Saint-Jean au Québec, à l'aide des satellites Landsat-1 et Landsat-2; Proceedings of the 4th Canadian Symposium on Remote Sensing, p. 305 - 312.

Keene, D.F. and Pearcy, W.G.
1973: High-altitude photographs of the Oregon Coast; Photogrammetric Engineering, v. 39, no. 2, p. 163 - 176.

Kozlovic, N.J.
1977: Aircraft and satellite remote sensing for biophysical analysis at Pen Island, northwestern Ontario; unpubl. M.Sc. thesis, McMaster University, Hamilton.

Kozlovic, N.J. and Howarth, P.J.
1977: Biophysical mapping in northwestern Ontario from aircraft and satellite remote sensing data; Proceedings of the 4th Canadian Symposium on Remote Sensing, p. 27 - 36.

Lowry, R.T., Goodenough, D.G., Zelenka, J.S. and Shuchman, R.A.
1977: On the analysis of airborne synthetic aperture radar imagery of the ocean; Proceedings of the 4th Canadian Symposium on Remote Sensing, p. 480 - 505.

Lucas, A.E.
in prep: Geobotanical sequences on barrier coastlines within the southern Gulf of St. Lawrence; unpubl. M.Sc. thesis, McMaster University, Hamilton.

McCandless, S.W., Jr.
1975: SEASAT-A: A product of user interest; Proceedings of the 10th International Symposium on Remote Sensing and the Environment, p. 39 - 44.

Morley, L.W., Clough, D.J. and McQuillan, A.K.
1977:   Ocean information and management systems; Proceedings of the 4th Canadian Symposium on Remote Sensing, p. 113 - 124.

Munday, J.C., Jr.
1974a: Lake Ontario water mass determination from ERTS-1; Proceedings of the 9th International Symposium on Remote Sensing of Environment, p. 1355 - 1368.
1974b: Water quality of lakes of southern Ontario from ERTS-1; Proceedings of the 2nd Canadian Symposium on Remote Sensing, p. 77 - 85.

NASA
1976:   Landsat data users handbook; Goddard Space Flight Center, Document No.765DS-4258.

Nye, J.F.
1975:   The use of ERTS photographs to measure the movement and deformation of sea ice; Journal of Glaciology, v. 15, no. 73, p. 429 - 436.

O'Neill, R.A.
1978:   The aerial hydrography project; in Remote Sensing in Canada (Newsletter); v. 6, no. 2, p. 13 - 18.

Paul, L.A.
1974:   Aspects of the coastal geomorphology of Les Îles de la Madeleine; unpubl. B.A. thesis, McMaster University, Hamilton.

Prout, N.A.
1979:   Analysis of Landsat imagery for coastal Nova Scotia; Proceedings of the 5th Canadian Symposium on Remote Sensing, p. 169 - 173.

Rochon, G.
1977:   Un système automatisé d'analyse des caractéristiques des lacs par satellite; Proceedings of the 4th Canadian Symposium on Remote Sensing, p. 313 - 324.

Sabins, F.F., Jr.
1978:   Remote sensing: principles and interpretation; W.H. Freeman and Co., San Francisco.

Shaw, E.
1975:   Near real-time transmission of sea-ice satellite imagery; Proceedings of the 3rd Canadian Symposium on Remote Sensing, p. 83 - 91.

Sherman, J.W., III
1977:   Current and future satellites for oceanic monitoring; Proceedings of the 9th International Symposium on Remote Sensing of Environment, p. 279 - 297.

Stafford, D.B., Bruno, R.O. and Goldstein, H.M.
1973:   An annotated bibliography of aerial remote sensing in coastal engineering; U.S. Army Corps of Engineers, Miscellaneous Paper 2-73.

Stewart, T.
in prep: A study of the suspended sediment patterns of the Minas Basin, Nova Scotia; unpubl. M.Sc. thesis, McMaster University, Hamilton.

SURSAT Project Office
1977:   Surveillance Satellite Project, Experiment Plan Part 1, Request for proposals for experiments; Government of Canada.

Taylor, M.M.
1974:   Principal components colour display of ERTS imagery; Proceedings of the 2nd Canadian Symposium on Remote Sensing, p. 295 - 313.

Taylor, M.M. and Langham, E.J.
1975:   The use of maximum information colour enhancements in water quality studies; Proceedings of the 3rd Canadian Symposium on Remote Sensing, p. 359 - 366.

Thomson, K.P.B.
1972:   Infrared scanner observations on Lake Ontario; Proceedings of the 1st Canadian Symposium on Remote Sensing, p. 173 - 181.

Tuyahov, A.J. and Holz, R.K.
1973:   Remote sensing of a barrier island; Photogrammetric Engineering, v. 39, no. 2, p. 177 - 188.

3

VARIATIONS IN TIDAL-INLET MORPHOLOGY AND STABILITY, NORTHEAST NEW BRUNSWICK

G.E. Reinson

Atlantic Geoscience Centre, Geological Survey of Canada
Dartmouth, Nova Scotia

Reinson, G.E., Variations in tidal-inlet morphology and stability, northeast New Brunswick; in The Coastline of Canada, S.B. McCann, editor; Geological Survey of Canada, Paper 80-10, p. 23-39, 1980.

Abstract

The tidal inlets in the barrier-island shorelines of northeast New Brunswick display considerable variation with respect to channel dimension, inlet plan form, associated delta sand bodies, and locational and cross-sectional stability. These morphology and stability conditions vary systematically from one barrier-island segment to another, being dependent upon three main variables: 1) the alignment of each barrier-island segment relative to direction of wave approach, 2) the size of the bay-river system that each barrier segment encloses, and 3) the availability of littoral sediment within each barrier system.

According to existing inlet morphology models that are based on tidal range, the large inlets and flood- and ebb-tidal deltas of the Miramichi are characteristic of mesotidal coastlines, whereas the small inlets and deltas of the Pokemouche and Tracadie barrier-island segments are more characteristic of microtidal barrier-island shorelines. The northeast coast of New Brunswick is entirely microtidal. This discrepancy between existing models and the northeast New Brunswick examples suggests that models for barrier-island morphogenesis that are based solely on tidal range, although sufficient for describing variations between regions with substantially different tidal ranges, are insufficient for categorizing the variations of depositional features along and between coastlines subjected to small tidal ranges. In regions subjected to small tidal ranges, barrier-island morphology may be dependent more on tidal prism, nearshore sediment availability, and even coastline physiography.

Résumé

Les inlets de marée qui existent dans le littoral d'îles-barrières du nord-est du Nouveau-Brunswick présentent des variations considérables pour ce qui est de la dimension des chenaux, de la configuration horizontale des inlets, des masses de sable deltaïque connexes et de la stabilité positionnelle et transversale. Ces conditions relatives à la morphologie et à la stabilité varient systématiquement d'un segment d'îles-barrières à l'autre, suivant trois facteurs principaux: 1) l'alignement de chacun des segments d'îles-barrières par rapport à la direction d'approche des vagues, 2) la taille de l'ensemble baie-rivière compris dans chaque segment de barrière et 3) l'apport possible en sédiments littoraux dans chaque ensemble de barrières.

D'après les modèles morphologiques actuels des inlets qui reposent sur l'amplitude de marée, les grands inlets et les deltas de flot et de jusant de la Miramichi sont caractéristiques des traits de côtes mésotidaux, tandis que les petits inlets et deltas des segments d'îles-barrières de la Pokemouche et de la Tracadie sont plus caractéristiques des lignes de rivage à îles-barrières microtidales. La côte nord-est du Nouveau-Brunswick est entièrement microtidale. L'écart qui existe entre les modèles actuels et les exemples considérés dans le nord-est du Nouveau-Brunswick laisse croire que, même s'ils pouvaient suffire à décrire certaines variations entre des régions d'amplitudes de marée sensiblement différentes, les modèles morphogénétiques des îles-barrières qui reposent uniquement sur l'amplitude de la marée seraient encore insuffisants pour catégoriser les variations des phénomènes de sédimentation le long des traits de côte, et entre ceux-ci, lorsqu'ils sont soumis à de petites amplitudes de marée. Dans les régions soumises à ces petites amplitudes, la morphologie des îles-barrières dépend généralement davantage de l'existence de sédiments littoraux, du prisme de marée et même de la physiographie du trait de côte.

INTRODUCTION

The tidal inlets in the barrier island shoreline of northeast New Brunswick (Fig. 3.1) display wide variations in morphology, stability and size. Such variations are not entirely consistent with existing morphological models for tidal inlets and barrier islands on microtidal coasts (Hayes, 1975, 1976). Given that the entire New Brunswick eastern shore is microtidal (tidal range <2 m), factors other than tidal range must control the morphology and stability variations displayed by the inlets. The purpose of this paper is first, to illustrate the range of inlet conditions present in northeast New Brunswick and second, to demonstrate the main controlling factors on inlet variability in this region.

Although the coastline of northeast New Brunswick was described originally by Ganong (1908) and Johnson (1925), much of our present knowledge of the barrier island shorelines of this region has resulted from the later works of Bryant and McCann (1972, 1973), McCann and Bryant (1973), and Owens (1974a, b, 1975). The recent studies provided a

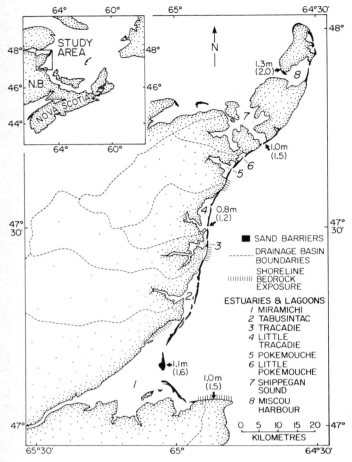

Figure 3.1. *Location map showing the regional setting of the barrier islands, lagoons and corresponding drainage areas. Metric measurements refer to mean tidal ranges and large tidal ranges and are taken from the 1977 tide tables of the Canadian Hydrographic Service.*

basis for the further investigations of specific areas (Munro, 1977; Reinson, 1977, 1979; Rosen, 1979, Bryant, 1979). The impetus to undertake this study stems in particular from the regional synthesis of Owens (1974b), which provided a depositional framework for the barrier island shoreline of northeast New Brunswick. This paper expands on Owens' studies by concentrating on the tidal inlets within that regional barrier island framework.

MARITIME SETTING

The southern Gulf of St. Lawrence is a shallow, semi-enclosed sea in which shore processes are curtailed for up to four months each year by pack and shorefast ice (Owens, 1975). Swell from the north Atlantic enters the southern Gulf for only 7 per cent of the year (Bryant and McCann, 1972), and consequently the wave climate is governed by wind generated within the Gulf itself. Maximum wind fetches, relative to the eastern New Brunswick shoreline, are 500-700 km in north-northeast to east-northeast orientations. However, the prevailing winds are generally offshore, and this inhibits wave generation during ice-free months.

The wave environment is characterized by short-period, locally generated storm waves (Bryant and McCann, 1972). Waves are generally steep with short wave length in relation

to height; wave periods greater than 9.5s, wave heights over 5 m, and wave lengths over 100 m are rare. Wave refraction diagrams indicate that orthogonals of long-period waves (8.8s) from the east converge on Miscou Island and Point Sapin, which are undergoing rapid cliff erosion (McCann and Bryant, 1973). Conversely, orthogonals diverge north of the Miramichi embayment and south of Kouchibouguac Bay, areas dominated by accretionary coastal features.

A dominant southerly directed littoral transport system for the barrier island shoreline of northeast New Brunswick has been inferred by Owens (1974b) on the basis of regional morphological trends. Owens proposed that such a littoral transport pattern occurs in response to wind-generated storm waves from the northeast, the direction from which major storms pass through the region. The suggestion that this section of the southern Gulf shoreline is affected primarily by storm waves has been further substantiated recently by Bryant (1979), who suggested that catastrophic aperiodic storm events play a significant role in effecting local nearshore and barrier morphological changes in the Kouchibouguac embayment south of the study area.

As mentioned previously, the northeast New Brunswick shoreline is essentially a microtidal environment, and the tides are mixed diurnal to semidiurnal. Mean tidal range at Portage Island in the Miramichi embayment is 1.1m, whereas farther north at Tracadie (Fig. 3.1), it is 0.8 m (Canadian Hydrographic Service, 1977).

PHYSIOGRAPHIC AND GEOLOGICAL SETTING

The coastal region of northeast New Brunswick lies in the Maritime Plain physiographic unit (Bostock, 1970). This is a region of low relief with inland elevations up to 180 m, which slope gently towards the coast. The terrain is made up of a thin, intermittent veneer of surficial deposits (glacial and proglacial sediments, peat bogs) overlying flat-lying Permo-Carboniferous sandstones and shales (Owens, 1974b). The drainage system predates glaciation and is developed along structural weaknesses which were modified, both before and after glaciation, by fluvial erosive processes to yield the present drainage configuration.

The entire coastline was submerged by rising sea level following the last Pleistocene glacial retreat, about 13 000 years BP (Prest and Grant, 1969). Consequently the coastal zone is characterized by reentrants or drowned river mouths, the largest of which is the Miramichi estuary (Fig. 3.2). After initial submergence sea level fell to 20 m below its present level around 10 000 years BP, as the result of the rapid isostatic rebound of the crust (Thomas et al., 1973). Over the past 8000 years sea level apparently has slowly risen (Thomas et al., 1973), although rates and fluctuations of Holocene transgression are not yet fully documented for this region. Kranck (1972), Owens (1974b) and Bartlett and Molinsky (1972) discussed the postglacial sea level history for this region as it is presently understood.

The relatively low-relief drainage basin divides, which were gradually submerged during the Holocene marine transgression, form flat-lying subdued headlands at the shoreline. The present barrier island configuration is the result of the landward reworking of glacial and proglacial sediments, to positions between the headlands.

This region is a transgressive shoreline, as are most of the world's coastal plain regions (Kraft, 1978). Comparative analysis of aerial photographs covering the last 30 years indicates that the northeast New Brunswick shoreline in most barrier areas is receding landward, and that sea level may still be rising. Owens (1974b) has observed peat and marsh deposits underlying contemporary beach deposits at some localities; this also indicates that the shoreline is still transgressive.

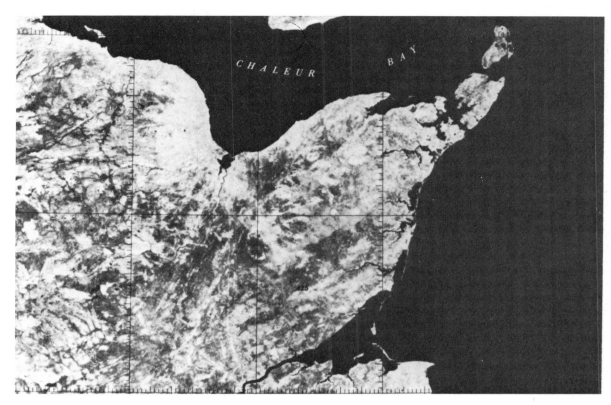

Figure 3.2. *ERTS satellite image mosaic of northeast New Brunswick illustrating the decrease in lagoon-estuary size in a northward direction. For scale: distance between vertical grid lines is 40 km (reproduced from NTS 1:1 000 000 mosaic series, published by Surveys and Mapping Branch, EMR, 1975). (BIO 4455)*

BARRIER ISLAND SYSTEMS

Much of the nearshore zone adjacent to the study area is nearly devoid of sediments (McCann and Reinson, unpubl. data) and foreshore areas adjacent to rocky headlands consist of rock pavement (Fig. 3.1) overlain by only a thin veneer of contemporary littoral sand. As first recognized by Ganong (1908), the headlands delineate four distinct barrier island segments: Miramichi-Neguac, Tabusintac, Tracadie and Pokemouche (Fig. 3.3).

The regional shoreline configuration defined by the four barrier beach segments is largely a function of the submerged topographic configuration of the ancestral pre-glacial, drainage system. The Miramichi-Neguac segment has a highly concave-seaward alignment terminated at the southern end by the most prominent bedrock headland in the region, Point Escuminac. The Tracadie and Pokemouche barrier segments are also concave to seaward, although the Tracadie barrier approaches linearity in its southern portion. Both segments are much less embayed than the Miramichi, because they enclose much smaller ancestral river mouths than that of the Miramichi-Neguac barriers, which extend across a wide, deep, in part structurally controlled reentrant of the Miramichi river valley. The only barrier segment which is convex seaward is Tabusintac, and this difference could exist because there is no prominent headland between Tabusintac and the Miramichi embayment (Fig. 3.4). The Miramichi estuary is separated from Tabusintac lagoon by low-relief 'peat-cliffs', which are receding slowly landward. The drainage basin divide between the Tabusintac and Miramichi river valleys is very subdued, and the presently submerged portion of the ancestral divide must have had a very subdued elevation

also, having been completely drowned during the Holocene transgression. The absence of a pronounced divide and bedrock headland between the Miramichi and Tabusintac systems may indicate that the Tabusintac River was once a large tributary of the Miramichi drainage system. Further, it is conceivable that at some time during the early Holocene an extensive barrier island system may have extended in a relatively straight line across a large combined bay system at the mouths of the two rivers. This would account for the eroding 'peat-cliffs' of the blacklands, which may represent freshwater marsh deposits that were initiated during a lower stand of sea level.

Ganong (1908) commented on the convexity of the Tabusintac barrier shoreline, in contrast to most of the other barriers along the entire eastern New Brunswick coastline, which displayed concavity, and also proposed an explanation for this difference in the following account (Ganong, 1908, p. 25, 26):

Of the beaches..., all are hung in the typical inbowed curves from headland to headland except three, -- the minor case..., and those of Tabusintac and Buctouche. The latter are attached only at one end but are free at the other, and are outbowed. Yet in both cases the explanation is plain. The Tabusintac beach has at present no southern headland except the peat-cliffs of the blacklands, which are being eroded with great rapidity, and which obviously the free end of the Beach is following steadily landward. Yet I have no question that in recent times this Beach had a southern headland, off to the eastward, towards which it ran inbowed, though only a suggestion of such a place is given by the charts. Not only is the existence of such a headland

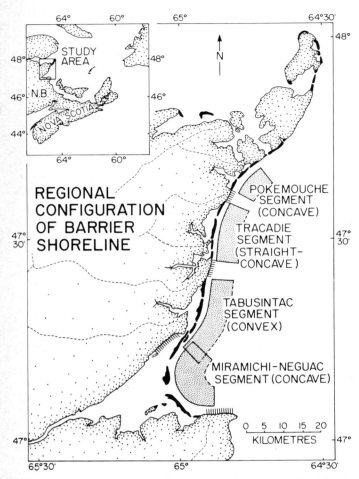

Figure 3.3. *Regional configuration of the barrier-island shoreline defines four barrier-island segments, some of which are separated by bedrock headlands. The segments are aligned either concave to seaward or convex to seaward.*

probable from the beach phenomena, but it is necessitated by the presence of the blacklands, whose great deposits of peat must have had an upland rise between them and the sea.

The four barrier island segments enclose six lagoons (or estuaries), which display a wide range of physical dimensions both in bay surface area and drainage-basin area (Table 3.1). The Miramichi estuary is extemely large, in terms of freshwater input and physical size, compared with the other enclosed bays, which decrease in size in a northward direction, as do the corresponding catchment areas. Both the Pokemouche and Tracadie barrier island systems contain two separate bays (Fig. 3.1). In the Pokemouche system the two lagoons have formed from a natural process of land reclamation by march growth and stabilization. However, at Tracadie the single bay that was fed by two rivers is now completely separated by a small causeway (constructed within the last decade) joining the barrier beach to the mainland (Figs. 3.1, 3.5).

There are presently eleven tidal inlets, or 'gullies' as they are locally referred to, in the four barrier island systems. The largest inlets are those of the Miramichi-Neguac, and the smallest are those in the Pokemouche barrier system, and the northernmost inlet in each of the Tracadie and Tabusintac barrier island systems.

Ten of the eleven inlets could be classified as permanent fixtures; some of them (with the aid of dredging) have been in existence for more than 40 years. Only one could be classified as ephemeral, having formed about four years ago at the northern end of the Tabusintac barrier system (Fig. 3.6).

The two physiographic parameters discussed above, the shoreline configuration or alignment of each barrier segment (Fig. 3.3), and the wide range in physical dimensions and hydraulic parameters of the lagoon-estuary systems (Table 3.1), must play a prominent role in controlling the variability of inlets along the northeast New Brunswick coast. The alignment of the barrier shoreline relative to dominant wave approach will affect the longshore transport conditions, and therefore inlet morphology and stability. Likewise, the size of the estuary (therefore tidal prism), and the magnitude of freshwater input, will control the morphology, size and stability of the tidal inlets within specific barrier segments.

The effects of the two physiographic parameters on the morphology and stability of the tidal inlets in each barrier segment are examined in detail in the following section.

Figure 3.4

Oblique aerial view of the southern part of the Tabusintac barrier segment showing the dual-channelled South Inlet, the overlapping barriers, and the peat cliffs of the "blacklands" that separate Tabusintac lagoon from Neguac bay in the northern part of the Miramichi estuary (view looking west, photo by D. Frobel, November 1977). (uncatalogued)

Table 3.1. Physical characteristics of estuaries and lagoons in the northeast New Brunswick region

Estuary, lagoon	Catchment area	Estimated mean annual runoff rate	Bay area	Inlets
	(km²)	(m³/s)	(km²)	
Little Pokemouche	8	-	3.4	1
Pokemouche	490	10.2	24	1
Little Tracadie	278	-	25	2
Tracadie	533	7.4	15	1
Tabusintac	770	11.6	36	3
Miramichi	13 980	235	295	3

Runoff data from Atlantic Development Board (1969) (in Owens, 1974b) is presented for comparative purposes only. Hydrological data for the Miramichi drainage basin has been recently updated in a comprehensive study by Ambler (1976).

MORPHOLOGY AND STABILITY OF INLETS

Four characteristics of the inlets in each barrier segment are discussed: inlet plan form, presence and nature of flood- and ebb-tidal deltas, locational stability, and cross-sectional stability.

A morphological classification of inlets based on plan form (Fig. 3.7) was devised by Galvin (1971). He recognized four types of inlets based on the offset of the barrier islands on either side and proposed that these configurations were related to three conditions: availability of littoral drift, relative strengths of tidal and longshore transport rates, and ratio of net to gross longshore transport rates (Table 3.2).

In the overlapping offset situation, one barrier extends seaward and downcoast across the entrance to the lagoon (Fig. 3.7). These inlets develop where the supply of littoral drift is adequate, where longshore transport rates are large but the tidal flow strong enough to maintain the inlet channel, and where the ratio of net to gross transport rates approaches 1:0.

An updrift offset occurs where the updrift barrier is offset seaward (Fig 3.7). This barrier is usually tapered toward the inlet. Such inlets occur under conditions similar to the overlapping type, except that a significant number of the waves approach from the downdrift side of the normal to the shoreline. Therefore the ratio of net to gross longshore transport rates is far less than one, but not zero.

Figure 3.5.   *Oblique aerial view (looking north) of the central inlet to Tracadie Lagoon. Note the bulb-shaped form of the barrier north of the inlet, and the highly modified and eroded barrier to the south which is also characterized by extensive washover features. This inlet displays a typical downdrift offset in plan form. Note also the small causeway, separating Little Tracadie from Tracadie Lagoon (left centre of photograph). (Photo by J.R. Belanger, May 3, 1977, winter ice still remains, abutting against the back barrier). (BIO 4405-7)*

Table 3.2. Hypothesis relating inlet offset to coastal processes

Offset	Availability of littoral drift	Ratio of tidal to longshore transport	Ration of net to gross longshore transport (wave direction)
Over-lapping	Adequate updrift source	Relatively equal	Near 1.0 (one side only)
Updrift	Adequate updrift source	Relatively equal	< 1.0 (one side dominant)
Down-drift	Beach is only updrift source	Relatively less long-shore transport	< 1.0 (one side dominant)
Neg-ligible	?	?	Near 0 (both sides equal)

From Galvin (1971). See Figure 3.7.

The downdrift offset displays a rounded or bulb-shaped downdrift barrier which is offset seaward (Fig. 3.7). Such an inlet plan form results when: (a) there is a limited availability of littoral drift, (b) longshore transport rates are small compared to tidal-current transporting capacity, and (c) there is a dominant direction of wave approach, but waves approach from the downdrift side most of the time. Hence the ratio of net to gross transport is less than one, but not zero. The downdrift offset results when there is a lack of source material for littoral drift, other than the beaches themselves. Outer bars adjacent to the inlet also contribute by causing waves to refract around and approach the downdrift as well as the updrift side (Hayes et al., 1970). This causes transport of sediment towards the inlet from both sides.

A negligible offset, or symmetrical inlet, has no offset, or one that is only a fraction of the minimum inlet width. Negligible offset inlets occur under conditions where wave directions are equally distributed about the normal to the shoreline, and where net to gross transport rates approach zero.

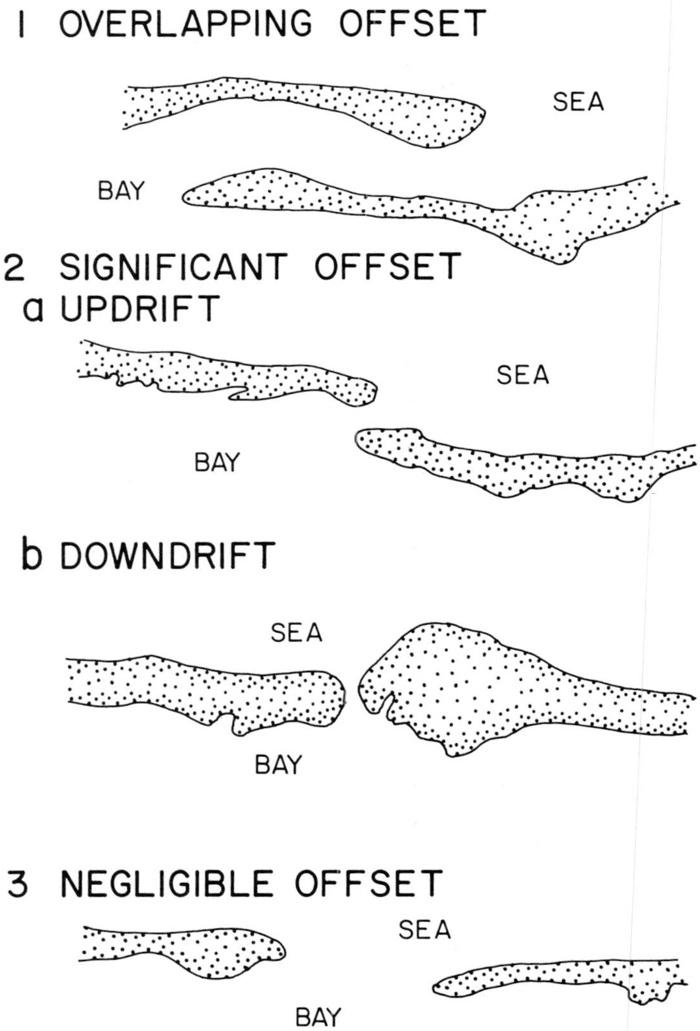

Figure 3.6. *Oblique aerial view (looking south) of the northern part of the Tabusintac barrier segment showing the extensive washover flats in the centre of the photograph, and North Inlet with its flood-tidal delta, at the top of the picture. (Photo by J.R. Belanger, May 3, 1977). (BIO 4404-6)*

1 OVERLAPPING OFFSET

SEA

BAY

2 SIGNIFICANT OFFSET
a UPDRIFT

SEA

BAY

b DOWNDRIFT

SEA

BAY

3 NEGLIGIBLE OFFSET

SEA

BAY

Figure 3.7. *Classification of inlets based on plan form (modified from Galvin, 1971).*

Miramichi-Neguac barrier segment

The Miramichi-Neguac barrier segment is characterized by three inlets, Portage Gully, Portage Channel and Huckleberry Gully (Fig. 3.8). Portage Channel and Portage Gully (Fig. 3.9) are extremely large, and have extensively developed flood-tidal and ebb-tidal delta shoals (Reinson, 1977, 1979). Huckleberry Gully is very small, and has a large inner shoal (flood delta), but no significant ebb delta development. Both Portage Channel and Huckleberry Gully are symmetrical in plan form and are locationally stable. Portage Gully is updrift offset (Table 3.3) and has migrated some 3 km southward since 1945 (Fig. 3.10).

The highly inbowed curvature of the Miramichi embayment induces a longshore sediment transport towards Huckleberry Gully and Portage Channel from both sides of the inlet. Consequently these inlets are symmetrical in plan form. The occurrence of a large ebb and flood delta associated with Portage Channel is related to the magnitude of the tidal prism that drains the inlet. The extremely large tidal prism is able to counteract the strong littoral drift, thereby forming a large ebb delta shoal. High freshwater discharge induces stratification in the water column, and this in turn favors landward transport of sediment to form a flood-tidal delta. In contrast, Huckleberry Gully accommodates a relatively small tidal prism, and therefore cannot flush the inlet of littoral drift. The bay behind is being filled in by littoral drift during flooding tides, but during the ebb phase the tidal currents are not strong enough to remove these sediments to form ebb delta shoals.

This variable morphology of the Miramichi inlets is reflected in the maintenance dredging pattern. Although dredging has been extensive in the Miramichi estuary (Reinson, 1977; McCann et al., 1977), the inlet throats of Portage Channel and Portage Gully have never been dredged. In contrast, Huckleberry Gully has to be dredged periodically to maintain a 2 m deep channel for use by small-draft vessels.

The inlet conditions displayed by Portage Gully, of being locationally unstable (Fig. 3.10) and yet having a large cross-sectional area (Fig. 3.8) with associated well developed ebb and flood delta (Fig. 3.9), are related to a combination of strong southerly littoral drift and a large tidal prism. Portage Gully receives abundant sediment from the Tabusintac barrier immediately to the north, but the tidal prism draining the inlet is large enough to maintain the deep channel even as it migrates. Evidence for a strong southerly drift component has been documented by Owens (1974a, 1975) and this is confirmed by the morphology and stability characteristics of the Tabusintac inlets, which are discussed later.

The cross-sectional stability of Portage Channel and Portage Gully through time are evident in Figure 3.11. Even though Portage Gully has migrated southward at the rate of about 100 m/a*, the cross-sectional area has been maintained and has, in fact, increased some 900 m² over the past 25 years. Similarly, the cross-sectional area of Portage Channel, although remaining constant from 1922 to 1954, increased by 1900 m² since then. The increase of 2840 m² in cross-sectional area for the two inlets combined implies that the volume of water (or tidal prism) draining these inlets, has increased since the early 1950s. An increase in flow volume at Portage Channel has been implied also from the bed form distribution pattern (Reinson, 1979). The increase in magnitude of tidal prism draining Portage Channel and Portage Gully can be attributed to the gradual shoaling over the past century of Neguac Bay and Baie Ste.-Anne (Fig. 3.12), and the closure of Fox Gully (Fig. 3.10) in the early 1970s (Reinson, 1977). These changes probably diverted some of the tidal prism to the two main inlets.

---

* a is the SI symbol for years.

Table 3.3. Inlet offset and stability as observed in vertical aerial photographs taken in 1945, 1963 and 1974

Segment and inlet	Offset 1974	Offset 1963	Offset 1945	Location stability since 1945
Pokemouche				
Little Pokemouche	D(S)	N	N	moved 350 m south
Pokemouche	N	D(N)	D(N)	stable
Tracadie				
North	N	N	N	moved 250 m north
Central	D(N)	N	N	stable
South	N	N	N	moved 1.7 km south*
Tabusintac				
North	D(S)	-	-	-
Tabusintac Gully	U(N)	U(N)	U(N)	moved 3 km south
South	O(N)	O(N)	U(N)	moved 1 km south
Miramichi-Neguac				
Portage Gully	U(N)	U(N)	U(N)	moved 3 km south
Portage Channel	N	N	N	stable
Huckleberry Gully	N	N	N	stable

* Due to relocation of inlet by dredging.
N negligible offset. D(N) downdrift offset on the north. D(S) downdrift offset on the south. U(N) updrift offset on the north. O(N) overlapping offset on the north.

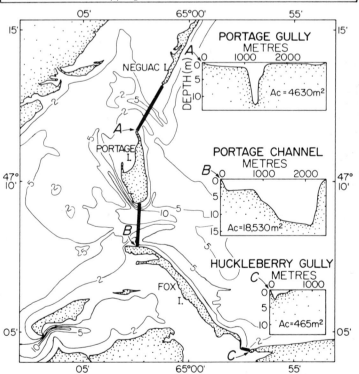

Figure 3.8. *Entrance to the Miramichi estuary showing the form of the flood- and ebb-tidal deltas as defined by the 2 m and 5 m isobaths. Minimum cross-sectional areas (A_C) relative to mean sea level are also illustrated. Portage Channel and Portage Gully sections are drawn from the 1974-1975 hydrographic field sheets, Huckleberry Gully is drawn from the 1922 field sheet.*

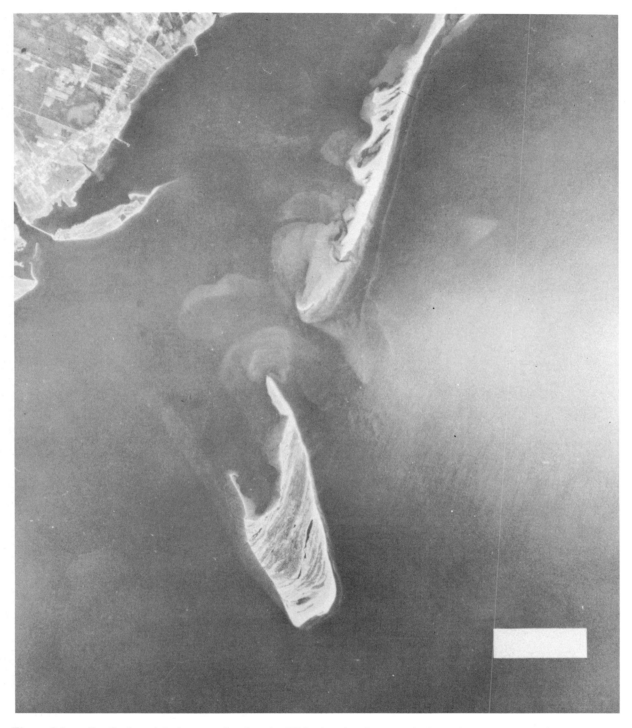

Figure 3.9. *Vertical aerial photograph taken in 1976, showing Portage Gully and corresponding flood- and ebb-tidal delta shoals. The stunted "drumstick" shape of Portage Island (bottom of photograph) contrasts with the long, linear shape of Neguac Island to the north of the inlet. Bar scale is 2 km (Source: NAPL Photo A24434-45).*

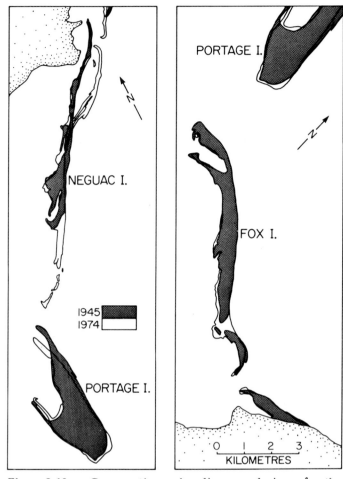

Figure 3.10. *Comparative shoreline analysis of the Miramichi barrier segment using 1945 and 1974 NAPL photo series (modified from Hunter, 1976). Note the former presence of an inlet, Fox Gully, about 2 km north of Huckleberry Gully.*

The entire Miramichi estuary can accommodate a spring tidal prism in the order of 3.8×10^8 m^3, and a mean tidal prism of about 3.3×10^8 m^3 (Table 3.4). According to O'Brien (1931, 1969), the flow area of an inlet in equilibrium is related to the tidal prism by the function $A_c = 2.0 \times 10^{-5}P$ where A_c is the minimum cross-sectional area (ft^2) of the inlet measured below mean sea level, and P is the volume of the tidal prism on a spring or diurnal tide expressed in ft^3. Using this relationship (and converting to metric units) the tidal prism obtained from the combined cross-sectional areas in 1975 of Portage Channel and Gully is 3.5×10^8 m^3, whereas in the 1950s it was 3.1×10^8 m^3. The 0.4×10^8 m^3 difference could easily be explained by a shift in flow volume to the main inlets as the result of peripheral sedimentation and inlet closure. The two main inlets evidently accommodate most of the tidal prism volume for the entire estuary, and Portage Channel alone accounts for up to three quarters of the tidal flow entering the estuary.

It is noteworthy that O'Brien's relationship predicts tidal prism volumes for Portage Channel and Portage Gully that when totalled, compare favourably with the estimated tidal prism for the entire estuary and with the total tidal inlet discharges calculated from the current-velocity measurements of Com Dev Marine (1975) (Table 3.4). However, the revised equation of Jarrett (1976), relating P to A_c for unjettied inlets on the Atlantic coast, predicts unrealistically low tidal prisms, which are not in the same range as the estimated tidal prism for the entire estuary, or the inlet tidal prisms calculated from current-velocity measurements.

Tabusintac Barrier Segment

The Tabusintac barrier is characterized by three main inlets, South Inlet, Tabusintac Gully and North Inlet (Fig. 3.12). Tabusintac Gully and South Inlet are dual channelled, exhibiting pronounced updrift and overlapping offset plan forms, respectively, whereas North Inlet (formed in 1976) is essentially symmetrical in plan at present. All of the Tabusintac inlets have small cross-sectional areas (Fig. 3.13) and the flood-tidal delta shoals (with the exception of the North Inlet delta) are not clearly defined morphological features. Ebb-tidal deltas are even less distinct morphologically than the flood deltas and are also smaller.

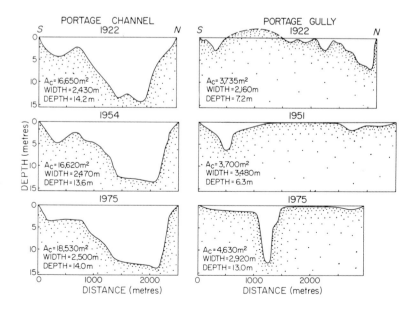

Figure 3.11

Comparison of inlet throat cross sections for Portage Channel and Portage Gully. Sections represent minimum areas measured below mean sea level. (All sections are constructed from CHS field sheets.)

Tabusintac Gully and South Inlet are locationally unstable, tending to migrate southward rapidly at rates of up to 100 m/a (Table 3.3, Fig. 3.14). The present form of North Inlet is rather different from the other Tabusintac inlets, and trends in stability and morphology are not yet evident because of this inlet's relative infancy. However, the more permanent or 'mature' Tabusintac inlets display characteristics that suggest that there is a strong southerly littoral drift along this barrier (or a ratio of net to gross transport approaching one, Table 3.2). The convex shoreline probably promotes this dominant southerly littoral transport. The

tidal prism is sufficiently large to promote tidal currents strong enough to maintain the inlet channels, even though these are laterally unstable.

The longshore drift system for the Tabusintac and Miramichi-Neguac barrier systems can be inferred, from the observations on inlet stability and morphology (Fig. 3.15), to be a composite system of sediment transport from the Tabusintac barrier into the Miramichi-Neguac embayment. Hence the lateral instability of Portage Gully, which receives strong longshore sediment input from the north. Such a longshore drift system for Miramichi-Tabusintac was originally inferred by Owens (1974a, 1975), based on a comparative airphoto analysis of the migrating barrier segments in the Neguac - south Tabusintac region.

Tracadie barrier segment

The Tracadie barrier segment (Fig. 3.3) begins north of the bedrock headland at Barreau Point (Fig. 3.12). The morphology and shoreline alignment of this barrier system is completely different from that of Tabusintac to the south (Fig. 3.16). Individual barrier islands do not overlap but are aligned in a straight to slightly concave shoreline orientation. There are three inlets in this barrier system (Fig. 3.17), two which drain the large lagoon of the little Tracadie River (Fig. 3.1), and a third draining the Tracadie River north of the Val Comeau peninsula (Fig. 3.16). All three inlets have cross-sectional areas estimated to be less than 500 m^2. Both flood- and ebb-tidal deltas are present, but the ebb deltas are small and ill defined compared with the flood deltas (Fig. 3.17).

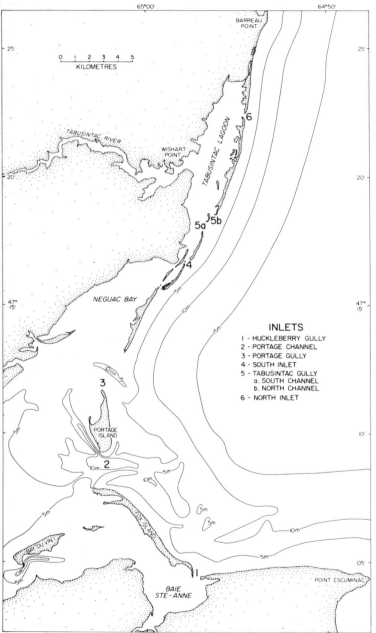

Figure 3.12. Map showing the geographic relationship between the Miramichi embayment and Tabusintac lagoon. Names of the major inlets are shown along with the generalized nearshore bathymetry.

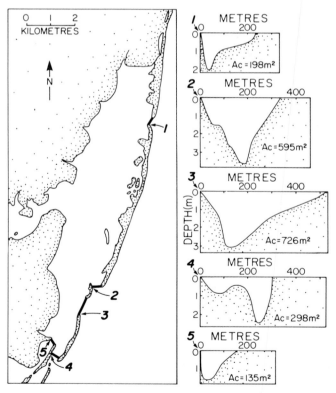

Figure 3.13. Map illustrating the location and configuration of inlet-throat cross sections of the Tabusintac inlets. Cross-sectional areas (A_C) represent the minimum areas measured below mean sea level. (Sections drawn from data collected by the author in July 1977.)

Table 3.4. Relationships between tidal prism and inlet cross-sectional areas for Portage Channel and Portage Gully

Estimated tidal prism for Miramichi estuary using a bay surface area of 295 km^2

3.8×10^8 m^3 (using a measured spring tidal range of 1.3 m for September, October 1974)

3.3×10^8 m^3 (using a predicted mean tidal range of 1.1 m)*

4.7×10^8 m^3 (using a predicted large tidal range of 1.6 m)*

Predicted tidal prisms for Portage Channel and Portage Gully (using O'Brien's relationship, $A_c = 2.0 \times 10^{-5}P$)

	1975	1954(51)
Portage Channel	2.8×10^8 m^3	2.5×10^8 m^3
Portage Gully	0.7×10^8 m^3	0.6×10^8 m^3
Total	3.5×10^8 m^3	3.1×10^8 m^3

Calculated tidal prisms for Portage Channel and Portage Gully (using current-velocity measurements for September, October 1974)**

Portage Channel	2.4×10^8 m^3
Portage Gully	0.5×10^8 m^3
Total	2.9×10^8 m^3

* From Canadian Hydrographic Service (1977).
** Taken by Com Dev Marine (1975). Discharges calculated by method of Jarrett (1976). Values are averages of eight flood and ebb cycles for Portage Channel, and six flood and ebb cycles for Portage Gully.

The central inlet (Fig. 3.5), which has been locationally stable for the last 30 years (Table 3.3), displays a pronounced downdrift offset in plan form (Fig. 3.7, 3.17). According to Galvin's theory, the dominant direction of wave approach at this inlet is from south of the normal to the shoreline, and net longshore drift is northwards. Galvin (1971) has suggested that downdrift offsets usually occur where there is a paucity of source material for littoral drift, the material being derived mainly from adjacent beaches. This situation is evident at the central inlet to Tracadie (Fig. 3.5), where the updrift barrier beach (south of the inlet) is receding rapidly by shoreline erosion, while the downdrift beach is accreting.

The southern inlet in the Tracadie barrier segment (Fig. 3.16, 3.17) displays negligible offset. Its present location is the result of dredging in 1964. Prior to 1964 it was some 1.7 km farther north, and between 1945 and 1963 the inlet migrated about 0.5 km northwards. The inlet migration would infer a net northerly littoral drift in this area, although this is not indicated by the present plan form configuration. The sediment cover in the littoral zone in this area southwards to Barreau Point is minimal. Sidescan and bottom profile records of the nearshore zone indicate that only a thin patchy veneer of sand is present on a predominantly bedrock seabed (McCann and Reinson, unpubl. data). Since the creation of the inlet in 1964, a large flood-tidal delta has formed landward of the barrier and beach erosion has ensued at Val Comeau beach (Fig. 3.5). This indicates

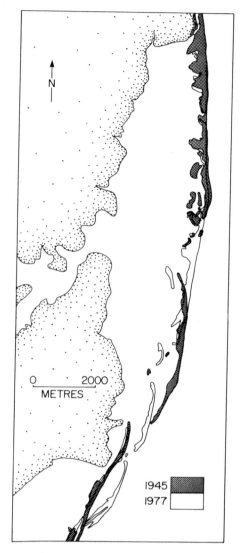

Figure 3.14. *Comparative shoreline analysis of the Tabusintac barrier segment using the 1945 and 1975, 1976 NAPL photo series, as well as oblique photos and aerial observations during May and July 1977. (1977 shoreline map compiled by D. Frobel, 1945 shoreline map interpreted from aerial photographs by P. Vilks.)*

that the littoral sediment is being supplied in large part from erosion of adjacent beaches, is carried into the lagoon by tidal currents, and is lost permanently from the nearshore zone.

The northernmost inlet in the Tracadie barrier segment has a negligible offset configuration and has remained relatively stable, migrating about 250 m northward in 35 years. There appears to be no predominant littoral drift direction in this area, although sand bypassing at the central inlet may be the cause of its slight northward migration. A very small inlet, it still remains open probably because the littoral sediment supply in this region is rather low. If there were an abundant sediment supply this inlet would have been filled in long ago. Under the present situation the tidal prism is large enough to maintain the inlet.

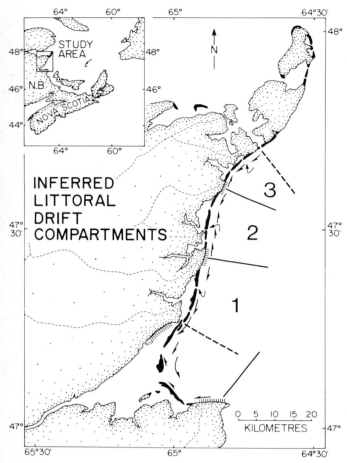

Figure 3.15. *Inferred littoral drift compartments for northeast New Brunswick, based on morphology and stability of the inlets (1 – Miramichi-Tabusintac, 2 – Tracadie, 3 – Pokemouche).*

The Tracadie inlets tend toward closure and both the central and southern inlets have had to be maintained by dredging. The shoaling of these two inlets has not been rapid and, even though the shoreline alignment is concave seaward, the available drift apparently is inadequate to force rapid closure.

The morphology and stability of the Tracadie inlets infer a littoral drift system which is closed at both ends and in which sediment supply is scarce, with no major replenishment from alongshore areas to the north or south of the system.

Pokemouche barrier segment

There are two inlets in the Pokemouche barrier segment (Fig. 3.18), both of which are extremely small, with cross-sectional areas estimated to be less than 300 m². The flood-tidal deltas are extensively developed and are being stabilized by marsh growth. In contrast ebb tidal deltas are virtually absent. The inlet to Pokemouche Lagoon has a negligible offset and has remained in its present position for the past 35 years (Table 3.3). Little Pokemouche inlet displays a slight downdrift offset to the south (Fig. 3.18), and has moved in this direction some 300 m in 30 years. Both inlets display a strong tendency toward closure, and dredging is probably the only reason that they remain open.

A closed littoral drift compartment for the Pokemouche barrier system can be inferred from the morphology and stability of the inlets (Fig. 3.15). Inlet plan forms suggest that the ratio of net to gross transport approaches zero at both inlets, and that waves approach an equal amount of time from all directions of the normal to the shoreline (perhaps a little more so from the north at Little Pokemouche inlet). The shoreline is aligned concave to seaward, and the littoral sediment supply is more abundant than in the Tracadie barrier system. In addition the tidal prisms are not large enough to promote a higher rate of tidal-current transport over longshore transport. All these conditions favour inlet siltation and closure

IMPLICATIONS OF INLET MORPHOLOGY AND STABILITY

A longshore sediment transport system, containing three littoral drift compartments, is inferred from the analysis of inlet morphology and stability (Fig. 3.15). The Miramichi-Tabusintac compartment is a combined system, in which a dominant southerly littoral transport occurs along the Tabusintac segment and enters the Miramichi embayment, where sediment is trapped. This sediment entrapment results from the drift reversal that is set up in the southern part of the embayment by the prominent north-facing headland west of Point Escuminac (Fig. 3.12) (Owens, 1975). The Miramichi-Tabusintac littoral drift system is open to the north, but probably very little sediment enters the system from this direction, because there simply is not enough material available for transport in the region of Barreau Point. The primary source of littoral sediment in the Tabusintac segment probably comes from within the system itself, by shoreface erosion and by landward recession of the barrier islands.

The Tracadie barrier segment is interpreted as a predominantly closed littoral drift system, in which the sediment supply is very low. The barrier beaches are eroding rapidly because they are the main sources of the littoral drift. Onshore reworking is probably not a major contributor to the littoral drift system because of the scarcity of sand in the nearshore zone. Pokemouche is interpreted as a partly closed littoral compartment also, but here the sediment supply from nearshore and alongshore sources appears to be higher than in the Tracadie system.

The littoral drift pattern, inferred from inlet morphology and stability (Fig. 3.15), does not completely fit the generalized southerly sediment dispersal pattern inferred by Owens (1974b) for the entire northeast New Brunswick coast. This does not mean that the model of Owens is not valid on a regional basis, for it is likely that Tracadie and Pokemouche are the only barrier island systems of substantial size on the entire New Brunswick coast (from Miscou Island south to Buctouche Spit in Northumberland Strait) that are not subjected to a dominant southerly longshore transport regime. These two barrier segments, and the one at Shippegan Sound (Fig. 3.1), are situated in a broad shallow-embayed region of the coast that is not entirely exposed to maximum fetches from north-northeast to east-northeast directions. Most of the other barrier island segments are completely exposed to the maximum fetch window.

The fact that the variations in inlet morphology and stability point to a rather complicated littoral drift system for the portion of coastline discussed here indicates the need for a comprehensive wave climate study for the entire southern Gulf of St. Lawrence. As pointed out by Bryant (1979), directional wave data, collected from stationary wave-rider buoys deployed for long periods are needed.

Figure 3.16. *Oblique aerial photograph (looking north) of the Tracadie barrier-island system, showing the Val Comeau peninsula in the foreground, and the downdrift offset central inlet near the top of the photograph. Note the relatively straight to concave alignment of the Tracadie barrier islands compared to those at Tabusintac (Fig. 3.4). (Photo by J.R. Belanger, May 3, 1977) (BIO 4405-3)*

Although hindcasted statistics and occasional wave observations are useful for depicting nearshore wave climates as they affect shorelines on a regional basis, they are not adequate for delineating process-response patterns of specific shoreline segments such as Pokemouche.

The variations in morphology and stability displayed by the inlets along the coastline of northeast New Brunswick are not consistent with the generalized morphological models of Hayes (1975, 1976) for inlet-barrier systems on microtidal coasts. According to Hayes, some major geomorphological differences exist between microtidal barrier island shorelines and mesotidal barrier island shorelines. Microtidal barrier islands are long and linear and characterized by abundant storm washovers, and the tidal inlets and deltas are minor in extent, with more prevalent flood-tidal deltas than ebb deltas. Mesotidal barrier islands are short and stunted (drumstick shaped), and the tidal inlets and deltas, especially the ebb deltas, large and distinct. Microtidal coasts are considered by Hayes to be wave-dominated, whereas mesotidal coasts are affected by both wave- and tidal current - generated processes. Hayes's morphogenetic differentiation, based on tidal range, applies in many barrier island systems throughout the world, but not in the northeast New Brunswick region. Here, there are wave-dominated inlets (Pokemouche), inlets influenced largely by tidal currents (Portage Channel and Portage Gully), large and small inlets, large and small ebb and flood-tidal deltas, and both drumstick and linear islands. (In two cases a drumstick island is situated adjacent to a linear island (Figs. 3.9, 3.17), yet the entire shoreline is microtidal (Fig. 3.1).)

It is suggested here that the tidal range theory for barrier island morphogenesis, although useful for describing variations between regions with substantially different tidal ranges, is certainly not sufficient for explaining the variations of depositional features along and between coastlines subjected to small tidal ranges.

In microtidal, and possibly also in some mesotidal regions, other factors may be as important or more important than tidal range variations in controlling the morphology of barrier island systems. In particular, variations in tidal prism, which is a function of bay surface area and tidal range, will be extremely important in regions of low tidal range.

To summarize, three factors control the variations in inlet conditions and morphology of barrier islands along the northeast coast of New Brunswick. These are (1) the physical dimensions of the bay-river systems that the barrier islands enclose (the tidal prisms), (2) the alignment of each barrier island segment relative to the direction of offshore wave approach, and (3) the variability in the supply of littoral sediment along the coast.

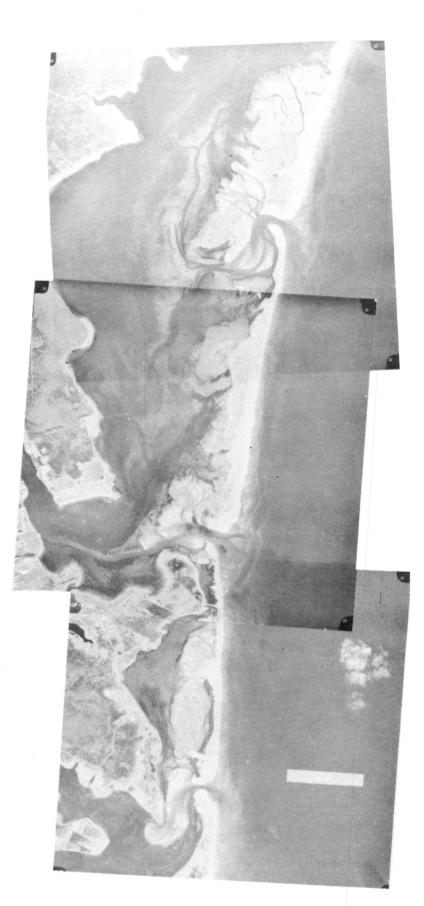

Figure 3.17

Vertical aerial mosaic (using 1974 NAPL photographs) of the Tracadie barrier-island system. Note the large size of the flood deltas relative to the ebb deltas at each inlet. Note also the drumstick-shaped island north of the central inlet and the long-linear island to the south. The barrier island north of the southernmost inlet has undergone extensive modification and erosion. (Bar scale represents 1 km) (BIO 4797-3)

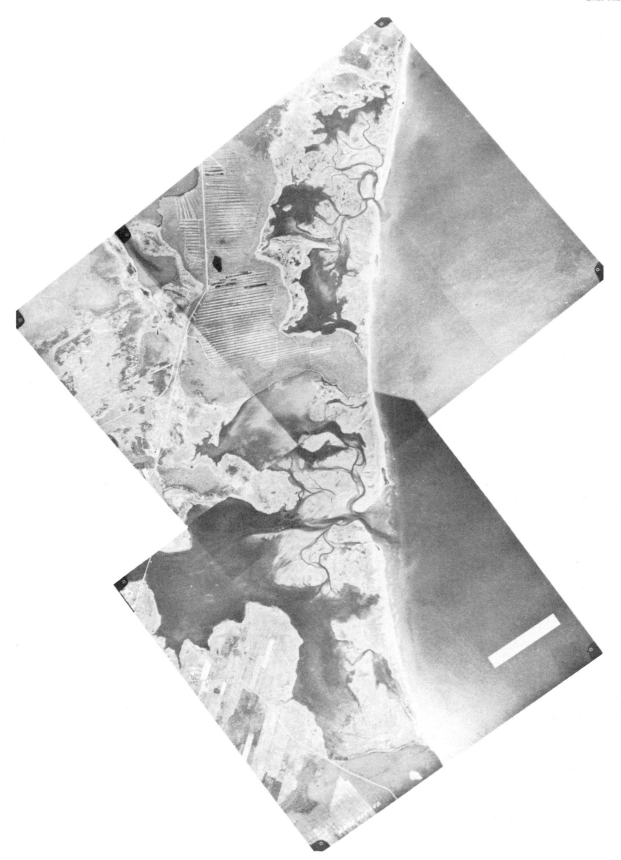

Figure 3.18. *Vertical aerial mosaic (using 1974 NAPL photographs) of the Pokemouche barrier-island segment, showing Little Pokemouche lagoon at the top and Pokemouche lagoonal estuary at the bottom of the composite photograph. Note the symmetry of the inlets, the large accreting flood-tidal delta shoals which are being stabilized by marsh, the lack of ebb-tidal deltas, and the general extremely shallow condition of the inlet channels. The linear striped pattern to the left of Little Pokemouche lagoon is caused by surface mining of peat deposits. (Bar scale represents 1 km) (BIO 4797-2)*

Acknowledgments

I thank S.B. McCann and E.H. Owens for critically reviewing the manuscript and P.S. Rosen, along with McCann and Owens, for providing stimulating discussions during the course of this work. W. Cooper, D. Frobel, M. Gorveatt, F. Jodrey, B. Murphy, and P. Vilks provided assistance during the field survey at Tabusintac, and K. Asprey assisted with laboratory data reduction and synthesis. The illustrations were prepared by A. Cosgrove, K. Hale and H. Slade of the drafting department of the Bedford Institute. I also acknowledge the Canadian Hydrographic Service for their co-operation in providing copies of various field-survey sheets, and Miramichi Channel Study (through K.L. Philpott) who provided a copy of the Miramichi Comparative Shore-line Study.

References

Ambler, D.C.
1976:   Miramichi River Navigation Channel Study, surface water and sediment investigation; Environment Canada, Inland Waters Directorate, Halifax, N.S., 103 p.

Atlantic Development Board
1969:   Maritime Provinces Water Resources Study, Appendix XII, Ground Water Resources, 288 p. and maps.

Bartlett, G.A. and Molinsky, L.
1972:   Foraminifera and Holocene history of the Gulf of St. Lawrence; Canadian Journal of Earth Sciences, v. 9, p. 1204 - 1215.

Bostock, H.S.
1970:   Physiographic subdivisions of Canada; in Geology and Economic Minerals of Canada, R.J.W. Douglas, ed.; Geological Survey of Canada, Economic Geology Series Report No. 1, 5th ed., p. 9 - 30.

Bryant, E.A.
1979:   Wave climate effects upon changing barrier island morphology, Kouchibouguac Bay, New Brunswick; Maritime Sediments (in press).

Bryant, E.A. and McCann, S.B.
1972:   A note on wind and wave conditions in the southern Gulf of St. Lawrence; Maritime Sediments, v. 8, p. 101 - 103.
1973:   Long and short term changes in the barrier islands of Kouchibouguac Bay, southern Gulf of St. Lawrence; Canadian Journal of Earth Sciences, v. 10, p. 1582- 1590.

Canadian Hydrographic Service
1977:   Canadian tide and current tables, 1977, v. 2, Gulf of St. Lawrence; Environment, 63 p.

Com Dev Marine
1975:   Miramichi Survey, Oceanographic Program Report No. 7300-1121 TR (Oceanographic); Atlantic Oceanographic Laboratory, Bedford Institute of Oceanography, Dartmouth, N.S. (unpubl.).

Galvin, C.J., Jr.
1971:   Inlets and wave direction, wave climate and coastal processes; in Symposium on Water, Environment and Human Needs; Massachusetts Institute of Technology, p. 44 - 78.

Ganong, W.F.
1908:   The physical geography of the north shore sand islands; New Brunswick Natural Society Bulletin, No. XXVI, v. VI, pt. 1, p. 22 - 29.

Hayes, M.O.
1975:   Morphology of sand accumulations in estuaries; in Estuarine Research, Vol. 2, Geology and Engineering, L.E. Cronin, ed.; Academic Press, New York, p. 3 - 22.
1976:   Transitional coastal depositional environments; in Terrigenous Clastic Depositional Environments, Some Modern Examples, M.O. Hayes and T.W. Kan, eds.; Technical Report No. 11-CRD, Department of Geology, University of South Carolina, p. I32 - I111

Hayes, M.O., Goldsmith, V. and Hobbs, C.H., III
1970:   Offset coastal inlets; Proceedings of the 12th Conference on Coastal Engineering, Washington, D.C., American Society of Civil Engineers, New York, p. 1187 - 1200.

Hunter, G.A.
1976:   Comparative shoreline analysis, 1837 - 1974; prepared for Miramichi Channel Study, Airphoto Analysis Associates Ltd., Toronto (unpubl.).

Jarrett, J.T.
1976:   Tidal prism - inlet area relationships; GITI Report No. 3, U.S. Army Corps of Engineers, Fort Belvoir, Virginia, 32 p. plus appendices.

Johnson, D.W.
1925:   The New England Acadian shoreline; Wiley and Sons, New York, 608 p. (Facsimile Ed., Hafner, New York, 1967).

Kraft, J.C.
1978:   Coastal stratigraphic sequences; in Coastal Sedimentary Environments, R.A. Davis, Jr., ed.; Springer-Verlag, New York, p. 361 - 380.

Kranck, K.
1972:   Geomorphological developments and post-Pleistocene sea-level changes, Northumberland Strait, Maritime Provinces; Canadian Journal of Earth Sciences, v. 9, p. 835 - 844.

McCann, S.B. and Bryant, E.A.
1973:   Beach changes and wave conditions, New Brunswick; Proceedings of the 13th Conference on Coastal Engineering, Vancouver, B.C., American Society of Civil Engineers, New York, p. 1293 - 1304.

McCann, S.B., Reinson, G.E. and Armon, J.W.
1977:   Tidal inlets of the southern Gulf of St. Lawrence, Canada; in Coastal Sediments '77, 5th Symposium of the Waterway, Port, Coastal and Ocean Division of the American Society of Civil Engineers, Charleston, S.C., American Society of Civil Engineers, New York, p. 504 - 519.

Munro, H.
1977:   Historical development of Neguac Island; Proceedings of the 4th Conference on Port and Ocean Engineering under Arctic Conditions, Sept. 26 - 30,, 1977, Memorial University, St. John's, p. 1 - 11.

O'Brien, M.P.
1931:   Estuary tidal prisms related to entrance areas; Civil Engineering, v. 1, p. 738, 739.
1969:   Dynamics of tidal inlets; in Coastal Lagoons, a Symposium, A. Castanares and F.B. Phleger, eds.; Universidad Nacional Autonoma, Mexico, p. 397 - 406.

Owens, E.H.
1974a: Coastline changes in the southern Gulf of St. Lawrence; in Report of Activities, Part A, Geological Survey of Canada, Paper 74-1A, p. 123, 124.
1974b: A framework for the definition of coastal environments in the southern Gulf of St. Lawrence; in Offshore Geology of Eastern Canada, B.R. Pelletier, ed.; Geological Survey of Canada, Paper 74-30, v. 1, p. 47 - 76.
1975:   Barrier beaches and sediment transport in the southern Gulf of St. Lawrence, Canada; Proceedings of the 14th Conference on Coastal Engineering, Copenhagen, Denmark; American Society of Civil Engineers, New York, p. 1177 - 1193.

Prest, V.K. and Grant, D.R.
1969:   Retreat of the last ice sheet from the Maritime provinces - Gulf of St. Lawrence region; Geological Survey of Canada, Paper 69-33, 15 p.

Reinson, G.E.
1977:   Tidal current control of submarine morphology at the mouth of the Miramichi estuary, New Brunswick; Canadian Journal of Earth Sciences, v. 14, p. 2524 - 2532.
1979:   Longitudinal and transverse bedforms on a large tidal delta, Gulf of St. Lawrence, Canada; Marine Geology, v. 31, p. 279 - 296.

Rosen, P.S.
1979:   Aeolian dynamics of a barrier island system; in Barrier Islands---From the Gulf of St. Lawrence to the Gulf of Mexico, S.P. Leatherman, ed.; Academic Press, New York, p. 81 - 98.

Thomas, M.L.H., Grant, D.R. and deGrace, M.
1973:   A Late Pleistocene marine shell deposit of Shippegan, New Brunswick; Canadian Journal of Earth Sciences, v. 10, p. 1329 - 1332.

Addendum

Since the writing of this paper two important papers have been published that are highly pertinent to the preceding discussions:

Hayes, M.O.
1979:   Barrier-island morphology as a function of tidal and wave regime; in Barrier Islands---From the Gulf of St. Lawrence to the Gulf of Mexico, S.P. Leatherman, ed.; Academic Press, New York, p. 1 - 27.

Reinson, G.E. and Frobel, D.
1980:   The effects of dredging activities on shoreline morphology and stability, northeast New Brunswick; Proceedings of Canadian Coastal Conference 1980, National Research Council, Ottawa.

4.

CHANGEABILITY IN SMALL FLOOD TIDAL DELTAS AND ITS EFFECTS, MALPEQUE BARRIER SYSTEM, PRINCE EDWARD ISLAND

John W. Armon
Department of Geography, McMaster University, Hamilton, Ontario

Armon, John W., Changeability in small flood tidal deltas and its effects, Malpeque barrier system, Prince Edward Island; in The Coastline of Canada, S.B. McCann, editor; Geological Survey of Canada, Paper 80-10, p. 41-50, 1980.

Abstract

Changes in flood tidal delta morphology from 1935 to 1976 were investigated for two small tidal inlets on northern Prince Edward Island. Both inlet systems have undergone considerable modifications since 1935, as a result of channels migrating on the flood tidal delta, new channels forming, and others closing. The stimulus to channel migration has generally been deposition along one channel margin, in response to sediment inputs from the littoral drift or an adjacent channel. Elsewhere, new channels have developed in situations providing direct water exchanges between the estuary and inlet throat. The impact of a flood tidal delta's channel configuration upon inlet behaviour was also investigated for the larger inlet, Hardys Channel, using current velocity data. Results indicate a relationship between flow conditions in the 1970s and recent inlet migration. Comparisons between these small inlets and larger inlets in this microtidal environment suggest that some inlet responses are influenced more by inlet size, or tidal prism, than by tidal range.

Résumé

Les auteurs ont étudié la modification du modelé des deltas engendrée par les courants de marée entre 1935 et 1976 et se sont plus particulièrement intéressés à deux petits inlets de marée situés dans le nord de l'Ile-du-Prince-Edouard. Les deux ensembles d'inlets ont subi des modifications considérables depuis 1935, par suite de la migration des chenaux sur le delta de marée, de la formation de nouveaux chenaux tandis que d'autres se refermaient. La migration des chenaux a généralement accompagné la sédimentation qui s'est effectuée le long d'une bordure de chenal, à la suite d'apports de sédiments provenant de la dérive littorale ou d'un chenal adjacent. Ailleurs, de nouveaux chenaux se sont formés dans des situations assurant des échanges d'eau directs entre l'estuaire et le goulot de l'inlet. L'effet de la configuration du chenal du delta sur le comportement de l'inlet a été aussi étudié dans le cas du plus grand des deux inlets, le chenal Hardys, au moyen des données sur la vitesse du courant. Les résultats obtenus indiquent un rapport entre les conditions d'écoulement dans les années 70 et la récente migration de l'inlet. Des comparaisons effectuées entre ces petits inlets et les plus grands dans ce milieu microtidal laissent croire que certaines réactions des inlets dépendent davantage de la taille des inlets ou du prisme de marée que de l'amplitude de marée.

INTRODUCTION

Sandy sections of shoreline fringing the southern Gulf of St. Lawrence in New Brunswick and Prince Edward Island are characterized by spits and barrier islands broken by small and large tidal inlets. The barrier islands and the nearshore zone have received much attention during the 1970s (Bryant and McCann, 1973; Greenwood and Davidson-Arnott, 1975; Owens, 1974; Armon and McCann, 1977a) but little has been published on the tidal inlets until recently (Reinson, 1977; McCann et al., 1977). The tidal inlets occurring around the southern Gulf are of interest because of their impact on barrier island dynamics (Armon and McCann, 1979) and their location in a coastal environment with small tidal ranges and restricted wind fetches. This latter aspect is important because detailed studies of inlet morphology, currents, bedforms and patterns of net sediment transport have generally been carried out along exposed ocean coasts possessing larger tidal ranges (e.g., Coastal Research Group, 1969; Byrne et al., 1974; Boothroyd and Hubbard, 1975). The resulting models of flood-tidal and ebb-tidal delta morphology and dynamics from such areas have been extended recently to inlets in other coastal environments (Hayes, 1975).

This paper considers changes on the inner sand bodies of two small tidal inlets along the Malpeque barrier system, northern Prince Edward Island (Fig. 4.1). The term 'flood-tidal delta' is applied here to the entire inner sand body, rather than to the more restricted zone considered by some workers. This study has three aims: to establish the degree and rate of changeability in channel patterns on the flood-tidal deltas of the inlets, to explain any changes in channel positions, and to assess the possible impact of such changes on inlet migration. Changes in channel patterns have been investigated using aerial photography flown since 1935, and the tidal current conditions and inlet responses have been recorded for one inlet. The results presented here provide the basis for evaluating Hayes's (1975) conclusions regarding tidal inlet systems in microtidal regimes.

FIELD AREA

The two tidal inlets, Hardys Channel and Palmer Inlet, are located 17 km apart, midway along the Malpeque barrier system (McCann et al., 1977). The adjacent sections of barrier shoreline are transgressive, maintaining their general character and dimensions under continuing landward retreat

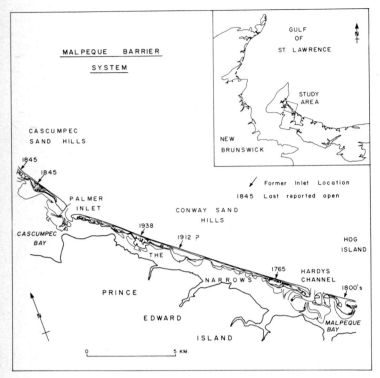

Figure 4.1. *Location map for Hardys Channel and Palmer Inlet, Malpeque barrier system, Prince Edward Island. Previous inlet sites are indicated by arrows.*

(Armon and McCann, 1977a). Wind fetches in the northeastern quadrant vary between 150 and 700 km, so that in the context of the southern Gulf this barrier shoreline is an exposed one. The longest fetch is to the northeast but storm waves are formed more commonly from the north, resulting in net southeastward sediment transport along the coast. The northwestern section of the barrier islands is partly sheltered from these northerly wave approaches and rates of net longshore sediment transport are lower there. Data on inshore wave conditions and other evidence suggest that rates increase from 40 000 m^{3}year^{-1} southeast at Palmer Inlet to 200 000 m^{3}year^{-1} southeast by Hardys Channel (Armon and McCann, 1977a, b). The difference in rates appears to be made up largely by the continuing erosion of the nearshore surface along Conway Sand Hills, down to 10 - 15 m water depths.

The tides are mixed mainly semidiurnal, with a maximum range in spring approaching 1.3 m, and mean tidal ranges of 0.67 - 0.77 m (Canadian Hydrographic Service, 1973). Characteristic spring tidal ranges are around 1.0 m. Freshwater inputs to the estuaries are relatively minor except during spring snowmelt, and waters at the inlets are unstratified (Armon, in prep.). Two large estuaries back the Malpeque barrier system but most of their tidal exchanges occur through the larger inlets, Alberton Harbour inlet in the north and Malpeque Channel in the south. The remaining limited catchment areas plus the microtidal ranges result in small tidal prisms and inlet dimensions for Hardys Channel and Palmer Inlet (Table 4.1). The dimensions of these inlets are an order of magnitude less than those of Malpeque Channel.

In spite of their minor dimensions, small inlets have had considerable impact on the Malpeque barrier system in the long term. Since the earliest map coverage in 1765 nine other inlets have been reported, seven of which are small inlets. Approximately 30 per cent by length of the shoreline has been influenced by present or former tidal inlets in the past 210 years, and over 90 per cent by volume of all measured landward sediment movements in the period 1935 - 1968 occurred at tidal inlets or former small inlet situations (Armon and McCann, 1979; Armon, 1979).

Hardys Channel is the larger of the two inlets, exchanging most of the waters from The Narrows (Fig. 4.1; S. Vass, pers. com., 1978) as well as from adjacent sections of Malpeque Bay. This inlet has existed for the last two centuries. Map and geomorphic evidence indicate that it has moved 1200 m to the southeast during that time, with 380 m recorded since 1935. The small ebb-tidal delta extends 400 - 500 m seaward from the inlet throat and links with the outer nearshore bar. In the estuary, the relatively large flood-tidal delta is 2500 m by 1100 m. Since 1970 small inlet channels have formed immediately southeast of Hardys Channel but their tidal prisms remain small and they have had little influence on the actions at Hardys Channel.

Palmer Inlet formed in this century between 1912 and 1935, and has remained open in spite of its rather small dimensions. In contrast to Hardys Channel this inlet has maintained its general position since 1935, showing no tendency to migrate downdrift. In fact, the inlet throat at Palmer Inlet has migrated 100 m to the northwest in the decades following 1935. The ebb-tidal delta is similar in seaward extent to that of Hardys Channel but is shallower across its outer margin or terminal lobe (0.5 - 0.7 m below low low water (LLW)). The flood-tidal delta extends 1800 m alongshore and 1000 m into the estuary.

The landward margins of the flood-tidal deltas at Hardys Channel and Palmer Inlet mark the limit of sand transport into the estuaries from these inlets. Eelgrass

Table 4.1 Inlet dimensions, Malpeque barrier system

	Width of throat	Maximum depth at throat	Mean depth at throat	Mean cross-sectional area
	(m)	(m)	(m)	(m^2)
Hardys Channel	130	7.9	3.5	720
Palmer Inlet	190	4.0	2.5	470
Malpeque Channel	1240	18	7.3	9000
Alberton Harbour inlet	470	6.3	3.5	1610

Source: Table 5.1, p. 175, Armon (1975), with modifications for Malpeque Channel.

(*Zostera marina*) grows on the estuary floor adjacent to the deltas and on the bottoms of channels emerging into the estuary, permitting only very limited sand transport. This situation for small tidal inlets supports Hayes's (1975) contention that in microtidal estuarine environments sand transport by tidal currents diminishes rapidly away from inlet locations. On the other hand, changes recorded in Malpeque Bay (Sheldon et al., 1968) plus the extensive sand bodies there indicate that sand transport may be active for much greater distances landward from larger inlets in some microtidal situations.

FLOOD TIDAL DELTA CHANGES

Hardys Channel

Hardys Channel is the more accessible and easily studied inlet of the two. In the seventies it consisted of four zones of clam flat separated by simple or complex channel sets (Fig. 4.2). The major channel set was directed to the west from the inlet throat, and depths of 3 - 4 m were maintained in the main west channel across the flood-tidal delta. The other major channels had maximum depths of 2.0 - 3.5 m, but were considerably shallower at estuary and inlet ends (0.5 - 1.5 m below LLW). The surface of the flood-tidal delta was 0.4 - 0.7 m above low low water, being completely covered during large and spring tides only.

Figure 4.3 presents the inlet morphologies recorded at Hardys Channel between 1935 and 1968. The striking differences between the conditions in 1935 and 1958 highlight the degree of changes in channel patterns that can occur at this inlet. In 1935 there was a simple bifurcation landward of the inlet throat into two channel sets, with a continuous clam flat zone backing these channels. By 1958 the major 1935 channel sets curved back into the flood-tidal delta, and additional channels were present in the west and southwest. The conditions recorded from 1958 to 1968 demonstrate the rate at which such changes can occur. In 1964 two channel sets existed where there was one in 1958, and elsewhere noticeable changes had also taken place. These trends continued through to 1968 and by that time the flood-tidal delta had much of its 1973 character (Fig. 4.2).

The extent of these changes is indicated on Figure 4.4 for the time periods 1935 - 1958 and 1958 - 1968. During the earlier 23-year period the southeastern channel system was deflected over 400 m landward, with a lesser deflection recorded for the main west channel. Subsequently a new channel set developed across the southeastern sand flat, other channel systems were reoriented, and the inner margin of Conway Sand Hills eroded. The inlet throat and ebb-tidal delta migrated continuously to the southeast in the decades following 1935. This migration has often been a factor influencing the changes on the flood-tidal delta.

The changes in channel patterns recorded here result from both channel migration and channel initiation or infilling. The impetus to channel migration commonly appears to have been a surplus of sediment deposited along one channel margin. For example, 1958 aerial photography shows a large accumulation on the updrift (northwest) margin of Hardys Channel, deposited from the littoral drift in association with the inlet's longshore migration. This deposition apparently forced the main west channel to curve landward into the delta. It also appears likely that the development of extensive sandflats immediately southeast of the 1958 inlet throat caused the migration of the southeastern channel set there. These sandflats developed from the eroding downdrift inlet margin as a result of landward sediment transport by storm overwash.

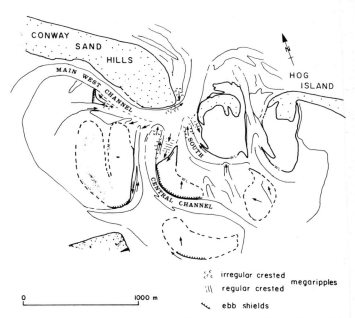

irregular crested
regular crested megaripples
ebb shields

0   1000 m

Figure 4.2.   *Hardys Channel flood tidal delta, June 8th, 1973. Source: CN 2482, frames 75-28; NAPL.*

Some channels have changed only in the orientation of their seaward margins, in response to the changing current deposition patterns in adjacent channels. For instance, the reorientation of the southeastern 1958 channel set through to 1968 resulted from the formation of an additional channel set immediately seaward (Fig. 4.3).

Channel initiation has also contributed to the changes in channel patterns. At present little is known of the mechanisms triggering the formation of new channels but several possibilities exist. In some circumstances ice might promote localized scour during spring breakup. Strong hydraulic currents resulting from a major storm surge may accentuate irregularities over the clam flats, if the surge coincides with spring high tide. Enhancement of local irregularities during normal spring tides is unlikely because water depths are shallow and current speeds over the higher clam flats are only 30 - 40 cm s^{-1} (Armon, in prep.).

Two characteristics of channel formation have become apparent from an analysis of aerial photographs. New channels have consistently developed in locations that have led to more direct channelized water exchanges between the inlet and estuary. In addition, channel formation appears to have occurred commonly in response to one set of currents (flood or ebb). For example, the precursor of the south channel system was evident in 1958, crossing the higher intertidal sandflats (Fig. 4.3). This channel's nonalignment with the axis of the inlet throat indicates that ebb currents rather than flood currents were important in forming it there.

Once initiated, channels tend to grow into full channels by positive feedback, as current speeds are higher in channels than on the clam flat and the currents are active for longer periods. That such a development can be rapid is revealed in the changes between 1973 and 1976 when a channel formed between central and south channel (Fig. 4.5). In 1973 the beginnings of the channel were seen at the junction with south channel; it was fully developed by 1976.

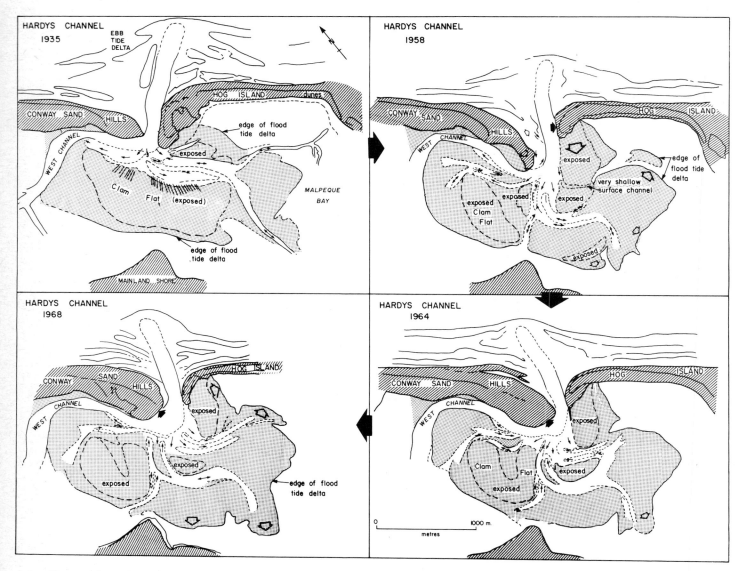

Figure 4.3. *Flood tidal delta morphology at Hardys Channel between 1935 and 1968. The major sand bodies are shaded. Source: Run numbers A5074, A16112, A18452, and A20356; NAPL.*

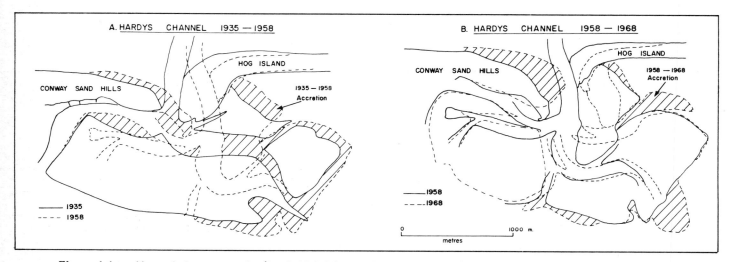

Figure 4.4. *Mapped changes on the flood tidal delta at Hardys Channel for the periods 1935-1958 and 1958-1968.*

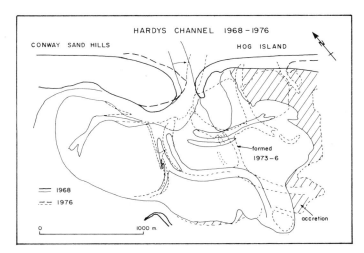

Figure 4.5. *Mapped changes on the flood tidal delta between 1968 and 1976. Source: Run numbers A20356, CN 2482, and A24328; NAPL.*

Palmer Inlet

The flood-tidal delta at Palmer Inlet (Fig. 4.6) resembles more closely than Hardys Channel the model proposed by Hayes et al. (1973) for mesotidal flood-tidal deltas. There are noticeable ebb shields and spillover lobes, a relatively large flood ramp, and a reduced clam flat zone. The characteristic bifurcation into two channel sets at the inlet throat, however, has not been evident at Palmer Inlet since 1958 (Fig. 4.7). For the last two decades there has been a major channel and flood ramp complex directed south-eastwards into the estuary, introducing an asymmetry to the channel system. Depths in the channels here are shallow (up to 2 m below LLW) and only 0.5 to 1.0 m deep at the estuary limits.

In 1935 this inlet was relatively symmetrical and the flood-tidal delta rather segmented (Fig. 4.7). However, by 1958 the asymmetry had developed in the channel pattern. Conditions were similar in 1971, but with a more pronounced curviness to the major channel set.

This flood-tidal delta system is smaller, simpler and less changeable than in Hardys Channel. In detail though, both channel migration and channel initiation or closure are evident (Fig. 4.8). Changes closest to the inlet have generally been a response to the continued landward migration of the inlet margins since 1935. Elsewhere the most noticeable changes have been in the zone of small channels with spillover lobes, located west of the flood ramp (Fig. 4.7). Contrasts in the channel numbers, sizes and locations in successive aerial surveys between 1958 and 1971 show they are constantly changing.

The most unexpected feature of inlet behaviour at Palmer Inlet has been the migration of the inlet throat 100 m northward since 1935 (Fig. 4.8), which occurred as the updrift and downdrift waterlines were migrating south-wards. The responses of the waterlines are an expected result of a southerly littoral drift, with deposition updrift and erosion downdrift of the inlet throat. Part of the reason for the unusual behaviour of the inlet throat is the small size of the inlet and ebb delta system, which has allowed the sediment moving along the coast to bypass the inlet easily.

The net longshore sediment transport rate at Palmer Inlet is also relatively low. A possible cause of the inlet's updrift movement, considered below, is the ebb current flow pattern at the inlet throat, produced by the configuration of channels on the flood-tidal delta.

CHANNEL CONFIGURATIONS AND EBB FLOW CONDITIONS

The investigation of current conditions at Hardys Channel suggests that channel patterns on flood-tidal deltas can influence inlet behaviour, in particular the direction and rate of inlet migration. This is due to the effect of channel configuration on water flow through the inlet throat during ebb tide conditions, at times when waters crossing the flood-tidal delta are largely carried in the channels.

At Hardys Channel, ebb flow conditions in the seventies were dominated by the waters driving in from the west in a channel 3-4 m deep, carrying up to 80 per cent of the ebb flow. Incoming waters from the other channels had maximum flow depths of 1.5 - 2.5 m and influenced the pattern of ebb currents mostly in the upper 2 m. During spring tide in 1977 (Fig. 4.9) the waters entering from the central channel contained the surface flow from the west against the north channel margin, where the highest current speeds (150 cm s^{-1}) were recorded. Elsewhere, high surface speeds were also measured towards the downdrift marginal shoal of the ebb-tidal delta.

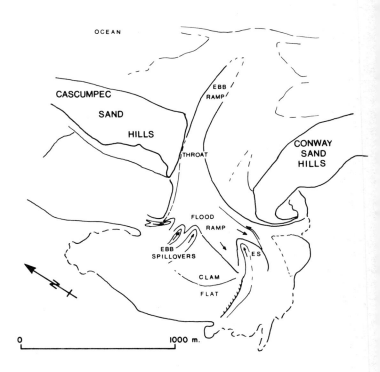

Figure 4.6. *Palmer Inlet flood tidal delta, 1971. Source: A22600, Number 47; NAPL.*

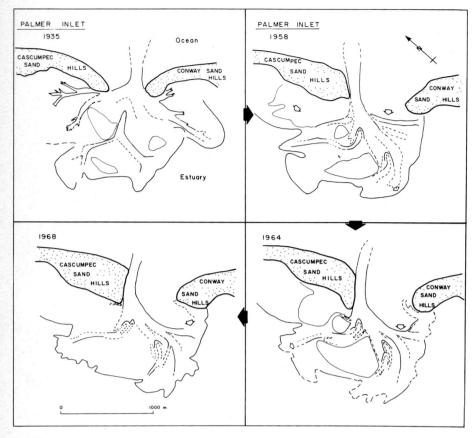

Figure 4.7

Flood tidal delta morphology at Palmer Inlet between 1935 and 1968. The major sand bodies are shaded. Source: Run Numbers A5076, A16096, A18452, and A20380; NAPL.

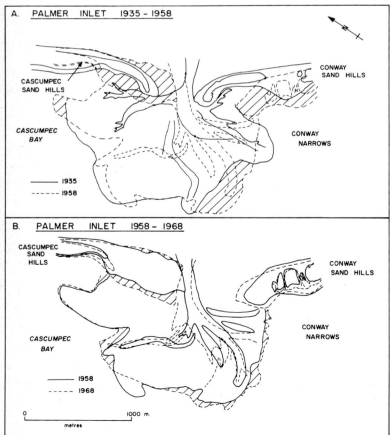

Figure 4.8

Mapped changes on the flood tidal delta at Palmer Inlet, for the periods 1935-1958 and 1958-1968.

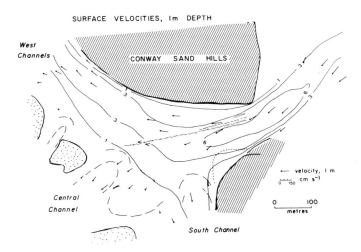

Figure 4.9. *A summary of ebb flow velocities at 1 m depth for spring tide conditions, July 1977. Major sand body locations mapped in the field and isobaths established from echo sounding.*

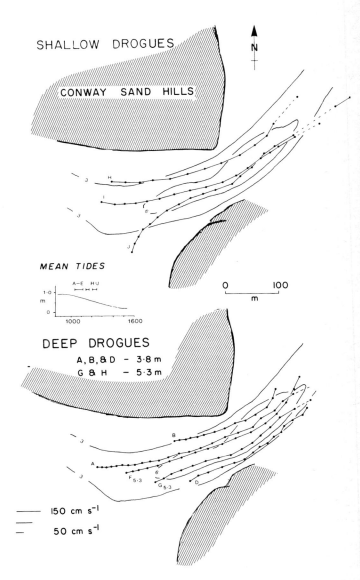

Figure 4.10. *Ebb current drogue tracks at selected depths, recorded during mean tide conditions in July 1977. The shallow drogues were suspended at 1.8 m depth. The deep drogues show the general character of the flow through the inlet throat.*

At depth, the flow pattern exhibited significant differences. Current drogue paths at 3.8 and 5.3 m (Fig. 4.10) and vertical water temperature profiles indicated that the flow from the west drove 30 - 50 m under the water from the central channel. Passing through the inlet throat, the deeper drogue tracks shown in Figure 4.10 maintained generally discrete and curvilinear paths. More significantly, there was a tendency for the curving flow to sweep against the southeastern inlet margin because the major water mass was approaching the inlet throat at a large angle from the west, and was forced to turn rapidly seaward. In doing so, its considerable momentum caused the flow to drive against the downdrift channel margin.

This current pattern has resulted in undercutting of the southeastern inlet margin. Bathymetric maps compiled from echosounding data show steeper slopes along part of the southeastern margin of Hardys Channel, in the zone where currents impinge on the channel side. Consequently, the migration rate of Hardys Channel during the seventies is a response to ebb current flow patterns as well as to the mechanisms usually advocated: updrift deposition and contrasts in channel margin materials (Hayes, 1976).

A similar situation appears to have existed at Palmer Inlet in recent decades, but with the major ebb flows approaching from the opposite of the inlet throat. The channel pattern has been noticeably asymmetrical since 1958, and dominant water exchanges occur between the inlet and the estuary to the southeast. This dominance is confirmed by photographic records of early ice-breakup conditions in 1973 (RSA30624, frames 33-36, National Air Photo Library, Ottawa). The asymmetry appears to produce ebb-tidal flows which curve against the northern channel margin in turning seaward, promoting its erosion, but profiles across the inlet throat in the seventies show similar slopes on both inlet margins, and the evidence remains unclear. However, updrift deposition at this inlet is not effective in promoting inlet migration, and tidal currents remove any sediment deposited subtidally on the updrift inlet margin.

DISCUSSION AND CONCLUSIONS

Aerial photographs flown since 1935 record details of major changes in channel patterns on the flood-tidal deltas of two small inlets on northern Prince Edward Island. There are contrasts between the inlets in flood-tidal delta size and morphology, as well as in the extent of the changes recorded. Hardys Channel is the larger of the two inlets, the most complex, and has undergone the most striking changes in channel patterns. New channels and channel sets have formed there since 1935, accompanied by marked changes in channel orientation or location for adjacent channels. Changes at Palmer Inlet were most evident for the 1935-1958 period, when marginal channels either infilled or migrated into the delta. In the decades following 1958 most changes there were recorded in the small channels with ebb spillover lobes, at both ends of the central clam flat.

Observations of these inlets indicate that considerable changes can occur rapidly in channel sets crossing flood-tidal deltas of small inlets in microtidal environments. Channel migration of more than 400 m has been recorded within 23 years and new channels have formed in 3 to 6 years. Such changeability has not been described previously although early writers incorporated changing channel patterns into their models of inlet evolution (Lucke, 1934). The changes reported have generally been in flood-tidal delta size (El-Ashray and Wanless, 1965; McCormick, 1973) or in small-scale features (Finley, 1975). Hine (1975) recorded the migration of flood spillover lobes on a newly formed, growing flood-tidal delta.

Johnson (1919) attributed developments in channel patterns at migrating inlets to the downdrift channels competing more successfully for waters discharging through the inlet. Analysis of the aerial photography at Malpeque has contributed new information on the factors influencing changes in channel patterns. The alongshore migration of Hardys Channel has affected some of the changes in channel positions, but more directly than proposed by early writers. Deposition associated with the migration of Hardys Channel between 1935 and 1958 forced some channels to move laterally. Most significantly, the downdrift channel set was deflected by more than 400 m as the washover flat developed on the southeastern inlet margin. Similar washover flats have also accumulated southeast of the small inlet channels opened in the seventies (Fig. 4.2). Channels formed on the flood-tidal delta at Hardys Channel since 1935 have competed successfully for inlet waters, but only the southern channel set developed downdrift. Other channels formed where extensive areas of clam flat had previously existed (Fig. 4.3) and their success resulted from providing more direct channelized exchanges between the inlet and estuary.

Reinson (1977) related historical changes in ebb-tidal delta morphology at Portage Channel, New Brunswick, to changing flow conditions through the inlet, induced by a dredged channel through the flood-tidal delta. At Hardys Channel the current and morphologic evidence recorded in the seventies similarly indicates that channel patterns of the flood-tidal delta can influence ebb flow conditions through the inlet throat. During ebb tides the major channelized water mass drove in at a large angle to the inlet throat and its considerable momentum caused the ebb flow to sweep against the southeastern channel margin in turning seaward. This caused undercutting of the southeastern inlet margin and probably contributed to the migration of Hardys Channel in the seventies. The degree to which migration rates have been affected by this action is not known, however, because of the additional effects of updrift deposition from the littoral drift and material differences between updrift and downdrift inlet margins.

This ebb flow condition at Hardys Channel appears to resemble the ebb current pattern occurring there since 1964. The aerial survey in 1964 was the first occasion when the seventies' channel configurations and alignments were observed on the flood-tidal delta. Prior to that survey major differences existed. In 1958 the western channels curved into the flood-tidal delta and approached the inlet throat at a small angle only. Downdrift undercutting due to the channel configuration would not have been active then. In addition, the 1958 inlet morphology and the 1935-1958 mapped changes confirm that updrift deposition has played an active role in diverting currents and promoting inlet migration. In 1935 two channel systems approached from opposite sides and the resulting flow conditions at the inlet would have contrasted markedly with those in the seventies.

The behaviour of Palmer Inlet since 1935 may have been similarly influenced by channel patterns on the flood-tidal delta and the resulting ebb flow conditions. The inlet throat has migrated in an updrift direction, an action which is best explained in terms of ebb waters driving in from the southeast and eroding the northern inlet margin.

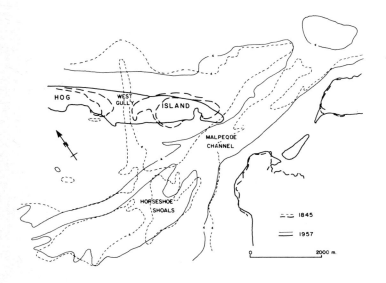

Figure 4.11

Malpeque Channel, southeastern Malpeque barrier system, showing mapped positions of the 12 foot (approx. 4 m) isobath in 1845 and 1957. The major changes are associated with the filling of West Gully inlet. Source: Bayfield (1845) and Canadian Hydrographic Service (1966).

The responses investigated here are for small tidal inlets in a microtidal regime, that is, inlets possessing small tidal prisms. The degree of changeability and the rate at which changes occur likely are different for larger inlet systems, whether in microtidal or mesotidal environments. At Hardys Channel and Palmer Inlet the inlet throats and adjacent channel sets are relatively shallow and unaffected by bedrock. Substantial changes can occur rapidly, often promoted by inlet migration landwards or along the coast. Larger, deeper channels crossing the flood-tidal deltas of major inlet systems may well resist change better because of their greater dimensions and the restrictive effect of bedrock. Thus Malpeque Channel maintained the same general morphology between 1845 and 1957 (Fig. 4.11), and the major changes on the flood-tidal delta (Horseshoe Shoals area) arose from closure of a nearby inlet. Evidence presented by Reinson (1977) similarly showed a relatively unchanging flood-tidal delta and channel complex at Portage Channel.

Hayes (1975) focussed on the influence of tidal range in controlling the distribution and form of sand bodies in estuaries. Some of his conclusions were (1) that sand transport in microtidal estuaries is largely restricted to the vicinities of tidal inlets, (2) that flood-tidal deltas in microtidal estuaries are generally small, and (3) that models established for flood-tidal deltas in mesotidal environments (tidal range 2 - 4 m) may well apply to inlets in microtidal environments. The evidence from the large and small inlets at Malpeque suggests that tidal prism (or inlet size) often requires as much consideration as tidal range. Sand transport diminishes rapidly away from the small inlets but continues much farther landward from Malpeque Channel. Variations in tidal range do not control this effect. The size of the flood-tidal delta increases with the size of the inlet (tidal prism). Reinson (1977) also considered tidal prism rather than tidal range to be the dominant factor influencing the size of flood-tidal deltas on the New Brunswick coast. The preceding discussion suggests that tidal prism may also be the more important factor affecting rates and magnitudes of changes in channel positions on flood-tidal deltas.

The observations at Malpeque support Hayes's (1975) contention that models of inlet morphology, established in mesotidal environments, can generally be applied to inlets in microtidal estuaries, but inlet size again introduces an element of variability for inlets around the southern Gulf of St. Lawrence. The flood-tidal deltas of larger inlets such as Portage Channel and Malpeque Channel are subtidal, whereas those of smaller inlets are exposed at low tide. In this respect, the smaller inlets in these microtidal estuaries resemble mesotidal inlets. Taken together, the comments made here concerning inlet size (tidal prism) indicate that it must be considered when drawing general conclusions about tidal inlet morphology and responses.

Acknowledgments

The field program was supported by funds from National Research Council, Canada, Grant Numbers A5082 and A4227, and an award from the Science and Engineering Research Board, McMaster University, Hamilton, Ontario. Much of the initial investigation was carried out as one part of the doctoral research into barrier island dynamics along the Malpeque coast, and the work benefitted from numerous discussions in the field and elsewhere with S. Brian McCann. Thanks are also due to Josephine Poon for typing the manuscript.

References

Armon, J.W.
1975: The dynamics of a barrier island chain, Prince Edward Island, Canada; Ph. D. thesis, McMaster University, Hamiton, 546 p.
1979: Landward sediment transfers in a transgressive barrier island system, Canada; in Barrier Islands, S.P. Leatherman, ed; Academic Press, New York, p. 65 - 79.

Armon, J.W. and McCann, S.B.
1977a: Longshore sediment transport and a sediment budget for the Malpeque barrier system, southern Gulf of St. Lawrence; Canadian Journal of Earth Sciences v.14, no.11, p. 2429 - 2439.
1977b: The establishment of an inshore wave climate and longshore sediment transport rates from hourly wind data; Discussion Paper No. 9, Monograph Series, Department of Geography, McMaster University, Hamilton, 76 p.
1979: Morphology and landward sediment transfer in a transgressive barrier island system, southern Gulf of St. Lawrence, Canada; Marine Geology, v.31, p. 333 - 344.

Bayfield, Captain
1845: Richmond Bay; National Map Collection, Public Archives of Canada, Ottawa.

Boothroyd, J.C. and Hubbard, D.K.
1975: Genesis of bedforms in mesotidal estuaries, Volume II; Proceedings of the Second International Estuarine Research Conference, L.E. Cronin, ed.; Academic Press, New York, p. 217 - 234.

Bryant, E.A. and McCann, S.B.
1973: Long and short term changes in the barrier islands of Kouchibouguac Bay, southern Gulf of St. Lawrence; Canadian Journal of Earth Sciences, v.10, p. 1582 - 1590.

Byrne, R.J., De Alteris, J.T. and Bullock, P.A.
1974: Channel stability in tidal inlets: a case study; in Proceedings of the 14th Coastal Engineering Conference, American Society of Civil Engineers, New York, p. 1585 - 1604.

Canadian Hydrographic Service
1966: Malpeque Bay; Hydrographic Chart No. 4491, Scale 1:37500.
1973: Canadian Tide and Current Tables, Vol.2, Gulf of St. Lawrence; Canadian Hydrographic Service, Marine Sciences Directorate, Department of the Environment, Ottawa.

Coastal Research Group
1969: Coastal environments: NE Massachusetts and New Hampshire; Society of Economic Paleontologists and Mineralogists Field Trip Guide Book, Contribution 1-CRG, University of Massachusetts, Department of Geology Publication Series, 462 p.

El-Ashray, M.T. and Wanless, H.R.
1965: The birth and growth of a tidal delta; Journal of Geology, v. 73, p. 404 - 406.

Finley, R.J.
  1975:   Hydrodynamics and tidal deltas of North Inlet, South Carolina, Volume II; Proceedings of the Second International Estuarine Research Conference, L.E. Cronin, ed.; Academic Press, New York, p. 277 - 291.

Greenwood, B. and Davidson-Arnott, R.G.D.
  1975:   Marine bars and nearshore sedimentary processes, Kouchibouguac Bay, New Brunswick; in Nearshore Sediment Dynamics and Sedimentation, J. Hails and A. Carr, eds.; Wiley, London, p. 123 - 150.

Hayes, M.O.
  1975:   Morphology of sand accumulations in estuaries: an introduction to the symposium, Volume II; Proceedings of the Second International Estuarine Research Conference, L.E. Cronin, ed.; Academic Press, New York, p. 3 - 22.
  1976:   Lecture notes; in Terrigenous Clastic Depositional Environments, M.O. Hayes and T.W. Kana, eds.; Technical Report No. 11-CRD, Coastal Research Division, Geology Department, University of South Carolina. p. I-1 - I-131.

Hayes, M.O., Owens, E.H., Hubbard, D.K. and Abele, R.W.
  1973:   The investigation of form and processes in the coastal zone; in Coastal Geomorphology, D.R. Coates, ed.; Publications in Geomorphology, State University of New York, Binghamton, p. 11 - 41.

Hine, A.C.
  1975:   Bedform distribution and migration patterns on tidal deltas in the Chatham Harbour Estuary, Cape Code, Massachusetts, Volume II; Proceedings of the Second International Estuarine Research Conference, L.E. Cronin, ed.; Academic Press, New York, p. 235 - 253.

Johnson, D.W.
  1919:   Shore processes and shoreline development; Wiley, New York, 584 p.

Lucke, J.B.
  1934:   A theory of evolution of lagoon deposits on shorelines of emergence; Journal of Geology, No. 42, p. 561 - 584.

McCann, S.B., Reinson, G.E. and Armon, J.W.
  1977:   Tidal inlets of the southern Gulf of St. Lawrence, Canada; in Coastal Sediments 77, Proceedings, American Society of Civil Engineers.

McCormick, C.L.
  1973:   Probable causes of shoreline recession and advance on the south shore of eastern Long Island; in Coastal Geomorphology, D.R. Coates, ed.; Publications in Geomorphology, State University of New York, Binghamton, p. 61 - 71.

Owens, E.H.
  1974:   Barrier beaches and sediment transport in the southern Gulf of St. Lawrence; in Proceedings of the 14th Coastal Engineering Conference, American Society of Civil Engineers, New York, p. 1177 - 1193.

Reinson, G.E.
  1977:   Tidal-current control of submarine morphology at the mouth of the Miramichi estuary, New Brunswick; Canadian Journal of Earth Sciences, v. 14, no. 11, p. 2524 - 2532.

Sheldon, R.W., Loring, D.H. and Deleum, S.
  1968:   Physiographic changes in Malpeque Bay, Prince Edward Island, between 1845 and 1955, and the possible effects on oyster production; Journal of the Fisheries Research Board of Canada, v. 26, p. 171 - 175.

5.　　　　　　　　　THE COASTAL GEOMORPHOLOGY OF THE MAGDALEN ISLANDS, QUEBEC

E.H. Owens[1] and S.B. McCann[2]

Owens, E.H. and McCann, S.B., The coastal geomorphology of the Magdalen Islands, Québec; in The Coastline of Canada, S.B. McCann, editor; Geological Survey of Canada, Paper 80-10, p. 51-72, 1980.

Abstract

The Magdalen Islands are a series of small rock outcrops in the central Gulf of St. Lawrence, six of which have been connected by long tombolo systems of double barrier beaches to form a continuous elongate island, 70 km long, including the terminal spits. The islands have been subdivided into nine geomorphic units, five of which are bedrock units with coastal cliffs and four of which are depositional units – sand barriers and spits. The characteristics of each unit are described and a morphological analysis of the depositional units is used to reconstruct the recent evolution of the islands. The narrow west-facing barriers in the tombolo systems are transgressive in character but the wider, east-facing barriers are basically progradational features. This reflects the differences in wave energy levels between the two sides of the islands, the west coast being the higher energy shore under the influence of the dominant wind waves from the west and northwest. Reworked glacial deposits on the shallow shelf have provided much of the sand for the development of the barriers and spits. At present the west coast beaches are zones of sediment bypassing and new supplies of sand from offshore are being transported alongshore towards the terminal spits.

Résumé

Les îles de la Madeleine sont formées d'une série de petits affleurements rocheux situés au centre du golfe du Saint-Laurent, six d'entre elles ayant été reliées par des ensembles de longs tombolos à double cordons qui donnent à l'île un aspect allongé et continu, sur une longueur de 70 km, y compris les flèches terminales. Les îles ont été réparties en neuf unités géomorphologiques, dont cinq sont formées de roches en place à falaises côtières, les quatre autres étant des unités sédimentaires: cordons et flèches de sable. Les auteurs décrivent les caractéristiques de chacune des unités et procèdent à une analyse morphologique des unités sédimentaires afin de reconstituer l'évolution récente des îles. Les étroits cordons à façade occidentale dans les ensembles de tombolos ont une nature transgressive tandis que les cordons plus larges et à façade orientale sont essentiellement des engraissements progradationnels. Ce phénomène reflète les différences dans les niveaux énergétiques des vagues entre les deux côtés de l'archipel, la côte ouest recevant les vagues les plus fortes en raison des vents dominants de l'ouest et du nord-ouest. Des dépôts glaciaires remaniés situés dans les eaux peu profondes de la plate-forme ont fourni presque tout le sable nécessaire à la formation des cordons et flèches. Aujourd'hui, les plages de la côte ouest sont des zones de passage des sédiments et du sable frais en provenance du large est transporté le long de la rive en direction des flèches terminales.

INTRODUCTION

The Magdalen* Islands, in the centre of the southern Gulf of St. Lawrence (Fig. 5.1), present a unique assemblage of coastal landforms dominated by extensive sand barriers and spits. Two large tombolo systems of double barriers enclosing extensive lagoons link the major rock islands and, together with complex terminal spits, constitute a narrow, continuous land area, extending for 70 km in a southwest-northeast direction along the crest of the shallow Magdalen shelf (Fig. 5.2). The barriers and spits have much in common with the other major coastal depositional systems of the southern part of the Gulf (Owens, 1974a, 1975; McCann, 1979) except that the islands are in a much more exposed location, with unrestricted fetches in all directions. Unlike the barrier coasts of New Brunswick and Prince Edward Island, the beaches of the Magdalen Islands are directly exposed to waves generated out of the west and northwest by the prevailing and dominant winds, so that energy levels on the west-facing coasts of the islands are higher than on other barrier systems in the southern Gulf. Because of the dominance of winds and waves out of the west, the contrasts between the major east- and west-facing beaches, separated often by only 2 to 3 km of shallow lagoon, are striking, and an analysis of the morphology of the beach and dune ridge systems of the barriers and spits provides a means of reconstructing the recent depositional history of the islands.

The principal concerns of this paper are to present an explanatory description of the coastal landforms of the islands, with emphasis on the depositional forms, and to provide an interpretation of their recent evolution from morphological evidence. Nine coastal subdivisions have been identified, described and analyzed. The data presented here were obtained from ground and aerial observations between 1972 and 1975 and from an interpretation of aerial photography (Paul, 1974). Investigations of the interrelationships between processes, sediment dispersal, and nearshore and littoral morphology of two contrasting 500 m sections of barrier beach in the Magdalen Islands are reported elsewhere (Owens, 1977a, b; Owens and Frobel, 1975, 1977).

[1] Woodward-Clyde Consultants, Victoria, British Columbia

[2] Department of Geography, McMaster University, Hamilton, Ontario

* Spelling as approved by Canadian Permanent Committee on Geographical Names is Madeleine Islands.　　　　51

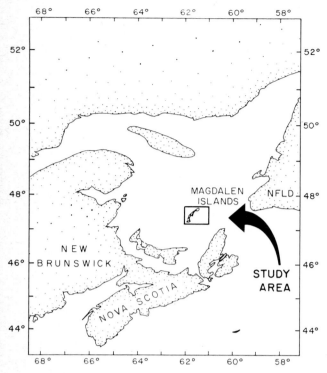

Figure 5.1. *Location of the Magdalen Islands, Quebec.*

GEOLOGICAL SETTING

Structurally, the islands are part of the Appalachian system and consist of Permo-Carboniferous strata deformed during the Acadian orogeny (Sheridan and Drake, 1968). The Magdalen Shelf is part of a broad anticlinal arch, which may be associated with the formation of salt diapirs in the region (Watts, 1972). The oldest outcrops are Mississippian shallow-marine limestones and gypsum interbedded with brecciated basaltic tuff and agglomerate (Alcock, 1941). The outcrops of volcanic rock form a resistant core to the four largest islands (Île d'Entrée, Île du Havre Aubert, Île du Cap aux Meules, and Île du Havre aux Maisons), producing numerous rounded hills with elevations up to 182 m. This Mississippian sequence is overlain unconformably by a Permo-Carboniferous sandstone series, the Cap-aux-Meules Formation, which grades from grey-green (marine) to red (aeolian) (Sanschagrin, 1968). Where bedrock is exposed along the coast, cliffs are generally 5 to 20 m high, but rise to 50 and 70 m in some locations.

Some authors (Goldthwait, 1915; Alcock, 1941; Dresser and Denis, 1964) believed that evidence from surficial sediments indicated that the area was glaciated by the Wisconsin Laurentide ice sheet. Others (Richardson, 1881; Chalmers, 1895; Clarke, 1910; Prest, 1970; Laverdière and Guimont, 1974) considered that the islands were not glaciated by the main ice sheets. Prest (1970) suggested that Laurentide ice reached the islands from the north and resulted in the deposition of an ice-contact drift or kame moraine on Île de la Grande Entrée, but that only shelf ice

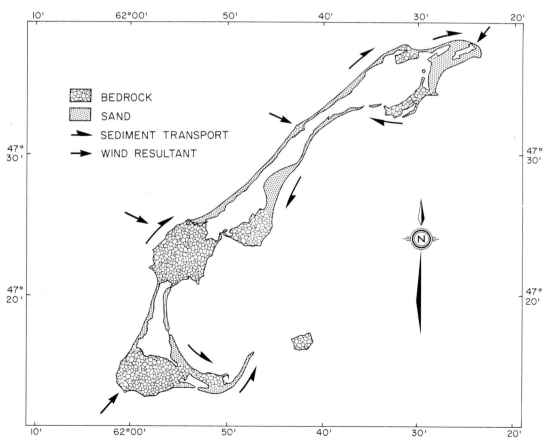

Figure 5.2. *Nearshore sediment dispersal patterns and bedrock outcrops, Magdalen Islands. The wind resultants are for onshore winds at the given location (from Owens, 1977a).*

reached the southern parts of the islands. Grant (1975a) found it difficult to reconcile this view with a unidirectional southeast flow of Laurentide ice across the west coast of Cape Breton Island, only 100 km to the southeast, but subsequently agreed (1976) that both the islands and parts of the adjacent shelf could have escaped glaciation. Recent interpretations by Prest and Terasmae (Prest et al., 1976) stress the essentially unglaciated character of the islands and conclude that they were "definitely not overriden by Laurentide or other ice sheets during the entire Wisconsinan glacial stage, though the ice was near at hand on the Magdalen Shelf." They suggested that the abundance of sand in the Quaternary deposits of the islands, which in turn has provided a readily available sediment source for the present system of tombolos and spits, reflects a long involved history of shifting ice fronts and changing water levels on the adjacent shelf. Though there are no data from the Magdalen Islands, the most recent phase of this history may be inferred from the findings of Grant (1970, 1975b) in the Maritime Provinces as a whole and Kranck (1972) in Northumberland Strait, to be one of relatively rapid coastal submergence. Grant (1970) indicated that submergence in the Maritime Provinces over the last 4000 years has been taking place at 30 cm per century, several times the worldwide eustatic sea level rise.

The barrier beaches and dunes of the Magdalen Islands are composed largely of medium sized sands which exhibit remarkably uniform grain size characteristics (Owens, 1975), with little difference between east and west coast or between littoral and dune samples. Where an intertidal zone is present at the base of coastal cliffs cobble and boulder beaches occur, but as these coarse sediments are composed predominantly of unresistant sandstone the material is rarely transported for any distance along shore before disintegrating. Cliff erosion is relatively rapid (up to 2 or 3 m/a*) and there is some contribution of sediment to the littoral zone but the sources are restricted in extent. The contribution from streams is negligible as drainage basins in the islands are small.

Owens (1975) suggested that the major contemporary source of sediment is the onshore movement of surficial material from the adjacent seafloor, and that the barrier systems also represent the accumulation of sand from the migration of beach deposits during the postglacial transgression. The bottom sediments on the Magdalen Shelf, which has low gradients off the islands (Fig. 5.3), consist of

glacial and fluvioglacial materials which have been reworked during this transgression (Fig. 5.4). Loring and Nota (1973) showed that to the west of the islands these deposits are being reworked by present processes and that sand-sized sediments are being redistributed landward. Direct evidence of the movement of sediments on the seafloor by tidal- and wave-generated currents is provided by bottom photographs and by sidescan sonar records that show fields of sand waves in water depths to 54 m (Loring et al., 1970). Mineralogical analysis of material from the littoral and offshore environments of the area (Loring and Nota, 1969) shows that these sediments are derived from the same source. Loring and Nota (1973) stated that bottom sediments on the seafloor to the west of the islands grade from poorly sorted sands to gravelly well sorted sands towards the coast. Dispersal of these sediments around the northern and southern extremities of the islands leads to deposition of fine-grained sediments in a sheltered zone, protected from waves out of the west and northwest.

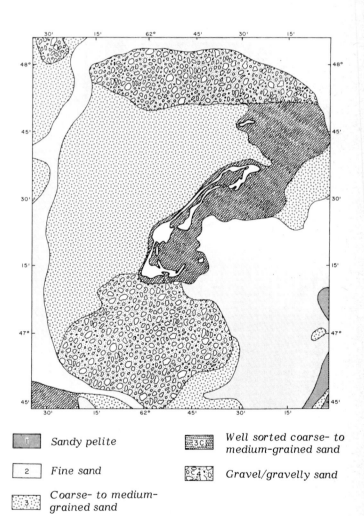

Figure 5.4. Distribution of surface sediments on the seafloor adjacent to the Magdalen Islands (adapted from Loring and Nota, 1973).

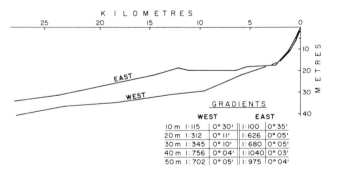

Figure 5.3. Offshore profiles and gradients, Magdalen Islands. Profiles are located in the central section of the northern tombolo and are perpendicular to the coast (from Owens, 1977b).

---

* a is the SI abbreviation for year.

COASTAL PROCESSES

The prevailing wind direction of the Magdalen Islands is from the northwest (Fig. 5.5a) and a vector of the resultant of direction and velocity computed from data collected at Grindstone over a 40-year period (Fig. 5.5b) shows the dominance of winds out of the west-northwest during the ice-free period. There is a distinct seasonal variation in mean monthly wind velocity values (Table 5.1), which results from the southerly displacement of the Polar Front and an increase in pressure gradients associated with low-pressure centres that pass directly over the region during winter months. The frequency of wind velocities over 90 and 115 km/h, calculated for the four major compass quadrants over 40 years (Table 5.2) clearly demonstrates the dominance of strong winds out of the west. One critical factor in limiting the effects of wind-generated processes is the presence of ice on the beach and the adjacent sea areas from January to April.

Fetch distances vary with aspect. The northwest-facing barriers have a fetch of approximately 300 km. The east-facing beaches are exposed to north Atlantic swell waves which can pass through the narrow (110 km) Cabot Strait. Ploeg (1971) presented a summary of deep-water wave data collected in an area adjacent to Bird Rocks, 25 km north-northwest of the islands, which gives the general pattern of wave characteristics from the end of June to early December 1967. Seasonal variations are evident from these data, particularly when the values are reduced into specific time periods (Table 5.3).

Although no data are available on the direction of wave approach, the dominant and prevailing winds are from the west and northwest and locally generated waves in this semienclosed sea would be associated with these winds. An indication of the predominance of waves out of the west is given by wave energy values which were computed from data collected on the east and west coasts during investigations in July, August and November, 1974 (Owens, 1977a). These data indicate that during summer months more than twice as much energy is dissipated on the west coast as compared with the east coast (Table 5.4). In winter the energy levels are greater on the west coast by a factor of 2.95. The wave climate on the west coast is characterized by a greater seasonal difference in wave energy levels than on the east coasts (Fig. 5.6), where the wave climate is dominated by the effects of storm waves which produce greater variation within each season (Owens, 1977a).

Table 5.1. Mean wind velocity and direction, Grindstone (1933-1972)

	Maximum mean wind velocity	Direction	Mean wind velocity
	(km/h)		(km/h)
January	47.2	NW	41.0
February	41.4	NW	37.2
March	40.6	NW	35.0
April	36.2	NW	33.0
May	35.2	NW	30.1
June	33.3	NW	28.7
July	30.6	SW	27.4
August	30.4	SW	28.2
September	35.7	NW	31.5
October	41.0	NW	35.7
November	41.7	NW	37.7
December	45.7	NW	40.0

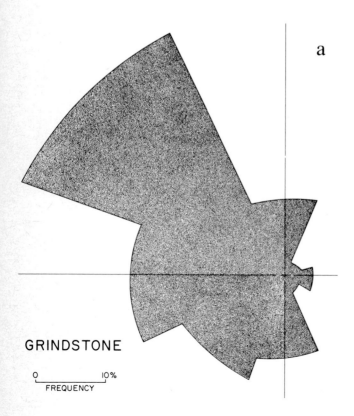

GRINDSTONE

0   10%
FREQUENCY

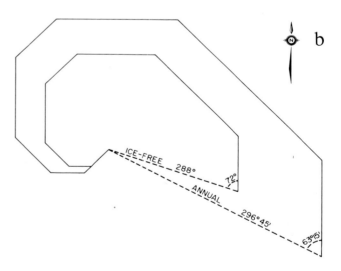

a.   *Annual wind frequency by direction at Grindstone, Magdalen Islands. (Source: Villeneuve, 1967).*

b.   *Vector diagram of winds greater than 25 km/h derived from data collected at Grindstone, 1933-68. The vector was computed by weighting the mean monthly wind velocity frequency classes. The ice-free period is defined as April to December.*

Figure 5.5

The predominance of locally generated waves out of the west and northwest would produce a pattern of nearshore currents and longshore sediment transport which is outlined in Figure 5.2. This is substantiated by current meter data obtained from the west coast (Owens and Frobel, 1975, p. 61, 99), which show that the predominant direction of nearshore currents measured in 6 m water depth was parallel to the shore towards the northeast. Maximum recorded bottom velocities from these meters were greater than 80 cm/s. Measurements of longshore currents adjacent to the beach show the same prevailing direction on the west coast but on the east coast, during the period of measurement, the longshore currents were to the north in summer and to the south in winter (Owens, 1977a).

Ice is present in the southern Gulf from January to late April or early May, with close pack ice during February and March. This general pattern varies greatly each year and local ice cover also varies throughout the winter. The prevailing winds cause accumulation of pack ice against the west-facing coasts and removal of ice from the sheltered east coast. No information is available on the length of time that an ice foot is present in the intertidal zone, although it would probably be as long, twelve to thirteen weeks per year, as that reported for the eastern New Brunswick coast (Owens, 1976).

The tides of the Magdalen Islands are mixed and semidiurnal types. Tidal predictions for the islands (Canadian Hydrographic Service, 1974) give mean and spring tidal ranges of 0.7 and 1.0 m, respectively, for the east coast, and 0.5 and 0.8 m for the west coast.

Table 5.2. Frequency of storms by quadrant

Duration:	Recorded velocity > 90 km/h		
	1 hour	> 3 hours	> 6 hours
NW-NNE	6.4/year	1.7/year	0.9/year
NE-ESE	1.5/year	1 in 3 years	1 in 13 years
SE-SSW	3.1/year	2 in 5 years	1 in 8 years
SW-WNW	3.0/year	2 in 5 years	1 in 4 years

Duration:	Recorded velocity > 115 km/h	
	1 hour	> 3 hours
NW-NNE	2 in 5 years	1 in 13 years
NE-ESE	--	--
SE-SSW	1 in 20 years	--
SW-WNW	1 in 5 years	1 in 40 years

Table 5.3. Summary of wave data from Bird Rocks, 1967, after Ploeg (1971).

	Whole season	June 27 - Sept. 15	Sept. 16 - Oct. 31	Nov. 1 - Dec. 11
Median significant wave height (cm)	137	107	146	189
Mean wave period (s)	5.9	5.4	5.9	7.0
Peak wave length (m)	55	48	55	76
1% significant wave height (cm)	457	335	427	564
1% wave period (s)	10.8	9.4	11.3	12.6
1% peak wave length (m)	183	137	183	244

Significant wave height expected once/year	762 cm
Wave period expected once/year	14.5 s
Peak wave length expected once/year	335 m
Maximum observed individual wave height during observations	1158 cm

Table 5.4. Summary of computed wave energy, from Owens (1977a).

		Wave energy (ergs/cm/3 h)		
		Mean	Minimum	Maximum
Summer	west	2.52×10^{11}	2.12×10^{9}	1.65×10^{13}
	east	1.12×10^{11}	2.12×10^{9}	1.10×10^{13}
Winter	west	2.51×10^{12}	1.68×10^{11}	7.38×10^{13}
	east	8.51×10^{11}	3.04×10^{10}	5.89×10^{13}

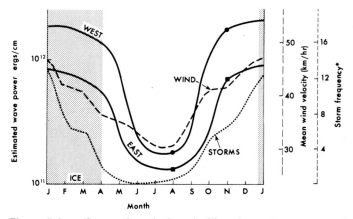

Figure 5.6. *Seasonal variations in (i) estimated wave power on the east and west barriers (solid lines), (ii) mean monthly wind velocity, and (iii) storm frequency. The period of sea ice cover or beach-fast ice is indicated by the shaded area. Wave power is estimated from Owens (1977a) and storm frequency (*) is the number of periods in each month when wind velocities exceed 55 km/h, based on mean data over 40-year period (from Owens, 1977b).*

COASTAL GEOMORPHOLOGY SUBDIVISIONS

The Magdalen Islands may be subdivided into nine geo-morphic units, five of which are bedrock units with coastal cliffs and four of which are depositional sand barriers and spit systems (Fig. 5.7). Two of the bedrock units, Île d'Entrée and Île Brion, are isolated islands, the other three act as rock anchors for the tombolo systems and for the terminal spits.

Bedrock units

Unit 1. Île d'Entrée

This hilly bedrock island has a cliffed shoreline with narrow pebble-boulder beaches. The eastern half is cored by vol-canic rocks, rising to a maximum elevation of 150 m, and where these rocks outcrop on the coast vertical cliffs up to 60 m high have been formed. The western half of the island is a flat marine terrace and cliffs are only 5 to 10 m high. On the west-facing coast, longshore drift of coarse inter-tidal sediments to the north has resulted in deposition against a jetty, which was constructed at the only location without a cliff. Beyond this jetty a small flying spit (200 m long) has grown from the northwest corner of the island where the shoreline orientation abruptly changes.

Unit 3. Île du Havre Aubert

The island is an outcrop of the Havre-Aubert anticline which trends east-west (Sanschagrin, 1968) and relatively resistant volcanics are exposed in the centre, giving a hilly topog-raphy that rises locally to 136 m. The shale, limestone and sandstone which surround the volcanic rocks form a low terrace that is rarely more than 15 m above sea level, so that coastal cliffs are generally only 10 to 15 m high. The coastline is relatively straight and there are few pocket beaches. Where beach and intertidal sediments occur they are generally of pebble to boulder size, derived directly from cliff erosion.

Unit 5. Île du Cap aux Meules and Île du Havre aux Maisons

These two bedrock outcrops are the focal point of the Magdalen Islands in terms of coastal geomorphology, as they provide the stable anchor for the two major tombolo systems to the north and south (Fig. 5.7). Although separated by a narrow channel, the islands are geologically one unit on the limb of the Cap-aux-Meules anticline, which trends N80°E (Sanschagrin, 1968). This geomorphic unit is very similar to Île du Havre Aubert and has a volcanic core surrounded by less resistant sandstone, limestone and shale. Where the sandstone outcrops on the coast, marine erosion forms vertical cliffs 10 to 15 m high (Fig. 5.8). Higher cliffs, up to 30 m above sea level, are found on the east of Île du Cap aux Meules and on the south and east coasts of Île du Havre aux Maisons, where the more resistant volcanics and older sedimentary rocks are exposed. Local shoreline config-uration is controlled by erosion along fault lines or joints but in general the coastline is relatively straight. Pocket beaches consisting of locally derived sediments have devel-oped in embayments, particularly on the sheltered east coasts of the islands. The channel between the islands has been narrowed by the growth of spits but infilling is prevented by strong tidal currents which maintain depths in the order of 15 m in the narrow inlet throat. Adjacent to this inlet are large ebb- and flood-tidal deltas.

Unit 7. Grosse Île and Île de la Grande Entrée

The low-lying islands of Grosse Île and Île de la Grande Entrée have short coastlines but are important as they serve as the downdrift anchors for the northern tombolo system and as the updrift anchors for the northern spit. Grosse Île has exposures of shale and sandstone rising inland to 90 m, with a cliff coastline 1.5 km long and up to 20 m high that is fronted by narrow beaches of reworked coarse talus de-posits. Inland, former active sea cliffs have been removed from marine action by deposition associated with the devel-opment of the tombolo and spit systems. Île de la Grande Entrée is a low (31 m maximum elevation) outcrop of red

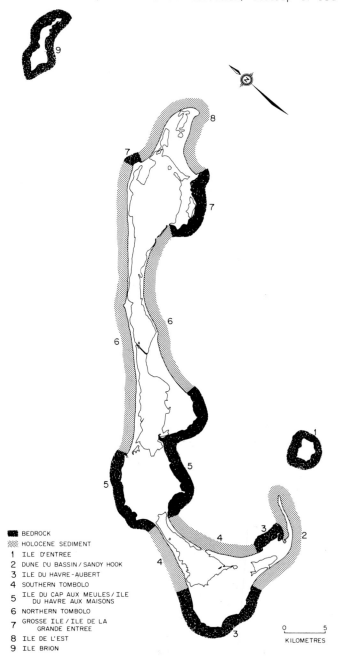

■ BEDROCK
▨ HOLOCENE SEDIMENT
1 ILE D'ENTREE
2 DUNE DU BASSIN / SANDY HOOK
3 ILE DU HAVRE-AUBERT
4 SOUTHERN TOMBOLO
5 ILE DU CAP AUX MEULES / ILE DU HAVRE AUX MAISONS
6 NORTHERN TOMBOLO
7 GROSSE ILE / ILE DE LA GRANDE ENTREE
8 ILE DE L'EST
9 ILE BRION

0   5
KILOMETRES

Figure 5.7. *Geomorphological subdivisions of the Magdalen Islands, showing the bedrock and depositional units.*

sandstone with an alternating sequence of low cliffs, generally less than 10 m in height, and small sandy beaches along the east coast. The northeastern promontory of Île de la Grande Entrée, Old Harry (Fig. 5.15), has acted as a large groin to sediment moving southwestwards from Pointe de l'Est, but Île Boudreau, which is composed largely of drift, is an important local source of beach material.

Unit 9. Île Brion

This isolated sandstone island (Fig. 5.7), 20 km north of Pointe de l'Est, is separated from the mainland of the archipelago by a wide channel 30 m deep. Only 2 km of the total coastline of 14 km are not cliffed. This one section is a large depositional cuspate foreland on the south shore which is migrating to the east: it is affected by waves out of the east and the west, which cause a convergence of long-shore currents. Elsewhere cliffs are generally 15 to 20 m high but rise to 60 m on the northern shore.

Depositional units

Unit 4. Southern tombolo (Dune de l'Ouest - Dune de l'Est)

The two barriers of the southern tombolo system that enclose the shallow, infilling lagoon of Havre aux Basques are quite different in character (Fig. 5.9). The western barrier, Dune de l'Ouest, is narrow and tenuous and the eastern barrier, Dune de l'Est, is wider and prograding. Both are oriented to face the respective prevailing direction of wave approach: the western barrier faces to the west-northwest and the eastern barrier to the east, so that the enclosed lagoon narrows to the north (Fig. 5.10). The former barrier is composed of very well sorted, medium-grained sands and the latter of well sorted medium- to fine-grained sands (Owens, 1974b).

The western barrier is migrating eastwards into the lagoon and peat outcrops are exposed in the intertidal zone of the ocean-side beach. This is a zone of sediment by-passing and there is a net movement of sediment away from the central section, which is very narrow and frequently overwashed (Fig. 5.11). Three inlets that existed in this barrier in 1917 (Sanschagrin, 1968) are now closed, although they are sites of continued washover.

The eastern barrier developed in the lee of the western as sediment moved into the area from the northeast and around Sandy Hook. The accumulation of sediment has resulted in the development of a series of progradational ridges in the southern section adjacent to Île du Havre Aubert (Fig. 5.12). The development of such a progradational series of parallel dune ridges required a wide gently sloping beach and nearshore zone, and a large input of sediment. In this type of progradational system each ridge is formed initially by the development of a low foredune, by wind action, on the berm at the rear of the beach. The front of the developing foredune may be trimmed into an erosional scarp by storm waves but, with a wide beach which absorbs much of the wave energy and a system of parallel bars and troughs in the nearshore zone which do not favour the concentration of wave energy at specific locations, the erosion produces a linear scarp rather than breaching the foredune. The developing dune ceases to grow when a new foredune begins to form on the berm, cutting off the supply of blowing sand, and progradation or shoreline advance occurs.

The older dune ridges in the sequence are uniformly low and are concave seawards, so that initially progradation must have been very rapid in a spitlike form across a shallow embayment northwest from Île du Havre Aubert. Subsequently, as the shoreline was straightened the rate of progradation slowed, allowing more time for dune accumulation, so that the most recent ridges are higher and parallel

Figure 5.8. *View to the south of cliffed coast near Fatima on the western coast of Île du Cap aux Meules, (loc. 1, Fig. 5.9). (BIO 3273A-16)*

to the shoreline. A large inlet with a well defined ebb- and flood-tidal delta system existed in 1952, breaking the continuity of Dune de l'Est to the north of the prograding section, but a road causeway has been constructed to close the inlet and the lagoon is no longer connected to the sea. The lagoon is infilling by washover and aeolian deposition and more than half of it is now occupied by marsh (Fig. 5.10).

Grandtner (1967, 1968) presented the typical dune vegetation succession for the Magdalen Islands. The mobile foredunes (Unit A, Fig. 5.13a) are dominated by *Ammophila breviligulata*, which is replaced in the fixed dune areas by *Emperrum nigrum* (Unit B). With landward succession into the older dune areas a greater variation in species develops but it is possible to recognize zones dominated by lichens (*Cladonia* - Unit C), *Juncus* (D), and *Sphagnum* (E). In addition to these species, which characterize the zonation, *Hudsonia tomantosa*, *Juniperus communis* and *Myrica pensylvanica* are common in the fixed dune areas. For the salt marshes Grandtner (1966) identified four major communities between the lagoons (Figs. 5.13b, 1) and the dunes (Fig. 5.13b, 6). On the margins of the lagoons, *Salicornia europaea* and *Salicornia laurentium* (Unit 2) give way to a zone of *Spartina alterniflora* (3) in the upper parts of the intertidal zone. This is followed landward by a progression from *Carex palaecea* (4) to *Juncus balticus* (5).

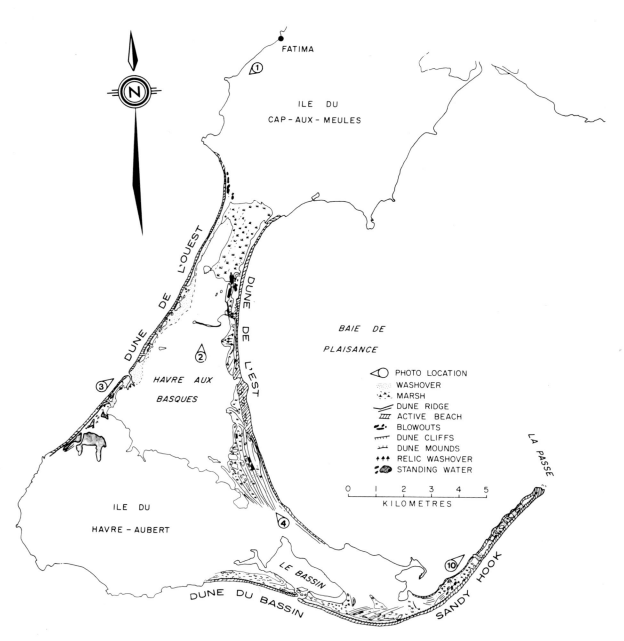

Figure 5.9. *Geomorphological features of the southern tombolo and Bassin-Sandy Hook units (after Paul, 1974).*

Figure 5.10. *View of the northern half of Havre aux Basques (loc. 2, Fig. 5.9). The former inlet on Dune de l'Est which was closed artificially is at bottom right and Ile du Cap aux Meules is at the top of the photograph (Photograph by P.R. Hague). (BIO 3273A-20)*

Figure 5.11. *Aerial view of the central section of Dune de l'Ouest, August 1972 (loc. 3, Fig. 5.9). This west-facing barrier is frequently overwashed and there is deposition and infilling of the lagoon on the landward side of the barrier (Photograph by P.R. Hague). (BIO 3273A-18)*

Figure 5.12. *Beach ridge complex on Dune de l'Est adjacent to Île du Havre Aubert. View to the northwest (loc. 4, Fig. 5.9) (Photograph by P.R. Hague). (BIO 3273A-18)*

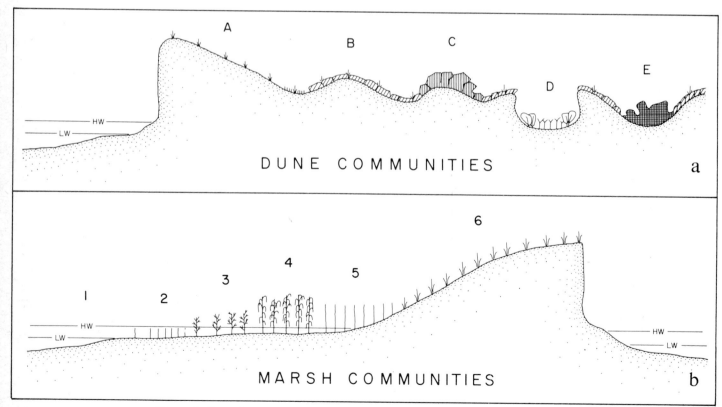

Figure 5.13. *Shore zone vegetation communities, Magdalen Islands (see text).*

Unit 6. Northern tombolo (Dune du Nord - Dune de Sud)

The northern tombolo is larger and more complex than the southern and this double barrier system encloses two large linked lagoons, Lagune du Havre aux Maisons and Lagune de la Grande Entrée, both of which are connected to the sea through the eastern barrier by tidal inlets (Fig. 5.14, 5.15). Again there is a contrast between the western (Dune du Nord) and eastern (Dune du Sud) barriers, the former (Fig. 5.16, 5.17) being narrower with little evidence of old dune ridges and the latter exhibiting the largest sequence of progradational ridges in the southern Gulf of St. Lawrence (Fig. 5.18). However, there are differences along each barrier and it is convenient to subdivide each into two sections. The western barrier consists of very well sorted, medium-grained sands, with little change in sediment type alongshore, and the eastern barrier of very well sorted medium- to fine-grained sands (Owens, 1974b).

Midway along the 35 km length of the western barrier there is a small rock island, Île de la Pointe au Loup (Fig. 5.14), which forms a convenient division and which has acted as a fulcrum for the development of the northern dune section. The presence of dune ridges in the wider parts of Dune du Nord between Île de la Pointe au Loup and Grosse Île (Fig. 5.15, 5.17) suggests that this section of the barrier developed as a spit which grew northwards from the former island. This spit growth must have occurred in relatively recent times, for open water conditions in the present Lagune de la Grande Entrée are necessary to explain the formation of Pointe de l'Est (see Unit 8 below). Except at the southern end adjacent to Île de la Pointe au Loup, this northern section of the western barrier is wider and the dunes less severely eroded than the southern section.

At the southern end of the southern section of Dune du Nord, near Fatima (Fig. 5.14) there is a large flat washover with maximum elevations less than 2 m above mean high

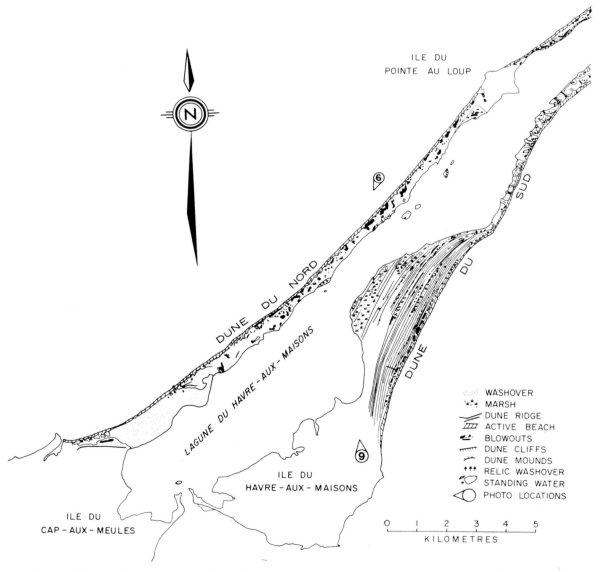

Figure 5.14. *Geomorphological features of the southern section of the northern tombolo unit (after Paul, 1974).*

water mark. Richardson (quoted in Sanschagrin, 1968) reported that prior to his visit in 1881, an inlet had been opened at this location which was used by local fishing boats for access to Lagune du Havre aux Maisons. The inlet had closed by 1881 but the area is still one of active storm erosion and overwash. To the north of Fatima the barrier is a relatively straight narrow feature with dunes up to 15 m high. The dunes have been eroded by storm waves which produce irregular scarps (Fig. 5.16) or, where the barrier is very narrow, washover channels. The irregular pattern of

cut and fill results from the concentration of storm wave energy, which is controlled by the complex system of rhythmic nearshore bars. The zones of storm erosion are subsequently infilled by littoral and aeolian deposition.

The eastern barrier again developed in the lee of a pre-existing western barrier. The bulk of the sediment was probably transported into this area from the northeast around Pointe de l'Est and redistributed towards the southwest by waves out of the east and northeast. The northern or updrift section is a zone of sediment bypassing and is

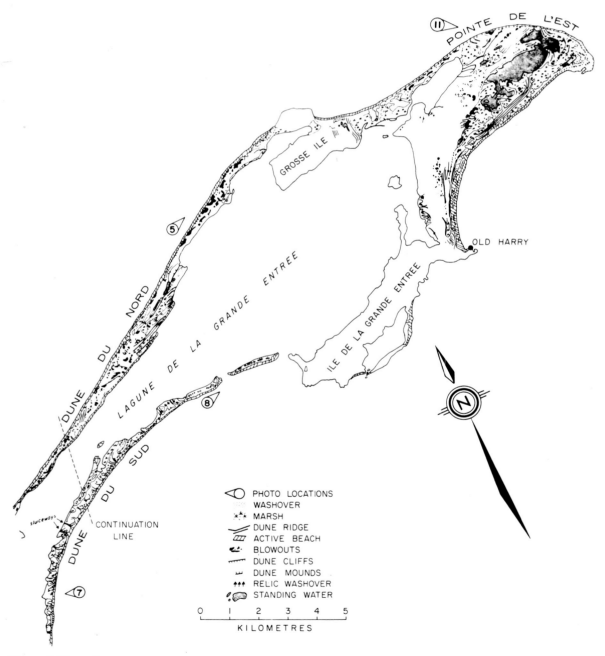

Figure 5.15. *Geomorphological characteristics of the northern section of the northern tombolo and the Île de l'Est units (after Paul, 1974). The limit of overlap with Figure 5.14 is indicated by the continuation line.*

Figure 5.16. *Effects of storm wave erosion on dune morphology, Dune du Nord (loc. 6, Fig. 5.14). This aerial view at low tide shows the dune scarps that result from storm wave erosion and the subsequent deposition which restores the equilibrium trend of the shoreline (Photograph by R. Belanger). (BIO 3242-2)*

Figure 5.17. *Waves breaking on the nearshore bars, Dune du Nord. Grosse Ile is at the top of the photograph (loc. 5, Fig. 5.15) (Photograph by P.R. Hague). (BIO 3273A-20A)*

consequently low, narrow and frequently breached and overwashed (Fig. 5.19), in contrast to the southern section which is an area of sediment accumulation with a wide series of progradational dune ridges (Fig. 5.14, 5.18). The ridges have developed in a similar manner and under similar environmental conditions to those described previously in the eastern barrier of the southern tombolo. Initially this dune-ridge complex developed in a shallow embayment between Île du Havre aux Maisons in the south and the small bedrock outcrop associated with Île Shag in the north. The inner or older ridges are low with a local relief, between ridge and swale, of less than 2 m, a condition which indicates rapid progradation. There are no washover channels in this earliest set of ridges and there is no evidence of wave erosion on the lagoonal shoreline, affording proof of the existence of a protective western barrier prior to development of the eastern arm of the tombolo. The newer ridges are higher than the older, indicating that as the beach assumed a more stable equilibrium plan shape the rate of progradation slowed and the available sediment was built into more substantial dunes. This section is still a zone of sediment accumulation and progradation, though some sediment is now bypassing and being transported to the south along the eastern shore of Île du Havre aux Maisons. Some aspects of the dune ecology and the effects of man on the vegetation of this area are discussed by Lamoureux and Grandtner (1977).

A complex and changeable inlet system, Grande Entrée, separates the Dune du Sud barrier from Île de la Grande Entrée. It is evident from aerial photography that the system had two inlets between 1952 and 1972 (Fig. 5.20), but that by 1974 the more southerly of these had become infilled. In August 1975, however, the system was characterized by three inlets, and the major channel was 400 m wide with a large ebb- and flood-tidal delta system, and with a depth of 10 m at the inlet throat.

Unit 2. Southern spit (Dune de Bassin - Sandy Hook)

This unit is a complex spit in a zone of sediment accumulation and has developed as a result of longshore transport to the east along the south coast of Île du Havre Aubert (Fig. 5.9, 5.21). The lagoon at Bassin has been enclosed by shoreline simplification (Fig. 5.9) but remains tidal and, as a result, a small ebb- and flood-tidal delta system has formed at the inlet to this lagoon. At present this updrift section is a zone of sediment bypassing as material is moved east towards Sandy Hook. The flying spit of Sandy Hook has grown towards Île d'Entrée but strong tidal currents through La Passe maintain a deep channel and have prevented closure.

Figure 5.18.   *Beach-ridge complex on Dune du Sud (loc. 9, Fig. 5.14) Île Shag is at top right and the bedrock outcrop of Île du Havre aux Maisons is at the bottom of this photograph (Photograph by P.R. Hague). (BIO 3273 A-13)*

Figure 5.19. *Washover channels and fans on the northeastern section of Dune du Sud (loc. 7, Fig. 5.15) (Photograph by P.R. Hague). (BIO 3273A-19)*

Figure 5.20. *Inlets at Grande Entrée on Dune du Sud, August 1972 (loc. 8, Fig. 5.15). A well developed ebb- and flood-tidal delta system has formed at the more southerly inlet. The larger inlet, at top right, is maintained by dredging (Photograph by P.R. Hague). (BIO 3273A-14)*

Interpretation of relict beach ridges provides information for the development of a model to illustrate the pattern of spit growth. At the point of attachment a series of parallel ridges, which are truncated by the present shoreline, converge against the bedrock outcrop. This set of ridges is replaced to the east by a sequence which is perpendicular to the present shoreline (Fig. 5.21a). It is difficult to develop a model of spit growth from these relict ridges without considering the effects of wave action out of the northeast during formation of the incipient spit. One interpretation, given in Figure 5.21b, is that a cuspate foreland migrated eastwards along the coast (Stage A) until accumulation extended beyond the bedrock island. At this time the downdrift section came under the influence of waves out of the northeast and this led to the development of a new set of ridges on the north shore of the advancing spit (Stage B). As spit growth continued a series of ridges was formed on the prograding north coast while the older ridges to the west were truncated as the remnant foreland

narrowed (Stage C). The penultimate sequence involved development of the flying spit by movement of sediment along the south shore while the north shore continued to prograde (Stage D). At present (Fig. 5.21a) the effects of wave action along the north shore have greatly diminished due to the development of a wide, shallow, nearshore terrace, which absorbs the energy of incident waves out of the north-northeast. A sequence of four or five parallel nearshore bars on the seaward margin of this terrace is replaced landward in shallower water by sets of intersecting diagonal bars (Fig. 5.22). On the open (southern) coast of the spit two large linear nearshore bars parallel the shoreline. At the distal point of the spit a large shoal extends eastwards for approximately 4000 m. This submarine extension of the spit is covered by fields of large sand waves (wave lengths up to 100 m) that result from wave- and tide-induced currents.

The spit is 400 to 500 m wide, the dunes are cut by numerous overwash channels and large fans have been deposited on the north shore. Overwash is an important

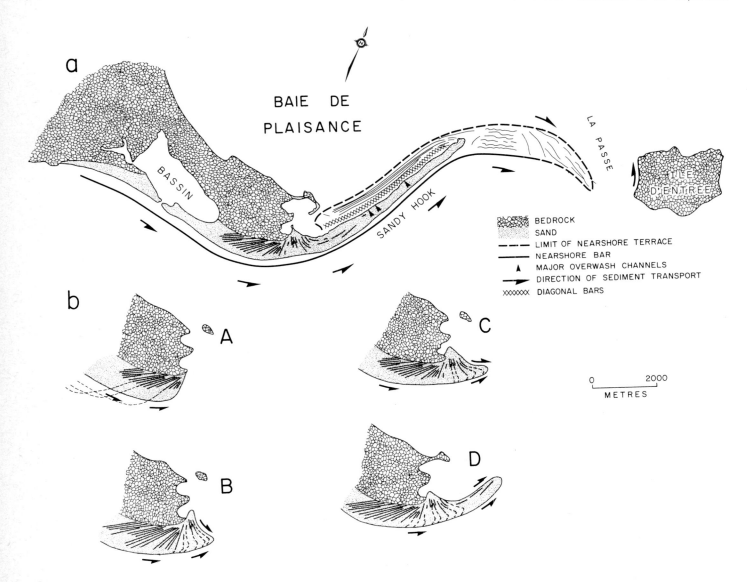

Figure 5.21. *Sandy Hook: (a) sketch of present geomorphological features from 1970 aerial photography (NAPL A21672); (b) four-stage model of spit development (see text).*

Figure 5.22. *Sandy Hook, looking towards the northeast (loc. 10, Fig. 5.9). This flying spit is subject to frequent overwash. The sheltered shore, to the left, has a shallow nearshore terrace on which a variety of bars have developed. By contrast, on the exposed shore (to the right of the spit) two linear bars parallel the beach (Photograph by P.R. Hague). (BIO 3273A-16)*

process by which sediment is transferred from the exposed shore to the sheltered north-facing coast. In the central section of the spit many isolated dune remnants have a concentric shape from erosion during washover (Fig. 5.22).

Historical evidence of shoreline change is given by Sanschagrin (1968), who shows that the width of La Passe narrowed from 5500 to 5200 m between 1765 and 1833. This was followed by sequences of opening (5500 m in 1916), closing (5011 m, 1917-1935), opening (5800 m, 1956) and closing (5000 m, 1959). These short-term cyclic changes can be attributed to the activity of storms but care must be exercised in determining small-scale changes from historical maps. Comparison of aerial photographs taken in 1952 and in 1970 shows that the distal point of the spit undergoes frequent modification but this is of smaller magnitude than that described by Sanschagrin.

Unit 8. Northern spit (Pointe de l'Est)

This complex depositional feature (Fig. 5.15) has developed at the end point of the west coast sediment transport system and extends northeastwards from the two rock islands, Grosse Île and Île de la Grande Entrée. Sediments in the littoral zone are similar to those found on the western barrier of the northern tombolo and consist of very well sorted, medium-grained sands (Owens, 1974b). As in the case of Unit 2 (Dune du Bassin - Sandy Hook) a model of spit growth can be developed from interpretation of relict beach

ridges (Fig. 5.23). The initial stage (Stage A) shows the development of a spit with recurved ridges, which grew to the northeast from Île de la Grande Entrée. This interpretation means that the present Lagune de la Grande Entrée had to be open to the west at this time for large waves to enter the area and generate longshore currents eastwards between Grosse Île and Île de la Grande Entrée. As the west-facing barrier of the northern tombolo system progressively closed off the lagoon, the wave and current system between the islands became less dynamic and parallel progradational ridges developed in front of, or north of, the initial spit (Stage B). Finally, the lagoon was closed on the west and the available sediment was transported around Grosse Île to form a new spit or barrier linking this island with the older spit system (Stage C). At present (Stage D) relict ridges are being truncated near the distal section of the compound spit (Fig. 5.24) and accretion is taking place at Pointe de l'Est. This indicates that the beach facing north is a zone of erosion and that the whole system is migrating southwards and growing to the east.

The nearshore bars on the coast facing north are linear and parallel to the coast. This is similar to the bar system on the exposed coast of Sandy Hook but is in marked contrast to the irregular crescentic bars which characterize the west-facing coast of the northern tombolo. This linear pattern of nearshore bars is evident on all vertical air photographs of the north coast of Pointe de l'Est and indicates unidirectional nearshore currents (Homma and Sonu, 1963).

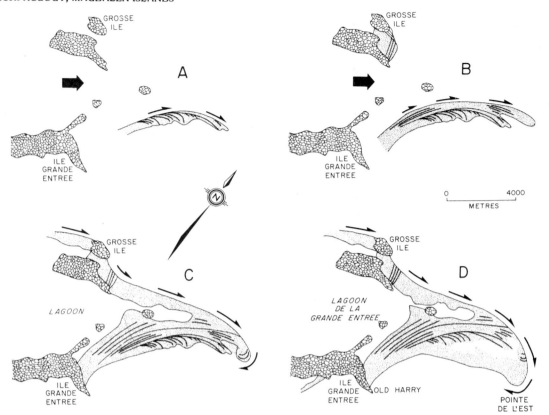

Figure 5.23. *Model of the growth of Ile de l'Est (the legend is given in Fig. 5.21). The sketch of the contemporary geomorphological features (D) is derived from 1970 aerial photography (NAPL A21672). The large arrow indicates open water.*

Figure 5.24. *Aerial view of Pointe de l'Est, taken towards the east (loc. 11, Fig. 5.15). Relict dune ridges are being eroded by wave action as the foreland is migrating to the east and to the south. The distal point is at top right in the photograph (Photograph by P.R. Hague). (BIO 3273 A-17)*

GEOMORPHOLOGICAL DEVELOPMENT OF THE BARRIER SYSTEM

In the present dynamic shoreline condition of the Magdalen Islands the long continuous barrier beaches of the west-facing coast are subject to greater inputs of wave energy, from the dominant waves out of the northwest, than the beaches facing east. Sand is still being supplied to the system, largely from the shallow offshore areas of the Magdalen Shelf, and inferences about the general pattern of longshore sediment dispersal (Fig. 5.25), based on consideration of the present wave climate, are substantiated by observations on the morphology of the beach zone on the two sides of the island. The west coast is essentially a zone of sediment bypassing, dominantly to the north, and sand is moving towards the two terminal spit systems. Pointe de l'Est in the north is a large, accretional foreland which is being built out into deeper water and Sandy Hook in the south, which receives less sediment, is a long, narrow, flying spit.

Longshore sediment transport rates are high on the west coast and the barriers are narrow with little development of regular dune ridge systems (Owens, 1977b). The barrier section north of Île du Cap aux Meules is subject to overwash in the updrift sections adjacent to the rock islands, and elsewhere the seaward front of the dunes is subject to frequent storm wave erosion and recovery. The southern section is low, frequently overwashed and clearly migrating landwards into the lagoon of Havre aux Basques.

The east coast barrier beaches have developed in a zone of sediment deposition as material has been transported around the extremities of the islands. Transport is generally from north to south under the influence of waves out of the northwest which have been refracted around Pointe de l'Est, but this coast is also affected by local waves out of the northeast and swell which passes through Cabot Strait to the east. The barriers are generally lower and wider than those on the west coast but are narrow in the updrift or northern sections. Inlets and overwash are restricted to these narrow sections where bypassing is prevalent. Sediment has accumulated in the downdrift sections adjacent to bedrock outcrops, which have acted as major groins. Two major zones of accumulation have well defined sequences of prograding beach ridges, which developed in the lee of the west coast barriers.

The oldest historical record of the coast of the Magdalen Islands, a chart surveyed by James Cook in 1765, shows a shoreline configuration very similar to the present one. The scale and detail of the chart do not permit detailed analysis but serve to show that there have been no major changes in coastal outline in the past 200 years. As in other barrier systems in the southern Gulf (Bryant and McCann, 1973) an indication of local changes and short term variability may be obtained from a compilation of the different positions of the tidal inlets in the system shown on a variety of charts and aerial photographs during the period (Fig. 5.26). There are presently no active tidal inlets on the west coast, but Cook's map, in addition to locating the former inlet at Fatima discussed previously, indicates the position of four former inlets in the southern section of the western barrier, which encloses the southern lagoon, Havre aux Basques. It appears that the low, overwashed, transgressing condition of this section of the west-facing barrier,

EROSION

a   ····   SEDIMENT OUTPUT > INPUT (SECTIONS OF WASHOVER)

b   ◊   SHELTERED UPDRIFT SITES OF OVERWASH OR INLET DEVELOPMENT

ACCRETION

c   ····   SPITS - TRANSPORT ENDPOINTS

d   ⅏   BEACH RIDGE COMPLEXES

→   DIRECTION OF LONGSHORE SEDIMENT TRANSPORT

     ○   INLET OPEN

     ●   INLET CLOSED

     *   MAN-MADE CLOSURE

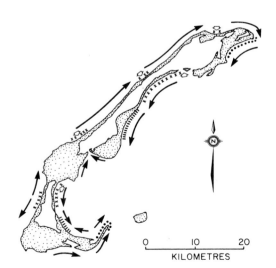

Figure 5.25. *Directions of net longshore sediment transport and areas of erosion or deposition, Magdalen Islands (Owens, 1977b).*

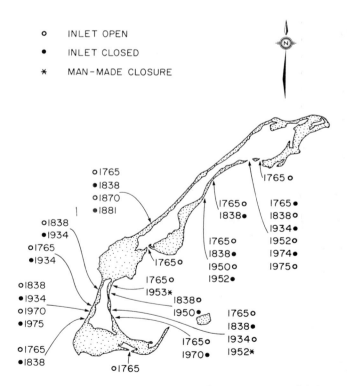

Figure 5.26. *Composite diagram of the location of inlets, derived from charts, aerial photography and Paul (1974).*

allied to shallow lagoon depths, no longer favours the development and maintenance of tidal inlets. The shallow lagoon condition has also enabled the artifical closure of the inlets on the opposite, eastern barrier to be successful, though this is also a relatively protected section of coast. Two inlets on the east coast appear to have been open throughout the two hundred year period, one between the two islands of Île du Cap aux Meules and Île du Havre aux Maisons is bedrock controlled, the other at Grande Entrée is the largest and most dynamic inlet in the Magdalen Islands. The latter is a complex system with two separate inlets, one of which shows a sequence of opening and closure that continues today.

A reconstruction of the earlier stages in the evolution of the barrier system must rest on the overall contrast between the western and eastern barriers, on the morphological evidence of the older dune ridge sequences and on assumptions concerning the operation of coastal processes during the postglacial rise in sea level.

During the early phase of the postglacial transgression, glacial and glaciofluvial sediments reworked by marine and littoral processes may be assumed to have formed beaches on the Magdalen Shelf, which with rising sea level migrated westwards towards the higher area and eventually stabilized around the bedrock outcrops of the Magdalen Islands, providing the antecedents of the present western barriers. The oldest extant dune ridges in the islands, at the rear of the progradational sequences on the east coast, appear to have been formed when sea level was below the present level, and their morphology dictates that protective barriers were present on the west coast at this time. The early development of the terminal spits was probably contemporaneous with the beginning of the progradational sequences, with deposition at Dune du Bassin in the south and with the growth of a spit northeast from Île de la Grande Entrée in the north, the latter implying that the northern section of the western barrier did not yet reach Grosse Île. When the western barrier system was complete the present pattern of longshore sediment transport was initiated and the eastern shore became a more pronounced zone of sediment accumulation: the rate of barrier development on this shore increased and the enclosed lagoons were formed.

The contrast between the western and eastern barriers may be expressed in the context of Swift's views (1975) of the two modes of barrier development during a marine transgression (Fig. 5.27). Following earlier work by Bruun (1962), Curray et al. (1969) and other workers, Swift suggested that when coastwise sand exports equal or exceed

coastwise sand imports then an erosional condition results with shoreface retreat or retrogradation: when there is an excess of sand imports over exports a depositional condition results with shoreface advance or progradation. The west coast barriers accord with the former condition and sections of the east coast barriers with the latter, though it is interesting to note that erosional and depositional shoreface deposits have developed adjacent to each other on the east coast.

SUMMARY

1. The coastline of the Magdalen Islands may be subdivided into nine geomorphic units, four of which are depositional units composed of medium-sized sands. The depositional units comprise two systems of double barrier beaches and dunes, enclosing shallow lagoons, and two terminal spits. The west-facing barriers in both tombolo units are narrow and in the south the barrier is migrating eastwards into the central lagoon. In contrast the east-facing barriers are generally wider and contain two progradational dune-ridge sequences. The west coast is the higher energy shore and is largely a zone of sediment bypassing, with sand moving towards the two terminal spits.

2. The unique assemblage of coastal depositional landforms in the Magdalen Islands represents a geomorphic response to a particular combination of environmental conditions in an unusual geological setting. The key environmental factor is the predominance of locally generated waves from the west and northwest. The key factors in the geological setting are the shallow, sediment-abundant shelf condition, and the spacing and alignment of the series of small rock islands in the centre of the shelf, which act as stable anchors for the double tombolos and terminal spits.

3. The present shoreline condition is the end product of a long period of fluctuating but, overall, rising sea level during which beach and shallow marine processes have reworked the sandy, glacial deposits of the Magdalen Shelf. The barriers and spits are the supratidal component of a suite of reworked shelf sediments.

4. The morphological analysis and interpretation of the recent development of the barrier beaches and spits of the Magdalen Islands presented here complement the detailed process studies made by Owens (1977a, b; Owens and Frobel, 1975; 1977). They provide a framework for the broader application of the findings related to shoreline dynamics, which by their nature are site specific. In this respect morphological analysis is an important tool in coastal geomorphology, which allows inferences to be made concerning evolutionary trends in shoreline development.

Acknowledgments

E.H. Owens' investigations were conducted as part of projects 730088 and 740009 at the Geological Survey's Atlantic Geoscience Centre; salary support during the preparation of the paper was provided by the Geography Programs, Office of Naval Research under a contract with the Coastal Studies Institute, Louisiana State University. S.B. McCann's investigations were supported by National Research Council of Canada Grant No. A5082. The figures were prepared by the Drafting and Illustrations Unit of the Atlantic Oceanographic Laboratory, Bedford Institute of Oceanography. The manuscript was critically reviewed by D.R. Grant and C.P. Lewis.

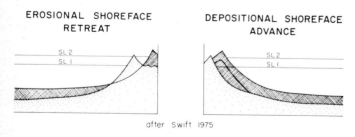

EROSIONAL SHOREFACE RETREAT

DEPOSITIONAL SHOREFACE ADVANCE

after Swift 1975

Figure 5.27. *Model of shoreface retreat or advance with a transgressing sea.*

References

Alcock, F.J.
1941:   The Magdalen Islands, their geology and mineral deposits; Canadian Institute of Mining and Metallurgy, Transactions, v. 44, p. 623 - 649.

Bruun, P.
1962:   Sea level rise as a cause of shore erosion; Journal, Waterways and Harbours Division, American Society of Civil Engineers, Proceedings, v. 88, p. 117 - 130.

Bryant, E.A. and McCann, S.B.
1973:   Long and short term changes in the barrier islands of Kouchibouguac Bay, Southern Gulf of St. Lawrence; Canadian Journal of Earth Sciences, v. 10, p. 1582 - 1590.

Canadian Hydrographic Service
1974:   Canadian Tide and Current Tables, 1975; Volume 2, Gulf of St. Lawrence; Department of the Environment, Ottawa, 67 p.

Chalmers, R.
1895:   Report on the surface geology of eastern New Brunswick, northwestern Nova Scotia, and a portion of Prince Edward Island; Geological Survey of Canada, Annual Report, 1894, (new ser.), 7, Part M, 144 p.

Clarke, J.M.
1910:   Observations on the Magdalen Islands; New York State Museum Bulletin, No. 149, 53 p.

Curray, J.R., Emmel, F.J. and Crampton, P.J.S.
1969:   Holocene history of a strand plain, lagoonal coast, Nayarit, Mexico; in Proceedings, International Symposium on Coastal Lagoons; A. Ayala-Castanaries and F.B. Phleger, eds.; UNAM-UNESCO, Nov. 28 - 30, 1967, Mexico, D.F., p. 63 - 100.

Dresser, J.A. and Denis, T.C.
1964:   La géologie de Québec; Ministère des Richesses Naturelles, Québec, Report 20, 2, 647 p.

Goldthwait, J.W.
1915:   The occurrence of glacial drift on the Magdalen Islands; Geological Survey of Canada, Museum Bulletin, No. 14, Geological Series No. 25, 11 p.

Grandtner, M.M.
1966:   Premières observations phyteopédologiques sur les prés salés des Îles-de-la-Madeleine; Le Naturaliste Canadien, v. 93, p. 361 - 366.
1967:   Les ressources végétales des Îles-de-la-Madeleine; Fonds de Recherches Forestières de l'Université Laval, Bulletin No. 10, 53 p. and map.
1968:   Quelques observations sur la végétation psammophile des Îles-de-la-Madeleine; Collectanea Botanica, VII, 25, p. 519 - 530.

Grant, D.R.
1970:   Recent coastal submergence of the Maritime Provinces, Canada; Canadian Journal of Earth Sciences, v. 7, p. 676 - 689.

Grant, D.R.
1975a: Surficial geology of northern Cape Breton Island; in Report of Activities, Part A; Geological Survey of Canada, Paper 75-1A, p. 407 - 408
1975b: Recent coastal submergence of the Maritime Provinces. Environmental change in the Maritimes; Nova Scotia Institute of Science, Proceedings, 3rd Supplement, v. 27, p. 83 - 102.
1976:   Late Wisconsinan ice limits in the Atlantic Provinces of Canada with particular reference to Cape Breton Island; in Report of Activities, Part C; Geological Survey of Canada, Paper 76-IC, p. 289 - 292.

Homma, M. and Sonu, C.J.
1963:   Rhythmic pattern of longshore bars related to sediment characteristics; in Proceedings, 8th Conference Coastal Engineering, Mexico City, 1962; American Society of Civil Engineers, New York, p. 248 - 278.

Kranck, K.
1972:   Geomorphological developments and Post-Pleistocene sea-level changes, Northumberland Strait, Maritime Provinces; Canadian Journal of Earth Sciences, v. 9, p. 835 - 844.

Lamoureux, G. and Grandtner, M.M.
1977:   Contribution à l'étude écologique des dunes mobiles. I---Les éléments phytosociologique; Canadian Journal of Botany, v. 55, no. 2, p. 158 - 171.

Laverdière, C. and Guimont, P.
1974:   Un froid à sol fendre; Geos, Department of Energy, Mines and Resources, Canada, fall edition, p. 18 - 20.

Loring, D.H. and Nota, D.J.G.
1969:   Mineral dispersal patterns in the Gulf of St. Lawrence; Revue du Géographie de Montréal, v. 23, p. 289 - 305.
1973:   Morphology and sediments of the Gulf of St. Lawrence; Fisheries Research Board, Canada, Bulletin No. 182, 147 p.

Loring, D.H., Nota, D.J.G., Chesterman, W.D. and Wong, H.K.
1970:   Sedimentary environments on the Magdalen Shelf, southern Gulf of St. Lawrence; Marine Geology, v. 8, p. 3337 - 3354.

McCann, S.B.
1979:   Barrier islands in the southern Gulf of St. Lawrence, Canada; in Barrier Islands, S.O. Leatherman, ed.; Academic Press, New York, p. 29-63.

Owens, E.H.
1974a: A framework for the definition of coastal environments in the southern Gulf of St. Lawrence; in Offshore Geology of Eastern Canada, Volume 1, Concepts and Applications of Environmental Marine Geology, B.R. Pelletier, ed.; Geological Survey of Canada, Paper 74-30, p. 47 - 76.

Owens, E.H.
1974b: Size analysis data of surface samples from the coastal zone of the southern Gulf of St. Lawrence, Bedford Institute of Oceanography, Dartmouth, Nova Scotia, Data Report B1-D-74-1, 106 p.

1975:   Barrier beaches and sediment transport in the southern Gulf of St. Lawrence, Canada; in Proceedings, 14th Conference, Coastal Engineering, Copenhagen, June 1974; American Society of Civil Engineers, New York, v. II, p. 1177 - 1193.

1976:   The effects of ice on the littoral zone, Richibucto Head, eastern New Brunswick; Revue de Géographie de Montréal, v. 30, no. 1-2, p. 95 - 104.

1977a: Temporal variations in beach and nearshore dynamics; Journal of Sedimentary Petrology, v. 47, p. 168 - 190.

1977b: Process and morphology characteristics of two barrier beaches in the Magdalen Islands, Gulf of St. Lawrence, Canada; in Proceedings, 15th Conference on Coastal Engineering, Honolulu, July 1976; American Society of Civil Engineers, New York, v. II, p. 1975 - 1991.

Owens, E.H. and Frobel, D.H.
1975:   Environmental, morphological, and sediment size data from two barrier beaches in the Magdalen Islands, Quebec; Bedford Institute of Oceanography, Dartmouth, Nova Scotia, Data Report B1-D-75-8, 447 p.

1977:   Ridge and runnel systems in the Magdalen Islands, Quebec; Journal of Sedimentary Petrology, v. 47, p. 191 - 198.

Paul, L.A.
1974:   Aspects of the coastal geomorphology of Îles-de-la-Madeleine using remote sensing techniques; unpubl. B.A. thesis, Department of Geography, McMaster University, Hamilton, 94 p.

Pleog, J.
1971:   Wave climate study, Great Lakes and Gulf of St. Lawrence; National Research Council Canada, Mechanical Engineering Report, MH-107A, v. 1, 160 p.

Prest, V.K.
1970:   Quaternary geology of Canada; in Geology and Economic Minerals of Canada, R.J. Douglas, ed.; Geological Survey of Canada, Economic Geology Report no. 1, 5th ed., p. 676 - 758.

Prest, V.K., Terasmae, J., Matthews, J.V. and Lichiti-Federovich, S.
1976:   Late-Quaternary history of Magdalen Islands, Quebec; Maritime Sediments, v. 12, p. 39 - 58.

Richardson, J.
1881:   Report of a geological exploration of the Magdalen Islands; Geological Survey of Canada, Report of Progress (1880 - 1881), Part G, p. 9 - 11.

Sanschagrin, R.
1968:   Magdalen Islands; Department of National Resources, Quebec, Geology Report 106, 58 p.

Sheridan, R.E. and Drake, C.L.
1968:   Seaward extension of the Canadian Appalachians; Canadian Journal of Earth Sciences, v. 5, no. 3, p. 337 - 373.

Swift, D.J.P.
1975:   Barrier-island genesis: evidence from the central Atlantic Shelf, eastern U.S.A.; Sedimentary Geology, v. 14, no. 1, p. 1 - 43.

Villeneuve, G.O.
1967:   Aperçu climatique des Îles-de-la-Madeleine; Ministère des Richesses Naturelles, Québec, Report M-21, 69 p.

Watts, A.B.
1972:   Geophysical investigations east of the Magdalen Islands, southern Gulf of St. Lawrence; Canadian Journal of Earth Sciences, v. 9, p. 1504 - 1528.

STORM WAVE CLIMATOLOGY: A STUDY OF THE
MAGNITUDE AND FREQUENCY OF GEOMORPHIC PROCESS

Peter B. Hale   and Brian Greenwood
Scarborough College, University of Toronto, West Hill, Ontario

Hale, Peter B. and Greenwood, Brian, Storm wave climatology: A study of the magnitude and frequency of geomorphic process; in The Coastline of Canada, S.B. McCann, editor; Geological Survey of Canada, Paper 80-10, p. 73-88, 1980.

Abstract

This paper provides a framework for detailed time series analysis of storm events and an assessment of their relative importance in controlling morphological changes in the coastal zone. A wave-hindcast procedure (S-M-B) is used to generate theoretical wave heights, periods and cumulative wave energies for specific storm events based on hourly wind data for Kouchibouguac Bay in the southern Gulf of St. Lawrence. The synthetic wave climatology provides: (a) measures of storm intensity, by maximum significant wave height, period or cumulative wave energy for the duration of the storm, (b) return periods for events of differing magnitude, and (c) a ranking scheme for the relative importance of storm events in terms of their geomorphological impact in the coastal zone.

Kouchibouguac Bay is a low-energy, storm-wave dominated environment, receiving 19 storms per ice-free year on average but these represent only 5.5 per cent of the total time. The dominant storm-wave direction is northeasterly for all return periods and the stormiest months are May followed by April and December. The largest most probable annual wave event produces significant wave heights of 1.3 m and a total storm wave energy of 13 344.5 x 10^3 J m^{-1} crest width from the northeast. The largest predicted wave has a return period of 34 years, a significant height of 2.6 m (maximum of 4.7 m) and a period of 7 s; extrapolation to the 100-year event suggests a maximum wave height of 5.6 m.

Morphological response in Kouchibouguac Bay is well-correlated with wave intensity: (a) rip-channel excavation in the inner bar system occurs with predicted waves 60-80 cm high and a return period less than one month; (b) the outer crescentic bar system responds extensively to the most probable annual maximum (significant height of 1.2 m); (c) barrier washover correlates with this latter event also; (d) barrier breaching occurs under storm conditions with return periods of between 4 and 12 years but the location is controlled by antecedent morphology.

Résumé

La présente étude se veut le cadre d'analyses détaillées de séries chronologiques d'apparitions de tempétes et d'évaluation de leur importance relative dans la lutte contre l'évolution morphologique des côtes. Les auteurs emploient une méthode de prévision à posteriori des vagues (S-M-B) afin de reconstituer la hauteur théorique des vagues, leurs périodes et l'énergie accumulée à l'occasion de certaines tempétes, à partir de données éoliennes horaires pour la baie de Kouchibouguac dans la partie méridionale du golfe du Saint-Laurent. La climatologie des zones synthétiques a permis de déterminer les facteurs suivants: (a) des mesures de l'intensité des tempétes, par la hauteur de houle significative et maximale, l'énergie périodique ou cumulative de la houle pour la durée de la tempéte; (b) la durée des cycles pour chacune des apparitions de tempétes de puissance différente et (c) un mode de classement pour l'importance relative des tempétes suivant leurs effets géomorphologiques sur la zone côtière.

La baie de Kouchibouguac constitue un milieu à faible énergie dominé par des vagues de tempéte; la baie essuie en moyenne 19 tempétes par année (période libre de glace) mais celles-ci ne représentent que 5,5 p. 100 de tout le temps écoulé. Les vagues de tempéte dominantes ont une direction nord-est pour tous les cycles, les mois les plus perturbés étant surtout le mois de mai, suivi d'avril et de décembre. La plus grande apparition probable d'onde annuelle produit des hauteurs de houle significative de 1,3 m et une énergie totale due aux vagues de tempéte de 13 344,5 x 10^3 J m^{-1} comme largeur de créte venant du nord-est. La plus grande vague prévue possède un cycle de 34 ans, une hauteur significative de 2,6 m (maximum de 4,7 m) et une période de 7 s; son extrapolation sur 100 ans laisse croire à la possibilité d'une hauteur de houle maximale de 5,6 m.

Les effets morphologiques dans la baie de Kouchibouguac sont étroitement liés à l'intensité de la houle: (a) le creusement du chenal d'arrachement dans le réseau de cordons intérieurs se produit lorsque les vagues prévues atteignent 60 à 80 cm de hauteur et possèdent un cycle de moins d'un mois; (b) les réseaux de cordons recourbés vers l'extérieur réagissent fortement au maximum annuel le plus probable (soit une hauteur significative de 1,2 m); (c) le washover de barrière se corrèle aussi avec cette dernière apparition; (d) l'ébrèchement des barrières se produit dans des conditions de tempéte avec cycles d'une durée de 4 à 12 ans mais l'emplacement est commandé par une morphologie antécédente.

INTRODUCTION

The relative magnitude and frequency of occurrence of specific geomorphological processes has been a recurrent conceptual problem for many years and was clearly identified in the classic paper by Wolman and Miller (1960). More recently the importance of morphological thresholds (Schumm, 1973, 1975) has been identified as a modulating influence on the absolute magnitude of process. Such concepts are particularly relevant in coastal studies in any attempt to define both the magnitude of process controlling the wave-induced rates of sediment flux through time (Komar, 1976) and the development of specific geomorphological features such as barrier breaches (Greenwood and Keay, 1979). The basic philosophical question thus still remains as to whether modern process studies should emphasize analysis of infrequent extreme events (e.g., Jackli, 1957; Ball et al., 1967; Hayes, 1967; Hayes and Boothroyd, 1969) under the framework of a 'catastrophic uniformitarianism' (Lyell, 1830; Gretener, 1967; Brenner and Davies, 1973; Kumar and Sanders, 1976), or more moderate events (e.g., Wolman and Miller, 1960). Indeed the very definition of 'extreme event' is unclear. Unfortunately, as in many other fields of geomorphology, assessing the significance of empirical studies of specific events is restricted by the limited time series of both process and form which are presently available.

Understanding morphological change in the coastal zone depends heavily upon an analysis of the effect of wave energy dissipation and its variation through time. This is particularly so in storm-wave dominated coasts (Davies, 1973), such as those of the Canadian Arctic, Great Lakes and sections of the Eastern Seaboard where geomorphological work is a distinctly discrete process; periods of intensive wave activity are associated with the intermittent passage of meteorological depressions of varying size (Fox and Davis, 1976) and frequently separated by long periods of near zero wave activity. While storm effects depend upon the character of individual event (size of waves generated, level of surge, etc.) modulated by the tidal regime, sediment texture and availability, and coastal configuration, the relative importance of any specific event depends upon its relationship to the local wave climate. To evaluate morphological change in the coastal zone in the long term it is necessary, therefore, to determine some index of storm magnitude, which will reflect a potential to do work, and also recurrence intervals for events of similar magnitude, which will reflect the pattern of total work over time. In this way specific empirical studies of the morphological change associated with known storm conditions can be placed in their true perspective with respect to the magnitude and frequency of occurrence of that specific event.

The aim of this paper is to present a method for evaluating the significance of specific storm events using a synthetic wave climatology and to illustrate its application in case studies of storm wave effects in Kouchibouguac Bay, New Brunswick, bordering the southern Gulf of St. Lawrence (Fig. 6.1). In this area, sheltered from swell wave penetration, morphological change results from local wave generation during the passage of extratropical depressions and studies have been made of the response of the nearshore zone to individual storm events (e.g., Greenwood and Davidson-Arnott, 1975; Greenwood and Keay, 1979; Greenwood and Hale, 1980). It is important, however, that these be placed in context with the long-term distribution of storm events of differing magnitudes.

The Kouchibouguac embayment has been described in detail previously (Davidson-Arnott, 1971; Bryant, 1972;

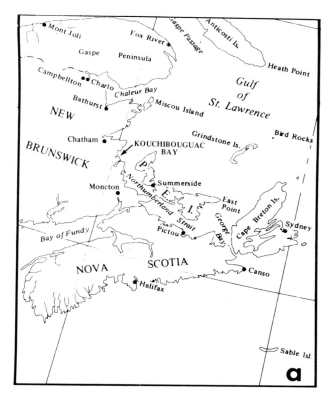

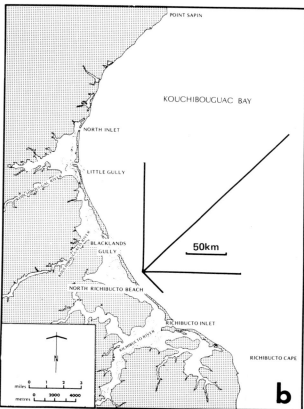

Figure 6.1. *Location of study area: (a) the southern Gulf of St. Lawrence; (b) Kouchibouguac Bay illustrating fetch lengths for North Richibucto Beach.*

Bryant and McCann, 1973; Greenwood and Davidson-Arnott, 1975, 1977) and it is sufficient to note that the area has a mixed microtidal regime and is storm-wave dominated with long intervals either free from storms or periods (generally 3 months) during which ice in the nearshore zone prohibits wave activity. No long-term wave records are presently available for the bay itself although shorter periods of recording are available for a station in 7 m water depth in the southern part of the bay (Davidson-Arnott, 1975; Mittler, 1977, pers. com.).

WAVE CLIMATOLOGY

Winds change not only by the minute, hour and day but also by the season and year. Since they are the generating force for the waves, the waves themselves exhibit this same variability. It is this long-term distribution of waves that constitutes a *wave climatology*. In addition to the temporal variations of winds and waves there are spatial variations and hence a wave climatology is unique to a particular area. Wave climatologies for large areas such as the Gulf of St. Lawrence (Quon et al., 1963; Environment Canada, 1972) are referred to as *regional* wave climates, those for specific localities such as Kouchibouguac Bay are termed *local* wave climates (Ploeg, 1971; Ashe and Ploeg, 1971; Environment Canada, 1977a). Furthermore, wave characteristics in shallow water will differ considerably in direction of approach, height and alongshore energy distribution from those in deep water. The amount of variation will depend upon the bathymetry, the initial angle of wave approach and the deep-water wave length. Both *nearshore* (Goldsmith, 1976) and *offshore* (Walton, 1973) wave climates can be recognized.

Attempts are being made with increasing frequency to monitor wave characteristics at these different scales ranging from the United States Hydrographic Office Global Wave Climate (Bigelow and Edmondston, 1947) and the wave study proposed by the Permanent International Association of Navigation Congresses (1973) to the highly localized monitoring of the Littoral Environment Observations Program (Berg, 1970). In Canada a continuing effort is being made to provide as wide a coverage of wave data as possible (Draper, 1970; Baird and Wilson, 1974; Environment Canada, 1977b). In most instances, however, the cost, both in time and money, of obtaining long-term wave records cannot be afforded. As a result lengthy time series suitable for compilation into a wave climatology are seldom available for the area of concern. Furthermore even where direct measurement has been undertaken the directional attributes of the waves (so important in coastal sediment transport) are frequently not available because of the difficulty or cost of determination (Mitsuyasu and Mizuno, 1976). One means of circumventing this problem involves the collection of wave data for a short period and using these data to calibrate a wave hindcasting procedure based on meteorological parameters and available fetch. After calibration to establish the validity of the procedure an extended time series of meteorological data can be used to generate a *synthetic* wave climatology (Hale, 1978).

SYNTHETIC WAVE CLIMATOLOGY

Since the early work of Suthons (1945), Arthur (1947) and Sverdrup and Munk (1947) there has been a continuing effort to perfect wave prediction procedures through either a significant wave determination or complete spectral estimation for given wave-generating events (Bretschneider,

1966). All methods depend upon semiempirical computations involving wind speed, duration and fetch length and to date it is not possible to clearly identify a superior method (Neumann and Pierson, 1957) although Komar (1976) argued a preference for spectral estimates on theoretical grounds. Neu (1971), in contrast, argued that it is difficult and impractical to apply spectral data to a wave climate investigation, and the description of the physical characteristics of the waves (height, period, etc.) is more useful and more adaptable to time series analysis.

In this study a synthetic wave climatology is developed using the Sverdrup-Munk-Bretschneider (S-M-B) significant wave approach (Sverdrup-Munk, 1947; Bretschneider, 1951, 1958, 1959, 1970). The relationships representing deep-water wave generation can be defined in dimensional equations (Johnson, 1950):

$$\frac{C}{V} = \psi_1 \left[\frac{gF}{V^2}, \frac{gt}{V} \right] \qquad (1)$$

$$\frac{gH}{V^2} = \psi_2 \left[\frac{gF}{V^2}, \frac{gt}{V} \right] \qquad (2)$$

where C = wave celerity; H = wave height (significant); V = wind speed; F = fetch length; t = duration; g = gravitational constant; ψ = constant of proportionality. The constants of proportionality depend upon empirical data and, as such, are revised as more information becomes available. Lalande (1975) developed two computer programs based on the above equations that allow simple incorporation of the constants as they are modified. One program employs average wind speed for the first six hours of the storm followed by hourly wind speeds. Significant wave height and period for the first six-hour interval are computed and printed. This is followed by an hourly computation of the wave parameters using the cumulative average wind speed. For this study the program was modified to provide an hour-by-hour printout of wave conditions from the first hour of the event. Procedures were added to compute the wave energy generated each hour and cumulative or total wave energy for the storm event.

The S-M-B relationships were derived for open coast situations where fetch width was at least as great as fetch length. In a study of measured versus predicted wave characteristics in a situation where fetch width was small in comparison with fetch length, Saville (1954; Saville et al., 1962) found considerably smaller measured waves. Furthermore for wind velocities over small fetch lengths at angles of 30° to 45° to the longer fetch lengths, an underprediction occurred using available fetch. Consequently a procedure was adopted that assumes that the effectiveness of any fetch segment is a function of the ratio of the actual length of the segment to the length it would be in a fetch of unrestricted width. It further assumes that the effectiveness of the wind in generating waves is proportional to the cosine of the angle from the average wind direction and that wind beyond 45° on either side of the principle direction is noneffective. In view of the limited fetch widths in the study area (Fig. 6.1b) effective fetch rather than available fetch was used in the modified Lalande (1975) program together with hourly wind data to generate a synthetic wave climatology.

To develop a storm wave climatology for any area using hindcasting techniques, exactly what constitutes a storm event must be defined on the basis of the meteorological data. Furthermore in a time series analysis some index of storm intensity must be derived.

Storm event criteria

No absolute definition of what constitutes a storm event exists and, in general, simple meteorological measures are used to identify the storm magnitude (barometric pressure, maximum hourly wind speed, maximum gust, etc.). From a wave generation point of view, however, a number of key variables need to be defined: wind directions determining the fetch lengths, wind speeds capable of wave generation and wind duration controlling the extent of wave buildup and period of wave activity. Again somewhat arbitrary decisions have to be made when working from meteorological data.

The following criteria, based on the hourly average wind speed and direction summaries provided by the Atmospheric Environment Service, Fisheries and Environment Canada, have been used in this paper to define a storm event.

1. Wind speed was defined as the cumulative average hourly value throughout the duration of the storm event and must not be less than 19 Km h^{-1} (12 mi h^{-1}) from an existing fetch direction. This latter value was adopted since a wind speed of 19 km h^{-1} will not theoretically generate significant waves greater than 1 m in height or 4 s period regardless of fetch length or duration and forms the lower limit of the S-M-B nomogram. A storm event was considered terminated when the cumulative average wind speed fell below 19 km h^{-1}.

2. The duration of wind speeds equal to or greater than 19 km h^{-1} must not be less than six hours. Waves take a certain length of time to develop over any significant fetch length and therefore a single hour of wind, no matter how strong, will not be particularly important unless it is preceded or followed by winds of similar intensity. An arbitrary value of six hours was, therefore, taken as the minimum duration of a storm event. This value proved to be conservative in subsequent time series analysis when the annual maximum series of storm events was considered.

3. Wind directional variability must be restricted to fluctuation less than ± 45° from the predominant direction except where (a) the fluctutions were for a period of time not exceeding two hours, or (b) the wind reverted to its original direction (and minimum speed or greater) for a further period of not less than six hours within a seven-hour interval.

The predominant direction was determined on the basis of the maximum number of hours of wind from a given direction. Where winds blew an equal number of hours from more than one direction the predominant wind was defined by the highest hourly average wind speed.

Storm intensity indices

Storm event classification by maximum significant wave height and the height of the highest one tenth of the waves, combined with information on storm surge, may provide a measure for determining the potential of a storm to produce barrier breaching, overwash, and flooding of low-lying coastal regions. It may not, however, be the best measure of intensity for predicting the potential impact on the nearshore zone in terms of both the quantity of longshore sediment transport and the resultant morphological changes. In this instance a storm index based on the cumulative energy or capacity to do work may be more applicable.

Two indices were used in the present study: (i) maximum significant wave height for a storm event and (ii) cumulative storm wave energy generated by an event. Furthermore an estimation of extreme wave heights for particular events was also possible using the relationships derived by Longuet-Higgins (1952).

KOUCHIBOUGUAC BAY: A CASE STUDY

Meteorological data

Three locations around Northumberland Strait provide hourly wind data: Chatham and Moncton, New Brunswick, and Summerside, Prince Edward Island (Fig. 6.1a). The Moncton station is a considerable distance from the Strait and is surrounded by heavy forest. Summerside is approximately 100 km south and east of the study area, whereas Chatham is only 60 km to the north. The Chatham station is about 30 m above sea level in an area of flat, open country, the only obstruction being to the south where there is a stand of heavy forest. The Miramichi Embayment is a short distance to the northeast and there is no intervening high ground. Similarly, the terrain to the east is low-lying. Therefore the Chatham wind data were selected for use in wave hindcasting.

Frequently in wave hindcasting overland winds are adjusted to represent those expected over water (Richards and Phillips, 1970; Resio and Vincent, 1977). The lack of overwater wind data for Northumberland Strait coupled with the unreliability of conversions (Cole, 1967) precluded such adjustments in this study.

A pilot study to compare Chatham winds with those measured at the exposed coast (North Richibucto Beach; Fig. 6.1b) was undertaken for the summer of 1976 and significant (0.05 level) correlations were obtained for all fetch directions except southeast. Figure 6.2 illustrates the wind roses for the same period and reveals the similarity of wind conditions for all fetch directions except the southeast; of particular significance is the similarity of the north and northeast components which are the dominant wave-generating directions. The greater magnitude and frequency of winds from the southeast at North Richibucto Beach reflects the sea breeze phenomena, which is only of minor importance in wave generation because of its limited fetch and duration. For this study the unaltered Chatham wind data for 33 ice-free years (1941 - 76) were used, since the high correlations suggest a strong relationship between the land-based versus shore-based readings. Even though the absolute speeds may vary, being higher at the beach, this can be considered a constant in the long time series used in generating a synthetic wave climatology.

Hindcast waves

The use of the S-M-B technique for limited fetch environments has been reasonably successful (Brebner and Kennedy, 1962; Brebner and Sangal, 1964; Cole, 1967, 1971) although it does underpredict at low wind speeds. A further check on its ability to predict real waves was carried out in this study for one specific wave-generating event. To do this it was necessary to have a distinct wave-generating event where the antecedent conditions were of no importance. The storm selected occurred between 1976-7-18-0800 h and 1976-7-18-1700 h and winds were mainly from the east. During the previous 19 hours the winds had been offshore from either the west or southwest and thus the storm is a good example of a discrete wave-generating episode. Figure 6.3 illustrates these winds and waves (both measured and predicted). Predicted values are lower than observed values for both wave height and period, even when shore-based winds are used, but the trend of observed and predicted waves is remarkably similar and there is no phase shift between wind and waves. This test indicates that the water body responds rapidly to local winds, suggesting that in a long-term comparative approach the S-M-B procedure will provide consistent, meaningful wave characteristics for the development of a wave climatology.

CHATHAM
JUNE1-AUGUST20

LEGEND:

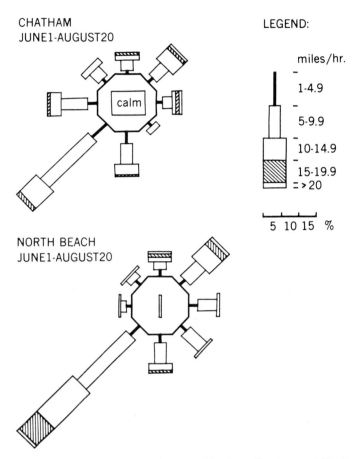

Figure 6.2. *Wind roses for the Chatham Station and North Richibucto Beach, 1976.*

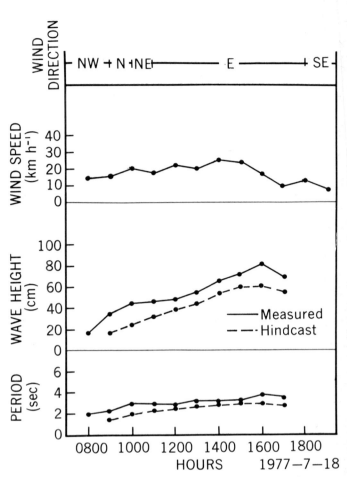

Figure 6.3. *Measured and predicted storm-wave characteristics, Kouchibouguac Bay. Winds were those recorded at North Richibucto Beach.*

Storm wave climatology

The storm wave climatology allows an assessment of the following characteristics: (i) the distribution of storm events by magnitude, direction and month to be expected in an average year; (ii) the annual variability in the number and intensity of storm events by direction and month of occurrence; (iii) the percentage frequency of occurrence of storm wave activity on an annual basis and the probabilities of occurrence of waves greater than a given size; (iv) the maximum significant and extreme wave heights and periods, plus total energies, to be expected from a given direction and the magnitudes of the average annual and most probable annual storm event by direction; (v) the recurrence interval for events of given magnitude (based on storm intensity indices) and direction. Thus, while a complete annual wave spectrum cannot be determined, the most important wave events from a geomorphological point of view can be derived.

Annual storm expectancy

Storm events abstracted from the Chatham wind record were first summarized in terms of the number of events by direction and month for an average year. Figure 6.4 shows that, of the 19 storms per year, 11 are from the northeast, 4 from the north, 2 from the east and 2 from the southeast.

The characteristic 'northeaster' is the major wave-generating event in this area, as it coincides with the maximum effective fetch (Fig. 6.1b). It is associated with the approach of depressions primarily along the eastern seaboard track (Fig. 6.5), and the termination of the storm is associated with a wind switch to the northwest and west as the centre passes. Storms tracking down the St. Lawrence Valley may be important if they veer southwards, but generally produce only strong southerly or southwesterly winds during their passage. Irrespective of direction, May is the stormiest month with an average of four storms, followed by April and December with three each. July, August and September, the quietest months, average only one storm each per year. These data reflect the characteristic annual pattern of storm tracks through this area (Fig. 6.5). Storm intensity is always greater in the fall, winter and spring in these latitudes simply because of the macroscale atmospheric conditions. In the fall and spring the east coast storm track lies over Nova Scotia and particularly strong northeasterly winds are generated in Northumberland Strait and the southern Gulf of St. Lawrence as storms approach. Bosserman and Dolan (1968) in their study of the Outer Banks, North Carolina found a frequency of extratropical storms almost double that for

Kouchibouguac Bay, but a similar dominance of northeast waves was noted by Hayden and Dolan (1977). Indeed, along the whole of the eastern seaboard, the 'northeaster' is the most important wave-generating event (Mather et al., 1964, 1967; Hayes and Boothroyd, 1969).

Storm frequency by magnitude and direction

Hindcast wave events were classified according to maximum significant wave height and cumulative storm wave energy (Tables 6.1, 6.2). The importance of fetch exposure is clearly illustrated by the dominant northeast component. Of the total period of ice-free years for a ten-year period (1965–75) storm waves were generated only 5.5 per cent of the time. However, of this percentage the largest contribution was from the northeast (3.3%) followed by north (1.6%) and east and southeast (0.3%). Thus, the wave climate is characteristically low-energy, punctuated by periods of moderate to high-energy conditions. Although the expected annual frequency of occurrence of storm wave heights and energies are shown in Tables 6.1 and 6.2, no indication of annual variability is given and examination of six discrete time intervals shows that this variability can be considerable. Table 6.3 documents this case for cumulative

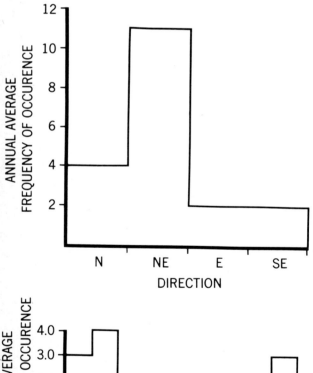

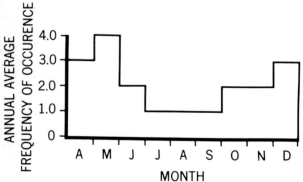

Figure 6.4. *Frequency distributions of storms by direction and month, Kouchibouguac Bay, for the period 1941–1976.*

storm wave energies. In one time interval (1972-8 to 1973-7) there were 28 storms, 9 above the average, while there were only 17 in the previous time segment. The distribution of storm events within each time interval also exhibits considerable variability. During the period August 1974 to July 1975 there were three events with total energy values greater than 3500×10^3 Jm^{-1} crest width, whereas events of similar magnitude occurred only twice in the other five time intervals (in both cases in the August 1970 to July 1971 time period).

Even though there is considerable annual variability it is possible to reveal important general patterns, particularly with respect to the larger events, using procedures originally developed in hydrology (Gumbel, 1941, 1960; Powell, 1943; Dalrymple, 1960; Chow, 1964) for the analysis of extreme values (Gumbel, 1960). Based on the Type I extreme-value distribution of Fisher and Tippett (1928) these techniques allow an analysis of the annual maximum storm wave series to determine the probability of occurrence or return period of a storm of given magnitude (Weibull, 1939; Gumbel, 1966; Khanna and Andru, 1974). Both the annual maximum and partial duration series of storms were examined for Kouchibouguac Bay. The former is more valuable for events with long return periods as it generates a smaller sampling variance (Cunnane, 1973), while the latter does yield more precise estimates of return period for the smaller storm events. Bores (1974) defined the annual maximum series as the "storm regime" but suggests that two consecutive hypercycles of 11 years provide an adequate data set for the series to be defined.

Examination of the distributions of both the annual maximum series and partial duration series for significant wave height (Figs. 6.6a, 6.6b) and cumulative storm energy (Figs. 6.7a, 6.7b) reveals that in all cases the largest magnitude event for any given return period is from the northeast. However, there is a tendency towards convergence for smaller return periods, particularly in the case of cumulative energy. This is to be expected as wave generation shifts from a fetch-limited to duration-limited condition. The dominance of the northeast component is particularly marked with respect to cumulative energy of storms with a less than 10-year recurrence interval (Fig. 6.7a) and reflects the duration of storms from the northeast. Convergence with storms from the north of longer return periods suggests that in the long-term record northerly winds may generate equally intense storms.

Tables 6.4 and 6.5 define the expected significant wave height and cumulative energy by direction for events of differing recurrence interval using the Hazen (1930) and Gumbel (1966) procedures. Besides indicating the general range of wave conditions and the probabilities of occurrence in Kouchibouguac Bay, the tables indicate a tendency for the Hazen technique to exaggerate the magnitudes for specific recurrence intervals. This results from the basic assumption of Hazen that, since the actual frequency of occurrence of the maximum event in n years is not known, it should be considered to be 2n.

The most probable annual storm wave event (recurrence interval 1.58 years) from the northeast is a significant wave height of 1.3 m or a cumulative energy of 1712.6×10^3 Jm^{-1} crest width. An event with an expected return period of 25 years, however, generates waves 2.6 m high with an energy value for the total storm of 1344.5×10^4 Jm^{-1} crest width. Thus it appears that a greater difference is produced in cumulative energy (by a factor of 8) than in wave height (by a factor of 2) as return periods increase. This can be expected as fetch restrictions limit wave height while storm duration increases total energy.

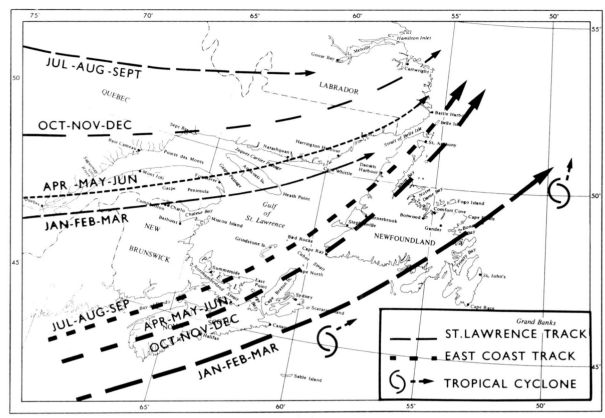

Figure 6.5. *Average storm tracks for Eastern Canada (after Watson, 1973).*

Table 6.1. Frequency of maximum significant wave height generated by storm events, classified by direction: (a) totals for period 1941-1976; (b) values for an average year. Figures in parentheses are percentages.

MAXIMUM SIGNIFICANT WAVE HEIGHT	N	NE	E	SE	ALL DIRECTIONS
(a) 1.0 – 1.9	5 (0.8)	11 (1.8)	1 (0.2)	8 (1.3)	25 (4.1)
2.0 – 2.9	55 (8.9)	154 (25.0)	27 (4.4)	51 (8.3)	287 (46.5)
3.0 – 3.9	31 (5.0)	98 (15.9)	26 (4.2)	11 (1.8)	166 (26.9)
4.0 – 4.9	15 (2.4)	58 (9.4)	16 (2.6)	1 (0.2)	90 (14.6)
5.0 – 5.9	5 (0.8)	25 (4.1)	4 (0.7)	0	34 (5.5)
6.0 – 6.9	2 (0.3)	8 (1.3)	1 (0.2)	0	11 (1.8)
7.0 – 7.9	1 (0.2)	1 (0.2)	0	0	2 (0.3)
8.0 – 8.9		2 (0.3)	0	0	2 (0.3)
TOTAL	114 (18.5)	357 (57.9)	75 (12.2)	71 (11.5)	617 (100.0)
(b) 1.0 – 1.9	0.15	0.34	0.03	0.25	0.77
2.0 – 2.9	1.69	4.73	0.83	1.57	8.82
3.0 – 3.9	0.95	3.01	0.80	0.34	5.1
4.0 – 4.9	0.46	1.78	0.49	0.03	2.76
5.0 – 5.9	0.15	0.77	0.12	0	1.04
6.0 – 6.9	0.06	0.23	0.03	0	0.34
7.0 – 7.9	0.03	0.03	0	0	.06
8.0 – 8.9	0	0.01	0	0	.01
TOTAL	3.49	10.92	2.3	2.19	18.9

Table 6.2. Frequency of cumulative storm energy generated by storm events, classified by direction: (a) totals for period 1941-1976; (b) values for an average year. Figures in parentheses are percentages.

TOTAL STORM ENERGY (ft·lbs/ftx10⁴)	N	NE	E	SE	ALL DIRECTIONS
(a) 0 – 10	81 (13.1)	257 (41.7)	54 (8.8)	66 (10.7)	458 (74.2)
10 – 50	27 (4.4)	62 (10.0)	19 (3.1)	5 (0.5)	113 (18.3)
50 – 100	4 (0.7)	27 (4.4)	1 (0.2)		32 (5.2)
100 – 150	1 (0.2)	3 (0.5)			4 (0.7)
150 – 200		5 (0.8)	1 (0.2)		6 (1.0)
200 – 250	1 (0.2)	1 (0.2)			2 (0.3)
250 – 300		1 (0.2)			1 (0.2)
300 – 350		1 (0.2)			1 (0.2)
TOTAL	114 (18.5)	357 (57.9)	75 (12.2)	71 (11.5)	617
(b) 0 – 10	2.50	7.89	1.66	2.03	14.08
10 – 50	0.83	1.90	0.58	0.15	3.46
50 – 100	0.123	0.83	0.03		0.98
100 – 150	0.031	0.09			0.12
150 – 200	–	0.15	0.03		0.18
200 – 250	0.031	0.03			0.06
250 – 300		0.03			0.03
300 – 350		0.03			0.03
TOTAL	3.51	10.95	2.30	2.18	18.94

height values are in feet.

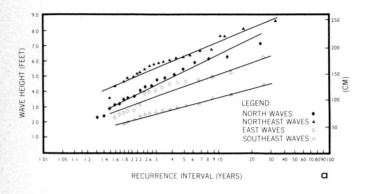

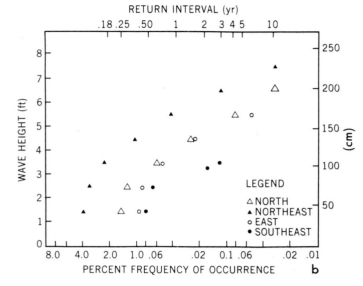

Figure 6.6. *Probability plots of the annual maximum series of significant wave heights using the plotting position n+1/m (a) and the partial duration series using the plotting position 2n/2m-1 (b).*

Table 6.3. Frequency of storm events classified by cumulative energy and direction for six time intervals 1970 to 1976.

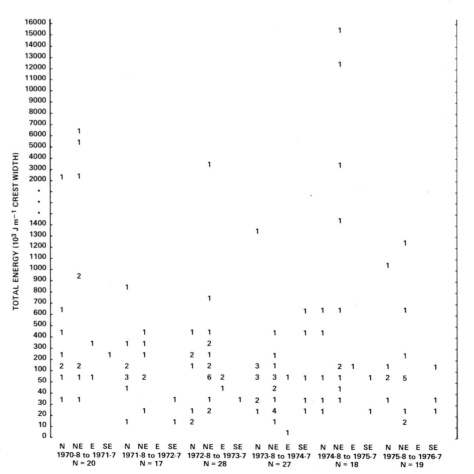

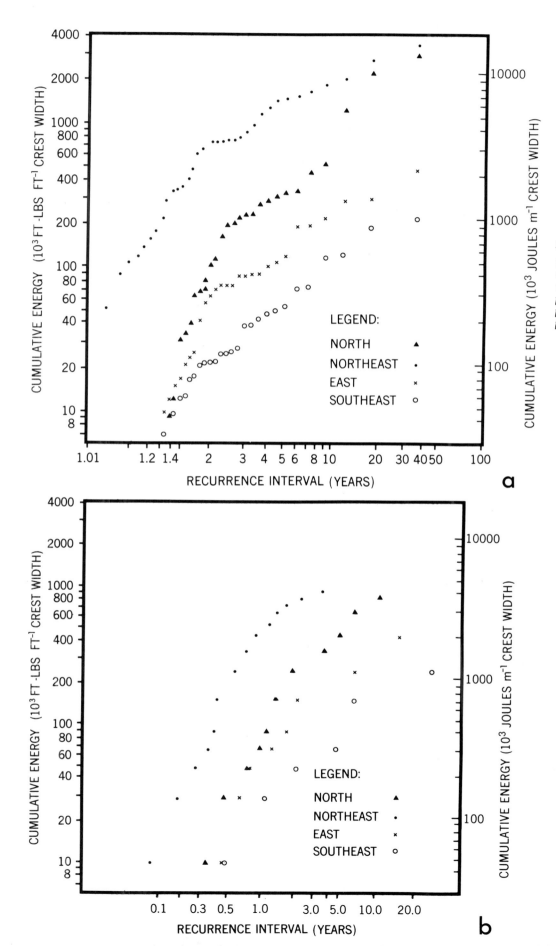

Figure 6.7

Probability plots of the annual maximum series of cumulative wave energies using the plotting position n+1/m (a) and the partial duration series using the plotting position 2n/2m-1 (b).

81

Table 6.4. Comparison of storm event magnitudes by maximum significant wave heights in centimetres for specified return periods as determined using the Hazen (1930) and Gumbel (1954) procedures.

RETURN PERIOD	METHOD	DIRECTION			
		North	Northeast	East	Southeast
Median Annual Event	Hazen	125	171	119	86
	Gumbel	116	152	95	61
Five Year Return Period	Hazen	174	213	162	122
	Gumbel	162	195	128	92
Ten Year Return Period	Hazen	198	229	174	137
	Gumbel	198	220	152	107

Table 6.5. Comparison of storm event magnitudes by cumulative wave energy (in joules per metre crest width $\times 10^3$) for specified return periods as determined using the Hazen (1930) and Gumbel (1954) procedures.

RETURN PERIOD	METHOD	DIRECTION			
		North	Northeast	East	Southeast
Median Annual Event	Hazen	400.3	2001.7	266.9	102.3
	Gumbel	444.8	3113.7	266.9	93.4
Five Year Return Period	Hazen	2046.2	6672.3	1023.1	444.8
	Gumbel	1334.5	7117.1	533.8	244.7
Ten Year Return Period	Hazen	3781.0	9786.0	1579.1	889.6
	Gumbel	2268.6	8451.6	889.6	467.1

The partial duration series (Fig. 6.6b) indicates that storms generating maximum waves of 1 m or greater occur every 0.2 years from the northeast, whereas the same condition is generated by a southeasterly storm only once in seven years on average. However, it must be remembered that the strong seasonal bias (particularly for northeast and north storms) may result in shorter return periods in those months of frequent storms (December, April, May) and longer return periods in the summer and fall.

Extreme storms

The maximum predicted deepwater storm wave in Kouchibouguac Bay has a significant height of 2.6 m and a 7 s period with a return period of 34 years. If the ratio between maximum and significant wave height of 1.8:1 is assumed (Longuet-Higgins, 1952; Thom, 1971) then the largest wave predicted is 4.7 m in height. The storm event generating these waves occurred 1974-11-21 during a 'northeaster' but there is no published record of its effects. The predicted 100-year significant wave is also from the northeast with a height of 3.1 m; an extreme height for such a storm would be 5.6 m. This does not seem an unreasonable prediction though fetch restrictions must place a finite limit on the maximum possible wave dimensions. There are two published accounts of major coastal storms which provide some comparative information. The June 1959 Northumberland Strait storm (McLeod, 1959) developed very rapidly and resulted in the loss of several lives. It was, however, these latter aspects rather than its absolute intensity, which in the popular perception gave it the status of an extreme event. The predicted wave height at Kouchibouguac was only 1.5 m and the recurrence interval only 2 years. The December 1964 storm over the Maritime Provinces (Tyner, 1965), which produced the lowest sea level barometric pressure ever recorded at Halifax, generated extremely high wind speeds (e.g., 160 km h^{-1} at Sydney, Nova Scotia). Nevertheless it did not greatly affect Kouchibouguac Bay, as winds were mainly from the south which is not an important fetch direction. The bay was only affected by the secondary depression which developed after the main storm. This emphasizes the often local effect of major storms and the importance of fetch.

MAGNITUDE AND FREQUENCY OF GEOMORPHIC EVENTS

Morphological changes in the coastal zone range from minor changes in swash slope morphology associated with water-level shifts and low-wave intensities on a minute-by-minute basis (e.g., Wadell, 1976), through changes in nearshore configuration associated with each storm event (e.g., Hayes and Boothroyd, 1969; Fox and Davis, 1976), to major changes in coastline form, such as barrier breaching associated with infrequent high wave-energy events (e.g., Hite, 1924; Stoddart, 1962; El-Ashry and Wanless, 1965; Greenwood and Keay, 1979). Correlation of observed changes with a wave intensity index or storm index is therefore useful in understanding the scale of process-response in a framework of total coastal change through time. An examination of changes monitored under specific storm wave conditions in Kouchibouguac Bay demonstrates the value of the synthetic wave climatology in this respect. Modifications of both inner and outer nearshore bar systems, barrier washover and barrier breaching are considered (Table 6.6).

The most mobile morphological unit is the inner bar system controlled by rip cell circulation. Rip channel excavation produced a 0.6 m deep, 25 m wide channel in one storm (1972-6-10, Fig. 6.8a) with coincident infilling of an old rip channel downdrift, and net displacement of the nearshore bar alongshore similar to the pattern observed by Davis and Fox (1972). Since such a storm may be expected approximately every month (29 days) in the ice-free year, considerable alongshore transport annually is achieved through transformations in the nearshore bar system. Changes in the beach face were volumetrically much smaller (Fig. 6.8b), emphasizing that the major response to the monthly storm was in the inner nearshore bar system where the bulk of the wave energy was dissipated by breaking on the bar rather than at the beach face. A second storm (1972-6-22) of similar magnitude enlarged the new channel and completely closed the old rip channel though a small storm (1972-6-17) with similar wave heights but much lower net energy, did not produce significant changes. The outer crescentic nearshore bar at Kouchibouguac responds to a rather limited spectrum of wave conditions. Table 6.6 indicates the maximum depth of activity and maximum bed surface change experienced by the bar crest, which lies approximately 2 to 3 m below mean water level, during two specific storm events. The larger storm had wave characteristics similar to the most probable annual storm and induced movement of sediment to the seaward foot of the bar, although net bed elevation change at this location was very small (Greenwood and Hale, 1980). This suggests an equilibrium relationship between the bar form and the most probable annual storm event. This storm, with a return period of 1.3 years, also created a minor washover on the barrier island with penetration into the dunes but not into the lagoon. The storm coincided with spring tides (0.9 m) and a storm setup of 1.2 m was measured in the backing estuary. The most probable annual storm event may well be, therefore, the minimum threshold of wave height and energy for this process in Kouchibouguac Bay.

Table 6.6. Morphological response to storms of varying magnitude and return periods.

Morphological response to storm waves	Storm Characteristics							
	Direction	Duration	Maximum wave ($H_{1/3}$) height	Return period	Cumulative energy	Return period	Extreme wave height	Date
		(h)	(m)	(yr)	($\times 10^3$ Jm^{-1} crest width)	(yr)	($H_{1/10}$-m)	
Rip-channel excavation (inner bar system)	NE	12	0.7	0.3	61.4	0.2	1.3	1972-6-10
	NE	7	0.6	<0.2	27.4	<<0.2	1.1	1972-6-17
	NE	7	0.8	0.3	58.3	0.2	1.4	1972-6-22
Maximum depth of scour (outer bar system) 46 cm 10 cm	NE NE	34 18	1.2 0.8	1.3 0.3	1207.7 41.8	1.4 0.1	2.2 1.5	1976-6-11 1976-8-14
Maximum bed surface change (outer bar system) 23 cm 10 cm	NE NE	34 18	1.2 0.8	1.3 0.3	1207.7 41.8	1.4 0.1	2.2 1.5	1976-6-11 1976-8-14
Barrier Washover	NE	34	1.2	1.3	1207.7	1.4	2.2	1976-6-11
Barrier breaching	NE NE	28 30	1.9 2.4	4 - 5 10 - 12	3232.7 6304.6	2 - 3 4 - 5	3.6 4.5	1970-12-24 1977-12-6

Two distinct episodes of barrier breaching have been studied in the barrier system and the storms generating the breaches have return periods of between 4 and 12 years depending on the storm index used. This return interval is close to the average breaching frequency in the bay (Bryant and McCann, 1973). However, this should not be considered a catastrophic event (Greenwood and Keay, 1979), for it is becoming increasingly clear that ephemeral tidal inlets are an integral part of the dynamic equilibrium of barrier islands and that in the long term the nature of barrier island sediments may reflect inlet infilling almost entirely (Kumar and Sanders, 1974).

Although the above discussion allows an assessment of the relative importance of storm events, the recurrence interval of an event cannot at present be related to absolute values of change such as volumes of sediment moved, which would then reflect total work. However, a framework (Table 6.6) within which this might be achieved has been outlined and an insight into possible thresholds for specific morphological responses has been given.

DISCUSSION AND CONCLUSION

The procedures outlined above enable a synthetic wave climatology to be developed for storm-wave dominated environments, where an extended time series of meteorological data is available. Determination of magnitudes and frequency of occurrence of specific storm wave events, and their annual, seasonal and directional distribution can then be made and related to known morphological responses.

The advantages of a hindcast approach are: (i) the site-specific nature of predictions; (ii) the availability of long periods of meteorological records for many coastal areas; (iii) the directional information derived (see Saville, 1974); (iv) the derivation of quantitative indices of storm magnitude (see Reid, 1957); (v) the speed and ease of computation; and (vi) the lack of sufficiently long measured wave records in most areas at present (Neu, 1972; Jahns and Wheeler, 1973). A number of inherent limitations, such as the accuracy of the S-M-B predictions (Brebner and LeMehaute, 1961; Lui, 1976), the use of a point source of land-based winds, the arbitrary nature of storm definition and the consideration of only the upper part of the energy spectrum in deep water without reference to wave duration, decay or transformation (Armon, 1975; Armon and McCann, 1977; Greenwood and McGillivray, 1978) should be noted. Nevertheless the wave parameters predicted are those most commonly used in geomorphological studies and the moderate to high wave events are most important in causing coastal change.

The case study of Kouchibouguac Bay in the southern Gulf of St. Lawrence illustrates the value of the technique. An empirical test of the wave-prediction procedure revealed a strong correlation between the observed initiation and development of waves over time and those predicted. While a discrepancy in absolute values was evident it was small and the variability over time (initial wave growth and the start of the decay) was faithfully predicted. The test suggests that values predicted for a long time series of meteorological data will conform in a relative sense.

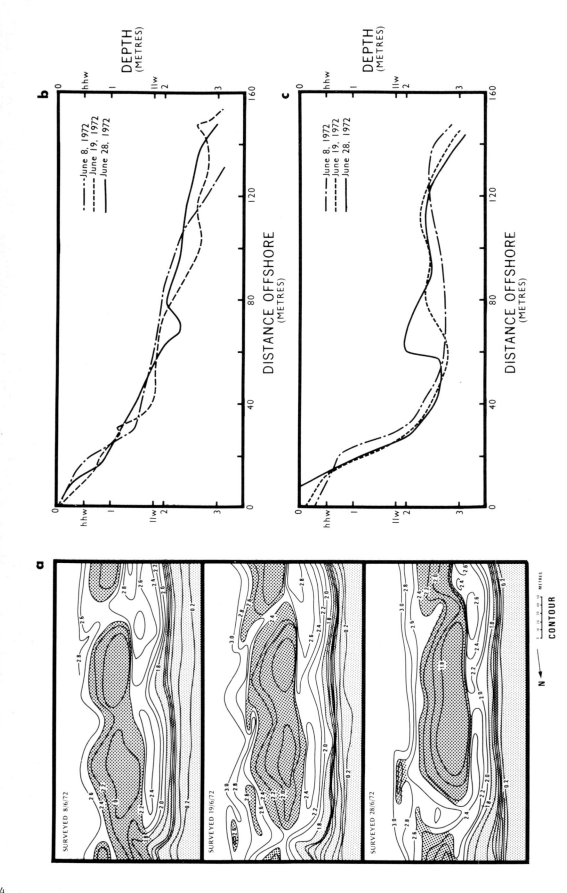

Figure 6.8. Morphological response in an inner bar system to events equivalent to the monthly storm: (a) bathymetric configuration prior to and succeeding storms dated 1972-6-10 and 1972-6-22; (b) profile along line of new rip channel; (c) profile along line of old rip channel.

Analysis of the complete time series allows determination of the variability of geomorphic process seasonally (Hayden and Dolan, 1977) or secularly (Hayden, 1975). Partial duration and annual maxima series give good estimates of the probable recurrence interval of specific magnitudes of storm event measured in terms of the maximum wave height (either $H_{1/3}$ or $H_{1/10}$) or cumulative storm wave energy.

Kouchibougac Bay receives 19 storm wave-generating events per year on average and the dominant wind direction is from the northeast (11 storms) followed by the north (4 storms). These are distributed unevenly throughout the year; May is the stormiest month with an average of four storms followed by April and December each with three while July, August and September experience only one storm on average and indeed storm wave conditions occur only 5.5 per cent of the total time. The area can be classified as a low-energy, storm-dominated environment. Examination of the annual maximum and partial duration series indicates that (i) for all return periods northeasterly storms produce the most intense wave conditions, (ii) the largest most probable annual wave event produces heights of 1.3 m and a total energy of $13344.5 \times 10^3 Jm^{-1}$ crest width from the northeast, (iii) the largest predicted wave has a return period of 34 years, a significant height of 2.6 m (maximum of 4.7 m) and a period of 7 s but extrapolation to the 100-year event suggests a maximum absolute wave height of 5.6 m.

Definitive statements cannot be made regarding the applicability of the storm intensity indices to either the type or the scale of changes in the coastal zone. It is, however, most likely that a good relationship will ultimately be found between total energy and quantity of sediment transported since both wave magnitude and duration are included in its computation. In contrast, the index of maximum significant wave height may be more applicable to subaerial changes associated with dune scarping, overwash and barrier breaching but the examples cited show the usefulness of both indices in assessing 'process thresholds' for the initiation of minor coastal changes such as nearshore bar migration or sediment flux in various depths of water, and major coastline changes such as barrier breaching. Rip channel excavation and inner nearshore bar modifications occur with maximum predicted significant wave heights of only 60 to 80 cm, which have a return period of less than one month, while extensive modification of the outer bar system requires significant wave heights of at least 1.2 m and appears to reflect the most probable annual maximum wave-generating event. Barrier washover is also correlated with the most probable annual maximum wave conditions whereas barrier-breaching conditions have return periods of between four and twelve years and reflect the importance of antecedent morphological as well as process thresholds.

Acknowledgments

Support for this research was provided by grants to one of us (B.G.) from the National Research Council of Canada (NRCA7956) and Imperial Oil Limited and forms part of a larger project on Coastal Sedimentation. Further assistance was provided by a contract from Parks Canada (AR076-21) to B.G. We would like to thank M.A. MacAulay and R.B. McLaughlin of the Atmospheric Environment Service, Atlantic Region, Environment Canada for help with the loan of wind-recording equipment and G.F. Pember and P.R. Mittler for assistance with data collection. The Graphics and Photography Department assisted with the illustrations and computer time was provided by the University of Toronto.

References

Armon, J.W.
1975: The dynamics of a barrier-island chain, Prince Edward Island, Canada; unpubl. Ph.D. thesis, McMaster University, Hamilton.

Armon, J.W. and McCann, S.B.
1977: Longshore sediment transport and a sediment budget for the Malpeque barrier system, southern Gulf of St. Lawrence; Canadian Journal of Earth Sciences, v. 14, p. 2429-2439.

Arthur, R.S.
1947: Revised wave forecasting graphs and procedures; Wave Report No. 73, Scripps Institute of Oceanography.

Ashe, G.W.T. and Ploeg, J.
1971: Wave climate study, Great Lakes and Gulf of St. Lawrence; Mechanical Engineering Report MN-107A, 2, 258 p., National Research Council, Ottawa.

Baird, W.F. and Wilson, J.R.
1974: Canadian wave-climate study---cost and application; Proceedings of an International Symposium on Ocean Wave Measurement and Analysis, v. 2, p. 55-61.

Ball, M.M., Shinn, E.A. and Stockman, K.W.
1967: The effects of hurricane Donna in South Florida; Journal of Geology, v. 75, p. 583-597.

Berg, D.W.
1970: Systematic collection of beach data; Proceedings of the 11th Conference on Coastal Engineering, v. 1, p.273-297.

Bigelow, H.B. and Edmonston, W.T.
1947: Wind waves at sea, breakers and surf; U.S. Navy Hydrographic Office, Washington, D.C., 177 p.

Bores, P.S.
1974: Sea observations in coastal areas: the Spanish offshore network; in Wave 74; Proceedings of the 1st International Symposium on Ocean Wave Measurement and Analysis, American Society of Civil Engineers, v. 1, p. 13-24.

Bosserman, K. and Dolan, R.
1968: The frequency and magnitude of extratropical storms along the Outer Banks of North Carolina; Technical Report 68-4, Coastal Research Association, Charlottesville, Virginia.

Brebner, A. and LeMehaute, B.
1961: Wind waves at Coburg, Lake Ontario, Queen's University, Civil Engineering Report, No. 19, 44 p.

Brebner, A. and Kennedy, R.J.
1962: Correlation of waves and shore winds, Lake Ontario; Publication No. 9, Institute of Science and Technology, University of Michigan, p. 116-122.

Brebner, A. and Sangal, B.P.
1964: A comparison of actual with predicted wave heights and periods for the north shores of Lake Ontario and Erie; The Engineering Journal, EIC-64-CIVI, p. 32 - 36.

Brenner, R.L. and Davies, D.K.
1973: Storm-generated coquinoid sandstone: genesis of high-energy marine sediments from the Upper Jurassic of Wyoming and Montana; Geological Society of American Bulletin, v. 84, p. 1685 - 1698.

Bretschneider, C.L.
1951: Revised wave forecasting curves and procedures; Technical Report No. HE-155047, Institute of Engineering Research, University of California.
1958: Revisions in wave forecasting: deep and shallow water; Proceedings of the 6th Conference on Coastal Engineering, p. 30 - 67.
1959: Wave variability and wave spectra for wind-generated gravity waves; U.S. Army Corps of Engineers, Beach Erosion Board Technical Memorandum, No. 118, 192p.
1966: Wave generation by wind, deep and shallow water; in Estuary and Coastline Hydrodynamics; A.T. Ippen, ed.; Ch. 3, p. 133 - 196.
1970: Forecasting relations for wave generation; Look Laboratory Quarterly, v.1, p. 31 - 34.

Bryant, E.A.
1972: The barrier islands of Kouchibouguac Bay, New Brunswick; unpubl. M.Sc. thesis, McMaster University, Hamilton, 277 p.

Bryant, E.A. and McCann, S.B.
1973: Long and short term changes in the barrier islands of Kouchibouguac Bay, southern Gulf of St. Lawrence; Canadian Journal of Earth Sciences, v. 10, p. 1582 - 1590.

Chow, V. T.
1964: Statistical and probability analysis of hydrologic data, Part I. Frequency Analysis; Section 8-1 in Handbook of Applied Hydrology: a Compendium of 'Water-resources Technology; McGraw-Hill, New York, p. 8-1 to 8-42.

Cole, A.L.
1967: An evaluation of wind analysis and wave hindcasting methods as applied to the Great Lakes; Proceedings of the 10th Conference on Great Lakes Research, p. 186 - 196.
1971: Hindcast waves for the western Great Lakes; Proceedings of the 14th Conference on Great Lakes Research, p. 412 - 421.

Cunnane, C.
1973: A particular comparison of annual maxima and partial duration series methods of flood frequency prediction; Journal of Hydrology, v. 18, p. 257 - 271.

Dalrymple, T.
1960: Flood frequency analysis: Manual of hydrology part 3, flood flow techniques; U.S. Geological Survey Water Supply Paper 1543-A, 80 p.

Davidson-Arnott, R.G.D.
1971: An investigation of patterns of sediment size and sorting in the beach and nearshore area, Kouchibouguac Bay, New Brunswick; unpubl. M.A. research paper, University of Toronto, 109 p.
1975: Form, movement and sedimentological characteristics of wave-formed bars —a study of their role in the nearshore equilibrium, Kouchibouguac Bay, New Brunswick; unpubl. Ph.D. thesis, University of Toronto, 226 p.

Davies, J.L.
1973: Geographical variation in coastal development; Hafner, New York.

Davis, R.A. and Fox, W.T.
1972: Coastal processes and nearshore sand bars; Journal of Sedimentary Petrology, v. 42, p. 401 - 412.

Draper, L.
1970: Canadian wave climate study — the formative year; Proceedings of the 12th Conference on Coastal Engineering, v. 1, p. 1 - 12.

El-Ashry, M.T. and Wanless, H.R.
1965: Birth and early growth of a tidal delta; Journal of Geology, v. 73, p. 404 - 406.

Environment Canada
1972: Summary of synoptic meteorological observations; Atmospheric Environment Service.
1977a: Waves recorded off Cape Tormentine, New Brunswick Stn. 59, July 9, 1976 to November 16, 1976; Marine Environmental Data Service, Fisheries and Marine Service.
1977b: A summary of available wave data products; Marine Environmental Data Service, Fisheries and Marine Service, 5 p., plus 3 appendices.

Fisher, R.A. and Tippett, L.H.C.
1928: Limiting forms of the frequency distribution of the largest or smallest member of a sample; Proceedings of the Cambridge Philosophical Society, v. 24, p. 180 - 190.

Fox, W.T. and Davis, R.A., Jr.
1976: Weather patterns and coastal processes; in Beach and Nearshore Sedimentation, R.A. Davis Jr. and R.L. Ethington, eds.; Society of Economic Paleontologists and Mineralogists, Special Publication, no. 24, p. 1 - 23.

Goldsmith, V.
1976: Wave climate models for the continental shelf: critical links between shelf hydraulics and shoreline processes; in Beach and Nearshore Sedimentation, R.A. Davis, Jr. and R.L. Ethington, eds.; Society of Economic Paleontologists and Mineralogists, Special Publication, no. 24, p. 24 - 47.

Greenwood, B. and Davidson-Arnott, R.G.D.
1975: Marine bars and nearshore sedimentary processes, Kouchibouguac Bay, New Brunswick, Canada; in Nearshore Sediment Dynamics and Sedimentation, J. Hails and A. Carr, eds.; Wiley, London, p. 123 - 150.

Greenwood, B. and Davidson-Arnott, R.G.D. (cont.)
1977: An interpretive study of coastal processes, Kouchibouguac National Park, New Brunswick; Parks Canada Contract Report, Department of Indian and Northern Affairs, 2 volumes, 398 p.

Greenwood, B. and Hale, P.B.
1980: Depth of activity, sediment flux and morphological change in a barred nearshore environment; in The Coastline of Canada: littoral processes and shore morphology, S.B. McCann, ed.; Geological Survey of Canada, Paper 80-10, Report 7.

Greenwood, B. and Keay, P.A.
1979: Morphology and dynamics of a barrier breach: a study in stability; Canadian Journal of Earth Sciences v. 6, p. 1533-1546.

Greenwood, B. and McGillivray, D.G.
1978: A theoretical model of the littoral drift system in the Toronto Waterfront Area, Lake Ontario; Journal of Great Lakes Research, v. 4. p. 84-102

Gretener, P.E
1967: Significance of the rare event in geology; American Association of Petroleum Geologists, Bulletin, v. 51, p. 2197 - 2206.

Gumbel, E.J.
1941: Probability interpretation of the observed return periods of floods; American Geophysical Union, Transactions Pt. 3, p. 836 - 850.
1954: Statistical theory of extreme values and some practical applications; National Bureau of Standard Applied Mathematical Series, no. 33.
1960: Statistics of extremes, Columbia University Press, New York.
1966: Extreme value analysis of hydrologic data; in Statistical Methods in Hydrology, Proceedings of Hydrological Sumposium No. 5; Department of Energy, Mines and Resources, Ottawa, p. 147 - 169.

Hale, P.B.
1978: Storm-wave sedimentation: the role of meteorological depressions as geological agents in a barred nearshore marine environment, Kouchibouguac Bay, New Brunswick; unpubl. M.Sc. thesis, University of Toronto, 188 p. plus appendices.

Hasse, L. and Wagner, V.
1971: On the relationship between geostrophic and surface wind at sea; Monthly Weather Review, v. 99, p. 225 - 260.

Hayden, B.P.
1975: Storm wave climates at Cape Hatteras, North Carolina, recent secular variations; Science, v. 190, p. 981 - 983.

Hayden, B.P. and Dolan, P.
1977: Seasonal changes in the planetary wind system and their relationship to the most severe coastal storms; Geoscience and Man, v. 18, p. 113 - 119.

Hayes, M.O.
1967: Hurricanes as geological agents: case studies of hurricanes Carla, 1961 and Cindy, 1963; University of Texas, Bureau of Economic Geology, Report of Investigations, v. 61, 56 p.

Hayes, M.O. and Boothroyd, J.C.
1969: Storms as modifying agents in the coastal environment; in Coastal Environments of Northeastern Massachusetts and New Hampshire; Contribution No. 1, Coastal Research Group, Geology Department, University of Massachusetts, p. 245 - 265.

Hazen, A.
1930: Flood flow; Wiley, New York.

Hite, M.P.
1924: Some observations of storm effects on ocean inlets; American Journal of Science, v. 7, p. 319 - 326.

Jackli, H.
1957: Gegenwartsgedogie des bundnerischen Gheingebietesin Beitrag zur exogenen Dynamik alpiner Gebirgslandschafen; Beitrage zur Geologie der Schweiz, Geotechnische Serie Lfg., v. 36.

Jahns, H.O. and Wheeler, J.D.
1973: Long term wave probabilities based on hindcasting severe storms; Journal of Petroleum Technology, v. 25, p. 473 - 486.

Johnson, J.W.
1950: Relationships between wind and waves, Abbots Lagoon, California, American Geophysical Union, Transactions, v. 31, p. 386 - 392.

Khanna, J. and Andru, P.
1974: Lifetime wave height curve for Saint John Deep, Canada; Waves 74, Proceedings of an International Symposium on Ocean Wave Measurement and Analysis; American Society of Civil Engineers, v. 1, p. 301 - 319.

Komar, P.D.
1976: Beach processes and sedimentation; Prentice-Hall, New Jersey.

Kumar, N. and Sanders, J.E.
1974: Inlet sequence: a vertical succession of sedimentary structures created by the lateral migration of tidal inlets; Sedimentology, v. 21, p. 491 - 532.
1976: Characteristics of shoreface storm deposits: modern and ancient examples; Journal of Sedimentary Petrology, v. 46, p. 145 - 162.

Lalande, M.E.
1975: A Fortran program to solve the Bretschneider wind-wave relationships for deep water; Atmospheric Environmental Service, Environment Canada, Technical Memorandum, TEC 816, 12 p.

Longuet-Higgins, M.S.
1952: On the statistical distribution of the height of sea waves; Journal of Marine Research, v. 11, p. 345 - 366.

Lui, P.C.
1976: Applications of empirical fetch—limited spectral formulas to Great Lakes waves; Proceeding of the 15th Conference on Coastal Engineering, p. 113 - 128.

Lyell, C.
1830: Principles of Geology, John Murray, London.

Mather, J.R., Adams, H.A. III and Yoshioka, G.A.
1964: Coastal storms of the eastern United States; Journal of Applied Meteorology, v.3, p. 693 - 706.
1967: Storm damage hazard along the east coast of the United States; Journal of Applied Meteorology, v. 7, p. 20 - 30.

McLeod, K.T.
1959: The Northumberland Strait Storm in Canada; Weatherwise, v. 12, p. 161 - 176.

Mitsuyasu, H. and Mizuno, S.
1976: Directional spectra of ocean surface waves; Proceeding of the 15th Conference on Coastal Engineering, p. 329 - 248.

Neu, H.A.
1971: Wave climate of the Canadian Atlantic coast and Continental Shelf, 1970; Atlantic Oceanographic Laboratory, Report 1971-10.

Neu, H.J.A.
1972: Extreme wave height distribution along the Canadian Atlantic Coast; Ocean Industry, v. 7, p. 45 - 49.

Neumann, G. and Pierson, W.J.
1957: A detailed comparison of theoretical wave spectra and wave forecasting methods; Deutsche Hydrographische Zeitschrift, v. 10, no. 2, p. 73 - 92, and no. 4, p. 134 - 146.

Permanent International Association of Navigation Congresses
1973: Report of the International Commission for the study of waves; Bulletin no. 15 (2), p. 1 - 40.

Ploeg, J.
1971: Wave climate study, Great Lakes and Gulf of St. Lawrence; Mechanical Engineering Report MH-107A, v. 1, National Research Council, Ottawa, 160 p.

Powell, R.W.
1943: A simple method of estimating flood frequencies; Civil Engineering, v. 13, p. 105, 106.

Quon, C., Keyte, F.K., and Pearson, A.
1963: Comparison of five years hindcast wave statistics in the Gulf of St. Lawrence and Lake Superior; Bedford Institute of Oceanography Report 63-2, 59 p.

Reid, R.O.
1957: On the classification of hurricanes by storm tide and wave energy indices; Meteorological Monographs, v. 2 (10), p. 58 - 66.

Resio, D.T. and Vincent, C.L.
1977: Estimation of winds over the Great Lakes; Journal of Waterway, Port, Coastal and Ocean Division, American Society of Civil Engineers, v. 103, no. WW2, p. 265 - 283.

Richards, T.L. and Phillips, D.W.
1970: Synthesized winds and wave heights for the Great Lakes; Canada Meteorological Branch, Department of Transport, Climatological Studies, No. 17, 53 p.

Saville, T., Jr.
1954: The effect of fetch width on wave generation; U.S. Army, Beach Erosion Board, Technical Memorandum, No. 70.
1974: Application of wave climatology and data for design; Waves 74, Proceedings of an International Symposium on Ocean Wave Measurement and Analysis; American Society of Civil Engineers, v. 1, p. 40 - 48.

Saville, T., Jr., McClendon, E.W. and Cochran, A.L.
1962: Freeboard allowances for waves in inland reservoirs; Journal of Waterways and Harbors Division, American Society of Civil Engineers, p. 93 - 124.

Schumm, S.A.
1973: Geomorphic thresholds and complex response of drainage systems; in Fluvial Geomorphology, M. Morisawa, ed.; State University of New York, Binghampton, ch. 13, p. 299 - 310.
1975: Episodic erosion: a modification of the geomorphic cycle; in Theories of Landform Development, W.N. Melhorn and R.C. Flemal, eds.; State University of New York, Binghampton, ch. 4, p. 69 - 86.

Suthons, C.T.
1945: The forecasting of sea and swell waves; British Naval Meteorological Branch, Memorandum No. 135/45.

Sverdrup, H.U. and Munk, W.H.
1947: Wind, sea and swell: theory of relations for forecasting; Hydrographic Office, Publication No. 601, U.S. Department of the Navy.

Thom, H.C.S.
1971: Asymptotic extreme-value distribution of wave heights in the open ocean; Journal of Marine Research, v. 29, p. 19 - 27.

Tyner, R.V.
1965: Storm of December 1-2, 1964, in the Maritime Provinces; Canada, Atmospheric Environmental Service, Technical Report No. 557, 6 p.

Wadell, L.
1976: Swash-groundwater-beach profile interactions; in Beach and Nearshore Sedimentation, R.A. Davis, Jr. and R.L. Ethington, eds.; Society of Economic Paleontologists and Mineralogists Special Publication, No. 24, p. 115 - 125.

Walton, T.L., Jr.
1973: Littoral drift computations along the coast of Florida by means of ship wave observations; Coastal and Oceanographic Engineering Laboratory, University of Florida, Technical Report No. 15, 80 p.

Weibull, W.
1939: A statistical theory of the strength of materials; Ingeniörsvetenskapsakademien Vetenskaps Handlingar (Stockholm), v. 151, p.15.

Wolman, M.G. and Miller, J.P.
1960: Magnitude and frequency of forces in geomorphic processes; Journal of Geology, v. 68, p. 54 - 74.

7.

DEPTH OF ACTIVITY, SEDIMENT FLUX, AND MORPHOLOGICAL CHANGE
IN A BARRED NEARSHORE ENVIRONMENT

Brian Greenwood and Peter B. Hale
Scarborough College, University of Toronto, West Hill, Ontario

Greenwood, Brian and Hale, Peter B., Depth of activity, sediment flux, and morphological change in a barred nearshore environment; in The Coastline of Canada, S.B. McCann, editor; Geological Survey of Canada, Paper 80-10, p. 89-109, 1980.

Abstract

Sediment flux and associated morphological change in a continuously submerged, nearshore, crescentic bar system is documented for discrete storm events using an array of depth of disturbance rods in conjunction with structural indices recorded in epoxy peels of box cores from the active layer. Steel rods (≈1 or 2 m in length, 0.5 cm in diameter) buried to a depth of 55 cm with a free sliding washer (≈0.6 cm internal diameter) accurately record the spatial variability of: (1) maximum depth of sediment activation; (2) net bed elevation changes; and (3) degradation-aggradation cycles. The depth of activity is related to the magnitude of the incident wave –(70 cm for deepwater waves of 2 m height, 6 sec period versus 23 cm for a height of 1.5 m and period of 5 sec)– and location within the bar system. Maximum values occur on the seaward side of the bar crest where wave breaking, asymmetric oscillatory motion and/or rip current flow would be a maximum during the storm. A secondary maximum is associated with longshore currents in the landward trough. Depths of activity minima occur on the landward slope in response to height loss due to breaking and increase in water depth. In general storms erode the bar profile with scour maxima on the seaward side of the crest and near the toe of the landward slope. Aggradation occurs on the upper landward and upper seaward slopes steepening both slopes and producing a seaward displacement of the bar crest over the crescent area. Structural indices suggest increasing rates of landward transport (through either ripple or lunate megaripple migration and sheet flow) as water depth decreases up the seaward slope. Landward transport across the bar crest and down the landward slope is also indicated. On the upper landward slope and bar crest of the crescent, however, small- to medium-scale seaward-dipping cross-stratification indicates a distinct seaward flux of sediment, which is interpreted as resulting from rip-type flow. This is not found on the shoal areas and this differentiation is instrumental in maintaining the on-offshore sediment balance as well as the crescentic form.

Résumé

Les auteurs donnent des précisions au sujet des apports de matériaux de l'évolution morphologique connexe dans un ensemble de cordons arqués, situé près du littoral et continuellement submergé afin de déterminer des apparitions de tempêtes discrètes au moyen d'un réseau de tiges de perturbation en profondeur combiné à des indices structuraux enregistrés dans des pelures d'époxy situées dans des carottes encastrées tirées de la couche active. Des tiges d'acier (≈1 ou 2 m de longueur et 0,5 cm de diamètre) enfouies à une profondeur de 55 cm et munies d'une rondelle mobile libre (≈0,6 cm de diamètre interne) enregistrent avec précision la variabilité spatiale des phénomènes suivants: (1) profondeur maximale de l'action sédimentaire; (2) les modifications altimétriques nettes du lit et (3) les cycles de démaigrissement-engraissement. La profondeur de l'action sédimentaire est liée à la force de la vague incidente –(70 cm dans le cas des vagues en eau profonde de 2 m de hauteur, une période de 6 s contre 23 cm pour une hauteur de 1,5 m et une période de 5 s)– et un emplacement situé à l'intérieur du réseau de cordons. On constate des valeurs maximales sur la façade maritime de la crête de cordon où le déferlement des vagues, le mouvement oscillatoire asymétrique ou le courant d'arrachement atteignent généralement un sommet au cours d'une tempête. Un maximum secondaire est associé à la dérive littorale dans le creux situé côté terre. Des profondeurs minimales d'action existent sur le versant intérieur par réaction à la perte de hauteur due au déferlement et à l'accroissement de la profondeur d'eau. De manière générale, les tempêtes contribuent à éroder le profil des cordons en pratiquant un affouillement maximal sur le côté maritime de la crête et près de l'encoche de la pente côté terre. L'engraissement se produit dans les parties supérieures des pentes situées tant du côté de la terre que du côté de la mer, ce qui accentue les deux pentes et engendre une migration vers la mer de la crête du cordon pardessus la zone arquée. Certains indices structuraux permettent de penser que les vitesses de transport en direction de la terre (soit par l'arrachement ou une forte migration parabolique des matériaux et un écoulement en nappe) augmentent à mesure que la profondeur de l'eau diminue en remontant le versant marin. Le transport vers la terre en travers de la crête du cordon et vers le pied du versant terrestre est aussi indiqué. Toutefois, sur la partie supérieure du versant terrestre et de la crête du cordon du croissant, des interlaminations de petite à moyenne échelle et à pendage orienté vers la mer indiquent la présence d'un transport de matériaux distincts en direction de la mer, ce qui peut s'expliquer par l'existence d'un écoulement d'arrachement. Le même phénomène est absent des zones de hauts-fonds et cette différenciation sert à maintenir tant l'équilibre des matériaux de va-et-vient que la forme arquée du relief.

INTRODUCTION

In coastal studies at present one of the most important problems being addressed concerns the direction and rate of sediment flux in the nearshore zone and its spatial and temporal variability. It is important, therefore, to develop techniques whereby sediment flux can be determined and related to both the transport mechanisms and morphological changes, particularly during high wave energy events. A number of approaches have been adopted in an effort to measure sediment flux (for a brief review see Dowling, 1977) including: (a) direct sensing of sediment load with various electro-optical, electromechanical, electroacoustical or entrapment devices (e.g., Watts, 1953; Fukushima and Mizoguchi, 1958; Bruun and Purpura, 1964; Sternberg and Creager, 1965; Thornton, 1968; Cook, 1969; Das, 1972; Fairchild, 1972; Swift and McGrath, 1972; Wenzel, 1974; Lee, 1975; Brenninkmeyer, 1976; Kana, 1976; Kilner, 1976; Lesht et al., 1976; Thornton and Morris, 1977); and (b) indirect determinations based upon either dispersion patterns of natural and artificial tracers (e.g., Goldberg and Inman, 1955; McMaster, 1960; Zenkovitch, 1960; Yasso, 1966; Ingle, 1966; Komar and Inman, 1970; Boon, 1970; Boone and Slowey, 1972; Nelson and Coakley, 1974; Judge, 1975; Heathershaw and Carr, 1977), or simple profile differencing procedures based upon bathymetric surveys (e.g., Davis and Fox, 1972; Coakley et al., 1973; Shaw, 1977). However, with the possible exception of the strain gage and almometer techniques (Shideler and McGrath, 1973; Brenninkmeyer, 1976) no method provides both sediment flux and bed elevation determinations; indeed at present no satisfactory technique exists for the determination of Lagrangian patterns of sediment transport and associated morphological changes during high wave conditions.

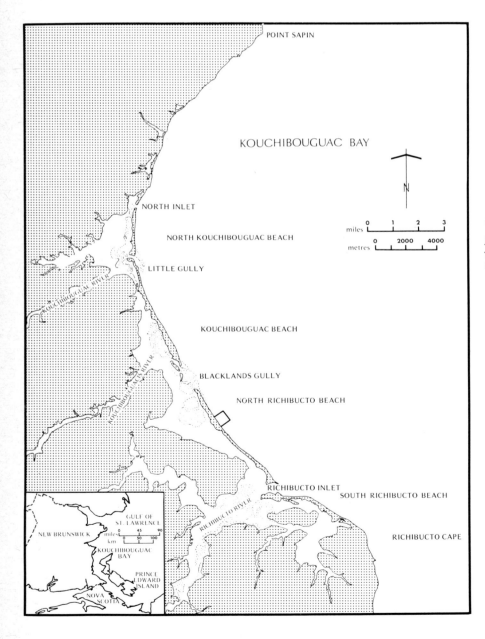

Figure 7.1

Location of the study area. Detailed work was carried out in the area of the nearshore zone shown by the box.

This paper describes a simple technique, the depth of disturbance rod, used to measure sediment flux (degradation-aggradation cycles) and bed elevation changes, which in conjunction with the analysis of sedimentary structures, provides a first approximation to the spatial and temporal patterns of sediment transport and associated morphodynamic behaviour of the nearshore zone. Experiments carried out during two discrete storm events are described from a barred nearshore environment in the southern Gulf of St. Lawrence.

The experimental site was established on an outer, crescentic nearshore bar system in Kouchibouguac Bay, New Brunswick (Fig. 7.1). Although the form of the nearshore bars, their spatial and temporal variability and basic sedimentary character have already been documented (Greenwood and Davidson-Arnott, 1972, 1975, 1979; Davidson-Arnott and Greenwood, 1974, 1976) some questions remain to be answered. Specifically, the relationship between the net alongshore sediment flux and the collective movement of sediments within the bar systems is still unclear. Estimates of the net alongshore sediment transport rate reveal values of approximately $10^5 \, m^3 \, a^{-1}$* to the south (Greenwood and Davidson-Arnott, 1977). In a single outer bar crescent, however, with a wavelength of 500 m there is approximately $2 \times 10^5 \, m^3$ of sediment. Since this outer bar occupies much of the length of the bay, it is evident that the net littoral drift is only a small part of the sediment available in the nearshore zone. Furthermore, collective movement of sediment through bar migration is only in the order of $10^2 \, m^3 \, a^{-1}$ (Greenwood and Davidson-Arnott, 1979) and bar stability is a strong characteristic of the outer system. Thus while the bar form does change under storm wave activity, it is in the nature of a quasi-equilibrium in an environment of high sediment flux. Under such conditions, therefore, pertinent questions arise:

(1) What proportion of sediment in the bar system becomes mobile?
(2) What is the relationship between the thickness of the active layer and form changes?
(3) What is the spatial pattern of the degradation/ aggradation cycles?
(4) What are the directional components of sediment transfer at different points in the bar during the period of sediment reworking and how are they related to the equilibrium form?

PROCEDURE

The depth of disturbance rod is a simple adaptation of the vigil network erosion pin (Leopold, 1962; Slaymaker and Chorley, 1964), which has previously been used in intertidal conditions (Clifton, 1969; Dolan et al., 1969; Williams, 1971; Knight, 1972; Dalrymple, 1972, 1973) but has not been tested in a continuously submerged nearshore situation. In this study a round steel rod (0.5 cm diameter, 1 - 2 m long) stamped with an identifier and tagged with a fluorescent streamer to aid recovery, is driven vertically into the sand until 0.45 m is left exposed above the surface; a loose-fitting washer (0.6 cm internal diameter) placed over the rod provides the control for determining bed surface scour or aggradation. Rods were deployed in two radial arrays using SCUBA prior to a storm event and re-examined in the immediate poststorm period. Rod measurements (Fig. 7.2) allowed determination of net surface change, maximum depth of activity relative to the prestorm surface and the total aggradation, if any. The only sequence of events that cannot be deciphered by the rod is an episode of aggradation followed by a smaller degree of degradation; the net result would appear as aggradation.

---

* a is the SI abbreviation for year.

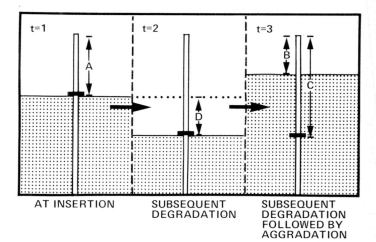

Figure 7.2. *Interpretation of depth of disturbance rod: t = 1,2,3 represent time intervals, stippling the sand bed and A,B,C,D measurements made relative to the top of the rod. The determinations to be made are: (a) net bed elevation change (A-B), this value may be positive or negative indicating aggradation or degradation; (b) maximum scour depth or depth of activity relative to the pre-storm surface (C-A); (c) total aggradation subsequent to maximum degradation (C-B).*

As with other techniques used in sediment flux determinations a calibration is necessary. A second estimate of the poststorm depth of activity and aggradation is indicated in epoxy peels of box cores by strong scour planes, structural or textural changes and truncation of bioturbation phenomena (Fig. 7.3). The good correlation achieved between rod values and core characteristics is illustrated in Figure 7.4a. A further estimate of the depth of activity can be made from the depth of burial of fluorescent tracers in core samples and Figure 7.4b illustrates again the good correlation with rod measurements. The consistency of the three measures of depth of activity indicates that no excessive scour or deposition is associated with flow interference from the rod itself. Direct observation of bedform generation and migration with no irregular surface deformation at the rod locations, at least under moderate energy conditions, provides further support for this conclusion.

The rods are reliable under both wave-induced oscillatory flow and longshore and rip current conditions, although difficulties of underwater measurement are encountered through failure to locate or identify the rod, rod bending, biogenic activity around the rod and difficulties of washer excavation in areas of high aggradation.

Besides providing a check on the accuracy of the depth of disturbance rods, box cores also indicate the assemblages of structures produced by bedforms during active sediment transport. Examination of these structures provides a measure of the type (and therefore relative rate) and direction of bedload movement, which is the dominant mode in the nearshore (Cook and Gorsline, 1972; Komar, 1976, 1977, 1978). For example, in Figure 7.3c the lowest sedimentation unit shows seaward-dipping, high-angle cross-stratification, indicative of the curved foresets of a dune form migrating seaward and obviously associated with a sediment flux in that direction. This unit is truncated above by a set of planar stratification dipping landwards at a lower angle, suggesting a shift through time to sheet flow and a probable reversal in the direction of sediment transport.

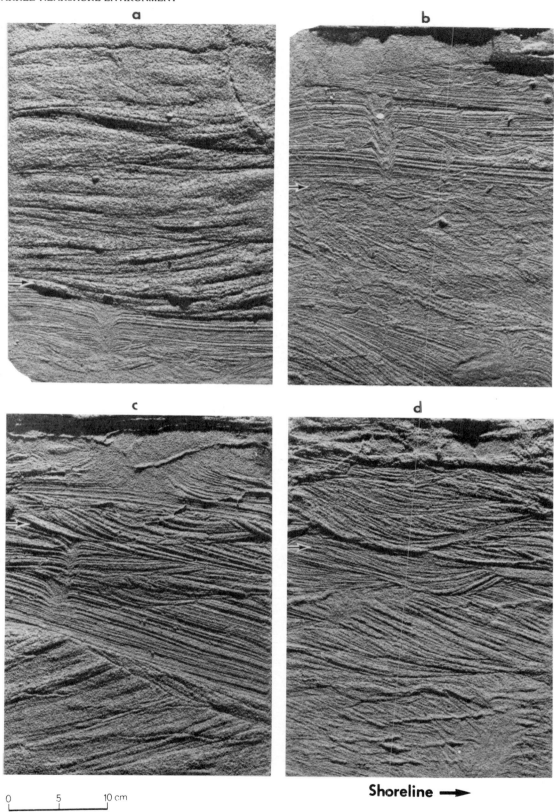

Shoreline ➡

(a) core illustrating distinct scour surface, textural and structure change and truncation of a bioturbation feature at the depth of disturbance

(b) core illustrating scour surface and truncation of bioturbation feature at depth of disturbance

(c) core illustrating simple scour surface at depth of disturbance

(d) core illustrating multiple scour surfaces with no clear indication of most recent depth of activity

Figure 7.3. Epoxy peels of box cores taken at the location of depth of disturbance rods illustrating scour sufaces: the depths of activity indicated by the rods are denoted by arrows.

Therefore, the rods may be used to determine the amount of sediment flux occurring spatially, but also, using the structural indices, possible sediment transport paths during individual storm events may be reconstructed.

SEDIMENT FLUX AND MORPHOLOGICAL CHANGE: A CASE STUDY

The results of monitoring arrays of 62 depth of disturbance rods deployed over a single crescentic bar form together with analysis of selected pre- and poststorm box cores give a coherent picture of the patterns of sedimentation and morphological change associated with high wave conditions in the barred nearshore of Kouchibouguac Bay.

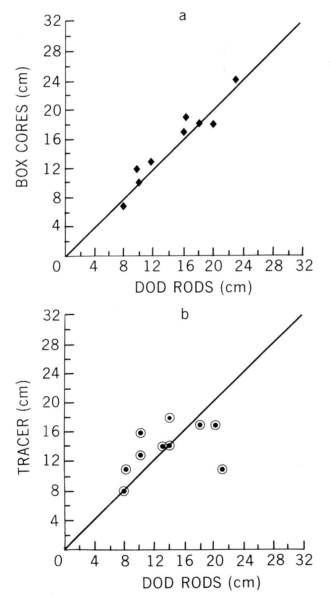

Figure 7.4. *Correlation between depth of activity determined from the depth of disturbance rods and: (a) sedimentary indicators in box cores; in these instances at least 3 of the indicators were present, (b) depth of incorporation of fluorescent tracers; 10 grains per 30 g sample was used as a cutoff concentration.*

Storm Event 1

A relatively shallow meteorological depression travelling southeast across New Brunswick on 1976-6-11 generated winds out of the northeast for 34 hours at North Beach in Kouchibouguac Bay (Fig. 7.5). Wave hindcasting (Hale and Greenwood, 1980) revealed maximum significant deep-water wave heights of 2 m with periods of 6 s (Fig. 7.5) and a return period for this storm of approximately 1.3 years. This is close to the return period of the most probable annual maximum storm, when the annual duration series is considered.

Figures 7.6a and 7.6c illustrate the values obtained for both depth of activity relative to the prestorm surface and the resulting bed elevation change. Scour depths range from a minimum of 6 cm on the landward slope of the bar to a maximum of 70 cm on the bar crest; bed elevation change reaches a maximum of 37 cm on the bar crest and a minimum of zero on the seaward slope. Clearly some areas have aggraded but the total pattern is one of surface lowering and apparent bar erosion. To examine sediment flux in greater detail variability normal to shore would seem an important aspect because wave approach approximates this after extensive refraction into Kouchibouguac Bay.

Figures 7.7a and 7.7b illustrate the changes revealed by the depth of disturbance rods along profiles across two areas of the outer bar system. Line BT illustrates the general one-bar profile of a simple crescent area whereas line CF illustrates a zone close to the shoal area where a distinct two-bar form is generated by a 'tail' extending landward from the southern crescent.

Line BT reveals maxima of depth of activity at two locations: seaward of the initial bar crest position (43 to 70 cm), and in the trough landward of the bar (43 cm). Depth of disturbance is relatively uniform over the landward slope (13 - 14 cm) whereas a general decrease is observed seaward over the seaward slope. Bed elevation change along the same line reveals: (a) maximum degradation on the seaward side of the prestorm bar crest (35 cm), coinciding with the zones of maximum depth of activity; (b) small but relatively constant lowering of the landward slope (1.5 - 4 cm); and (c) net aggradation at only one location, i.e., seaward of the zones of maximum scour and thus well seaward of the prestorm bar crest position. The rod data indicate a general deepening of the trough (up to 21 cm), seaward shift of the bar crest position and slight steepening of the seaward slope.

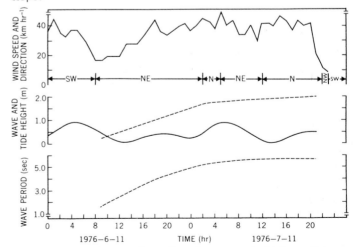

Figure 7.5. *Winds and predicted wave and tidal conditions, North Beach, Kouchibouguac Bay, 1976-6-11 to 1976-6-12.*

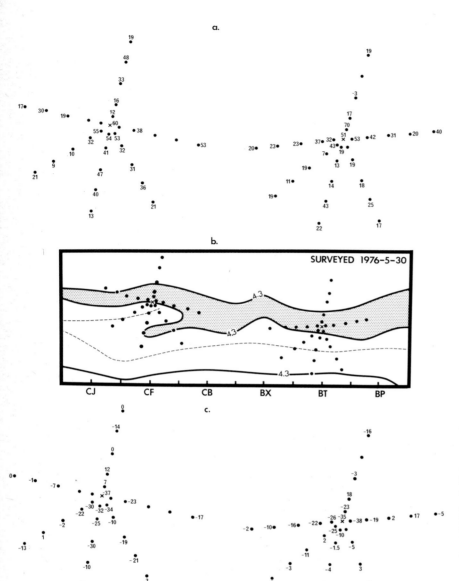

Figure 7.6

Depths of disturbance (a) and net bed elevation changes (c) from two radial grids centred on the bar crest along lines BT and CF (b) for the storm event 1976-6-11. Rods were spaced at 10, 25, 50, 75 and 100 m intervals from the centre along lines running approximately N, E, S, SW, W and NW. Rod locations lacking values reflect loss of rods. The contour line is referenced to a datum 1.1 m above mean water level.

Examination of the structures preserved in the active storm layer (this time relative to the poststorm bed surface) gives a clear indication of the directional component of the sediment flux. On the seaward slope significant sediment motion was initiated in 5.3 m of water. Figure 7.8 illustrates the structural indices developed at this location during the storm. The depth of activity is 14 cm and the plane bedding, dipping gently seaward, was generated by near-symmetrical oscillatory flow at the bed under conditions of wave shoaling. If the large pebble incorporated in the stratification was in motion during the storm then it may be possible to estimate the orbital velocity existing at the time (Komar and Miller, 1973, 1974, 1975a, b). For this pebble (sandstone S.G. = 2.6, average diameter = 5 cm) an orbital velocity of 183 cm s^{-1} is necessary for the initiation of motion with a 6 s wave period. As the pebble was in approximately 5.3 m of water, the necessary wave height would be 2.5 m, close to that hindcast for deep water during

this storm. Thus with high velocities near the bed but near symmetric flow, upper flat bed conditions (Southard, 1975) would exist; however, the depth of activity was still relatively small and certainly bed elevation change was low.

On the bar crest, the zone of maximum activity (both depth of scour and bed elevation change) is clearly associated with the development and migration of large asymmetrical dunelike bedforms (lunate megaripples: Clifton et al., 1971; Davidson-Arnott and Greenwood, 1976), which are preserved as distinct sets of trough cross-stratification (Fig. 7.9b). The marked scour plane identified in Figure 7.9b separates the storm-generated megaripple cross-stratification and massive bedding from the small-scale ripple cross-stratification built up under low waves before the storm. A prestorm peel from the same location consists of small- to medium-scale trough cross-stratification and massively bedded medium sand in sequence (Fig. 7.9a).

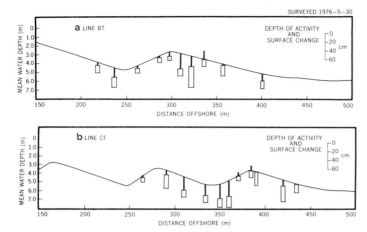

Figure 7.7. *Pre-storm profiles illustrating net bed elevation change (solid bar) and depth of active layer (open bar), relative to the pre-storm surface, along: (a) line BT and (b) line CF (Fig. 7.6). Note the scale difference for the depth of disturbance rod data.*

These structures are indicative of landward and oblique migration of ripples and megaripples. There is no evidence from this peel for seaward migration of bedforms at this point, in contrast to the poststorm peel. The juxtaposition of seaward- and landward-dipping cross-stratification in Figure 7.9b indicates that the direction of sediment movement varied greatly during the storm. However, it is extremely important to note that the major set of cross-stratification illustrates a clear seaward dip, and therefore seaward transfer of sediment at this point during the storm. Overlying this unit is a set of plane bedding dipping gently landward. This sequence is interpreted as representing lunate megaripple migration seaward under 'rip-type' currents generated during intense wave breaking on the seaward side of the bar crest followed by upper flat bed generated either as the storm abates and the rip currents decay, or as the rip migrates and asymmetric oscillatory flow over the bar crest is strong as the high waves continue to shoal. Furthermore, it is evident from the bed elevation change data that the location from which this core was taken changed from a position on top of the bar crest to one on the landward slope. This correlates well with the idea of erosion of the bar crest under rip-type flow and deposition seaward of the breaker line, producing a seaward migration of the highest point of the bar crest (see Figs. 7.6, 7.7).

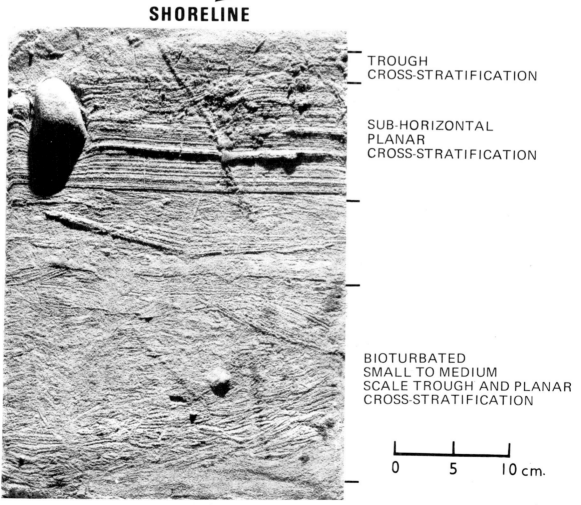

Figure 7.8. *Epoxy peel of box core from the active storm layer on the seaward slope in 5.3 m of water on line BT illustrating the structural indices of sediment transport.*

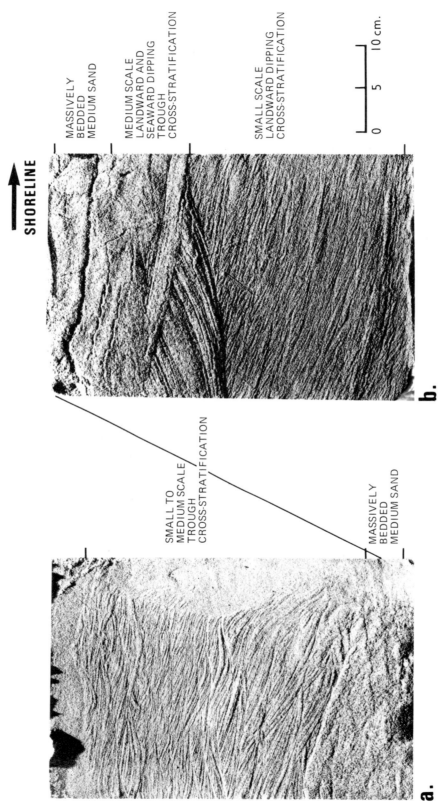

Figure 7.9. *Epoxy peels of prestorm (a) and post-storm (b) box cores from the bar crest in 2.5 m of water on line BT; the solid line marks the equivalent stratigraphic position.*

A pre- and poststorm sequence of cores was also taken from the bar crest north of the previous area at line BW (Fig. 7.10), at the northern limit of the depth of disturbance rods. Similar patterns emerge. The prestorm peel (Fig. 7.10a) consists of small- to medium-scale, trough cross-stratified indicative of ripples and megaripples migrating landward and oblique to shore. The direction and intensity of currents near the bed in this area must have fluctuated throughout the storm because both landward- and seaward-dipping cross-stratified units can be seen in the poststorm peel (Fig. 7.10b). The angle of dip is greatest for the seaward-dipping cross-stratification, suggesting that seaward migration may have been more or less normal to shore whereas landward migration was slightly oblique. The uppermost unit of small-scale trough cross-stratification is typical of ripple generation by low wave conditions following the storm.

On the bar crest it is evident that water and sediment flowed seaward over the crescentic area during the storm either as a very broad flow over 100 m wide, or as two distinct flows separated spatially or temporally. At present it is not possible to state unequivocally which interpretation is correct, but because the structural analogy is most closely correlated with rip currents in a measured inner system (Davidson-Arnott and Greenwood, 1974), then the most likely explanation is that narrow rips shifted spatially and temporally over a wide area of the crescent as the storm wave breaking conditions change.

Figure 7.11 illustrates the peel taken after the storm in the trough landward of the crescent (40 m landward of BT grid centre). Since no peel was taken before the storm and there was no DOD rod in the immediate area, the depth of disturbance can only be surmised from this peel, much of which is structureless. Unlike most other peels from the outer bar system this one contains a wide range of sediment sizes and several large shells. The only structures visible are seaward-dipping trough cross-stratification. These were formed by seaward-migrating dunes or megaripples; thus there must at some time have been a relatively strong seaward-flowing current in this area.

Some 60 m landward of the previous location on the seaward slope of the inner bar, two cores were taken, one before the storm and another following (Fig. 7.12). Both peels consist of cross-stratification indicative of ripple bedforms migrating normal, oblique and parallel to shore. Since the water depth averages just over 4 m the velocities near the bed generated by short-period waves will be low. These may or may not have been sufficient to initiate sediment transport and ripple formation; this will depend on the wave period at the time. Although low wave activity may account for the generation of ripples migrating normal or oblique to shore it could not account for ripple migration parallel to shore. Longer period waves break on the outer bar thus expending much of their energy. Hence the wave-induced velocities near the bed on the seaward slope of the inner bar are relatively low. The longshore current produced by the breaking waves, however, may be sufficient to generate ripple bedforms which migrate parallel, oblique or seaward depending on the direction and intensity of flow at that particular location. Since the peels were taken landward of the trough it seems unlikely that the longshore current would be flowing seaward in this location. The seaward return flow from a rip channel in the inner system 60 m north of the core location (line BV, Fig. 7.6) may, however, have produced sufficient seaward flow to generate migration of ripples in this location.

Storm effects in the area of line CF differ in several ways from those in the previous area considered, but the major distinction is in the increase in both depth of activity and bed elevation change (Figs. 7.6, 7.7b). This reflects the larger area of the bar form in shallower water which is thus subject to more intense wave and current activity. The zone of maximum depth of activity occurs again on the seaward side of the bar crest (both the outer and inner bar tail), reflecting the zone of wave breaking during the height of the storm. Excessive scour on the seaward margin of the seaward trough is also evident. Net bed lowering is again the general rule, although here aggradation on the landward side of the bar crest occurs, in contrast to line BT. In 5.3 m of water, at the seaward limit of the grid, depth of activity is considerable although there is zero bed elevation change as a result of the storm. As in the area discussed previously, the upper seaward slope steepens in association with aggradation seaward of the bar crest (Figs. 7.6, 7.7b). Sediment flux in this area can again be related to the bedforms active during the storm and preserved at depth; the inferred magnitude and direction of sediment transport correlates well with observed morphological changes.

At the seaward limit of the grid in 5.5 m of water the prestorm sediments were almost fully bioturbated (Fig. 7.13a), illustrating a lack of wave or current activity. In contrast, the poststorm peel (Fig. 7.13b) illustrates truncation of this deposit and the formation of interbedded sets of subhorizontal plane bedding together with small-scale ripple cross-stratification typical of the seaward slope. This indicates sediment transport under the nearly symmetrical oscillatory currents during wave shoaling (Davidson-Arnott and Greenwood, 1976). While considerable depth of activity occurred during the storm (19 cm below prestorm surface) bed elevation change was zero. This suggests a surface in dynamic equilibrium with these particular storm wave conditions and may well reflect directly the nearly symmetrical sediment flux indicated by the structures at this location. If this is the case, a point equivalent to that of oscillating equilibrium for single particles (Johnson and Eagleson, 1966) can be defined. Figure 7.4 illustrates structures generated in the active layer on the upper seaward slope of the bar (28 cm depth of activity relative to the poststorm surface). They form composite bedsets of plane-to-ripple bedding typical of wave shoaling with nearly symmetrical oscillatory flow (Davidson-Arnott and Greenwood, 1976), overlain by a distinct small- to medium-scale set of trough cross-stratification with dips oriented landward. The composite bedsets, characteristic of wave shoaling on both seaward and landward slopes, were probably developed during storm wave buildup and the landward-dipping cross-stratification is associated with peak conditions close to or at wave breaking, when strongly asymmetrical oscillatory flow covered parts of the seaward slope as well as the bar crest. Since the small-scale ripple cross-stratification is interbedded between sets of plane bedding the flow regime likely shifted during the period of active entrainment. Either wave energy fluctuated or water level shifted. The wind, tide and predicted wave characteristics for this storm, have already been shown in Figure 7.5 and energy dissipation in the nearshore clearly peaked during the falling cycle of a spring tide with a pure tidal fluctuation in water level of 85 cm, while predicted wave heights (at least in deep water) did not vary. It is interesting to note that aggradation of the bed occurred here and was about 12 cm, which would include this upper unit. Since the area immediately seaward experienced no net surface change but extensive scour (33 cm), while the area landward also experienced net aggradation, a net landward transport from the seaward side to the landward side of the bar crest can be inferred.

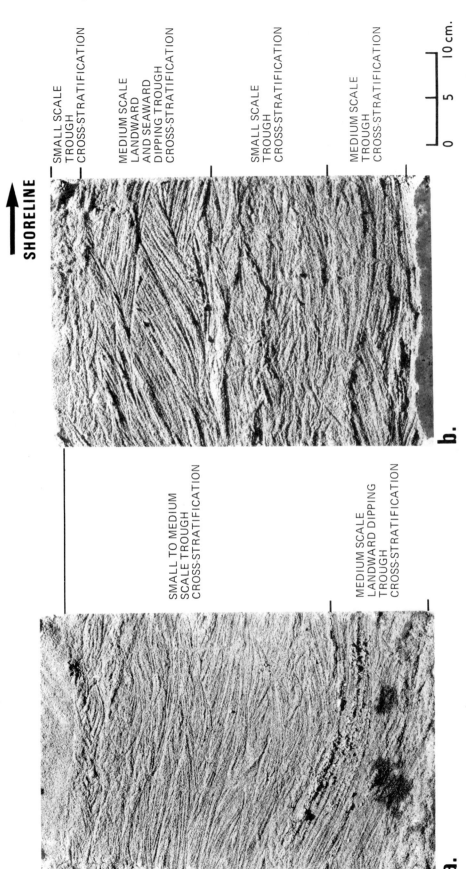

SHORELINE →

SMALL SCALE
TROUGH
CROSS-STRATIFICATION

MEDIUM SCALE
LANDWARD
AND SEAWARD
DIPPING TROUGH
CROSS-STRATIFICATION

SMALL SCALE
TROUGH
CROSS-STRATIFICATION

MEDIUM SCALE
TROUGH
CROSS-STRATIFICATION

10 cm.

5

0

b.

SMALL TO MEDIUM
SCALE TROUGH
CROSS-STRATIFICATION

MEDIUM SCALE
LANDWARD DIPPING
TROUGH
CROSS-STRATIFICATION

a.

Figure 7.10. *Epoxy peels of box cores from the bar crest line BW: (a) prestorm deposits; (b) post-storm deposits.*

SHORELINE

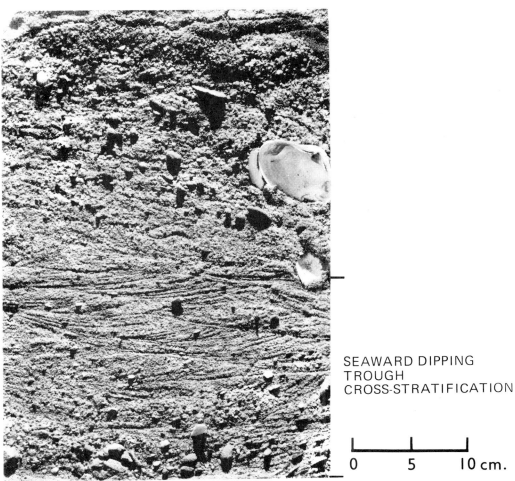

SEAWARD DIPPING
TROUGH
CROSS-STRATIFICATION

0   5   10 cm.

Figure 7.11   Epoxy peel of box core from the trough in 4 m of water on line BT.

Twenty-five metres shoreward of the previous location on the landward slope of the bar (see grid centre, line CF on Fig. 7.6) a prestorm peel illustrates features typical of the landward slope facies (Fig. 7.15a). Landward-dipping planar stratification up to 20° dip is the major set on this morphological slope of 2 to 3°. It is underlain and super-imposed by landward-dipping trough cross-stratification and a small unit of plane bedding. During the storm, 37 cm of material was scoured away and the depth of disturbance reached 23 cm relative to the poststorm bed. Thus relative to the prestorm bed, the depth of activity was 60 cm, or almost twice the depth visible in the prestorm peel. For this reason one would not expect the prestorm structures in the poststorm peel (Fig. 15b). In the latter there is a distinct break, not only in the sequence of sedimentary structures, but also in the sediment size at a depth correlating closely with the rod measurement. The structures below this break are typical of the landward slope facies where the wave-generated oscillatory currents produce flat bed and ripple bedforms. In contrast, the overlying cosets of seaward-dipping cross-stratification indicate seaward-migrating megaripple bedforms. These must have been gen-erated by seaward return of the longshore current similar to

that of a rip current in the inner bar system. That such structures formed on the landward slope of the bar suggests that the speed of this current was considerable and that significant quantities of sediment were being transported obliquely upslope. The massively bedded units near the top of the peel may reflect extremely rapid sedimentation as a result of the interaction between the seaward-flowing current and waves.

The rod data combined with the structural indices illustrate distinct but complex patterns of sediment flux over one crescentic bar during this storm. As the storm represents the most probable annual maximum event in intensity (measured by wave height and cumulative energy) it is probably the controlling event in nearshore equilibrium. This is supported by the depth at which significant sediment movement initiates morphological change: on line CF in 5.5 m of water, for example, the rod indicates considerable depth of activity but zero bed elevation change. On line BT again significant depth of activity occurs but bed elevation change is restricted to 18 cm, this time in 4.5 m of water.

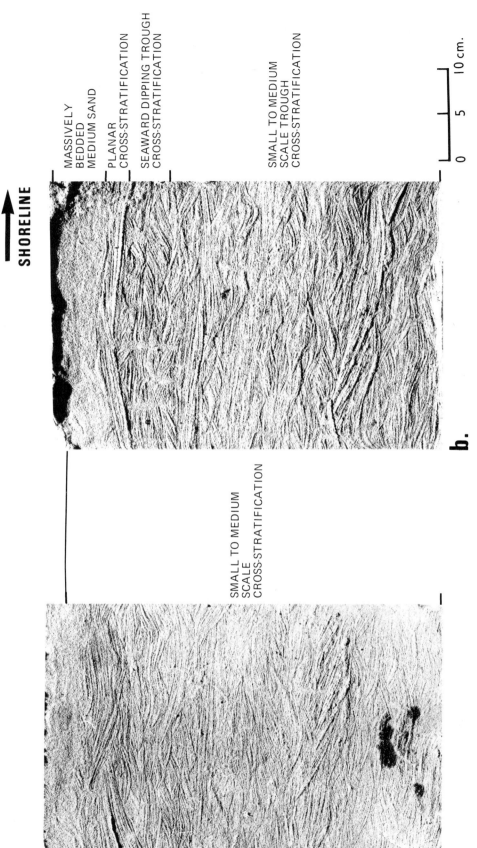

Figure 7.12. *Epoxy peels of box cores from the seaward slope of the inner bar line BT: (a) prestorm; (b) poststorm.*

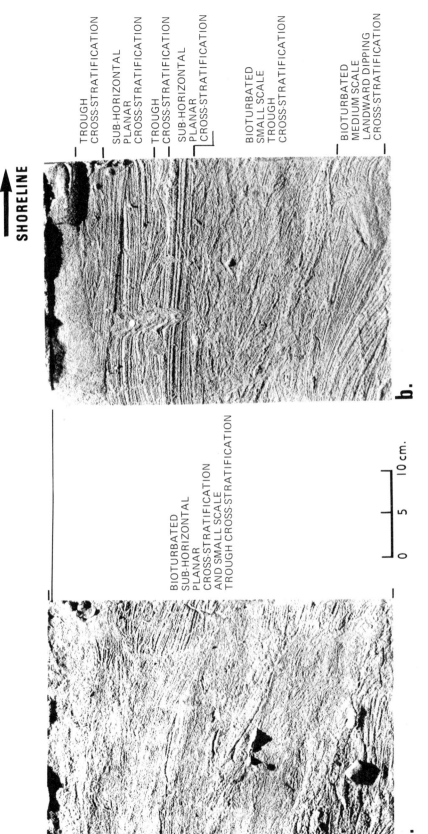

SHORELINE

TROUGH
CROSS-STRATIFICATION

SUB-HORIZONTAL
PLANAR
CROSS-STRATIFICATION

TROUGH
CROSS-STRATIFICATION

SUB-HORIZONTAL
PLANAR
CROSS-STRATIFICATION

BIOTURBATED
SMALL SCALE
TROUGH
CROSS-STRATIFICATION

BIOTURBATED
MEDIUM SCALE
LANDWARD DIPPING
CROSS-STRATIFICATION

b.

BIOTURBATED
SUB-HORIZONTAL
PLANAR
CROSS-STRATIFICATION
AND SMALL SCALE
TROUGH CROSS-STRATIFICATION

10 cm.

5

0

a.

Figure 7.13. Epoxy peels of prestorm (a) and poststorm (b) box cores from the seaward slope in 5.3 m water depth on line CF.

SHORELINE

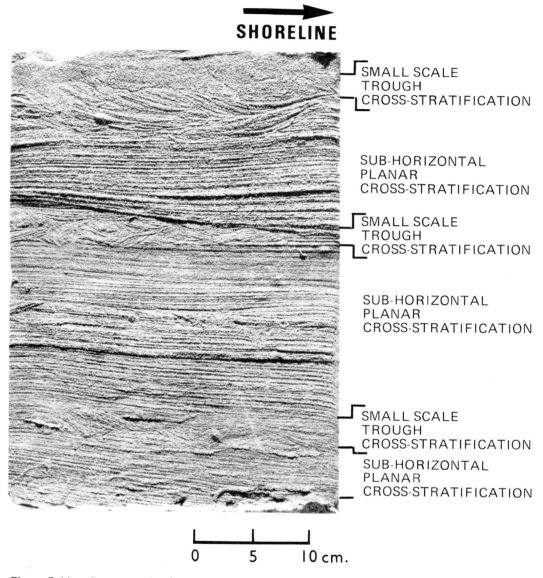

SMALL SCALE
TROUGH
CROSS-STRATIFICATION

SUB-HORIZONTAL
PLANAR
CROSS-STRATIFICATION

SMALL SCALE
TROUGH
CROSS-STRATIFICATION

SUB-HORIZONTAL
PLANAR
CROSS-STRATIFICATION

SMALL SCALE
TROUGH
CROSS-STRATIFICATION

SUB-HORIZONTAL
PLANAR
CROSS-STRATIFICATION

0   5   10 cm.

Figure 7.14   Epoxy peel of post-storm box core from the bar crest line CF in 2.5 m water depth.

Thus as one moves seaward bed elevation change approaches zero, even though sediment reactivation is considerable. It is also important to note that the point of zero bed elevation change is very close to the marked break-in-slope at the seaward foot of the bar. This clearly suggests that the seaward slope represents a dynamic equilibrium controlled by wave oscillatory currents and secondary rip currents with the seaward foot of the bar marking a point of initiation of the equilibrium slope probably associated with some threshold value of wave asymmetry which produces landward transport. General bar stability will thus be a result of a sediment balance maintained by a seaward flux of sediment in the rip-type currents. This equilibrium is further emphasized when the percentage of the total bar sediment in motion during the storm is computed and compared with the percentage change in bar form. On profile BT approximately 25 per cent of the bar form is mobilized,

whereas for line CF it is 32 per cent. Thus large volumes of sediment were set in motion while the bar form remained relatively stable (per cent sediment loss: line BT = 4; line CF = 7).

Storm Event 2

On 1976-8-14 a stationary front situated south of Northumberland Strait generated winds out of the north and northeast in Kouchibouguac Bay, which persisted for almost two days during which maximum hourly wind speeds reached 38 km h^{-1} at North Beach (Fig. 7.4). Hindcast wave conditions gave deep water values of 152 cm for significant height and 5 s for period. Such a storm would have a return period of approximately one month (Hale, 1978) and thus represents a very frequent event in the nearshore time series.

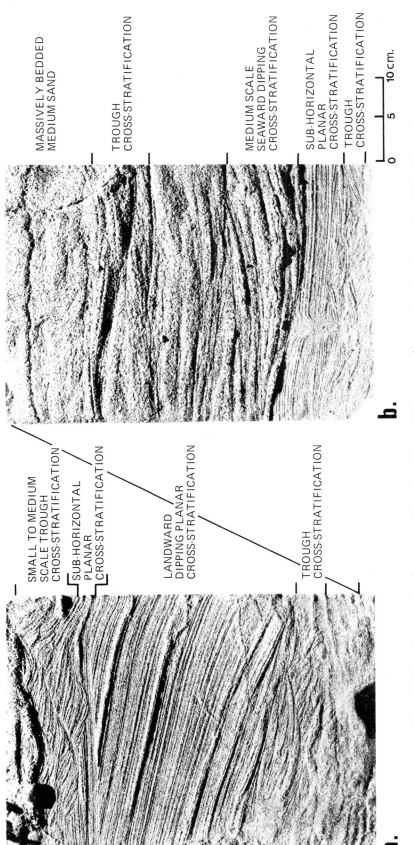

MASSIVELY BEDDED MEDIUM SAND

TROUGH CROSS-STRATIFICATION

MEDIUM SCALE SEAWARD DIPPING CROSS-STRATIFICATION

SUB-HORIZONTAL PLANAR CROSS-STRATIFICATION

TROUGH CROSS-STRATIFICATION

10 cm.

5

0

b.

SMALL TO MEDIUM SCALE TROUGH CROSS-STRATIFICATION

SUB-HORIZONTAL PLANAR CROSS-STRATIFICATION

LANDWARD DIPPING PLANAR CROSS-STRATIFICATION

TROUGH CROSS-STRATIFICATION

a.

Figure 7.15. *Epoxy peels of prestorm (a) and poststorm (b) box cores from the landward slope line CF in 4.5 m of water.*

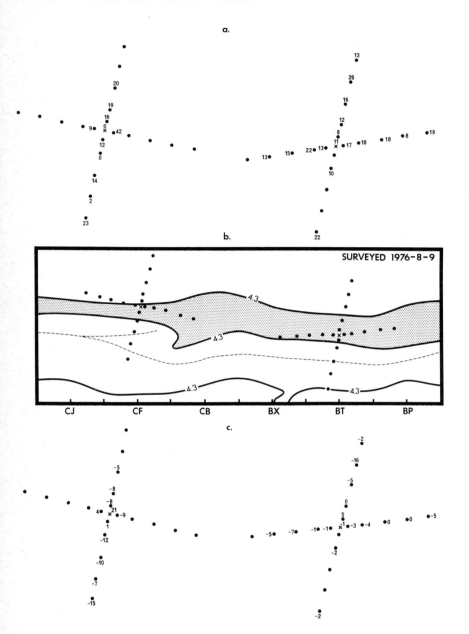

Figure 7.16.

Depths of disturbance (a) and net bed elevation change (c) from two radial grids centred on the bar crest along lines BT and CF (b) for the storm event 1976-8-14. Rods were spaced at 10, 25, 50, 75 and 100 m intervals from the centre along lines running approximately N, E, S and W. Rod locations lacking values reflect loss of rods. The contour line is referenced to a datum 1.1 m above mean water level.

Figures 7.16c and 7.16a illustrate the rod readings for bed elevation change and depth of activity, respectively, and show, as might be expected, the relatively smaller changes generated by this smaller storm. Shore normal changes are again illustrated with reference to prestorm profiles along lines BT and CF (Fig. 7.17a, b). While the degree of change was small (maximum depth of active layer = 33 cm; maximum bed elevation change = +21 cm) the type of change was similar to that of the first storm for similar locations within the bar system. The trough, bar crest and upper seaward slope again exhibit greatest depths of activity while net aggradation is experienced only in areas just seaward of the prestorm crest; all other locations experienced net degradation. The landward slopes in these areas again experienced uniform depth of activity and lowering.

An examination of structures preserved in the crescent area (line BT) reveals the difference between sediment flux under this storm and the previous storm event. Figure

7.18a-c illustrates the structures found on the seaward side of the bar crest (a), the bar crest itself (b), and the landward slope (c). The depth of activity relative to the poststorm surface was 12 cm, 24 cm and 7 cm, respectively. The sequence of structures preserved is subhorizontal plane bedding on the seaward side of the bar crest, small- to medium-scale sets of trough cross-stratification dipping landward on the top of the bar crest, and massively bedded sand on the landward slope. All of this suggests landward migration (if any) of sediments over this crescent area during the storm and in fact a buildup and increase in height of the bar crest itself. However, the structures preserved from previous storms show that this had once been a zone of seaward-migrating megaripples, as evidenced by the sets of medium-scale seaward-dipping cross-stratification shown in Figure 7.18a-c. This suggests that this magnitude of storm did not generate a significant seaward flow of water over the bar crest since wave breaking was not intense enough to

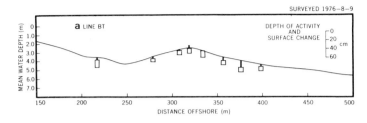

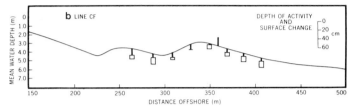

SURVEYED 1976-8-9

Figure 7.17. *Prestorm profiles illustrating net bed elevation change (solid bar) and depth of activity (open bar), relative to the pre-storm surface along: (a) line BT and (b) line CF. Note the scale difference for the depth of disturbance rod data.*

cause rip currents in this outer bar system. This further suggests a bar response characterized primarily by sediment flux landward and alongshore in the trough. It is interesting that a series of cores taken across the bar crest and landward slope at a shoal area, line BZ (Fig. 7.19b), illustrate structures indicating landward sediment movement across the crest and avalanching down the landward slope. The peel from the crest (Fig. 7.19a) illustrates landward-dipping trough cross-stratification overlain by landward-dipping tabular cross-stratification, trough cross-stratification and finally, small-scale landward-dipping cross-stratification. With the exception of the uppermost unit all others are indicative of high wave energy conditions. The fact that tabular units of steeply dipping cross-stratification are present suggests very strongly that asymmetrical currents were generated in this area, even that a surf zone may have developed and that the bores produced these units. The trough cross-stratification and small-scale landward-dipping cross-stratification associated with megaripple and ripple bedforms, which overlie the tabular units, reflect decreasing wave energy conditions or increasing water depth. The cores from the landward slope at the shoal (Fig. 19b, c) are dominated by avalanche bedding (up to 17° dip) which at the toe of the bar overlies fine sands and silts of the trough and in turn is overlain by massive very fine sands. The bar foresets meet abruptly with the trough sediments; no distinct toesets are present. This is similar to the observations made by Davidson-Arnott and Greenwood (1974) at the base of a migrating slip face on the inner bar system. They concluded that the longshore currents in the trough during high energy conditions, when the bar is actively migrating shoreward, prevent deposition of material from suspension, thus accounting for the lack of distinct toesets. The same situation likely existed on the outer bar during the storm event. The massively stratified unit above the planar cross-stratified unit may reflect settling out of suspension after the peak of the storm whenever wave energy conditions subsided. Although no depth of disturbance rods were present in this area, the incorporation of tracer in the box cores and the soft, unstable nature of the landward slope indicate that the structures represent this small storm event. Undoubtedly the shallow water depth over the shoal would be conducive to greater activity than over the crescent area.

CONCLUSIONS

The depth of disturbance rod is clearly successful in determining the depth of the active sediment layer during a storm event at a point permanently submerged in the nearshore zone, the temporal sequence of degradation-aggradation at that point, and the net bed elevation change resulting from the gross sediment flux induced by storm waves. The rod is more accurate, simpler and quicker than other methods presently employed to study depth of activity (compare King, 1951; Kolp, 1958; Kumar and Sanders, 1976; Vvedenskaya, 1977). Although continuous monitoring of absolute values of sediment flux is not possible with this technique, its simplicity permits deployment of considerable numbers of rods for the detection of spatial variability of net flux through time. Furthermore the directions and relative rates of sediment transport can be interpreted from the structural indices preserved in the active layer and recorded in box cores. Even where direct measurement devices have been deployed either in numbers (Brennink-meyer, 1974) or as a mobile system (Kana, 1976; Coakley, 1978) they were restricted to measuring only part of the total sediment load and generally give no indication of the direction of transport.

The study of sediment flux over two discrete storm events affecting a nearshore crescentic bar system in the southern Gulf of St. Lawrence produced the following conclusions:

1. As might be expected, depths of activity are greater under more severe storms. Maximum depths of scour during the two storms were 70 cm for predicted deep-water significant wave heights of 2 m and periods of 6 s, and 23 cm for wave heights of 1.5 m and periods of 5 s.

2. In both storms maximum depths of activity were on the seaward side of the bar crest, where wave breaking would be most intense and where asymmetrical oscillatory flows or rip current flows at the bed would be at a maximum under all wave conditions. In contrast minima occurred on the upper part of the landward slope. A secondary maximum of depth of activity was associated with the trough where longshore currents caused considerable scour, although in these depths of water (4 to 5 m) they would be active for only a relatively short time during the most intense phase of wave breaking on the bar. This short time period, however, is clearly compensated for by the higher rates of sediment flux associated with unidirectional as opposed to oscillatory flow (whether symmetrical or asymmetrical).

3. In general net bed elevation changes were negative, revealing erosion of the bar form during storms. Maxima of bed surface change were located on the seaward side of the bar crest (35 cm of erosion) and in the trough close to the foot of the landward slope (37 cm of erosion) for Storm 1. Net aggradation was found either on the upper landward slopes (12 cm) or upper seaward slope (21 cm), although the latter was found following the lower wave activity of the second storm.

4. An examination of the structural indices preserved in the poststorm active layer allows an interpretation of water and sediment transport conditions during the storm. On the seaward slope of the bar sediment was being transported in a minimum depth of 4.8 m for both storms. Landward of this, in approximately 4.5 m of water, the structures indicate a transition from small-scale ripples and flat bed of the seaward slope subfacies to flat bed and megaripples of the bar crest subfacies. This reflects increasing asymmetry and speed of oscillatory flow and greater rates of sediment transport towards the crest. On the bar crest the inferred direction of bedform migration

SHORELINE

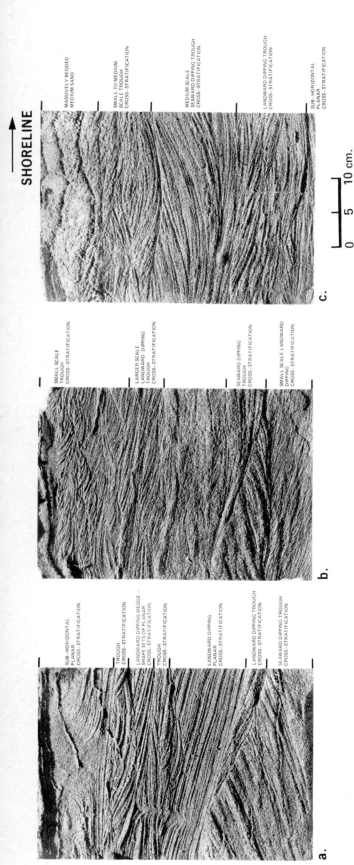

c.

MASSIVELY BEDDED
MEDIUM SAND

SMALL TO MEDIUM
SCALE TROUGH
CROSS–STRATIFICATION

MEDIUM SCALE
SEAWARD DIPPING TROUGH
CROSS–STRATIFICATION

LANDWARD DIPPING TROUGH
CROSS–STRATIFICATION

SUB–HORIZONTAL
PLANAR
CROSS–STRATIFICATION

0 5 10 cm.

b.

SMALL SCALE
TROUGH
CROSS–STRATIFICATION

LARGER SCALE
LANDWARD
DIPPING
TROUGH
CROSS–STRATIFICATION

SEAWARD DIPPING
CROSS–STRATIFICATION

SMALL SCALE LANDWARD
DIPPING
CROSS–STRATIFICATION

a.

SUB–HORIZONTAL
PLANAR
CROSS–STRATIFICATION

TROUGH
CROSS–STRATIFICATION

LANDWARD DIPPING WEDGE –
SHAPE SETS OF PLANAR
CROSS–STRATIFICATION

TROUGH
CROSS–STRATIFICATION

LANDWARD DIPPING
PLANAR
CROSS–STRATIFICATION

LANDWARD DIPPING TROUGH
CROSS–STRATIFICATION

SEAWARD DIPPING TROUGH
CROSS–STRATIFICATION

Figure 7.18. *Epoxy peels of box cores from the active storm layer line BT: (a) seaward side of bar crest; (b) top of bar crest; (c) landward slope of bar.*

SHORELINE

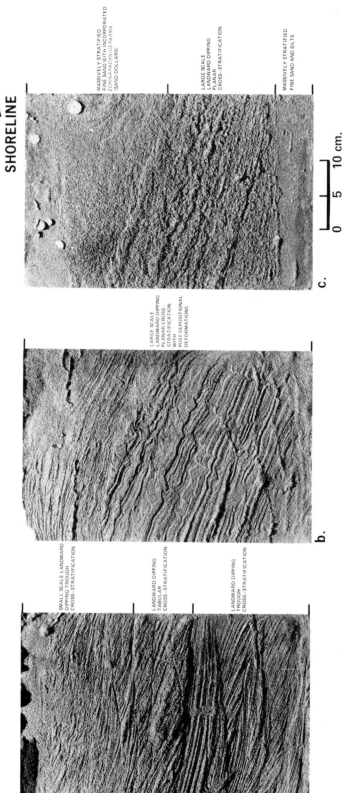

c.

MASSIVELY STRATIFIED
FINE SAND WITH INCORPORATED
ECHINARACHNIUS PARMA
(SAND DOLLARS)

LARGE SCALE
LANDWARD DIPPING
PLANAR
CROSS–STRATIFICATION

MASSIVELY STRATIFIED
FINE SAND AND SILTS

0 5 10 cm.

b.

LARGE SCALE
LANDWARD DIPPING
PLANAR CROSS–
STRATIFICATION
WITH
POST DEPOSITIONAL
DEFORMATIONS

a.

SMALL SCALE LANDWARD
DIPPING TROUGH
CROSS–STRATIFICATION

LANDWARD DIPPING
TABULAR
CROSS–STRATIFICATION

LANDWARD DIPPING
TROUGH
CROSS–STRATIFICATION

Figure 7.19. *Epoxy peels of poststorm box cores from the bar crest (a), mid-landward slope (b) and toe of the landward slope (c) on line BZ.*

106

varied considerably from place to place and even at a single location. With the exception of the shoal areas, where bedform migration was consistently shoreward, all other areas of the crescentic form showed evidence of megaripple migration in several directions during the storm. A distinct seaward component could be identified, however, suggesting that a seaward return flow of sediment was dominant at times but that either it was dispersed between the shoal areas, or the position of the return flow varied with time. The evidence of seaward-migrating megaripples on the landward slopes indicates that at some time during the storm the speed of the return flow must have been considerable. It seems highly unlikely that such currents could have existed simultaneously throughout the length of the crescent. The lack of a well defined channel to confine the return flow further suggests that it may shift in position. This could account for the juxtaposition of landward- and seaward-migrating bedforms on the bar cresent.

5. The sediment flux patterns derived from the depth of disturbance rods and structural indices support the conceptual model of bar stability based on rip cell circulation proposed by Greenwood and Davidson-Arnott (1979). The idea is supported that the bars are indeed equilibrium forms in a very dynamic sedimentological environment and respond to storm magnitudes close to that of the most probable annual maximum.

Acknowledgments

Support for this research has been provided by grants to the senior author (B.G.) from Imperial Oil Limited and the National Research Council of Canada (NRCA7956). A research contract from Parks Canada (ARO 76-21) assisted with summer work in 1976. We would like to thank R.G.D. Davidson-Arnott, P.R. Mittler, and G. Pember for their invaluable assistance in the field; the Graphics Department, Scarborough College assisted with the illustrations.

References

Boon, J.D. III
1970: Quantitative analysis of beach sand movement, Virginia Beach, Virginia; Sedimentology, v. 17, p. 85 - 103.

Boone, C.G. and Slowey, J.F.
1972: Stable isotope tracing of coastal sand transport using dysprosium oxide; Old Dominion University, Institute of Oceanography Technical Report 3, 56 p.

Brenninkmeyer, B.M.
1974: Mode and period of sand transport in the surf zone; Proceedings of the 14th Conference on Coastal Engineering, p. 812 - 827.
1976: *In situ* measurements of rapidly fluctuating, high sediment concentrations; Marine Geology, v. 20, p. 117 - 128.

Bruun, P. and Purpura, J.
1964: Quantitative research on littoral drift in field and laboratory; Proceedings of the 9th Conference on Coastal Engineering, v. 2, p. 267 - 288.

Clifton, H.E.
1969: Beach lamination: nature and origin; Marine Geology, v. 7, p. 553 - 559.

Clifton, H.E., Hunter, R. and Phillips, R.L.
1971: Depositional structures and processes in the non-barred, high energy nearshore; Journal of Sedimentary Petrology, v. 41, p. 651 - 670.

Coakley, J.P.
1978: Study of littoral drift in suspension: the S.O.L.I.D.S. project; Proceedings, 2nd Workshop on Great Lakes Coastal Erosion and Sedimentation, N.A. Rukavina, ed.; Hydraulics Division, National Water Research Institute, p. 17 - 20.

Coakley, J.P., Haras, W. and Freeman, N.
1973: The effect of storm surge on beach erosion, Point Pelee; Proceedings of the 16th Conference on Great Lakes Research, p. 377 - 389.

Cook, D.O.
1969: Sand transport by shoaling waves; unpublished Ph.D. thesis, University of Southern California, 148 p.

Cook, D.O. and Gorsline, D.S.
1972: Field observations of sand transport by shoaling waves; Marine Geology, v. 13, p. 31 - 55.

Dalrymple, R.W.
1972: Preliminary investigation of an intertidal sand body Cobequid Bay, Bay of Fundy; McMaster University Geology Department Technical Memorandum 72-1.
1973: Sediment texture and transport studies in an intertidal environment: a progress report; Maritime Sediments; v. 9, p. 45 - 58.

Das, M.
1972: Suspended sediment and longshore sediment transport data review; Proceedings of the 13th Conference on Coastal Engineering, v. 2, p. 1027 - 1048.

Davidson-Arnott, R.G.D. and Greenwood, B.
1974: Bedforms and structures associated with bar topography in the shallow-water wave environment, Kouchibouguac Bay, New Brunswick, Canada; Journal of Sedimentary Petrology, v. 44, p. 698 - 704.
1976: Facies relationships on a barred coast, Kouchibouguac Bay, New Brunswick, Canada; in Beach and Nearshore Sedimentation, R.A. Davis, Jr. and R.L. Ethington, eds.; Society of Economic Paleontologists and Mineralogists, Special Publication 24, p. 149 - 168.

Davis, R.E. and Fox, W.T.
1972: Coastal processes and nearshore bars; Journal of Sedimentary Petrology, v. 42, p. 401 - 412.

Dolan, R., Ferm, J.C. and McArthur, D.S.
1969: Measurements of beach process variables, Outer Banks, North Carolina; Coastal Studies Institute, Louisiana State University, Technical Report 64, 16 p.

Dowling, J.P.
1977:   Sediment transport measurement in the near-shore environment: a review of the state of the art; in Nearshore Sediment Transport Study, Workshop on Instrumentation for Nearshore Processes; Institute of Marine Resources, University of California, La Jolla, Sea Grant Publication No. 62, p. 58 - 83.

Fairchild, J.C.
1972:   Longshore transport of suspended sediment; Proceedings of the 13th Conference on Coastal Engineering, v. 2, p. 1069 - 1088.

Fukushima, H. and Mizoguchi, Y.
1958:   Field investigation of suspended littoral drift; Coastal Engineering in Japan, v. 1, p. 131 - 134.

Goldberg, E.D. and Inman, D.L.
1955:   Neutron-irradiated quartz as a tracer of sand movements; Bulletin of Geological Society of America, v. 66, p. 611 - 613.

Greenwood, B. and Davidson-Arnott, R.G.D.
1972:   Textural variation in the sub-environments of the shallow-water wave zone, Kouchibouguac Bay, New Brunswick; Canadian Journal of Earth Sciences, v. 9, p. 679 - 688.
1975:   Marine bars and nearshore sedimentary processes, Kouchibouguac Bay, New Brunswick; in Nearshore Sediments and Sediment Dynamics, J. Hails and A. Carr, eds.; Wiley, p. 123 - 150.
1977:   An interpretive study of coastal processes, Kouchibouguac National Park, New Brunswick; Parks Canada, Department of Indian and Northern Affairs, Halifax, 398 p.
1979:   Sedimentation and equilibrium in wave-formed bars: a review and case study; Canadian Journal of Earth Sciences, v. 16, p. 312 - 332.

Hale, P.B.
1978:   Storm-wave sedimentation: the role of meteorological depressions as geological agents in a barred, nearshore marine environment, Kouchibouguac Bay, New Brunswick; unpubl. M.Sc. dissertation, University of Toronto, 188 p.

Hale, P.B. and Greenwood, B.
1980:   Storm wave climatology: a study of the magnitude and frequency of geomorphic process; in Coastline of Canada: Littoral Processes and Shore Morphology, S.B. McCann ed.; Geological Survey of Canada, Paper 80-10, Report 6.

Heathershaw, A.D. and Carr, A.P.
1977:   Measurements of sediment transport rates using radioactive tracers; in Coastal Sediments '77, 5th Symposium, Waterway, Port, Coastal and Ocean Division, American Society of Civil Engineers, p. 399 - 416.

Ingle, J.C., Jr.
1966:   The movement of beach sand. Developments in Sedimentology, 5; Elsevier, New York, 221 p.

Johnson, J.W. and Eagleson, P.S.
1966:   Coastal processes; in Estuary and Coastline Hydrodynamics, A.T. Ippen, ed.; McGraw-Hill, New York, ch. 9, p. 404 - 492.

Judge, C.W.
1975:   Use of radioisotopic sand tracer (RIST) system; U.S. Army Coastal Engineering Research Center, Technical Memorandum 53, 75 p.

Kana, T.W.
1976:   A new apparatus for collecting simultaneous water samples in the surf zone; Journal of Sedimentary Petrology, v. 46, p. 1031 - 1034.

Kilner, F.A.
1976:   Measurement of suspended sediment in the surf zone; Proceedings of the 15th Conference on Coastal Engineering, v. 2, p. 2045 - 2059.

King, C.A.M.
1951:   Depth of disturbance of sand on sea beaches by waves; Journal of Sedimentary Petrology, v. 21, p. 131 - 140.

Knight, R.J.
1972:   Cobequid Bay sedimentology project: a progress report; Maritime Sediments, v. 8, p. 45 - 60.

Kolp, O.
1958:   Sediment sortierung und Umlagerung am meeresboden durch Wellenwirkung; Petermans Geographische Mitteilungen, v. 102, p. 173 - 178.

Komar, P.D.
1976:   Currents and sand transport on beaches: a review; Proceedings of Conference on Natural Water Resources and Ocean Engineering, American Society of Civil Engineers, New York, p. 1 - 27.
1977:   Beach sand transport: distribution and total drift; Journal, Waterway, Port, Coastal and Ocean Division, American Society of Civil Engineers, v. 104, no. WW2, p. 225 - 239.
1978:   Relative quantities of suspension versus bed-load transport on beaches; Journal of Sedimentary Petrology, v. 48, p. 921 - 932.

Komar, P.D. and Inman, D.L.
1970:   Longshore sand transport on beaches; Journal of Geophysical Research, v. 75, p. 5914 - 5927.

Komar, P.D. and Miller, M.C.
1973:   The threshold of sediment movement under oscillatory water waves; Journal of Sedimentary Petrology, v. 43, p. 1101 - 1110.
1974:   Sediment threshold under oscillatory waves; Proceedings of the 14th Conference on Coastal Engineering, v. 2, p. 756 - 775.
1975a: On the comparison between the threshold of sediment motion under waves and unidirectional currents with a discussion of the practical evaluation of the threshold; Journal of Sedimentary Petrology, v. 45, p. 362 - 367.
1975b: The initiation of oscillatory ripple marks and the development of plane-bed at high shear stresses under waves; Journal of Sedimentary Petrology, v. 45, p. 697 - 703.

Kumar, N. and Sanders, J.E.
1976:   Characteristics of shoreface storm deposits: modern and ancient examples; Journal of Sedimentary Petrology, v. 46, p. 145 - 162.

Lee, K.K.
1975:   Longshore currents and sediment transport in west shore of Lake Michigan; Water Resources Research, v. 11, p. 1029 - 1032.

Leopold, L.B.
1962:   The vigil network; Bulletin of International Association of Hydrological Sciences, v. 7, p. 5 - 9.

Lesht, B., White, R.V. and Miller, R.L.
1976:   A self contained facility for analysing near-bottom flow and associated sediment transport; National Oceanic and Atmospheric Administration, Technical Memorandum ERL MESA-9, 38 p.

McMaster, R.L.
1960:   Mineralogy as an indicator of beach sand movement along the Rhode Island shore; Journal of Sedimentary Petrology, v. 30, p. 404 - 413.

Nelson, D.E. and Coakley, J.P.
1974:   Techniques for tracing sediment movement; Environment Canada, Scientific Series, No. 32.

Shaw, J.R.
1977:   Coastal response at Point Pelee, Lake Erie; in Coastal Zone '78, Symposium on Technical, Environmental, Socioeconomic and Regulatory Aspects of Coastal Zone Management, American Society of Civil Engineers, v. 3, p. 1937 - 1953.

Shideler, G.L. and McGrath, D.G.
1973:   Evaluation of submarine strain gage systems for monitoring coastal sediment migration; Institute of Oceanography, Old Dominion University, Technical Report 11, 52 p.

Slaymaker, H.O. and Chorley, R.J.
1964:   The vigil network system; Journal of Hydrology, v. 2, p. 19 - 24.

Southard, J.B.
1975:   Bed configurations; chapter 2, in Depositional Environments as Interpreted from Primary Sedimentary Structures and Stratification Sequences, J.C. Harms et al., eds.; Society of Economic Paleontologists and Mineralogists, p. - 43.

Sternberg, R.W. and Creager, J.S.
1965:   An instrument system to measure boundary-layer conditions at the sea-floor; Marine Geology, v. 3, p. 475 - 482.

Swift, D.J.P. and McGrath, D.G.
1972:   Laboratory and field evaluation of an underwater sand height gage; Institute of Oceanography, Old Dominion University, Technical Report 4, 17 p.

Thornton, E.B.
1968:   A field investigation of sand transport in the surf zone; Proceedings of the 11th Conference on Coastal Engineering, v. 2, p. 335 - 351.

Thornton, E.B. and Morris, W.D.
1977:   Suspended sediments measured within the surf zone; in Coastal Sediments '77, 5th Symposium, Waterway, Port, Coastal and Ocean Division, American Society of Civil Engineers, p. 655 - 668.

Vvedenskaya, A.I.
1977:   Layer of storm reworking of sediments in Rudnaya Bay (Sea of Japan); Oceanology, v. 17, p. 333 - 335.

Watts, G.M.
1953:   Development and field test of a sampler for suspended sediment in wave action; Beach Erosion Board, Technical Memorandum 34.

Wenzel, D.
1974:   Measuring sand discharge near the sea-bottom; Proceedings of the Conference on Coastal Engineering, v. 2, p. 741 - 755.

Williams, A.T.
1971:   An analysis of some factors involved in the depth of disturbance of beach sand by waves; Marine Geology, v. 11, p. 145 - 158.

Yasso, W.E.
1966:   Formulation and use of fluorescent tracer coatings in sediment transport studies; Sedimentology, v. 6, p. 287 - 301.

Zenkovitch, V.P.
1960:   Fluorescent substances as tracers for studying the movement of sand on the sea bed, experiments conducted in the U.S.S.R.; Dock and Harbour Authority, v. 40, p. 280 - 283.

EDGE WAVES IN A CRESCENTIC BAR SYSTEM

D.A. Huntley
Department of Oceanography, Dalhousie University, Halifax, Nova Scotia

Huntley, D.A., Edge waves in a crescentic bar system; in The Coastline of Canada, S.B. McCann, editor; Geological Survey of Canada, Paper 80-10, p. 111-121, 1980.

Abstract

Measurements have been made of waves and currents in the nearshore crescentic bar system of a beach near Tracadie, New Brunswick to determine whether edge waves were present and could be responsible for forming the crescentic bars. The observations show that standing edge waves do occur in this system within a broad low frequency (18-32 s period) band, and that their energy increases greatly during storm conditions. The bandwidth of edge wave energy suggests that modes n = 1 to 4 are present with the wavelength predicted to form the observed crescentic bars. During a summer storm, estimated drift velocities under these edge waves are comparable with measured longshore drift currents of up to 60 cm/s. However, it is argued that the measured edge waves in this case were more likely to be a response to a pre-existing topographic wavelength rather than being directly responsible for forming the bars.

Résumé

Les auteurs ont mesuré les vagues et les courants d'un ensemble de cordons en forme de croissant situé à proximité du littoral sur une plage voisine de Tracadie, au Nouveau-Brunswick, afin de déterminer s'il y avait de la houle transversale et si celle-ci pouvait avoir contribué à former les cordons arqués. Les observations ont démontré qu'il existait effectivement une houle transversale constante dans cet ensemble en deçà d'une vaste bande de basse fréquence (période de 18-32 s), et que son énergie s'accroissait considérablement à l'occasion des tempêtes. La largeur de bande de l'énergie produite par la houle transversale permet de supposer que des modes n = 1 à 4 existent dans la longueur d'onde qui forme probablement les cordons arqués observés. Au cours d'une tempête d'été, les vitesses de dérive estimées dans le cadre d'une telle houle transversale sont comparables à des courants de dérive littorale pouvant atteindre 60 cm/s. Toutefois, certains prétendent que la houle transversale mesurée dans ce cas serait plus vraisemblablement une suite d'une longueur d'onde topographique pré-existante plutôt que la source directe de la formation des cordons.

INTRODUCTION

Complex offshore bar systems are frequent along coastlines with an abundance of beach sediment, and are very common features along the eastern shores of North America. The offshore bars generally run parallel to the shoreline and commonly exhibit undulations in their distance from the shoreline, with longshore spacings which can be regular over many wavelengths. Such bars are termed crescentic bars since they assume in plan the shape of crescents with their horns pointing landwards. They are frequently associated with cusps at the shoreline which have the same wavelength and have points opposite crescentic bar horns (e.g., Hom-ma and Sonu, 1963).

In attempting to explain the existence of these regular longshore features Bowen and Inman (1971) found that boundary layer drift velocities under standing edge waves form convergence zones which assume crescentic shapes in the nearshore zone. Edge waves are free modes of water motion trapped against a shoaling beach by refraction. Their amplitude varies sinusoidally along the shore and diminishes rapidly seawards from the shoreline. Bowen and Inman found that to match the drift velocity convergence zones to observed crescentic bar and cusp wavelengths the edge waves would have to be of low frequency, with periods of about 40 to 60 s. They also described laboratory experiments which confirm that standing edge waves can form crescentic bars and cusps. Sonu (1973), however, has questioned the importance of edge waves in generating regular longshore features, particularly on long unbroken shorelines where there are no obvious longshore boundaries to reflect progressive edge waves. Sonu (1973), Schwartz (1972) and others suggested instead that rhythmic topography on an unbounded coast is caused by sand-wave trains resulting from an instability of the surf-zone bed under longshore currents and waves, just as dunes and antidunes form in fluvial systems.

More recently Guza and Inman (1975), in discussing beach cusps, have suggested that edge waves provide an initial longshore perturbation in the topography, which then grows through positive coupling between the incident waves and the perturbed bed form. They cite laboratory experiments which indicate that edge wave-induced topographic changes in fact provide negative feedback to the edge waves, at least for subharmonic edge waves. Thus they suggest that although initial edge wave motion may be responsible for rhythmic nearshore topography, edge wave motion may become negligible as the topography forms.

Recent measurements of the nearshore velocity field and shoreline run-up on beaches of relatively simple topography have shown that low-frequency edge waves are very common, and their periods, typically from 10 to 70 s, are in the range predicted from observed crescentic bar wavelengths (Huntley, 1976; Huntley et al., 1977; Sasaki et al., 1977; Holman, 1977). These waves, while decaying rapidly offshore, are found in many cases to dominate the velocity field close to the shore. Both progressive and standing edge waves have been observed on long unbounded beaches; these observations suggest that relatively in-substantial longshore boundaries such as subaqueous reefs or even a gently curving shoreline may provide sufficient reflection to produce significant standing waves. The hypothetical relationship between these long-period edge waves and rhythmic nearshore topography has remained untested, however, since no hydrodynamic measurements have previously been reported from beaches where crescentic bar systems are forming or are already present.

The field program discussed here was designed to measure the velocity field on a beach with a well developed complex bar system in order to see whether edge waves are present in such systems and if so, whether they could be considered responsible for the formation of the bar systems.

EDGE WAVES

The theory of edge waves is well established and for beaches of simple profile, in particular a linear slope (Ursell, 1952; Eckart, 1951) and an exponential slope to a constant shallow

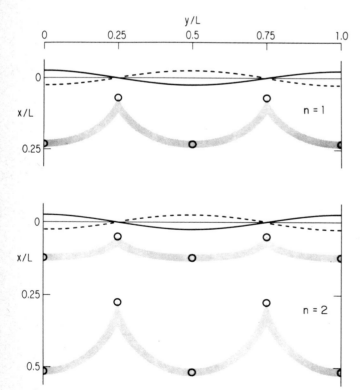

Figure 8.1. *Schematic diagram of the crescentic bars formed by drift velocities under edge waves of modes n = 1 and 2. The horizontal motion of the edge wave at the shoreline is illustrated and suggests a possible mechanism for forming cuspate features (from: Bowen and Inman, 1971).*

depth offshore (Ball, 1967), analytic expressions have been derived to describe the spatial distribution of amplitude and velocities, and to relate the longshore wave length to the wave period (the dispersion relationship). These theories have recently been reviewed in several papers (Bowen and Inman, 1969, 1971; Huntley, 1976; Guza and Inman, 1975). Only the features of significance to the present measurements need be pointed out.

For a beach of linear slope angle β, Ursell (1952) found a dispersion relation of the form

$$L = \frac{gT^2}{2\pi} \sin (2n + 1)\beta \qquad (1)$$

where L is the longshore wave length of the edge wave, T is its period and n is an integer, known as the mode number, which physically specifies the number of zero crossings in the rapid decay of amplitude and velocity with offshore distance. Equation 1 predicts a family of edge wave modes for any specified longshore wave length, each mode having a distinct period.

Bowen and Inman (1971) considered the drift velocities under standing edge waves using a general expression derived by Hunt and Johns (1963) for the drift velocity at the top of a boundary layer for a wave propagating in two horizontal directions. This expression involves quadratic terms in the offshore (u) and longshore (v) velocities and their offshore and longshore gradients. Substituting for u and v expressions appropriate to a single edge wave mode on a beach of linear slope (Eckart, 1951) they found a drift velocity field which has zones of convergence occurring in crescentic bands within one edge wave length of the shore; Figure 8.1, taken from their paper, shows the predicted bands of accretion for modes 1 and 2. They estimate the maximum drift velocity ū for a mode n edge wave with a shoreline amplitude a_n, a frequency (1/period) ν, and a linear beach slope tan β, to be

$$\bar{u} = \frac{a_n^2}{4g} \left(\frac{2\pi\nu}{\tan \beta}\right)^3 \qquad (2)$$

They also show that edge waves of wave length L, which are not synchronous with the incident waves, would produce crescentic bars and cusps with a longshore spacing of L/2 (see also Bowen, 1973).

In distinguishing between edge waves and incident waves in nearshore velocity records, the relative phases between the three orthogonal velocity components are important. Four cases are considered. Purely progressive gravity waves are assumed to travel towards the shore at some oblique angle to the shore normal, and to loose their energy by breaking at the shoreline so that no reflection takes place. Standing gravity waves on the other hand are reflected from the shoreline, though still progressive in the longshore direction. Progressive edge waves travel parallel to the shoreline while standing edge waves have nodes and antinodes at fixed locations along the shore. Using gravity wave theory and Ursell's theory for edge waves the phase relationships between the offshore (u), longshore (v) and vertical (w) velocities shown in Table 8.1 can be deduced. Here 'in phase' can mean a relative phase of 0° or 180° and 'quadrature' a relative phase of 90° or 270°. Although standing gravity waves and progressive edge waves are not distinguished by phase the other cases show a unique combination of phases.

Table 8.1. Phase relationships between velocity components

Wave type	offshore (u) vs longshore (v)	longshore (v) vs vertical (w)	offshore (u) vs vertical (w)
Progressive gravity	in phase	quadrature	quadrature
Standing gravity	quadrature	quadrature	in phase
Progressive edge	quadrature	quadrature	in phase
Standing edge	in phase	in phase	in phase

Several mechanisms for generating edge waves have been suggested. The specific case of subharmonic edge waves (with twice the incident wave period) on reflective beaches has been well studied and the generation mechanism, approximate growth rates and equilibrium amplitudes have been calculated. Long-period edge wave generation has been less studied, primarily because of the difficulty of modelling a system in which wave dissipation is significant. Gallagher (1971) considered edge wave generation by nonlinear interaction between pairs of incident waves with different frequencies and different longshore components of wave number. This idea was further studied by Bowen and Guza (1978), who confirmed the importance of the mechanism by laboratory experiments. Another possible mechanism for putting energy into low-frequency edge waves is through interaction between edge waves of higher frequency (Kenyon, 1970).

In the absence of external constraints the edge wave dispersion relation allows for a continuous range of possible frequencies and wave lengths, and yet observations of regular rhythmic topography suggest that edge waves of a specific wave length and mode frequently dominate on natural beaches. Several hypotheses exist to explain this. Where longshore boundaries to a beach exist, boundary conditions require that only edge waves with an integral number of half wave lengths between boundaries be resonant. Some observations suggest that this is an important constraint in some locations (Bowen and Inman, 1971; Holman, 1977) though it cannot explain the observation of regular spacing on unbounded beaches. On beaches with profiles which level to a constant depth offshore, edge waves at the cutoff frequency may occur preferentially (Ursell, 1952; Huntley, 1976). Generation of edge waves by interaction between waves in a narrow band of incident frequencies should also result in only a relatively few specific edge wave lengths (Bowen and Guza, 1978). However, the relative importance of these constraints in forming rhythmic topography with a single dominant wave length is not resolved.

THE FIELD SITE

Field measurements were made in July 1977 in association with the Geological Survey's Atlantic Geoscience Centre (AGC), Bedford Institute of Oceanography. The site chosen for the measurements was on the Gulf of St. Lawrence

shoreline of New Brunswick, near Tracadie (Fig. 8.2). This coastline forms part of a long, relatively unbroken shore of sandy barrier beaches and spits with a complex system of multiple offshore bars trending parallel to the shoreline but frequently showing crescentic features (Owens, 1975; McCann and Bryant, 1973; Greenwood and Davidson-Arnott, 1975). At least two bar systems were present when the measurements were made. An offshore bar, clearly visible in an aerial photograph (Fig. 8.3), ran approximately 190 m offshore and was essentially linear, while an inshore system 20-30 m offshore was much more complex, and showed distinct longshore variations in offshore distance and relief. At the shoreline itself beach cusps occurred.

Very little mobility of the offshore sand bar was expected during July wave conditions, so it was decided to make velocity measurements in the vicinity of the inshore system. Figure 8.2 shows the location chosen and Figure 8.4 shows the beach profiles to about 80 m offshore near the beginning and end of the measurement period.

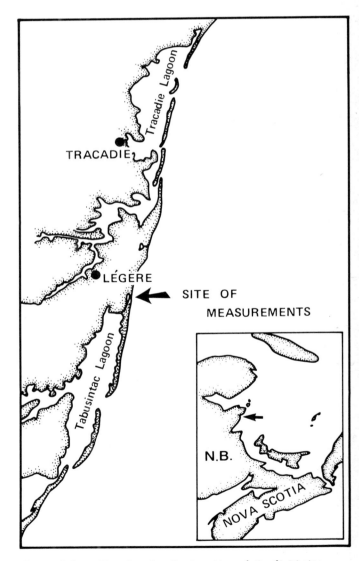

Figure 8.2. *Map showing the location of the field site.*

The beach profiles show the inshore bar system, but clearly changes of profile were considerable. The nature of these changes could be studied more closely using profiles measured by the AGC group on July 10 and July 27. On these dates one profile at the measurement location and two farther south separated alongshore by 20 m intervals, were measured and allow rough contour plots of the beach to be drawn. These are shown in Figure 8.5; the contour values are in centimetres below an arbitrary horizontal datum plane. These plots indicate that the profile changes at the

measurement site were probably the result of alongshore movement of an undulating bar system. The two northernmost profiles for the two days are strikingly similar but form mirror images of each other, and the plots, particularly for July 10, suggest a scale length of about 80 m for the alongshore wave length of the undulations. These observations, while too incomplete to allow definitive conclusions, suggest that the nearshore bar formed a crescentic system, with a wave length of around 80 m, which progressed alongshore with little change in relief.

Further evidence for a regular longshore wave length associated with nearshore features was found from observations of cuspate features at the shoreline. Table 8.2 shows the wave lengths of some of the cusps, measured on July 21; the measurements run from south to north and span the instrumented profile line, which was positioned about 426 m north of the southernmost point. The two larger distances clearly suggest that cusp relief varied and cusp horns were missed at several points but by assuming that these larger distances formed multiples of the basic wave length an average wave length of 75 m with a standard deviation of 7 m is obtained. Since shoreline cusps and offshore crescentic bars are common together, with beach cusp horns and crescentic points lying opposite each other (e.g., Hom-ma and Sonu, 1963) these observations support the suggestion that the nearshore bar formed a relatively regular crescentic bar system with a wave length of about 75 m. Thus, if low-frequency edge waves are responsible for these features the edge wave wave length expected is about 150 m.

It is instructive to compare the position of these crescentic bars with predictions made on the basis of edge wave drift velocities on a beach of linear slope (Fig. 8.1). Clearly modelling the present beach with linear slope is a gross simplification of the true profile and there are indications that the edge wave parameters may be considerably modified by undulations in the profile, especially if

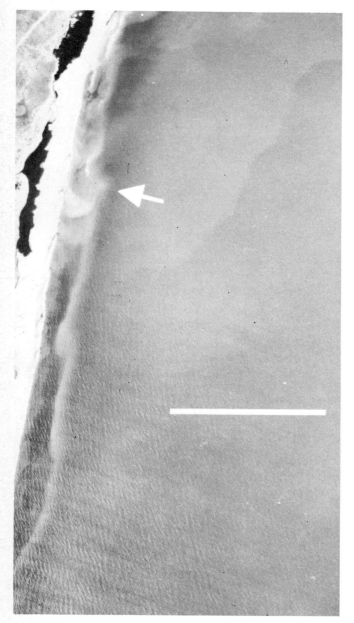

Figure 8.3. *Vertical aerial photograph of the field site taken in August 1976. The outer bar is clearly visible and parts of the inner bar system can also be seen. The bar scale represents 1 km and the arrow points to the approximate site of the measurements.*

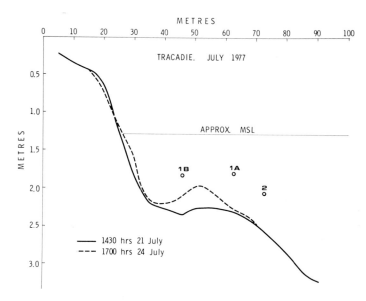

Figure 8.4. *Profiles of the beach taken near the beginning and end of the field program. The open circles show the locations, vertically and horizontally, of the flowmeters.*

they occur at or very close to the shoreline (Holman, pers. com.). Nevertheless, observations of long-period edge waves on a beach with an offshore bar (Huntley, 1976) suggest that the linear slope theory provides a reasonable approximation to the spatial variation of edge wave amplitude and velocities and to the dispersion relationship in such a case.

The arrows on Figure 8.5 show the predicted locations of the farthest inshore and farthest offshore points of the crescentic bars for modes 1 and 2 and a longshore wave length of 150 m. The observed bar position agrees well with predictions for a mode 1 edge wave. In calculating the period of such an edge wave using the dispersion relationship (Equation 1) the choice of a mean linear beach slope is clearly difficult for this profile, but we are helped by the fact that the period depends essentially only upon $\beta^{1/2}$. For edge waves, which decay rapidly offshore within one wave

length, the appropriate mean beach slope should be some form of average over an offshore distance equal to the longshore wave length. Two values are considered. Taking a mean beach slope which ignores the bar system gives a value of approximately 0.038; alternatively if the shoreline slope is the appropriate one, β is 0.074. The periods predicted for a mode 1 edge wave with a longshore wave length of 150 m for these two values of β are 29.1 s and 20.8 s, respectively.

FIELD MEASUREMENTS

The apparatus for the field measurements consisted of three two-component electromagnetic flowmeters (two Marsh-McBirney Inc. Model 711s and one Cushing Engineering Inc. Model 612) and a capacitance elevation sensor. The flowmeters were mounted on aluminum tripods 0.3 m high, which were placed on the seabed and held in position using lead weights (Huntley and Bowen, 1975). Two flowmeters were mounted 0.5 m off the seabed on one tripod, one oriented to measure offshore and vertical flows and the other, horizontally displaced about 0.3 m from the first, oriented to measure offshore and longshore flows; in this way the three orthogonal flow components were measured simultaneously essentially at a single location. For the measurements discussed here, this tripod was placed in the trough shoreward of the inshore bar at position 1B (Fig. 8.4). A second tripod, holding the remaining flowmeter 0.5 m up and oriented to measure offshore and longshore flows, was placed on the seaward slope of the bar at position 2 (Fig. 8.4). The elevation sensor, a capacitance device based on

Table 8.2. Measured beach cusp wavelengths, July 21, 1977

Distances in metres between cusp points
74, 70, 80, 72, 142 (= 2 × 71 ?), 80, 90, 218 (= 3 × 73 ?), 87, 66, 75
Mean and standard deviation of wave length of cusps = 75 ± 7 m.

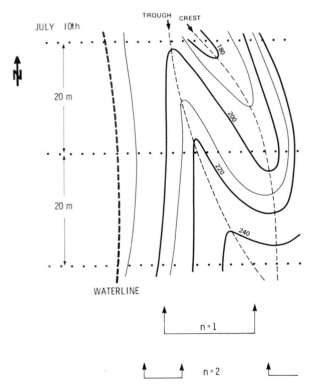

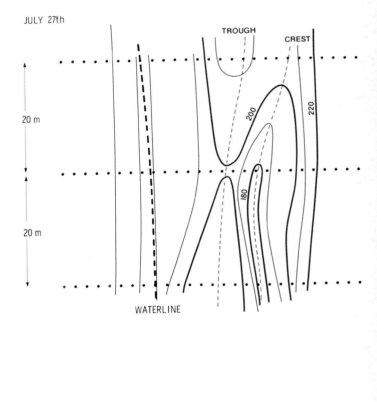

Figure 8.5. *Contour maps of a section of the beach based on three profiles measured on July 10th (a) and July 27th (b). The contours represent vertical distances, in centimetres, below an arbitrary horizontal reference plane. The arrows represent the inshore and offshore extent of crescentic bars predicted for edge waves of mode numbers n = 1 and 2 (see Fig. 8.1). The velocity measurements were made on the northernmost profile line.*

the design of Waddell (1973), was placed in the shoreline surf zone, but was found to change calibration because the wires stretched during the measurements, and has not been used in the present analysis. Cables ran up the beach from each of these sensors to a vehicle parked at the top of the beach, which contained battery-powered electronics and a magnetic tape analogue data logger. The data were subsequently digitized at a sampling interval of 0.33 s for computer analysis.

A variety of summer wave conditions were experienced during our field program. The first record discussed here, TR02, was measured on July 21, a day of predominantly long-crested low waves of period 4.5 to 5.0 s; no breaking on the inshore bar system was observed and the flowmeters were well seaward of the narrow surging surf zone. Record TR03 was measured on July 23, at the height of a mid-summer storm when breakers of about 1.1 m height were breaking on the inner bar and the wave period was irregular but centred at 5 to 6 s; on this day the outer flowmeter (position 2) was approximately at the outer breakerline and the inner flowmeters (position 1B) were in the quiet zone of reforming waves between the bar surf zone and the shoreline surf zone. The storm waves approached the beach from the northeast at an angle of 45 ± 5° to the normal at the bar breakerline, and drove a mean (50 minute average) longshore current of 25 cm/s at position 2 and 57 cm/s at position 1B. The third record TR04 comes from the day after the storm when the incident wave climate was predominantly long-crested swell of period about 7.5 s, breaking at a height of 0.75 m at the inner bar. For this record the inshore bar system had moved, presumably under the southerly longshore currents generated in the storm, to form the second profile of Figure 8.3, partly burying the mount at 1B.

Figure 8.6 is an example of the measurements made from TR03. The irregularity of the incident wave period on this day is apparent in the offshore velocity records. The mean currents have been removed from the longshore current records, but the unsteadiness of these currents is revealed in the residual; flow reverses occasionally at position 2. The vertical component of velocity appears to show considerably more high-frequency variability than the horizontal velocities, perhaps because of turbulent velocities which are made visible at this smaller velocity scale. Large peaks of upward velocity occur under the steep faces of incoming breakers, but there is no clear indication of the rapid drawdown just prior to the arrival of a breaker, as suggested by some authors. The rapid upward velocity as the onshore current increases towards the crest would result in a very sharp peak in the time series of the product of onshore and vertical velocities, which would require very rapid sampling times to resolve satisfactorily, and which consequently would make accurate evaluation of a mean Reynold's stress under combined waves and current difficult.

The different incident wave conditions for the three days are well shown in spectra of the offshore velocities at 1B (Fig. 8.7). The spectrum for TR02 shows that the dominant wave energy occurred at a period of 4.2 s, with a much smaller swell peak at 7.5 s. The incident storm waves of TR03 occupy a broad, high-energy spectral band with periods from 5 to 7 s, while the poststorm swell of TR04 is clearly seen as a dominant peak at 7.5 s period with a smaller broad energy peak at around 4.5 s because of choppy wind waves superimposed on the swell.

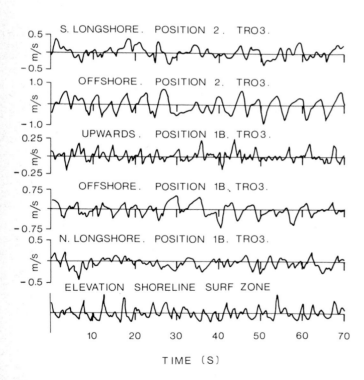

Figure 8.6. *A typical section of record from the flowmeters and elevation sensor. The elevation sensor was uncalibrated.*

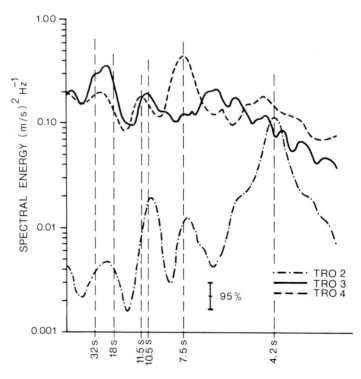

Figure 8.7. *Spectra of offshore velocity at position 1B for records for three days.*

LOW-FREQUENCY ENERGY

Of particular interest in the context of this paper are the clearly defined, low-frequency peaks in the spectra for all three of these days. A broad, low-frequency peak in the period range 18-32 s is present in all records and appears remarkably stable in period range despite the big changes in incident wave conditions. The same may be said of a second low-frequency peak at 10.5-11.5 s period, although there is some shifting of frequency apparent in this peak.

The relative phases of the velocity components have been used to identify the wave motion responsible for these peaks. Figure 8.8 shows coherence and phase spectra between offshore and longshore currents (Fig. 8.8a) and offshore and upward currents (Fig. 8.8b); the 32 s line in Figure 8.7 corresponds to a frequency of 0.031 Hz, 18 s to 0.056 Hz, and 11 s to 0.091 Hz. Figure 8.8a has significant coherence in the lower frequency band and a coherence peak at about 0.11 Hz, a somewhat higher frequency than the power spectral peak but within its band width. Phase values are clearly centred about 0° for frequencies above 0.1 Hz. Below 0.1 Hz lower coherences result in unsteadier phases, but in the low-frequency band the phase again centres around 0° with an uncertainty of about ± 30°. Comparing this with the predictions in Table 8.1 suggests that either progressive gravity waves or standing edge waves were occurring in all frequency bands. Figure 8.8b shows significant coherence for all frequencies above 0.08 Hz but the lowest frequency band has an unsteady coherence level, which is significant at the high-frequency end but barely significant at the lower frequency end. The phase shows a dramatic change at a frequency of 0.075 Hz. Above this frequency the phase is very close to 270°, suggesting, when taken with Figure 8.8a, that the energy in this range was due to the progressive gravity waves. Below 0.075 Hz the phase in the low-frequency band falls to around 0° where the coherence is significant, though becoming closer to -45° at the low-frequency side of the band where the coherence is low. A zero phase here suggests, when taken with Figure 8.8a, that the lower of the low-frequency bands of energy is the result of standing edge wave motion. Both coherence and phase plots show significant coherence also at frequencies below the resolution of the spectra, and the power spectra of Figure 8.7 also suggest a rise in spectral energy at very low frequencies; much longer record lengths would be required to identify the nature of this energy.

The data of Figure 8.8, therefore, suggest that the peak of energy centred around 11 s period is due to progressive incident waves. A period of 11 s is surprisingly long for incident waves on the Gulf of St. Lawrence coast of New Brunswick, where the longest fetch lengths are less than 600 km, from the northeast. However, meteorological observations summarized by the Atmospheric Environment Service, Toronto (quoted in Armon and McCann, 1977) show that the significant wave period exceeds 9 s 7 per cent of the time, predominantly during northeasterly fall storms, so waves of this long period certainly do occur.

Despite the relative constancy of the period range of the low-frequency edge wave band, it is clear from Figure 8.7 that energy contained in this band is strongly dependent on the total energy in the incident wave spectrum. In quantifying the energy in the edge wave band it is necessary to make some estimate of the bandwidth appropriate to the band, and integrate under the spectrum over this band. The true bandwidth of the low-frequency bands cannot be accurately deduced from Figure 8.7 since the resolution bandwidth of the spectra is about 0.017 Hz and the

bandwidths of the observed low-frequency peaks are only about 2 or 3 times this. However a higher resolution spectrum, for TR03, with a resolution bandwidth of 0.0044 Hz but with commensurately larger 95 per cent confidence limits on the size of the spectral curve (Fig. 8.9), shows that the energy level in the edge wave band is relatively flat between 0.028 and 0.058 Hz and falls off rapidly on either side. We have therefore chosen to integrate energy between the lower and upper halfpower frequencies of this band, and have assumed that edge wave energy outside this bandwidth is negligible. For TR04, where the low-frequency side of the edge wave band does not fall to half the peak level before rising again to the very low frequency level, we have taken the appropriate bandwidth to be twice the width from the peak to the upper half power level.

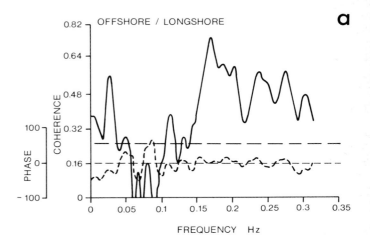

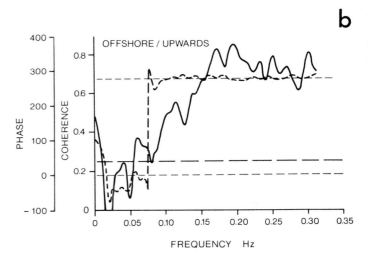

Figure 8.8. *Coherence and phase spectra between offshore and longshore (a) and offshore and upward (b) records from position 1B. The solid line shows the coherence and the dashed line the phase. The horizontal heavy dashed line represents the 95 per cent confidence level for zero coherence; the fine dashed lines mark phases of 0° and 270°.*

Integrating over these bandwidths gives the results for mean square amplitudes of offshore velocities shown in Table 8.3. The total mean square amplitudes are the result of integrating the area under the spectra over the whole frequency range out to the Nyquist frequency of 1.5 Hz. Mean square amplitudes of the 11 s swell peak are also shown for comparison. The large value of edge wave energy during the summer storm is strikingly apparent. Between TR02 and TR03 the energy in the edge wave band increased by a factor of 66 to contribute 19 per cent of the total wave energy, while the total energy level increased by a factor of 8 and the 11 s peak by a factor of 15; between TR04 and TR02 these factors are 49 for the edge wave band, 13 for the 11 s swell peak and 10 for the overall energy.

Thus it appears that edge wave energy at low frequencies increases greatly during storm conditions. Holman et al. (in press) have made extensive measurements of low-frequency energy in the nearshore velocity field on a beach of relatively simple topography and their observations also suggest a rapid increase in low-frequency energy with incident wave energy. Indirect support for this observation may also come from the common observation that crescentic bar systems and cusps are most active during storms

(e.g., Sonu, 1973). Guza and Inman (1975), in dicussing beach cusps, suggested that two different regimes occur in the action of edge waves to produce rhythmic topography, depending on whether the incoming waves are mainly reflective or dissipative. In reflective systems, with surging and surging/plunging breakers, subharmonic zero-mode edge waves appear to dominate but disappear rapidly as incident wave amplitude increases and wave dissipation by breaking increases above a critical level. Observations in the field confirm that subharmonic edge waves can occur on reflective beaches (Huntley and Bowen, 1973). The present observations show that in dissipative systems, on the other hand, edge waves with periods much longer than the incident waves dominate, and their amplitude increases with incident wave amplitude.

The bandwidth of the edge wave peak encompasses both the 29 s (β = 0.038) and the 21 s (β = 0.074) periods predicted for mode 1 edge waves of wave length 150 m, such as are expected to generate the observed crescentic bars. However, the edge wave band is very broad and there is no clear evidence for a single peak corresponding to either of these periods. In fact, Figure 8.9 suggests rather that the edge wave band is somewhat flat topped, with the energy falling off distinctly on either side of the band.

If we calculate the frequencies of 150 m edge waves of modes n = 1 to 4 using the smaller beach slope, they span the low-frequency band, though the resolution bandwidth of the spectra, even in Figure 8.9, is insufficient to resolve individual peaks corresponding to these modes. The good agreement between these predicted frequencies and the observed edge wave band suggests that, rather than a single mode, several modes are being excited in this band.

DRIFT VELOCITIES

It is of considerable interest to estimate the size of the drift velocities under the low-frequency edge waves observed on this beach. Although it is not clear that the observed edge waves were responsible for forming the beach cusps and crescentic bars, the rhythmic system itself appears to have moved slowly alongshore, essentially intact, during July and a drift velocity field must therefore have existed to maintain the crescentic features during this longshore movement. Such a drift velocity field may be due either to interaction between the incoming waves and the bottom topography forming rip currents and nearshore circulation cells (Sonu, 1973), or to boundary layer effects under the edge waves themselves (Bowen and Inman, 1971), or to a combination of both effects. In this section the magnitude of the edge wave drift velocities is estimated and compared with observed mean flows well above the boundary layer, in order to assess the relative importance of these two effects.

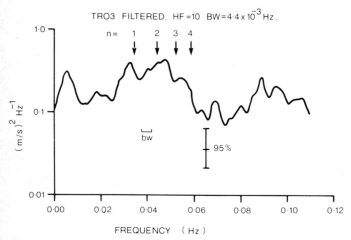

Figure 8.9. *A high resolution spectrum of offshore velocity at position 1B. The interval marked "bw" represents the resolution bandwidth. Vertical arrows show predicted frequencies of modes n = 1 to 4 edge waves with wavelength 150 m.*

Table 8.3. Mean square offshore velocity amplitudes, position 1B

Run ID	Total $(m/s)^2 \times 10^{-3}$	11 s peak $(m/s)^2 \times 10^{-3}$	% of total	Edge wave band $(m/s)^2 \times 10^{-3}$	% of total
TR02	6.9	0.33	4.8	0.15	2.2
TR03	54.0	4.9	9.1	10.0	18.5
TR04	67.0	4.4	6.6	7.4	11.0

The present data set (from just two points on an offshore line) is unfortunately too incomplete to allow mapping of the velocity field in the detail required to estimate the spatial gradients of velocities in the direct Hunt and Johns expression for drift velocity used by Bowen and Inman (1971). Furthermore, application of the Bowen and Inman edge wave drift velocity expressions is complicated by two factors. First we might expect that the edge wave velocity fields for a beach profile containing a well developed bar system could deviate markedly from velocity fields predicted by assuming that the beach profile was linear with the average slope (Holman, pers. com.). Secondly their theory applies to a single edge wave mode. When several modes are present, such as is observed here, the drifts for each mode cannot be directly summed to form the total drift velocity since the boundary layer expressions are obviously nonlinear in the orbital velocities. Accurate determination of the edge wave drift velocities therefore requires either much more extensive measurements along both offshore and longshore lines or a numerical calculation using the observed beach profile and assuming that particular edge wave modes were present on this beach. Nevertheless, we might hope to get at least an order of magnitude estimate of the maximum drift velocities by ignoring these complications and applying the Bowen and Inman theory (Equation 2) to each edge wave mode separately.

Using the data for the day of maximum low-frequency energy, TR03, we begin by assuming that the energy is equally distributed among the first four edge wave modes (Fig. 8.9). The rms amplitude of the offshore current at position 1B for each mode is therefore 5 cm/s, i.e., 7 cm/s peak amplitude. The low-frequency peak at position 2 is much less clearly defined than at position 1B, possibly due to a stronger, slowly varying mean flow system on the outer flank of the bar (see below) resulting in a higher overall low-frequency energy. Nevertheless, the energy level in the edge wave band suggests a peak amplitude of 5.3 cm/s. These measurements were taken close to high tide when the instruments were 27 m and 53.5 m offshore, respectively. To estimate maximum drift velocities under these waves, linear beach profile theory has been used to extrapolate the measured velocities to shoreline velocities $u(0)$. This offshore velocity is then used to estimate a_n, which is finally used in Equation 2 to provide an estimate of the maximum drift velocity. Generally a correction to the extrapolated velocity $u(0)$ would have to be made if the measurement position did not coincide with an offshore velocity antinode of the standing edge wave. However, for the TR03 data no low-frequency peaks were observed in the longshore spectra, and the general level of the longshore spectra in the low-frequency band suggests that measurements were made within about 15 m of an offshore current antinode, so that any corrections to $u(0)$ are estimated to amount to less than 20 per cent. This is consistent with the fact that measurements were made in a trough between two crescentic bar horns, where an offshore velocity antinode and longshore velocity node occurs. We have therefore assumed that the extrapolated value of $u(0)$ corresponds approximately to the value at an antinode.

The results of these calculations are shown in Table 8.4. The amplification factor k is the amount, based on linear slope theory, by which the measured values are multiplied to obtain the estimated value of $u(0)$. The values for $u(0)$ and a_n calculated by extrapolation from position 1B and position 2 are similar, suggesting that the use of theory based on a linear slope provides a reasonable estimate of the real offshore variation of velocity, at least at the offshore distance of the flowmeters. The exception to this occurs for

Table 8.4. Drift velocities under low-frequency edge waves

Mode	Position	Amplification factor k	$u(0)$	a_n	ν	$\bar{u}$
			cm/s	cm	Hz	cm/s
1	1B	13	92	16.4	0.034	12.0
	2	17	88	15.7		11.0
2	1B	10.5	73	10.0	0.044	9.9
	2	16	86	11.8		13.7
3	1B	7.5	53	6.2	0.052	6.2
	2	56	295	34.3		190.7
4	1B	15	106	10.9	0.059	27.9
	2	19	100	10.3		24.9

position 2 and mode number 3, where the simple theory suggests that the sensor is very close to a node of offshore velocity and the amplification factor is therefore large. Since the resolution of the spectrum is insufficient to resolve energy due to individual modes such a node could not be observed and the assumption of equipartition of low-frequency energy between the modes results in a large value of $u(0)$ and a_n. The values of a_n and $\bar{u}$ are calculated using the mean beach slope, $\tan\beta = 0.038$; if the foreshore slopes, $\tan\beta = 0.074$, were used instead, a_n would be multiplied and $\bar{u}$ would be divided by the ratio $0.074/0.038 \approx 2$.

The largest values of drift velocity occur for mode 4, mainly because of the ν^3 dependence of $\bar{u}$. The drift velocity values of Table 8.4 can be compared to measured mean longshore currents for TR03 of 57 cm/s at position 1B and 25 cm/s at position 2 and onshore mean currents of less than 5 cm/s (the resolution limit of the instrument) at position 1B and about 11 cm/s at position 2. In view of the assumptions involved in deriving drift velocities under the low-frequency edge waves the drift velocities in Table 8.4 must be considered only as order of magnitude estimates, but they do nevertheless suggest that they are of comparable magnitude to mean flows due to longshore currents and mean circulation cells.

DISCUSSION

These observations show that edge waves can exist in the presence of nearshore rhythmic topography and their periods agree well with the long periods required to generate that topography. However, two factors argue against the measured edge waves being directly responsible for the observed bars and cusps.

The first factor is the insensitivity of the edge wave frequency band to the incident wave climate. In the absence of pre-existing topography, both proposed mechanisms for the generation of long-period edge waves, interaction between different wave trains (Gallagher, 1971; Bowen and Guza, 1978) and a cascade from higher frequency edge waves (Kenyon, 1970) indicate that periods generated are strongly dependent on incident wave conditions. Mechanisms which have been proposed to single out specific long-period edge waves do not appear appropriate on this beach either. There are no obvious longshore boundaries which might cause a resonance for standing waves of 150 m wave length. Cutoff mode periods do not fit this broad band either. Long beach profiles, extending to 400 m offshore, suggest that the profile does flatten to almost constant depth within 150 m of the shoreline, but only the n = 2 cutoff mode occurs within the observed band. The first mode edge wave has a period of 39 s and a longshore wave length of 270 m. It is hard to escape the conclusion that the rhythmic topography itself is controlling the wave length of edge waves induced on this beach.

This conclusion is supported by the second feature of the observed edge wave band, that it appears to be made up of several edge wave modes whose only common feature is a wave length of about 150 m. No published theoretical work on edge wave generation has considered the importance of topographic effects, though some laboratory experiments (Guza and Inman, 1975) appear to suggest a negative feedback between edge waves and a growing rhythmic topography, at least for subharmonic edge waves. The present observations, on the other hand, suggest that the interaction between incident waves and a pre-existing topography can generate the edge waves of wave length appropriate to that topography and that these waves can become large during high-incident wave conditions. Surprisingly, however, the edge wave mode fitting the observed topography most closely does not appear to dominate over other low modes of the same wave length.

The observation of low mode number edge waves in the low-frequency band is consistent with previous indications that the low modes are preferentially generated (Huntley, 1976; Holman, 1977), though for waves generated by nonlinear interaction between incident waves Bowen and Guza (1978) suggested that many modes, including high modes, may be excited. It is not clear why the observed band shows a rapid fall in energy above the 4th mode frequency.

Drift velocities estimated for these low-frequency edge waves are surprisingly large and show that edge wave motion can provide velocities comparable with nearshore circulation cell velocities and sufficiently large to generate and move cuspate and crescentic features particularly during storms. More accurate estimates of drift velocities on this kind of complex topography could be made by mapping low-frequency velocity fields in more detail, either by much more extensive instrumentation in the field or possibly by numerical calculation using the observed beach profiles.

There remains the unresolved problem of how the rhythmic topography, pre-existing these measurements, was originally formed. One possibility suggested by the spectra (Fig. 8.7) is that the two swell peaks observed in the TR02 and TR04 records at about 7.5 s and 11 s could interact to form mode 1 edge waves at their beat period, and these waves could have a longshore wave length of 150 m if the swell waves approached from specific angles. Bowen and Guza (1978) looked at interactions between pairs of waves approaching a beach and, following Gallagher (1971), suggested that edge waves can be generated if the difference frequency and difference of the longshore components of the wave numbers of the approaching waves satisfy the edge wave dispersion relation. They found that

$$\nu_e^2 = |\nu_1^2 \sin \alpha_1 - \nu_2^2 \sin \alpha_2| \sin (2n+1) \beta$$

where ν_e, ν_1 and ν_2 are the edge wave and incident swell frequencies, respectively, and α_1 and α_2 are angles (to the beach normal) of approach of the incident swell waves in deep water.

Using this equation, and assuming that the longer swell waves must approach from the longest fetch direction, between Anticosti Island and the Madeleine Islands, it is possible to calculate the directions of approach required of 7.5 s waves in order to be able to generate the correct edge waves. Two possible angles of approach in deep water are found, N32°E and E22°S. Although fetch is limited by Anticosti Island, the first of these directions is consistent with observations during our measurements that these swell waves approached the beach approximately from the northeast. The second direction faces towards Cape Breton Island, to the south of the Madeleine Islands, and forms the only other appreciable fetch length from this beach. Either direction seems plausible therefore.

The basic drawback of this hypothesis, however, is the high sensitivity of the edge wave to the incident swell frequencies, and their angles of approach. The interaction equation suggests that the edge wave wave length for a particular mode (which is inversely proportional to the square of the frequency) depends on something like the difference of the squares of swell frequencies, and is thus extremely sensitive to small changes in these frequencies. In fact, interactions between different components within the bandwidths of the two swell peaks could change the wave length by at least a factor of two.

As a result of the present observations of edge waves in the presence of rhythmic topography, with bottom drift velocities estimated to be appreciable, we are one step closer to establishing a link between edge waves and the formation of such topography. However, since the definitive field experiment, measurement of the nearshore velocity field during the formation of a predicted rhythmic topography, will probably have to rely on serendipity, further theoretical work on the coupled water-sediment system is needed to establish whether edge waves alone can allow rhythmic topography to grow to the commonly observed sizes.

Acknowledgments

Considerable logistic help and supporting data for this field experiment was provided by the Coastal Geodynamics Section of the Geological Survey's Atlantic Geoscience Centre, Bedford Institute of Oceanography, and without this assistance the field program could not have been carried out. The author particularly thanks Brian McCann and Gerry Reinson, with Dave Froebel and others, for providing this support and for helpful discussions. This work was funded by a Research Agreement with the Department of Energy, Mines and Resources, and by the National Research Council of Canada.

References

Armon, J.W. and McCann, S.B.
1977:   The establishment of an inshore wave climate and longshore sediment transport rates from hourly wind data; Discussion paper No. 9. Department of Geography, McMaster University, Hamilton, Ont.

Ball, F.K.
1967:   Edge waves in an ocean of finite depth; Deep Sea Research, v. 14, p. 79 - 88.

Bowen, A.J.
1973:   Edge waves and the littoral environment; in Proceedings of the 13th Coastal Engineering Conference, p. 1313 - 1320, Council on Wave Research, London.

Bowen, A.J. and Guza, R.T.
1978: Edge waves and surf beat; Journal of Geophysical Research, v. 83, p. 1913 - 1920.

Bowen, A.J. and Inman, D.L.
1969: Rip currents; 2 laboratory and field observations; Journal of Geophysical Research, v. 74, p. 5479 - 5490.
1971: Edge waves and crescentic bars; Journal of Geophysical Research, v. 76, p. 8662 - 8671.

Eckart, C.
1951: Surface waves in water of variable depth; Wave report, Scripps Institution of Oceanography, S.I.O. ref. 51-12. 100, 99 p.

Gallagher, G.
1971: Generation of surf beat by non-linear wave interactions; Journal of Fluid Mechanics, v. 49, p. 1 - 20.

Greenwood, B. and Davidson-Arnott, R.G.D.
1975: Marine bars and nearshore sedimentary processes, Kouchibouguac Bay, New Brunswick; in Nearshore Sediment Dynamics and Sedimentation, Hails and Carr, eds.; Wiley, London.

Guza, R.T. and Inman, D.L.
1975: Edge waves and beach cusps; Journal of Geophysical Research, v. 80, p. 2997 - 3012.

Holman, R.A.
1977: Low frequency energy in the nearshore environment. EOS; Transactions, American Geophysical Union, v. 58, no. 6, p. 403.

Holman, R.A., Huntley, D.A. and Bowen, A.J.
in press: Infragravity waves in storm conditions; in Proceedings of the 16th Coastal Engineering Conference, American Society of Civil Engineers, New York.

Hom-ma and Sonu, C.
1963: Rhythmic pattern of longshore bars related to sediment characteristics; in Proceedings of the 8th Coastal Engineering Conference, Council on Wave Research, London, p. 248 - 278.

Hunt, J.N. and Johns, B.
1963: Currents induced by tides and gravity waves; Tellus, v. 15, no. 4, p. 343 - 351.

Huntley, D.A.
1976: Long period waves on a natural beach; Journal of Geophysical Research, v. 81, p. 6441 - 6449.

Huntley, D.A. and Bowen, A.J.
1973: Field observations of edge waves; Nature, v. 243, no. 5403, p. 160 - 162.
1975: Field measurements of nearshore velocities; in Proceedings of the 14th Coastal Engineering Conference, American Society of Civil Engineers, New York, p. 538 - 557.

Huntley, D.A., Guza, R.T. and Bowen, A.J.
1977: A universal form for shoreline run-up spectra?; Journal of Geophysical Research, v. 82, p. 2577 - 2581.

Kenyon, K.E.
1970: A note on conservative edge wave interactions; Deep-Sea Research, v. 17, p. 197 - 201.

McCann, S.B. and Bryant, E.A.
1973: Beach changes and wave conditions, New Brunswick; in Proceedings of the 13th Coastal Engineering Conference, American Society of Civil Engineers, New York, p. 1293 - 1304.

Owens, E.H.
1975: Barrier beaches and sediment transport in the southern Gulf of St. Lawrence; in Proceedings of the 14th Coastal Engineering Conference, American Society of Civil Engineers, New York, p. 1177 - 1193.

Sasaki, T., Horikawa, K. and Kubota, S.
1977: A study on nearshore currents (report No. 5); Long period fluctuations in nearshore currents; in Proceedings of the 24th Conference on Coastal Engineering in Japan; cited in: Horikawa, K., 1977, Nearshore current treatments and their applications to engineering problems, in Proceedings of the 4th P.O.A.C. Conference, Memorial University of Newfoundland, St. John's.

Schwartz, M.L.
1972: Theoretical approach to the origin of beach cusps; Geological Society of America, Bulletin, v. 83, no. 4, p. 1115, 1116.

Sonu, C.J.
1973: Three-dimensional beach changes; Journal of Geology, v. 81, p. 42 - 64.

Ursell, F.
1952: Edge waves on a sloping beach; Royal Society, London, Proceedings, Series A, p. 79 - 98.

Waddell, E.
1973: Dynamics of swash and implication to beach response; Coastal Studies Institute, Louisiana State University Technical Report No. 139, March 1973.

9. THE SEDIMENTARY CHARACTER OF THE MINAS BASIN, BAY OF FUNDY

C.L. Amos and B.F.N. Long
Atlantic Geoscience Centre, Geological Survey of Canada,
Dartmouth, Nova Scotia

Amos, C.L. and Long, B.F.N., The sedimentary character of the Minas Basin, Bay of Fundy; in The Coastline of Canada, S.B. McCann, editor; Geological Survey of Canada, Paper 80-10, p. 153-180, 1980.

Abstract

An analysis of the present sediment character and distribution, and sediment budgets and transport conditions was made. The various physical processes that affect these features were measured. The materials are derived mainly from cliffs bordering Minas Basin. They are well mixed within the water column. Most of the material within the intertidal zone is sand whereas the subtidal zone comprises glacial marine silts overlain by postglacial marine sediments. The study indicates a steady increase in the supply of material since 6300 B.P.

Résumé

L'auteur analyse la nature et la distribution des sédiments en question, le bilan sédimentaire et les modes de transport. Il mesure aussi les différents processus physiques qui influent sur ces phénomènes. Les matériaux proviennent principalement des falaises en bordure du bassin Minas et sont bien mélangés aux colonnes d'eau. Dans la zone intertidale, il y a principalement du sable et, dans la zone subtidale, des silts marins glaciaires recouverts de sédiments marins post-glaciaires. L'étude démontre que les matériaux s'accumulent de façon constante depuis 6 300 B.P.

INTRODUCTION

The Minas Basin, a semienclosed, macrotidal embayment at the head of the Bay of Fundy, Nova Scotia, is characterized principally by semidiurnal tides that have extreme tidal ranges of 16.3 m (Dawson, 1917). Such tides induce currents with maximum speeds from 2 to 3 m s^{-1} in the basin itself to more than 5 m s^{-1} (Cameron, 1961) in restricted channelways such as Minas Passage (Fig. 9.1a).

Evidence of sedimentation and sediment movement is abundant in the region. Widespread intertidal sandflats and sand wave fields are visible during low water (Fig. 9.2a, b). The tidal waters are red because high concentrations of suspended material are maintained and transported in suspension by turbulent tidal flows.

Because it is highly dynamic the region has received considerable attention from researchers interested in the behaviour of sediments under the influence of currents. More recently research has been stimulated by the potential of tidal power development. Generally studies have been site- or topic-specific and consequently the regional patterns of sedimentation remain largely unknown. In view of this a study was undertaken during 1975-77 to relate "the many parts of the Minas Basin system to the whole". The research addressed such aspects as the post-glacial evolution of the Minas Basin system, the sediment budget, and the sediment transport and depositional characters of the system.

PREVIOUS RESEARCH

Summaries of the major papers dealing with the geological, hydrological, and sedimentological aspects of the Minas Basin are to be found in a series of recently completed Ph.D. theses (Dalrymple, 1977; Knight, 1977; Lambiase, 1977). A collection of general papers dealing with many environmental aspects of the Bay of Fundy is to be found in *Fundy Tidal Power and the Environment* (Daborn, 1977).

PHYSIOGRAPHY

The general physiography of the Bay of Fundy region was documented by Goldthwait (1924) and later by Crosby (1962) and the Atlantic Tidal Power Programming Board (ATPPB) (1969). The general geological evolution of the system is described by Swift and Lyall (1968) and more recently by Fader et al. (1977) and Stephens (1977). Stephens has likened the structural setting of the Minas Basin system to the Red Sea-Sinai system. He suggested that large-scale earth movements have controlled the general, physiographically distinct, development of the Bay of Fundy.

The Minas Basin system is subdivided into several physiographic regions.

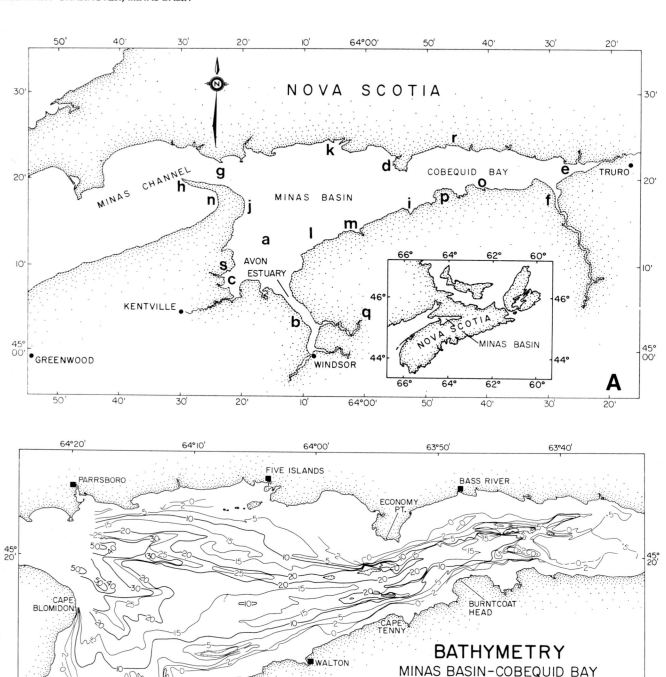

BATHYMETRY
MINAS BASIN-COBEQUID BAY

BASED ON SURVEY CONDUCTED
DURING JUNE 1976

DEPTH CONTOURS IN METRES
BELOW CHART DATUM

1. Minas Basin, *sensu stricto* is an enclosed basin comprising most of the Minas Basin system. It includes Windsor Bay and for convenience is considered to include the Avon, the Cornwallis and the Gaspereau river estuaries. It is surrounded by steep, eroding cliffs of variable composition (Fig. 9.2c). These cliffs have regressed up to 7 km and a marginal, smooth, wave-cut platform has been formed. Most of this platform is visible in the intertidal zone during periods of low tide, when the platform can be observed to be overlain by ephemeral features such as migrating sand wave fields (Klein, 1970), gravel and cobble storm beaches (Owens, 1977), the occasional pocket beach, and transgressing mudflats and salt marshes (Grant, 1970a, b; Fig. 9.2d). In contrast, the subtidal region is typically hummocky and irregular. The basic dimensions of the system are listed in Table 9.1.

2. Cobequid Bay is east of the Minas Basin and is separated from it by a 'narrow' to the south of Economy Point. It is considered to include the Salmon and Shubenacadie river estuaries. During periods of low tide, two thirds of the bay is exposed, revealing a wide expanse of sand bars (Amos and Joice, 1977; Dalrymple et al., 1975) and fringing salt marshes, partly enclosed within reclaimed marshlands and sections of low erosive cliffs.

3. Minas Passage connects the Minas Basin system to the Bay of Fundy, *sensu stricto*. It is 11 km long and 4 km wide, and is the conduit for the flooding and ebbing tidal waters of the Minas Basin. It is scoured of sediment by turbulent 5 m s^{-1} currents, generated by the passage of a tidal prism the volume of which may be as much as 15.3 km^3. The passage is contained between a fault scarp along its northern margin and an arcuate promontory to the south known as Cape Split.

METHODOLOGY

Conceptual model

The dynamic sedimentary character of any marine environment may be considered to be the response of that environment in terms of sediment erosion, transport and deposition, to the processes active at that time, and to the cumulative effect of the process/response relation with respect to time. This concept is expressed graphically in Figure 9.3a and forms the basis of this research. The three axes displayed in the figure represent process, result and time. It is considered that any physical phenomenon may be expressed in this manner. However, the processes and subsequent results will vary according to the researchers' specific interest.

In the present study, the processes measured were the major hydrological controls. The results measured were sediment erosion, transport and deposition, and the time framework considered, for convenience, was from the end of the glacial period to the present. From a conceptual point of view, the research was considered to fall within three areas of study.

1. The present sediment character (Fig. 9.3b). The sediment character was defined in terms of the budget of materials of varying sizes, their sources and the types of sediments found presently occurring at the seabed. Where applicable, sediments were classified into biogenic, organic and clastic types. However, no geochemical analyses were undertaken.

Facing page

a. *Windsor Bay*
b. *Avon River estuary*
c. *Cornwallis, Habitant and Canard River estuaries*
d. *Economy Point*
e. *Salmon River estuary*
f. *Shubenacadie River estuary*
g. *Minas Passage*
h. *Cape Split*
i. *Cape Tenny*
j. *Cape Blomidonk*
k. *Five Islands*
l. *Hog's Back*
m. *Walton Bar*
n. *Scot's Bay*
o. *Noel Head*
p. *Burntcoat Heads*
q. *Herbert River*
r. *Bass River*
s. *Kingsport*

Figure 9.1A. *The geographic location of the Minas Basin system and the associated place names cited throughout the text.*

Figure 9.1B. *The contoured bathymetry of the Minas Basin system in metres below Burntcoat Head chart datum (i.e. 9.13 m below GSCD). The bathymetry is based on 1976 soundings and has been tidally corrected both for stage of the tide and for spatial variations in tidal amplitude and phase.*

Table 9.1 A summary of the general dimensions of the Minas Basin system.

Length (max)	77 km	
Width (max)	31 km	
Depth (av)	15 m	(below lowest low water)
Perimeter	320 km	
Surface area	(km^3)	
Minas Basin	805	(intertidal 172; subtidal 633)
Cobequid Bay	306	(intertidal 186; subtidal 120)
Intertidal	358	
Subtidal	753	
Saltings	107	(Grant, pers. com.)
Volume	(km^3)	
Minas Basin	22.8	(intertidal 13.3; subtidal 9.5)
Cobequid Bay	3.2	(intertidal 2.0; subtidal 1.2)
Intertidal	15.3	(max)
Subtidal	10.7	(min)
Cross-section area	(m^2)	
Minas Passage	3.4 x 10^5	(below mean sea level)
Economy Point/ Cape Tenny	1.5 x 10^5	(below mean sea level)

Mean chart datum (lowest low water) = GSCD -8.126 m.
Error limits ±10% (P < 0.05).

Opposite

Figure 9.2 A. *Sand waves on Economy Point sand bar occurring during the deployment of radioisotopic glass (within the lead container) during October 1977. A scintillometer (in view) is used to monitor the radioactive contamination throughout the experiment.*

Figure 9.2 B. *Sand waves and megaripples on Economy Point sand bar. The orientation of the sand waves show a general direction of sediment transport taking place from left to right.*

Above

Figure 9.2C. *The erosive cliffs at Five Islands. The cliffs are 152 m high and are composed of Triassic sandstone overlain by Cretaceous basalt.*

Figure 9.2D. *Recent marginal salt marshes and mud flats developed in Windsor Bay. Cape Blomidon is in the background.*

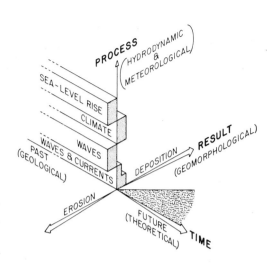

Figure 9.3A. *The conceptual model relating process and the ensuant result through time. This model formed the basis of the study. Several of the particular parameters measured have been included as examples.*

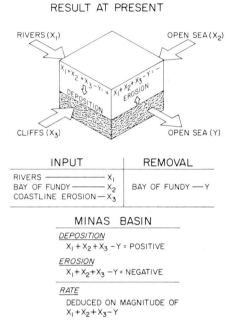

Figure 9.3B. *The components measured in the sediment budget study.*

MODEL I
SEDIMENT BUDGET
IN THE MINAS BASIN
RESULT AT PRESENT

INPUT		REMOVAL
RIVERS ——————— X_1		
BAY OF FUNDY ——— X_2		BAY OF FUNDY —— Y
COASTLINE EROSION — X_3		

MINAS BASIN

DEPOSITION
$X_1 + X_2 + X_3 - Y$ = POSITIVE

EROSION
$X_1 + X_2 + X_3 - Y$ = NEGATIVE

RATE
DEDUCED ON MAGNITUDE OF
$X_1 + X_2 + X_3 - Y$

MODEL II
SEDIMENT BUDGET
IN THE MINAS BASIN
RESULT FOR PAST,
PRESENT AND FUTURE

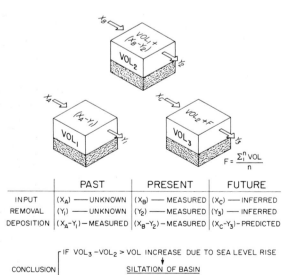

	PAST	PRESENT	FUTURE
INPUT	(X_A) —— UNKNOWN	(X_B) —— MEASURED	(X_C) —— INFERRED
REMOVAL	(Y_1) —— UNKNOWN	(Y_2) —— MEASURED	(Y_3) —— INFERRED
DEPOSITION	(X_A-Y_1) -MEASURED	(X_B-Y_2) -MEASURED	(X_C-Y_3) -PREDICTED

CONCLUSION
IF $VOL_3 - VOL_2$ > VOL INCREASE DUE TO SEA LEVEL RISE
↓
SILTATION OF BASIN

IF $VOL_3 - VOL_2$ < VOL INCREASE DUE TO SEA LEVEL RISE
↓
ENLARGEMENT OF BASIN

Figure 9.3C. *The components considered in the postglacial reconstruction of the sediment budget.*

MODEL III
SEDIMENT BUDGET
IN THE MINAS BASIN
TRANSPORT AND
PROCESS/RESPONSE MECHANISM

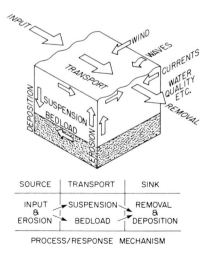

SOURCE	TRANSPORT	SINK
INPUT & EROSION	SUSPENSION / BEDLOAD	REMOVAL & DEPOSITION

PROCESS/RESPONSE MECHANISM

Figure 9.3D. *The components measured in the study of the sources, the transport and the ultimate deposition sites of sediments moved both as bedload and suspended load.*

2. The past sediment character (Fig. 9.3c). The nature of the present-day sediment character of Minas Basin largely depends on its historical development. Many of the features observed today are considered the cumulative effect of conditions over a time interval conveniently considered to have begun during deglaciation of the region. Vibrocores, gravity cores and seismic surveying of the post-glacial sedimentary column were conducted. Sedimentation rates following deglaciation were calculated from volumetric estimates of deposition between carbon-dated (total carbon-14) horizons. Inferences were drawn on the tidal and wave processes active during each period of sedimentation examined.

3. The processes controlling the sedimentary character (Fig. 9.3d). The interaction of process and result behave according to physical laws that are considered constant through time. However, the results of a complex interaction of several processes are not so readily definable (Buller and McManus, 1976). The interaction of the hydrological, meteorological, biological and geological processes need not have been constant through time. Hydrological parameters such as tide height, current speed and direction, temperature, salinity and wave spectra were measured periodically, in most cases for not less than one complete tidal cycle. Wherever possible the specific relationships governing sedimentation, sediment transfer and the measured processes were tested. Some of the results are presented in the text.

HYDROGRAPHY

Tides

The Bay of Fundy tides have a semidiurnal period. They vary in range from 2.4 m at the bay mouth to 16.3 m in Minas Basin (Greenberg, 1977). The mean tidal range at Burntcoat Head is 11.9 m and is subject to diurnal inequalities of up to 1.5 m (during spring tides). The tide is manifest as a standing wave in the open Bay of Fundy, but becomes modified in Minas Basin and Chignecto Bay where it is typically an intermediate standing/progressive wave. Within tidal estuaries and intertidal channels the tide becomes more progressive and often exhibits a tidal bore.

The near-standing-wave, subtidal oscillations are generally symmetrical about mean sea level. Any one tidal cycle from low water to the subsequent low water can be approximated by a fourth order polynomial ($r^2 = 0.999$). The points of inflection of the tidal curve (dh/dt max.) occur almost exactly at midflood and midebb stages of the tide. The maximum measured rate of sea level change (dh/dt) resulting from a 13.6 m normal tide is 3.5 m h^{-1} (Station 13, Fig. 9.4a).

The phase lag and amplitude increase from the mouth of the Bay of Fundy into Minas Basin is 10 to $20°$ and 200 to 300 per cent respectively. However, the tidal cycle in the higher parts of estuaries (such as the Avon) suffer much larger phase shifts, show decreases in tidal amplitude, and become progressively more asymmetrical.

A proportionality exists between tidal amplitude and current speed. The greater the tidal amplitude, the faster the current. This proportionality has been used to predict barotrophic tidal currents in Minas Basin (Greenberg, 1977). Perhaps more important, however, are the relationships of the rates of changes in these variables. The rate of change in tidal elevation (dh/dt) and the rate of change of current speed at any point are assumed to be proportional. Data sets of various tidal cycles were chosen from six weeks'

current records made at Station 13 using three Aanderaa current meters. The rate of change of current speed was compared to the rate of change of tidal elevation. The graph of the two variables (plotted in polar co-ordinates), generally follows a cardioid function of the equation

$$f(\theta) = a + b \cos \theta \qquad (1)$$

The graph of this function is plotted in Figure 9.5 and shows the relationship for the flood and ebb tides during an autumn period of observation in Minas Passage. The specific solution for the flood tide is:

$$f(\theta) = 18.1 + 9.6 \ (\cos\omega t - \sin\omega t) = \sqrt{\left|\frac{dh}{dt}\right|^2 + \left|\frac{du}{dt}\right|^2} \qquad (2)$$

for the interval $0 \leq \omega t \leq \pi$, $\quad \omega = \dfrac{2\pi}{T}$

where t = time; ω = angular velocity; T = tidal period; h = tide height; $dh/dt = \text{ms}^{-1}$, $d\bar{u}/dt = \text{mms}^{-2}$, u = current speed; and $\bar{u} = \int_0^h u(Z)dz$.

The specific solution for the ebb tide is

$$f(\theta) = 18.6 + 12.0 \ (\cos\omega t - \sin\omega t) = \sqrt{\left|\frac{dh}{dt}\right|^2 + \left|\frac{du}{dt}\right|^2} \qquad (3)$$

The basic function is modified by tidal harmonics that cannot be represented by a simple cosine term. In the case above, the mean current speed over a tidal cycle is computed from at least one value of current speed and the specific relationship of the rate of change in current speed to rate of change in tidal elevation (which varies with changing cross section and tidal prism). To use absolute values of tidal elevation does not account for variations in tidal amplitude nor for diurnal inequalities and therefore rate of change terms are preferred.

The tides observable today are the largest since glacial times (Amos, 1978). Evidence from vibrocores collected in the Minas Basin subtidal region, and from the rate of burial of salt marshes around the margin of Minas Basin (Grant, 1970a), were used to show that recognizable tidal activity began 6300 years BP. The tidal range has been increasing in an approximately linear fashion at a rate of 0.15 m per century since that time.

Currents

Currents in the Bay of Fundy are tidally controlled. They are generally strongly anisotropic, but are subject to inertial (Tee, 1975, 1976, 1977), geomorphic, frictional and meteorological modifications (Swift et al., 1973). These modifications result in rectilinear, residual circulation patterns and asymmetries in current speed and volume transfer of water between the flood and ebb tide. However, in Minas Basin, circulation patterns are mainly a function of inertial and geometric effects only (Tee, 1976).

The mean tidal streams have been documented by the Canadian Hydrographic Service (1966). It was shown that current speeds vary from 0.7 m s^{-1} at the mouth of the Bay of Fundy to 1.3 m s^{-1} in Minas Basin.

More recently, longer term (six weeks) current measurements (using Aanderaa self-recording current meters) have been made in the Minas Basin (Tee, 1975; and herein: 20 May - 25 June 1976, Station 13, see Fig. 9.4a). More general data on the distribution of current speed and direction through the water column were collected using an Endeco 110 current meter. Measurements were made over complete tidal cycles at the sites indicated in Figure 9.4a. Some of these data are illustrated in Figures 9.6a and 9.6b.

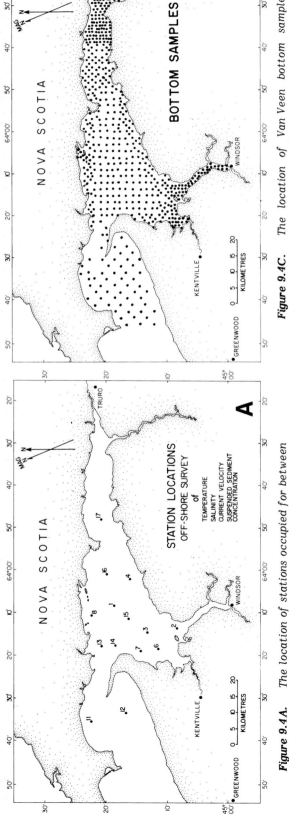

Figure 9.4A. *The location of stations occupied for between 1 and 4 tidal cycles (from low tide to successive low tide). At each station measurements were made of SSC, current velocity, temperature and salinity.*

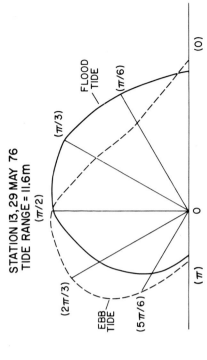

Figure 9.4C. *The location of Van Veen bottom samples collected for the interpretation of sediment distribution.*

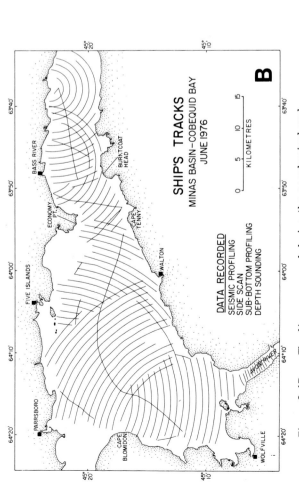

Figure 9.4B. *The lines surveyed during the geophysical and hydrographic survey of the Minas Basin in 1976. A total of 996 km of sounding lines was completed.*

Figure 9.5. *The relationship of the rate of change of mean current speed (dū/dt) and rate of change in tidal elevation (dh/dt) plotted in polar co-ordinates. The function is determined from actual measurements made at station 13 (tide range = 11.6 m).*

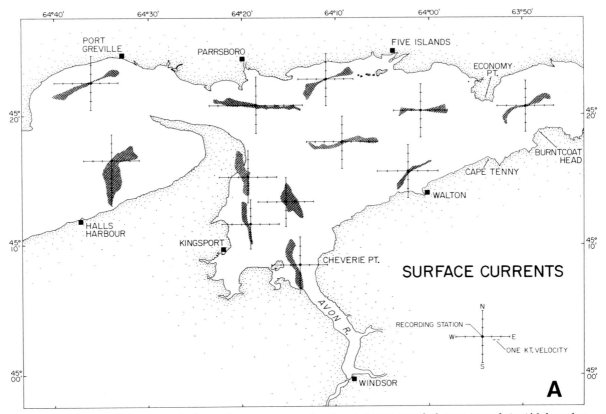

Figure 9.6 A. *Rose plots of the surface current velocity vectors recorded over complete tidal cycles at each of 12 stations. The currents are strongly bipolar (east-west into Cobequid Bay and north-south into Windsor Bay).*

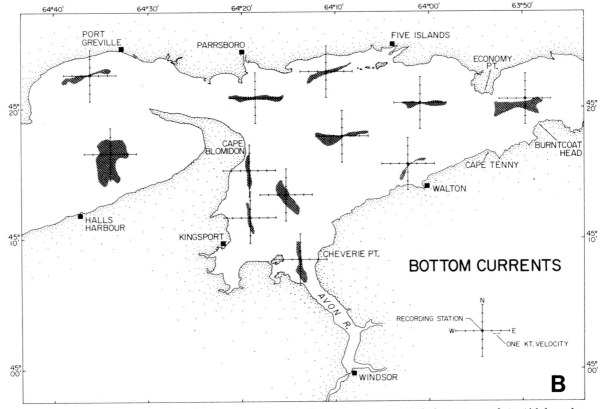

Figure 9.6 B. *Rose plots of the bottom current velocity vectors recorded over complete tidal cycles at each of 12 stations. These current measurements were made at 1 to 2 m above the sea bed.*

Maximum, nonrestricted, tidal currents in Minas Basin are between 2.5 m s^{-1} and 3.0 m s^{-1}. The current velocities increase by 30 to 50 per cent from neap to spring tides. In the subtidal region maximum currents occur during midflood and midebb stages of the tide; the maximum current accelerations occur at the beginning of the ebb (20 mm s^{-2}); maximum current decelerations occur at the end of the flood (18.6 mm s^{-1} min^{-1}) and at the end of the ebb (15.0 mm s^{-1} min^{-1}) (see Fig. 9.7).

The second derivative of the measured current speed (d^{2}u/dt^2) interpreted as the rate of change of acceleration shows maximum absolute values at the beginning of the flood (0.20 mm s^{-1} min^{-2}) and ebb (0.24 mm s^{-1} min^{-2}). There is no obvious relationship between these maxima and turbulence maxima (based on visual observation). The point of inflection (d^{2}u/dt^2 = 0) at or near the end of each phase of the tide indicates that the function defining flood or ebb flow is not affected by the preceding nor succeeding tidal phases. It is considered more justifiable, therefore, to rectify tidal current measurements and to consider the flood and the ebb current series of measurements as separate populations. The flood tide currents are generated principally by the hydraulic gradient of the tide while the ebb tide currents are more often a function of channel slope (chezy function $\bar{u} = C\sqrt{Rh.s.}$ where C = friction, Rh = hydraulic radius, and s = slope (Graf, 1971)) and the hydraulic gradient of the tide (Johns, 1976).

The current velocity in the intertidal zone has speeds equivalent to those observed in the subtidal region. However, the temporal fluctuations in speed and the flood-to-ebb asymmetries are greater. In the examples shown in Figure 9.7, taken from Economy Bar (near Economy Point), the flood tide current exhibits two maxima. The first is interpreted to be the result of an initial progressive tidal wave moving within the tidal channels. During subsequent inundation of the bar, sheet flow (more typical of subtidal flow) prevails, the current subsequently accelerating and decelerating in the manner exemplified in the subtidal region. The ebb tidal current conforms to the subtidal pattern. However, maximum midebb flows are much less than the flood tide equivalents.

The current acceleration (du/dt) is greatest during the first phase of the flood tide (2872 mm s^{-1} h^{-1}), and for a brief period after bar submergence and just prior to midflood (145 mm s^{-1} h^{-1}). Maximum decelerations occur during bar submergence (79 mm s^{-1} h^{-1}) and at the end of the flood tide (826 mm s^{-1}). These changes in current velocity and acceleration, which are much greater than over the subtidal zone, are thought to play a role in resuspension of material during initial inundation of the intertidal zone.

The complicated current patterns in the intertidal zone have been measured and discussed by Dalrymple (1977), Knight (1977), and Lambiase (1977) and the reader is referred to these sources for further information.

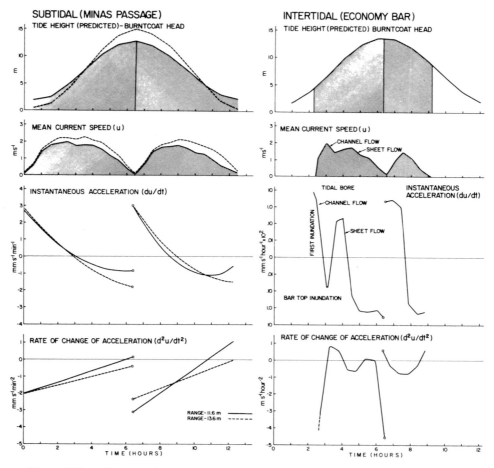

Figure 9.7. *Current data recorded at station 13 (subtidal) and on Economy Bar (intertidal). In each example, the current speed, instantaneous current acceleration and the rate of change of acceleration are plotted. The examples show the marked difference in currents between the two locations.*

The spatial distribution of tidal currents over a tidal cycle has been modelled by Tee (1976) and by Greenberg (1977). Tee calculated the general pattern of residual currents and identified a clockwise gyre in Minas Basin. The centre of this circulation is located 5 km east of Cape Blomidon. Tee showed that the current patterns are controlled by inertial forces (east-west into Cobequid Bay) and by geometry (north-south into Windsor Bay, i.e., the southern part of Minas Basin). The circulation patterns are remarkably consistent with time and are not influenced by tide range nor by meteorological influences. The absolute magnitude of the residual currents, however, is a function of tidal range (Tee, 1976).

Waves

The waves in the Minas Basin are principally locally generated. The region is sheltered from the larger swell and storm waves of the Bay of Fundy by the arcuate promontory known as Cape Split.

During 1975 (30 June - 1 December) and 1976 (13 April - 1 October) wave data were collected from a Datawell 6000 wave rider buoy moored at the approximate centre of Minas Basin. A total of 741 hours of data was collected and analyzed spectrally using the root mean square method (Marine Environmental Data Service, 1977). Measurements were made at three-hour intervals for periods of 20 minutes. Monthly averages of waves greater than 2 s period were computed and the results listed in Table 9.2. Plots of the measured waves are shown in Figure 9.8.

Table 9.2 Monthly mean wave data (significant height, peak period, and computed wavelength) for monthly intervals from April to December inclusive. The data were recorded by a Datawell wave rider buoy at the approximate centre of Minas Basin during 1975 and 1976. A total of 741 hours of records was analyzed.

	Significant height			Peak period		Wavelength
	(m)	(ft)	S.D.	(s)	S.D.	(m)
1975						
April	--	--	--	--	--	--
May	--	--	--	--	--	--
June	0.15	0.50	0.21	2.42	--	9.14
July	0.18	0.58	0.44	2.59	0.64	10.47 ± 0.64
Aug.	0.20	0.64	0.60	2.76	0.77	11.89 ± 0.93
Sept.	0.33	1.09	0.88	2.86	0.81	12.76 ± 1.02
Oct.	0.31	1.01	0.68	2.79	0.79	12.15 ± 0.97
Nov.	0.43	1.40	0.82	3.16	0.68	15.58 ± 0.72
Dec.	0.61	2.00	--	3.14	--	--
1976						
April	0.27	0.88	0.90	2.91	1.02	13.22 ± 1.62
May	0.33	1.09	0.98	3.21	1.13	16.08 ± 1.99
June	0.27	0.87	0.82	2.99	0.92	13.95 ± 1.32
July	0.24	0.78	0.72	3.37	1.14	17.72 ± 2.03
Aug.	0.20	0.66	0.61	2.74	0.91	11.72 ± 1.29
Sept.	0.24	0.80	0.62	2.77	0.77	11.97 ± 0.93
Oct.	0.28	0.93	0.95	2.72	0.67	11.55 ± 0.70
Nov.	0.51	1.61	0.86	3.30	0.96	16.99 ± 1.44
Dec.	--	--	--	--	--	--

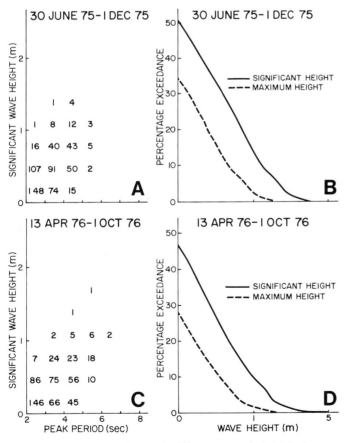

Figure 9.8. *Plots of the significant wave height (m) versus peak period(s) and the percentage exceedance of various wave heights for the periods 30 June to 1 December, 1975 and 13 April to 1 October, 1976. The data were recorded from a Datawell 6000 wave rider buoy situated at the centre of the Minas Basin.*

Local variations in wind conditions often complicate the sea surface because several sets of high-frequency wave trains (0.5 < T < 2 s period) interfere. However, the following general trends are defined for longer period waves (2 s ≤ T).

The wave height increases from a summer minimum of 0.15 m (S.D. = 0.56 m) to a maximum of 0.61 m during December. The maximum significant wave height recorded was 1.8 m. The computed wave lengths (Coastal Engineering Research Centre, 1973) vary from 9.2 m to 17.0 m and generally increase from summer to winter. During the winter the wave climate is subdued because of the 80 to 90 per cent ice cover (ATPPB, 1969). For 46 per cent of the period of observation conditions were calm.

In all cases, the waves were deep-water types (d/Lo > 0.5, where d is the water depth and Lo is the wave length).

Computations of the expected wave spectra and wave refraction under varying wind conditions have been presented by ATPPB (1969). They anticipate waves in Minas Basin 1 m in height and 3.5 s period under 20 mph (32 km h^{-1}) winds. To test the validity of such computations the observed wave height has been plotted against the synoptic wind speed for various wind directions and stages of the tide (see Fig. 9.9). There is only a poor relationship between the two variables plotted. It is concluded, therefore, that the characteristics of waves in this tidally active region are complex, and cannot be predicted using only wind information, fetch data and depth of water.

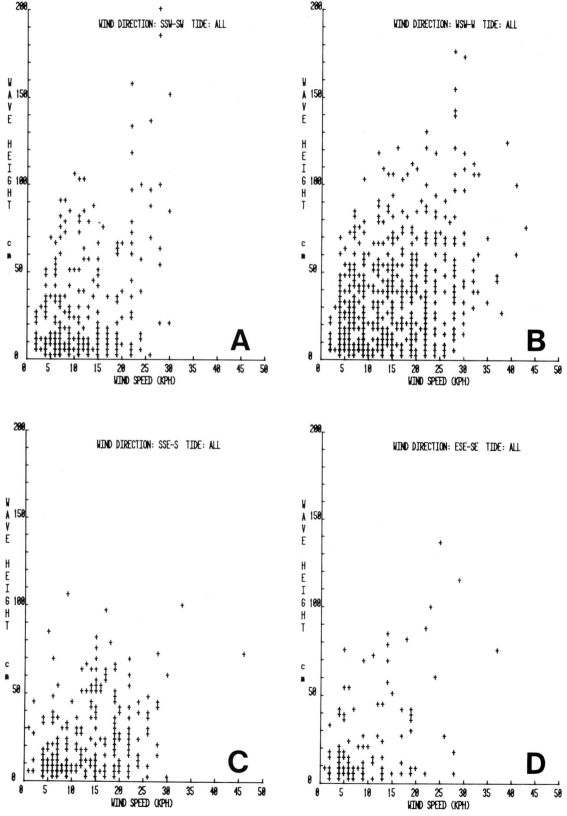

Figure 9.9. *The observed wave height (m) plotted against wind speed (km/h) for winds blowing from the eight octants of the compass. The wave data were gathered at all stages of the tide. The wind data were derived from available meteorological reports on Truro, Kentville, Greenwood, and Avon River, Nova Scotia.*

No information on the direction of wave propagation is available. ATPPB (1969) attempted to predict the wave ray paths under a variety of wind directions. No doubt the changing effects of water depth, tidal currents, hydraulic gradient and fetch distance preclude the use of conventional wave refraction models. However, the dominant direction of wave propagation is evidently to the northeast to north-northeast in response to the dominant wind patterns.

Temperature and salinity

The water column of the Bay of Fundy is stratified in its southern part, intermediate in type near its centre and becomes well mixed towards the head of the bay (Greenberg, pers. com.). In Minas Basin mixing is extreme (1 m s^{-1} vertical velocity components; visual observation).

In Minas Basin water properties are generally constant with depth. More than 200 hours of water monitoring were made at various locations throughout the basin (see Fig. 9.4a). At these locations the temperature and salinity distribution were measured with respect to depth and time. The results of Station 1 are illustrated as an example in Figure 9.10. Temperature was measured against depth using an Endeco 110 (accuracy 0.5% at 5°C) and temporally using the Aanderaa gauge (accuracy 0.15°C). Salinity was measured using an Autolab salinometer (accuracy ±0.1°/oo).

At any particular depth or location, temperature increases from less than 0°C (winter conditions) to a maximum of 21.0°C. The seasonal increase in temperature is linear (dC/dt = 0.2°C day^{-1}) and is independent of the tide range. In subtidal regions the spring tide temperature differences between high and low water increase from 0.3°C during the early spring to 2.0°C during the summer. The lower temperature occurs at high tide. In the nearshore region during the summer months, the temperature variation over the tidal cycle can be as much as 5.0°C and results from solar heating of the intertidal zone during low tide. Heat is conducted from the substrate to the water column during tidal inundation.

No abrupt changes in temperature or salinity were measured either spatially or temporally. No data are available on the synoptic spatial distribution of surface temperature or salinity.

Short-lived thermal gradients may occur under conditions of maximum solar heating of the surface. At Station 13 the top 4 m of the water column was observed to be 2.0°C higher than the lower waters during short periods (several hours) of June 1976. However, under peak currents stratification is destroyed by turbulence (Tee, 1976).

Salinity measured in Minas Channel during a five-week period showed no seasonal variation. However, differences over the tidal cycle were apparent. During neap tides these differences were 0.6°/oo and during spring tides 1.6°/oo. Salinity is highest at high tide.

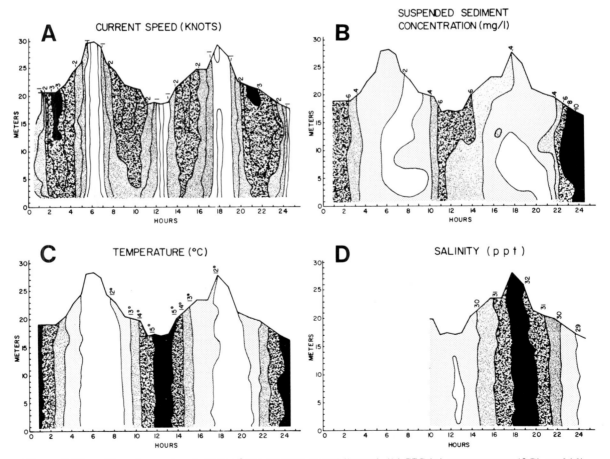

Figure 9.10. *Two-dimensional plots of (a) current speed (knots), (b) SSC (c) temperature (°C), and (d) salinity (°/oo), plotted versus depth over a tidal cycle recorded at station 1 during 18 August 1975.*

The mean salinities are 31.1⁰/oo to 32.9⁰/oo in the lower bay and between 30.0⁰/oo and 32.7⁰/oo in the higher regions. This measurable dilution increases within Minas Basin where salinities have been recorded at 26.1⁰/oo (Station 9, 22 June 1976). It has been intimated that measurable dilution of Bay of Fundy waters results from glacial meltwater transported from the Canadian Eastern Arctic by the Labrador current (Vandall, pers. com.). However, river discharge is the principal agent of seawater dilution in these landward regions.

THE PRESENT SEDIMENT CHARACTER

Distribution of sediments

Bottom sediments. The distribution of surface sediments was determined from 281 Van Veen grab samples collected in Minas Basin and 198 Van Veen grab samples collected from Cobequid Bay. The analysis of these samples supplemented data presented by Forgeron (1962), Huntec (1966), McMullen and Swift (1967), Swift et al. (1966, 1967), Swift and McMullen (1968), Pelletier and McMullen (1972), Dalrymple (1972, 1973), Klein (1963, 1970), Middleton (1972), Pelletier (1974), and Middleton et al. (1976). Figure 9.11 shows the distribution of sediments.

Within the northern Minas Basin, linear sand bars are found parallel to shore. The associated tidal channels are lined by gravelly sand, sand and gravel, and gravels. South of Five Islands to a depth of 5 m (below chart datum) there is a north-south oriented delta that grades seawards into gravels, cobbles and pebbles, and sand and gravels. The percentage of sand also decreases (< 20%) south of Economy Point.

Bordering the south shore of Minas Basin there is more sand. A large part of the intertidal wave-cut platform is veneered with a thin (30 to 50 cm) layer of sand. Most of Windsor Bay is underlain by a complex ebb delta, which no doubt is a sink to sand-sized sediment derived locally. This ebb delta is modified by freshwater discharges from the Cornwallis and the Avon river estuaries. The main flood and ebb channels, similar to the north shore situation, are lined with sandy gravel. Near the entrance to the Cornwallis River estuary (C in Fig. 9.1), the sediments become finer with the ultimate deposition of silt-size material in the intertidal region. Channel bottoms in this region are lined with sand.

The southern Minas Basin sand complex extends eastward without interruption and is manifested as the intertidal Hogsback and Walton Bar (L and M in Fig. 9.1). These features are aligned east-west parallel to shore and owe their existence to an ebb-dominant current, flowing east-west from Cobequid Bay along the south shore. In the subtidal region the sand bars are aligned northwest-southeast. This alignment is parallel to the lines of separation of the ebb-dominant current, which becomes deflected offshore towards Minas Passage (visual observation of turbid plumes).

Minas Channel, of which Minas Passage is a part, shows evidence of extreme scouring. At Cape Split, the tidal channel is scoured through bedrock to depths of 120 m. The entire channel bottom is lined with bedrock. The northern and southern margins of the channel are covered with gravel and cobbles derived locally. Farther westward, where Minas Passage becomes wider, two arcuate regions of sandy material are found. These sandy regions result from the

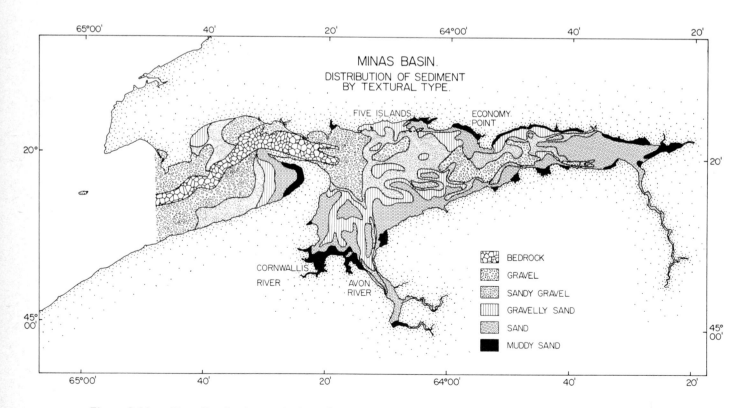

Figure 9.11. *The distribution and size of bottom sediments in Minas Basin, Minas Channel, and Cobequid Bay determined from 700 grab samples analyzed granulometrically at 1 φ intervals.*

Figure 9.12. *Eastern Cobequid Bay during low tide, showing the large expanse of sand flats visible during periods of low tide. (NAPL 11787-55)*

complex residual currents of this region (Tee, 1975), and from the sheltering effects of such topographic features as Scots Bay. Here the bottom sediments grade shorewards regularly from gravels and cobbles to silt and clay.

The distribution of bottom sediments in Cobequid Bay shows two distinctly differing regions. The western section, west of Noel Head, has many of the characteristics observed in Minas Basin. The central region shows signs of scour. The main tidal channel is lined with gravels and cobbles in its deepest parts. Shoreward, to both north and south, the sediments become finer, grading into gravelly sand, sandy gravel, and sand. In contrast to Minas Basin, the north shore of western Cobequid Bay has much more sand than the south shore.

East of Noel Head the distribution of bottom sediments changes markedly. In this region the main, gravel- and cobble-lined tidal channels occur close to the north and south shores, respectively, and are separated by a wide intertidal expanse of sand. This sand body has been the subject of intensive research (Middleton, 1977; Dalrymple, 1977; Knight, 1977; see Fig. 9.12).

Suspended sediments. The spatial distribution of suspended sediments in tidal regions varies considerably with the stage of the tide (Miller, 1966). Large-scale turbulences and strong tidal currents cause high temporal fluctuations of suspended sediment concentration (SSC). A single sediment particle may be transported 40 km in one tidal excursion. Consequently the spatial distribution of suspended sediment could not be determined by conventional sampling, so it was determined from LANDSAT radiometric data, which records sea surface colour in digital format and, for the Bay of Fundy area, gives quasisynoptic information.

During a two-year period, a calibration has been established between LANDSAT multispectral radiance data (recorded digitally in 6-bit format on high-density computer-compatible tapes (NASA, 1976)) and SSC (Amos and Alföldi, 1979; Alföldi and Mundy, 1977). The calibration is based on 42 points of data, collected under six differing atmospheric conditions, and representative of SSCs from less than 1 mg L^{-1} to 1200 mg L^{-1}. It is accurate to ±12 per cent (r = 0.96) and corrects for surface brightness variations and atmospheric interference and is not affected by variations in salinity, temperature, sediment shape, composition or size. The relationships between SSC (log$_e$ mg L^{-1}) and multispectral scanner (MSS) radiance (mW (cm^2)$^{-1}$ steradian^{-1}) in band 4 (0.5 to 0.6 μ) and band 5 (0.6 to 0.7 μ) are shown in Figures 9.13a and 9.13b, respectively.

Seventeen tapes of Minas Basin radiance, representative of a variety of seasons, stages of the tide and meteorological conditions, have been analyzed for SSC. Maps plotting the distribution of surface SSC are being generated with a spatial resolution of 80 m on the ground. The entire Minas Basin system has been mapped using 0.23 x 10^6 surface point discriminations of SSC.

Figures 9.14a and 9.14b show the interpreted surface SSC at 1430 GMT on 3 May 1974 and 24 August 1973, 20 minutes and 2 hours after high tide, respectively. In both images there is a consistent increase in SSC from Minas Passage into Cobequid Bay and Windsor Bay, increasing from 1.5 mg L^{-1} to > 100 mg L^{-1}. In the May 1974 image SSCs are less than 1.5 mg L^{-1} in the outer Minas Passage, increasing to 1.5 - 3.0 mg L^{-1} in Minas Basin, to 12 - 25 mg L^{-1} south of Economy Point and to 50 - 100 mg L^{-1} in Cobequid Bay. The SSC is generally higher along the south shore of Minas Basin. This conforms with the general residual current patterns proposed by Tee (1976). The cleaner flooding waters move into Cobequid Bay along the north shore.

The August 1973 image shows that SCCs are higher at all locations throughout the basin, and range from 6 to 10 mg L^{-1} in Minas Channel, to 10 - 34 mg L^{-1} in Minas Basin, and greater than 203 mg L^{-1} in Cobequid Bay. The image was created during maximum ebb currents. The increase in SSC in Minas Passage reflects this increase in current speed. Material presumably resuspended from the bed can be seen on the basin side of the passage. As in the previous example, SSCs are higher along the south shore of the basin than the north. Wave stirring has been eliminated as the cause of the high SSCs, as conditions were nearly calm during both overpasses. It is more probable that it demonstrates the existence of a seaward residual current along the south shore.

The volume of material suspended in Minas Basin waters was determined from the calibrated imagery. From the mean water depth and the appropriate surface area of each SSC level, it was calculated that during creation of the May 1974 image 0.25 x 10^6 m^3 of sediment was in suspension. During the August 1973 image creation, 0.50 x 10^6 m^3 of sediment was suspended.

The temporal and vertical distribution of suspended sediments was determined from 200 hours of water monitoring at the sites shown in Figure 9.4a. Each site was occupied for at least one tidal cycle from low tide to the succeeding low tide. At several sites two successive cycles were monitored to evaluate the reliability of the sampling interval and method. Sediment concentrations were determined from 1.25 L Knudsen bottle samples taken at 30 minute intervals at five depths through the water column. Five hundred mL of each sample were vacuum filtered through a 0.47 m Nuclepore filter pad and the concentration by weight determined. Measurements were also made on current velocity, temperature and salinity (see Fig. 9.10).

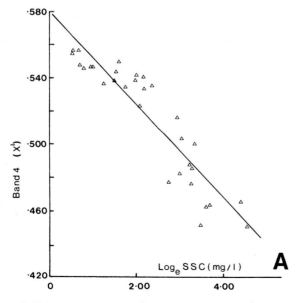

Figure 9.13 A. *The correlation between Landsat MSS band 4 and log$_e$ suspended sediment concentration based on 32 data points.*

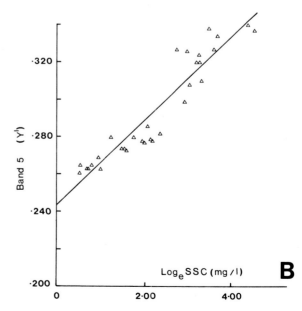

Figure 9.13 B. *The correlation between Landsat MSS band 5 and log$_e$ suspended sediment concentration based on 32 data points.*

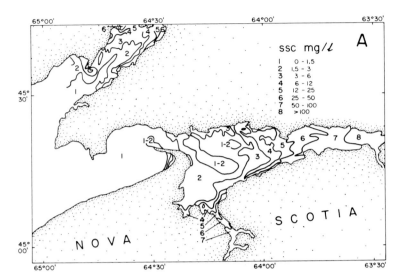

Figure 9.14 A.

The discriminated surface SSC determined from the Landsat sediment calibration for an image created 1430 GMT on 3 May 1974, i.e. 30 minutes after high tide.

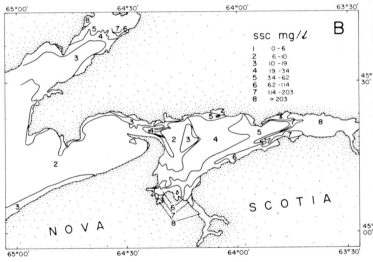

Figure 9.14 B.

The discriminated surface SSC determined from the Landsat sediment calibration for an image created 1430 GMT on 24 August 1973, i.e. 2 hours after high tide.

Within the nearshore subtidal regions of Minas Basin, the suspended particulate matter (SPM) was well mixed throughout the water column. The SSC was usually constant with depth at all stages of the tide. Farther from shore (Stations 13 and 14) there is evidence of gravity settling during low and high tide stands. At low and high tide the surface SSCs at these two stations were consistently 30 to 40 per cent less than in bottom waters. Without exception, the SSC was highest at low water and decreased progressively to high water. The tidal fluctuations in concentration vary from a factor of 10 in Cobequid Bay to a factor of 2 in Minas Channel. There is no relationship between current speed and SSC. The absolute sediment concentration at any site seems to be controlled by such processes as wave stirring, turbulence and biological activity (Risk et al., 1977) on the intertidal zone, rather than from any measurable phenomenon at the site of sampling.

Sediment sources

The present sediments in Minas Basin are derived from four major sources: the eroding cliffs bordering the systems, the rivers draining into the system, the Bay of Fundy, via Minas Passage, and the seabed by reworking.

The first three sources physically contribute material to the system and are therefore active components of the sediment budget of the Basin. Reworking of the seabed, on the other hand, redistributes material already within the system, and will therefore be considered under the section dealing with the transport of sediment.

The eroding cliffs. The cliffs surrounding Minas Basin have been known to be regressing at rates up to 2 m a^{-1}* and therefore supplying large quantities of sediment to the system (Churchill, 1924). Cliff-derived sediments have been identified by Klein (1963, 1970) and Middleton and Davis (1979). Of the 320 km perimeter, 79 per cent is occupied by eroding, unstable cliffs of Triassic sandstone (Fig. 9.2c), glacial till and outwash, Cretaceous basalt or Paleozoic sedimentary rocks.

The present cliff recession rates were determined from an examination of successive aerial photographs (from 1939 to 1964) at 105 sites regularly spaced around the system. Each recession rate was a computed mean of four independent measures. The population error of any single computation was a maximum of 22 per cent (P < 0.05). The recession rates are shown in Figure 9.15a.

---

* a is the SI abbreviation for year.

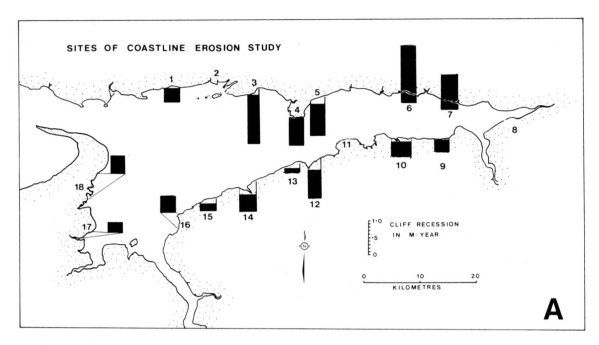

Figure 9.15A. *The rates of cliff line recession around the Minas Basin, based on sequential aerial photography between 1939 and 1974. The rates are based on measures at 105 sites spaced around the system.*

The mean cliff recession rate is 0.55 m a^{-1} (S.D. = 0.27 m a^{-1}); however, this rate varies considerably around the basin. Rates are maximum at Five Islands (1.5 m a^{-1}) and along the north shore of Cobequid Bay (1.6 m a^{-1}). These regions have cliffs composed of Triassic sandstone and glacial material, respectively. Along the south shore recession rates are lower. At Burntcoat Head no appreciable recession was measured, whereas the remainder of the south shore shows a mean regression rate of 0.5 m a^{-1}.

Cliff recession is a function of (1) the degree of exposure to wave attack during high tide inundation of the cliff foot, (2) the cliff composition (Triassic sandstone and glacial material erode faster than indurated Paleozoic rocks), and (3) the depth of cliff foot inundation. Along the north shore, recession rates are high because of exposure to the dominant southwest winds, because of the friable nature of the cliffs, and because cliff foot inundation is 2 m (during spring tides).

The volume of material put into the system from regressing cliffs is a function of cliff height. Heights were measured stereoscopically from aerial photographs at 158 sites representing points equidistantly spaced around the basin. Results were compared to field measurements made at a number of sites and errors were estimated to be ±5 per cent. The cliffs are up to 180 m high and have a mean height of 23 m (S.D. = 15.2 m).

The volume of sediment derived from cliff erosion is estimated to be 3.09 x 10^6 m^3 a^{-1} (±0.93 x 10^6 m^3 a^{-1}). The sources of this material are illustrated in Figure 9.15b. Minas Basin, *sensu stricto*, receives 2.72 x 10^6 m^3 a^{-1} and Cobequid Bay, 0.38 x 10^6 m^3 a^{-1}. Most material is derived from the Five Islands (0.85 x 10^6 m^3 a^{-1}) and Cape Blomidon (0.68 x 10^6 m^3 a^{-1}) regions, which are predominantly composed of Triassic sandstone. The south shore of Minas

Basin contributes 0.31 x 10^6 m^3 a^{-1} (10% of the total supply of cliff material). This material is principally Paleozoic sandstone, shale and quartzite, and breaks down into pebbles, gravel and silt. The volume of material derived from erosion of the wave-cut platform may be approximately equal to that volume derived from the regressing cliffs. The erosion rate normal to the platform, resulting from a cliff recession of 1.5 m a^{-1}, is 0.006 m a^{-1}. Let us assume that the erosion is linear across the intertidal zone and that this zone of erosion is 2000 m wide. Let us also assume that this erosion is typical of the cliffed perimeter of Minas Basin (~ 240 km). Then 2.9 x 10^6 m^3 of material are eroded from this source annually. Although this represents a large volume of material being broken down into transportable sizes, it does not alter the volume of the system, the material being derived below the high tide level. Furthermore the assumptions made cannot be verified easily. For these reasons this source does not appear in the sediment budget calculations.

Rivers. Data compiled by the Atlantic Tidal Power Programming Board (1969) shows that fluvial sediments are entering the Minas Basin system at rates as high as 7.1 x 10^4 tonnes river^{-1} a^{-1}. However, the debouched material has not been analyzed and, indeed, only one river has been examined in detail. The Salmon River, one of the larger rivers debouching to the system, has a mean sediment discharge of 21.6 tonnes day^{-1} (based on the mean daily discharge of 8.8 m^3 s^{-1}) derived from a catchment area of 363 km^2. These data were supplemented by sediment flux calculations made on the Herbert River from 25 September to 26 December 1975 and 1 May to 31 July 1976 (mean discharge = 5 m^3 s^{-1}), to determine the approximate fluvial input of sediment.

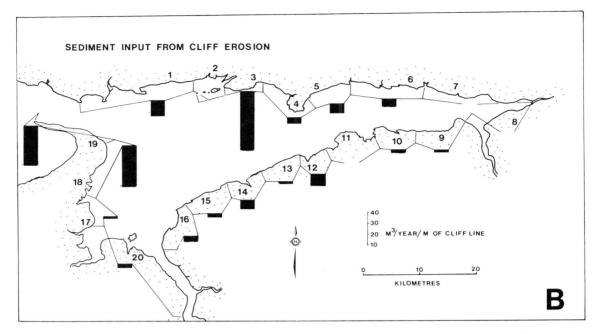

Figure 9.15B. *The volumes of sediment released annually from 20 segments of cliff line around the system. The volumes were computed on the basis of 158 cliff height measures and the cliff recession data.*

The sediment discharge from the Herbert River is highly variable over time; however, several trends emerged:

(1) There is only a moderate relationship between discharge and suspended sediment concentration ($f(x) = -1.91 + 1.32 \log_e (x)$; $r = 0.84$). This relationship is illustrated in Figure 9.16a.

(2) There is no obvious relationship between catchment area and sediment discharge (when compared to Salmon River data).

(3) There is a negative logarithmic relationship between sediment discharge and frequency of occurrence (0 to 0.5 m^3 day^{-1} - 78%; 0.5 to 5 m^3 day^{-1} - 18%; 5 to 50 m^3 day^{-1} - 4%; >50 m^3 day^{-1} - 0.5%).

(4) Most of the material in suspension is organic detritus (mean value of 60%). The remaining fraction is silt/clay-size material.

(5) There is a moderate logarithmic relationship between percentage organic detritus and total particulate matter ($f(x) = 15 \log_e x + 20$; $r = 0.89$; see Fig. 9.16b).

The mean sediment (inorganic) discharges from the Herbert River to Minas Basin were 1.38 m^3 day^{-1} and 0.82 m^3 day^{-1} for the autumn and spring survey periods, respectively. This is equivalent to an annual discharge of 680 m^3.

The total volume of inorganic SPM derived from a fluvial source has been computed to be 5.9×10^4 m^3 a^{-1}. This volume is equivalent to 1.91 per cent* of the yearly volume derived from cliff erosion.

Open sea. The transfer of a tidal volume of 15.3 km^3 (maximum) through Minas Passage over the tidal cycle no doubt causes mixing of SPM between the Minas Basin and the more open Bay of Fundy. But how much net residual sediment transfer is there either into or out of Minas Basin?

Two stations east (13 and 14) of Minas Passage and two stations to the west (11 and 12) were monitored for a total of 11 tidal cycles. Water samples were collected using Knudsen bottles at each 0.25 water depth interval every half hour, to determine the vertical distribution of suspended particulate matter throughout the tidal cycle. A flux profile, measured in g m s^{-1} was determined from synoptic current velocity data for each station monitored. The depth integration of the flux profile was the instantaneous mass transport of suspended sediment across a unit area of the water column. The flux was recorded in units of g m^{-2} s^{-1}. The residual transport of material was the difference between the time-integrated flux measure over the flood and ebb stages of the tide.

The results were recorded in units of grams per tide per metre width and are listed in Table 9.4 and plotted in Figure 9.17.

There is a headward residual movement of sediment at points immediately east of Minas Channel (2.6×10^6 g tide^{-1}) and a lesser, seaward residual to the west of the channel 1.1×10^6 g tide^{-1}. If the results are extrapolated over the entire cross-section, a net influx of 3.3×10^6 m^3 a^{-1} of SPM to Minas Basin is calculated.

Suspended material was examined after filtration, using a binocular microscope. Mica fragments in the silt range were abundant, as was the biogenic material. There also was an abundance of fibrous organic detritus, which was determined (by combustion at 900°C) to represent 50.6% by weight of the sample. The computed input of inorganic suspended particulate matter to Minas Basin was therefore 1.6×10^6 m^3 a^{-1}.

* These data are revised from those presented in Amos (1977).

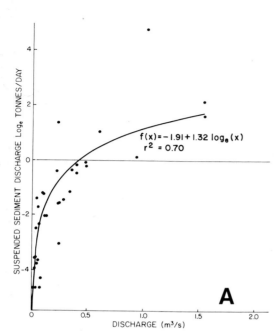

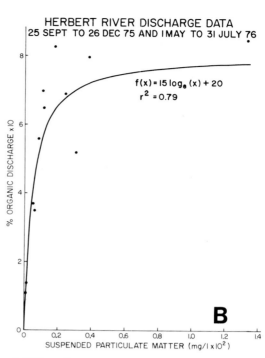

Figure 9.16 A. *The relationship between suspended sediment discharge and total water discharge for the Herbert River during 25 September-26 December, 1975 and 1 May-31 July, 1976.*

Figure 9.16 B. *The relationship between percentage organic discharge (based on combusion at 900ªC) and SPM for the Herbert River.*

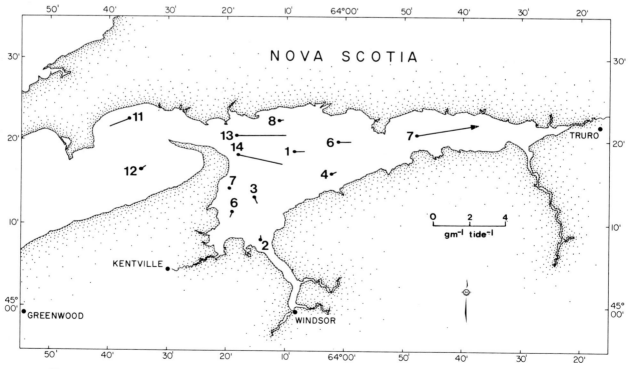

Figure 9.17. *The residual transport of SPM determined by direct monitoring over complete tidal cycles (from low tide to successive low tide) at 12 sites. The residual vector is the difference between the depth and time integrations of half hourly flux profiles with respect to the flood and ebb phases of the tide.*

Table 9.3 A summary table of the postglacial annual sediment budget (m^3a^{-1}), subdivided into three components.

Sediment	Location	Postglacial to 6300 years B.P.	6300 years B.P. to near-present	Present
		(m^3a^{-1})	(m^3a^{-1})	(m^3a^{-1})
Silt/clay	Intertidal[1]	-	-	-
	Subtidal[2]	0.5×10^6	-	-
	Marginal[3]	-(?)	0.1×10^6	1.7×10^6
Sand	Intertidal	-	2.8×10^6	2.8×10^6
	Subtidal	-	-	-
	Marginal	-(?)	-	-
Granules, pebbles or cobbles	Intertidal	-	0.6×10^5	0.3×10^6
	Subtidal	-	-	-
	Marginal	-(?)	-(?)	-
Total (sediment budget)		0.5×10^6	3.0×10^6	4.8×10^6
Maximum tide range		0-2 m	2-16 m	>16 m

[1] between high and low water levels
[2] below low water
[3] at, or outward of the high tide line

It will be shown later that SSC in the vicinity of Minas Passage is related to the residual tidal current (r = 0.90). According to the laws of continuity the net residual tidal current across Minas Passage (assuming no river input or evaporation) is zero. Is the residual sediment movement also zero, and therefore are the extrapolations made above in error?

Groen (1967) showed that tidal waters subject to the effects of bottom friction develop asymmetries in tidal current accelerations over the flood and ebb stages of the tide that are independent of tidal amplitude. He showed that a headward residual transport of suspended material can occur irrespective of the residual currents. He further proposed that under conditions of constant sediment type, the lag in gravity settling of sediment, combined with the acceleration/deceleration asymmetry over a tidal cycle, can cause a preferential headward transfer of suspended material, and that this may be 30 per cent higher than the return transport. This hypothesis requires that the maximum accelerations occur at the beginning of the flood tide and the maximum decelerations occur during the latter stages of the ebb. At Station 13, the flood transport of sediment exceeded the ebb transport by 35 per cent (see Table 9.4), a result remarkably close to that predicted by Groen. However, the times of maximum current acceleration and deceleration differ from those used by Groen. At Station 13 the mass transport of suspended sediment is a direct function of the mass transport of water induced by the residual tidal current (r = 0.90). At Station 14, however, though the residual sediment movement is headwards, only 10 per cent of the volume advected can be accounted for by the weakly, flood-dominant residual currents. At this location, mass sediment movement headwards is controlled by the asymmetries in maximum tidal current. The flood maximum was 1.85 m s^{-1}, while the ebb maximum current was 1.70 m s^{-1}. The conclusion is that at Station 14, the material is only partly suspended and behaves more like silt/sand-sized material, while at Station 13, material moves as a wash load over the complete tidal cycle. The integration of sediment flux across tidal entrances such as Minas Passage still remain subject to doubt. The solution lies in representative sampling at a number of sites across the entrance.

General. The total annual influx of sediment to the Minas Basin system is calculated to be 4.8×10^6 m^3 a^{-1}. Sand comprises 58 per cent of this volume, silt and clay 35 per cent, and coarser material only 7 per cent (see Table 9.3).

The relative difference between basin infill due to sedimentation and basin enlargement due to sea level rise is used to determine the evolutionary trend in basin size. It will be shown later that mean sea level is rising relative to a fixed datum at a rate of 15 cm per century. The volume increase of the basin resulting from sea level rise and from enlargement due to erosion amounts to 3.4×10^6 m^3 a^{-1}. As the annual sediment influx amounts to 4.8×10^6 m^3 a^{-1}, the Minas Basin system must be diminishing in volume at a rate of 1.4×10^6 m^3 a^{-1}.

The transport of sediment

Bed material transport and deposition. With the exception of Windsor Bay, the distribution of bottom sediments shows that bed material is transported principally in the intertidal zone. Wide expanses of sand wave and megaripple fields are visible during low tide covering a large area of the marginal wave-cut platform. These features have been used to infer the direction of bedload transport. The results have been documented by McMullen and Swift (1967), Klein (1970), Middleton (1972), Dalrymple (1977), Knight (1977), Lambiase (1977), Long (1977), and Long and Belanger (1978).

In the subtidal region, the surficial material is dominantly gravels, pebbles and cobbles, which, in view of biogenic overgrowths, are thought to be stationary.

As previously discussed, most sand in the sand bars scattered around the Minas Basin is derived from a limited number of sites along the local regressing cliffs. Some statements, therefore, on the rate and direction of transport of this material can be made.

Along the western shore of Minas Basin up to 0.49×10^6 m^3 of sand is being transported annually into Windsor Bay. Some of this is no doubt accumulating on the Avon estuary ebb delta and in the Avon River estuary itself. The remainder is thought to pass through this region and move eastward to supply sediment to Hogsback and Walton Bar. The sediment is prevented from moving farther by the ebb residual to the east.

The sand found along the north shore of Minas Basin and Cobequid Bay is principally derived from the Five Islands region. The general distribution of this sand indicates an eastward transport. The volume input from the cliffs gives the approximate sediment transport rate under steady state conditions (0.85×10^6 m^3 a^{-1}). This material moves past Economy Point and forms the tongue of sand extending beyond Bass River (Figure 9.11).

Table 9.4 The computed mass transport of suspended particulate matter, determined at various locations within Minas Basin. The estimated residual movements, based on the differences in volumes integrated over the flood and ebb phased of the tide are also given.

Station	Date	Burntcoat tide range	Water depth below GSCD	Flood transport	Ebb transport	Residual
		(m)	(m)	$(g\ m^{-1}\ tide^{-1} \times 10^6)$		
1	10/ 7/75	13.6	16.4	2.1	1.1	+1.0
1	10/ 7/75	14.3	16.4	1.6	2.0	−0.4
2	23/ 7/75	12.1	5.5	2.7	2.9	−0.2
3	8/ 8/75	14.6	11.0	1.2	0.9	+0.4
4	24/ 8/75	11.1	3.6	1.0	0.7	+0.3
6	10/ 8/75	15.4	3.7	1.9	1.6	+0.3
7	11/ 8/75	14.9	18.3	0.71	0.70	+0.1
8	6/ 9/75	15.1	5.5	1.2	1.0	+0.2
9	22/ 6/76	8.4	11.0	5.0	1.5	+3.5
10	9/ 6/76	13.3	7.3	2.6	1.9	+0.7
11	10/11/75	10.3	27.4	1.60	1.51	+0.1
11	10/11/75	9.9	27.4	1.69	3.04	−1.4
11	11/11/75	9.4	27.4	1.39	3.51	−2.1
12	11/11/75	9.0	29.3	2.3	2.1	+0.2
12	12/11/75	7.7	29.3	2.9	2.4	+0.5
13	22/ 5/76	9.1	62.2	9.5	6.7	+2.8
13	22/ 5/76	9.3	62.2	9.1	6.5	+2.6
13	23/ 5/76	8.7	62.2	8.1	6.2	+1.9
13	23/ 5/76	9.0	62.2	8.5	6.6	+1.9
14	24/ 5/76	8.8	51.2	10.9	8.3	+2.6

Within the western part of Cobequid Bay, sand moves from west to east along the northern intertidal margin. However, farther east the transport of material is more complex but is generally redistributed westwards along the centre of the Bay (Middleton, 1977). This redistribution has resulted in a complex sand bar extending throughout eastern Cobequid Bay.

The long-term transport of material should be manifested by changes in the bathymetry and in the distribution of the various bottom sediment and morphological types. During 1976 the bathymetry of the Minas Basin was resurveyed in conjunction with the Canadian Hydrographic Service (see Fig. 9.1b) to a vertical precision of ±10 cm and a navigational accuracy of less than 5 m (using a range-range system). The bathymetry was compared to soundings made by the British Admiralty during 1858 (taken from copies of the original field sheets).

The accretion and erosion in Cobequid Bay during the 118 years separating the surveys is shown in Figures 9.18a and 9.18b. The areas of maximum accretion correspond to the complex sand bar in eastern Cobequid Bay. In this region between 5 and 10 m of accretion has taken place. At the same time, the previously mentioned tongue of sand, found along the north shore of Cobequid Bay, experienced up to 2 m accretion. The south shore region shows similar net accretion.

The erosion patterns in Cobequid Bay between 1858 and 1976 are shown in Figure 9.18b. The central tidal channel south of Economy Point has been scoured in places to 5 m. In eastern Cobequid Bay the scoured channel bifurcates, one channel running close to the north shore and the second

close to the south shore. The comparison of charts of Cobequid Bay shows that each year $5.3 \times 10^6\ m^3$ of sediment is eroded (mostly from the tidal channels) and $6.0 \times 10^6\ m^3$ of sediment is deposited. There is, therefore, a net accretion of $0.7 \times 10^6\ m^3\ a^{-1}$. This is equivalent to almost the entire supply of sediment derived from the north shore of Minas Basin by cliff erosion.

The flux of bed material transport was determined from two series of experiments using irradiated synthetic sand. The first experiment was conducted on an intertidal sand bar near Economy Point during the period 27 October – 17 November 1976 (Long, 1977). The experiment was based on a method established by Crickmore and Lean (1962), Courtois and Hours (1965), Courtois and Sauzay (1966), and Sauzay (1968). One kilogram of glass, having the same hydrodynamic properties as the natural sediment and containing 0.5 per cent gold was irradiated to form the isotope ^{198}Au (half life 2.7 days) to a radiation level of 2 Ci. During successive low tides after sample release, the isotope radiation was measured in situ and the dispersing radioactive centroid was plotted with respect to time. The migration of the centre of gravity of the centroid was measured. The migration rate is proportional to the mean bedload transport rate. The 16 days of the experiment showed that the centroid centre of gravity migrated 67 m day^{-1}. The thickness of the mobile layer, determined from the depth of reworking of irradiated sand, was 14 cm. It was calculated that $1\ m^3\ day^{-1}\ m^{-1}$ was transported eastwards into Cobequid Bay during the experiment.

A similar series of experiments was conducted in the same general location at two different sites simultaneously.

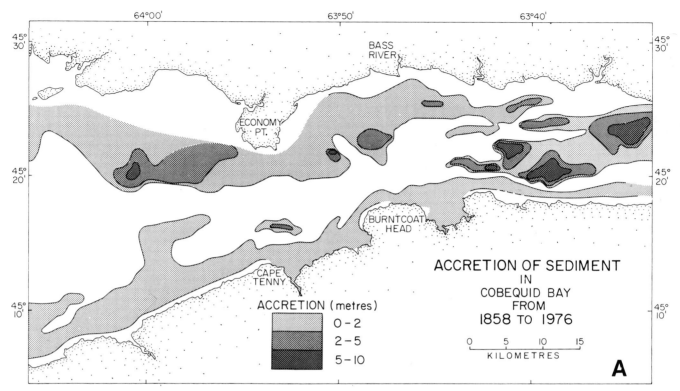

Figure 9.18 A. *The accretion of sediment in Cobequid Bay between 1858 and 1976. The depths were compared using the original bathymetric field sheet data, and not the bathymetric charts which are published showing only the shallowest depths.*

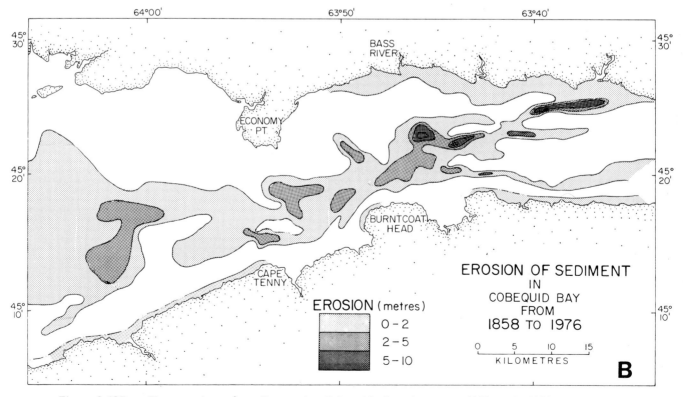

Figure 9.18 B. *The erosion of sediment in Cobequid Bay between 1858 and 1976, based on bathymetric field sheet data.*

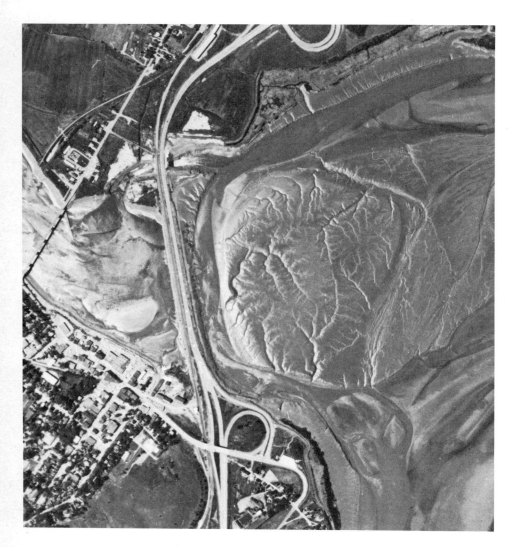

Figure 9.19A.

The Windsor causeway, on the Avon River estuary, and the accumulation of mud to its seaward side (right). The mud flat has developed since causeway construction in 1970, and continues to accrete during summer months.

Figure 9.19B. *The Moncton causeway, on the Petitcodiac River estuary, N.B., showing a dramatic accumulation of muddy sediments since causeway construction in 1969. The mud flat, which had developed seaward of the causeway, extends 20 km down the estuary and is colonized by halophitic marsh plants.*

Figure 9.19C. *The Upper Dorchester causeway, on the Memramcook River estuary, N.B., showing signs of sediment accretion on its seaward side. This causeway was built in 1974. Notice the accumulation of sediment is less in the channel leading from the sluice, due, no doubt, to fresh water flushing.*

Figure 9.19D. *An Aboideau and land reclamation dyke constructed at Palmers Creek, Memramcook River estuary, during 1955. The area behind the reclamation dyke is composed of marginal marine deposits, now used as farming land.*

This second study was carried out from 4 October to 7 November 1977. One site was located on the northern part of the intertidal sand bar, and the other site was situated immediately below low water on the southern margin of Economy Bar.

The technique was similar to that used in the first experiment; however, the radioisotope used was ^{147}Nd (half life 11.1 days). The tracer was activated to 1 Ci prior to immersion.

Unlike the first experiment, an integrator was used to record continuously the cumulative activity along each survey line. This so-called 'dynamic detection' was conducted daily for 30 days. The mean residual movement of the dispersing isotope was determined and the volume transport of sediment calculated to be 0.75 m^3 day^{-1} m^{-1} in an eastward direction (for the northern site) and 0.60 m^3 day^{-1} m^{-1} in a westward direction (for the southern site). The net movement of sediment as bedload was 460 000 m^{3}a^{-1} in an easterly direction through a belt from the north shoreline to the centre of the subtidal main channel.

Suspended sediment transport and deposition. The suspended sediment transport was determined for the stations indicated in Figure 9.4a by sediment flux calculations (based on SSC and current velocity measurements) made throughout the water column at half-hour intervals and integrated over the tidal cycle (see previous section). The residual transport of suspended sediment (measured in grams per metre) at each site has been computed and listed in Table 9.4. Results from duplicate surveys are also shown and were performed to assess the reproducibility of this technique. Applying the central limit theorem (Spiegel, 1961) the mean error of the duplicate surveys approximates the population error and was ±0.3 x 10^6 g m^{-1} tide^{-1} (i.e., ±26%).

The residual transport of suspended material is shown in Figure 9.17. There is a notable transport eastward into Cobequid Bay (0.1 to 3.5 x 10^6 g m^{-1} tide^{-1}) and southward into Windsor Bay (0.1 to 0.4 x 10^6 g m^{-1} tide^{-1}). In most cases, there is a positive correlation between the residual sediment transport and residual current (r = 0.90) and only a poor relationship between SSC and current speed (r = 0.31). However, at Stations 3, 6 and 7 the suspended sediment residual transport is opposite to the current residual flow predicted by Tee (1975) and measured herein. This suggests temporary deposition of the suspended load at these sites. The computed residence time of material moving in suspension is 0.15 years.

Suspended sediments in the greater part of Minas Basin behave, to a large extent, as wash load. Settling rates, determined from settling experiments in seawater, are no greater than 6.7 cm min^{-1}. Material deposits only under quiet conditions. These conditions are created artificially by the construction of earth fill causeways across tidal estuaries. Accumulations of fine-grained material are dramatic to seaward of such structures. The accumulation rate of such material with respect to depth below high tide, distance from the causeway and time after construction is the subject of ongoing research at the Avon River causeway (Fig. 9.19a), the Petitcodiac River causeway (Fig. 9.19b), the Memramcook River causeway (Fig. 9.19c) and the Palmers Creek causeway (Fig. 9.19d). Rates of sedimentation of 0.5 cm month^{-1} have been measured during summer months, balanced by up to 1.0 m of ice plucking during the winter.

The past sedimentary character

The postglacial sedimentary column. The distribution and interpretation of the postglacial sediments were determined from 12 vibrocores (Amos, 1978; Dames and Moore, 1969),

from seismic profiling (Huntec, 1966; Swift et al., 1966, 1967, 1973; Swift and McMullen, 1968; ATPPB, 1969; Fader et al., 1977), from echo sounding records and from existing data on the marginal sediments (Grant, 1970a, b; Welsted, 1976).

In the subtidal region the surface is occupied by either glacial or postglacial sediments. Bedrock outcrops only in the deeper parts of Minas Passage. The glacial deposits are compacted marine silts, which range in age from 14 180 (±710) years BP to >37 000 years BP. They underlie most of the Minas Basin seaward of the wave-cut platform to a depth below the seabed not greater than 8 m. These deposits are at the surface in the tidal narrow south of Economy Point and in a belt seaward of the south shore wave-cut platform (see Fig. 9.11).

Four distinctly different sedimentary units were deposited over the glacial deposits. There are (from top to bottom): surficial sand, gravel, pebbles and cobbles; poorly sorted shelly gravels; well sorted sands; and watery silts and clays.

The above sequence exhibits an increase in grain size to the surface and is illustrated schematically in Figure 9.20.

The watery silts and clays form a lens-shaped unit, thickest (7 m) near the centre of the basin and becoming thinner radially. It contains open marine assemblages of Mollusca (Wagner, pers. com.) and Foraminifera (Schafer, pers. com.) and was deposited at a maximum rate of 0.05 cm a^{-1} during the postglacial period until 6300 years BP. During this time the sedimentological evidence indicates low tidal activity.

The well sorted sand is a current-laid deposit, composed of medium/fine sand. The sands transgressed the underlying muds in response to increasing tidal currents from 6300 to 1000 years BP. They formed in a similar manner to the Sambro sands, which are presently forming in the outer Bay of Fundy (Fader et al., 1977).

The poorly sorted, shelly gravel unit is a lag deposit derived initially by ice rafting. Material incorporated into intertidal anchor ice is transported seaward by tidal action and subsequently dropped during spring thaws. The so-formed deposit of disarticulated shells (*Macoma baltica*), pebbles, gravel and sand protected the underlying sand from the increasing tidal currents subsequent to 1000 years B.P.

The surficial pebbles and cobbles occupy most of the subtidal seabed (see earlier section). This deposit is derived from ice rafting, but is coarser in grain size than the underlying ice-rafted sediments (Fig. 9.20). Subject to random lifting of ice a wide variety of material must have been transported seaward in this manner. However, only the pebbles and cobbles presently remain immobile within the 100 to 300 cm s^{-1} tidal currents. The finer material has no doubt been winnowed.

The postglacial, subtidal stratigraphy is fully developed for the period up to 6300 years B.P. However, the sequence laid down subsequently is relatively condensed. During this subsequent period deposition was preferentially taking place in the marginal, developing intertidal region. These latter deposits are the previously described sand bars, and sequences of mud flats and salt marshes. They are tidal in their mode of origin and constitute a fully developed sequence. None of the sediments has been dated older than 4500 years B.P. The age of the deposits increases with depth below present high water. Using this relation, Grant (1970a, b) showed that high tide has been rising in this region at a rate of 30 cm century^{-1}. Over the last 6300 years mean sea level has been rising at a rate of 15 cm century^{-1} so the tidal range has been increasing at a rate of 30 cm century^{-1} (Amos, 1978).

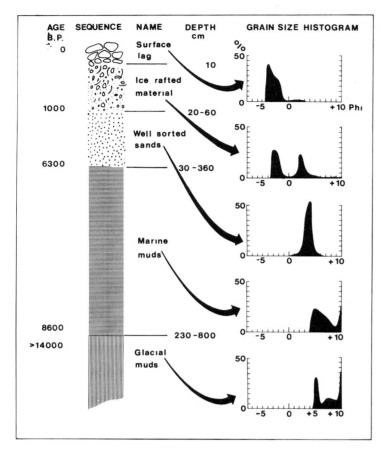

Figure 9.20. *A composite, schematic stratigraphic sequence of the postglacial subtidal sediments. The ages, depth ranges and grain size characteristics are also shown. The sequence exhibits a coarsening of grain size to the surface in response to increasing tidal activity.*

The postglacial to near-recent sediment budget. Volumetric estimates have been made of the sediments occurring between radiocarbon-dated horizons. The variations in sediment supply and type of sediment can thus be determined for the time interval represented by the sampled sedimentary column.

It has been shown that prior to 6300 years BP deposition of silt/clay material took place under quiet water conditions. The basin at this time would have been narrower and therefore wave activity would have been subdued. This would limit the sand supplied to the system. That portion that did enter would no doubt remain nearshore to protect the cliffs from further erosion by the creation of a beach or spit (Komar, 1976, p. 25). The absence of tidal currents limited the introduction of sediments from the Bay of Fundy, and also limited marginal (cliff line) sediment reworking. Therefore, the fine material deposited during the period up until 6300 years BP must have been derived from the rivers debouching into the basin. A minimum average of 0.5×10^6 m³ of sediment was debouched annually into Minas Basin. This is more than an order of magnitude higher than is presently derived from the same source. Perhaps during early postglacial times exposed glacial debris

would have been easier to winnow because vegetation cover was thinner and presumably because unstable slopes, were more abundant.

Throughout the period of increasing tidal activity after 6300 years BP, the supply of river-derived silt/clay appears to have been reduced (Table 9.3). This conclusion is based on volumetric estimates of marginal and intertidal mud flats and salt marshes (Grant, pers. com.).

Sand enters the system primarily by erosion of bordering cliffs. This erosion has resulted in the development of a wave-cut platform varying in width from 6000 m along the north shore of the basin to 1000 m along the south shore. Cliff recession, a function of cliff foot inundation, must have begun at the time of tidal inundation of the edge of the presently existing wave-cut platform. The depth of this edge is used (assuming 30 cm century⁻¹ rise in the high tide level) to infer incipient cliff erosion. The depth varies from 13 m below GSCD near Kingsport and Blomidon to 10 m below GSCD near Five Islands and Economy Point, to 8 m below GSCD in Cobequid Bay. The average age of the wave-cut platform was therefore computed to be 4900 years (S.D. = 740 years).

At 12 sites around the system, the calculated mean past cliff recession rate was compared to the measured present recession rate. The results, which are given in Table 9.5, show no significant change in this rate. This implies that cliff recession has been constant since it commenced approximately 4900 years B.P. and that (assuming similar mean cliff heights) the input of sand-sized material to the system must have been constant at 2.8×10^6 m³a⁻¹.

Table 9.5 The relationship between the present day cliff line recession (based on sequential aerial photographs) and the computed mean postglacial cliff recession based on sea level rise and tidal amplitude change data.

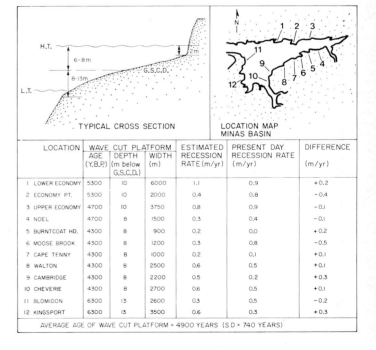

LOCATION	WAVE CUT PLATFORM			ESTIMATED RECESSION RATE (m/yr)	PRESENT DAY RECESSION RATE (m/yr)	DIFFERENCE (m/yr)
	AGE (Y.B.P.)	DEPTH (m below G.S.C.D.)	WIDTH (m)			
1 LOWER ECONOMY	5300	10	6000	1.1	0.9	+ 0.2
2 ECONOMY PT.	5300	10	2000	0.4	0.8	− 0.4
3 UPPER ECONOMY	4700	10	3750	0.8	0.9	− 0.1
4 NOEL	4700	8	1500	0.3	0.4	− 0.1
5 BURNTCOAT HD.	4300	8	900	0.2	0.0	+ 0.2
6 MOOSE BROOK	4300	8	1200	0.3	0.8	− 0.5
7 CAPE TENNY	4300	8	1000	0.2	0.1	+ 0.1
8 WALTON	4300	8	2500	0.6	0.5	+ 0.1
9 CAMBRIDGE	4300	8	2200	0.5	0.2	+ 0.3
10 CHEVERIE	4300	8	2700	0.6	0.5	+ 0.1
11 BLOMIDON	6300	13	2600	0.3	0.5	− 0.2
12 KINGSPORT	6300	13	3500	0.6	0.3	+ 0.3
AVERAGE AGE OF WAVE CUT PLATFORM = 4900 YEARS (S.D = 740 YEARS)						

CONCLUSIONS

The regional evaluation of the Minas Basin system entailed an analysis of the present sediment character and distribution, the budget of the various types of sediments and their sources, the transport of sediment both in suspension and as bedload from source to the ultimate site of deposition, and the postglacial historical development of these variables. In association with these studies, measures on the physical processes were made to define the various process/response relations for interpretive and predictive purposes. Below are the major points of conclusion derived from the study.

1. Most of the system is lined by postglacial deposits or bedrock. The surface deposits are predominantly gravels, pebbles, and cobbles subtidally, sand intertidally, and mud marginally. Bedrock crops out throughout the intertidal wave-cut platform, but only sparingly in the subtidal zone.

2. The material distributed through the water column is well mixed vertically but becomes more concentrated headwards within the basin. Concentrations range from less than 1 mg L^{-1} to greater than 2700 mg L^{-1}. Lines of equal SSC generally follow a consistent pattern; however, the absolute SSC value varies according to physical factors, such as wave stirring, proximity to the intertidal zone, and season.

3. Most of the material entering Minas Basin is derived from the bordering eroding cliffs and is predominantly sand-sized; 3.1×10^6 m^3 a^{-1} of sand is derived from this source. Silt/clay-size material is derived principally from the Bay of Fundy (up to 1.6×10^6 m^3 a^{-1}) and to a much lesser extent from the rivers debouching into the system (0.06×10^6 m^3 a^{-1}).

4. Bed material consists mostly of sand that moves in the intertidal zone. Material moves south into Windsor Bay and east towards Cobequid Bay. Radioisotope tracing of irradiated sands has shown an eastward migration of 0.46×10^6 m^3 a^{-1} of sand through the intertidal zone at Economy Point.

5. There is a strong flux of suspended material, which is principally controlled by the residual tidal current in the subtidal region and perhaps by current speed nearer to shore. Suspended material is being advected eastward into Cobequid Bay and south into Windsor Bay at rates from 0.1×10^6 g m^{-1} $tide^{-1}$ to 3.5×10^6 g m^{-1} $tide^{-1}$.

6. The subtidal stratigraphy is markedly different from that developing within the intertidal zone. The subtidal zone has glacial marine silts overlying bedrock, which in turn are overlain by 8 m of postglacial marine sediments. These latter sediments show four distinct horizons, which together define a coarsening-upwards sequence. The sequence has been interpreted as a period of nontidal conditions to 6300 years BP followed by a linear increase in tidal current activity through to the present. The rate of tidal amplitude increase has been calculated to be 0.15 m per century.

7. Volumetric estimates of differing sediment types between carbon-dated sediment horizons show a steady increase in the supply of material. Prior to 6300 years BP only 0.5×10^6 m^3 was supplied annually. This volume increased to 3.0×10^6 $m^3 a^{-1}$ during 6300 years BP to the near present, and to 4.8×10^6 $m^3 a^{-1}$ today. The proportion of silt/clay material has decreased through time in keeping with the interpreted increase in tidal conditions.

8. The determination of surface SSC spatially was made from LANDSAT data on sea surface reflectance within the visible part of the electromagnetic spectrum, which was calibrated to various concentrations of SPM. The technique can discriminate SSC levels to an accuracy of ±12 per cent and is independent of salinity, temperature, grain size, shape or composition.

9. The residual transport of suspended material was determined from flux profiles at hourly intervals from one hour before low tide to one hour after the succeeding low tide, giving results that can be reproduced within ±26 per cent. The results produced herein make sense when interpreted against the framework of geological evidence and this technique is considered valid for general interpretation.

10. The accelerations and decelerations of currents over a tidal cycle are computed differently depending on whether the flood and ebb phases of the tide are considered to represent a continuous function, or are independently governed. In the present study, each phase of the tide is considered independent and the current patterns were determined accordingly.

References

Alföldi, T.T. and Munday, J.C.
1977:   Progress toward a LANDSAT water quality monitoring system; in Proceedings of the 4th Canadian Symposium on Remote Sensing, p. 325 - 340.

Amos, C.L.
1977:   Effects of tidal power structures on the sediment transport and loading in the Bay of Fundy - Gulf of Maine system; in Fundy Tidal Power and the Environment, G. Daborn, ed.; Acadia University Press, p. 233 - 253.
1978:   The post glacial evolution of the Minas Basin, N.S. - A sedimentological interpretation; Journal of Sedimentary Petrology, v. 4, no. 2 (in press).

Amos, C.L. and Alföldi, T.T.
1979:   The determination of suspended sediment concentration in a macrotidal system using LANDSAT data; Journal of Sedimentary Petrology, v. 49, no. 1, p. 159-174.

Amos, C.L. and Joice, G.H.E.
1977:   The sediment budget of the Minas Basin, Bay of Fundy, N.S.; Bedford Institute of Oceanography, Data Series, BI-D-77-3, p. 411.

Atlantic Tidal Power Programming Board
1969:   Feasibility of tidal power development in the Bay of Fundy; Board report and committee report, Halifax, Nova Scotia.

Buller, A.T. and McManus, J.
1976:   Fluctuations of suspended sediment in estuaries. A descriptive review; Publication of Tay Estuary Research Centre, no. 3, p. 39.

Cameron, H.C.
1961:   Interpretation of high-altitude small-scale photography; The Canadian Surveyor, v. 110, p. 567 - 573.

Canadian Hydrographic Service
1966:   Bay of Fundy data report on tidal and current survey, 1965; Bedford Institute of Oceanography, Data Series, 66-2-D.

Churchill, F.J.
1924:   Recent changes in the coastline in the County of Kings; Nova Scotia Institute of Science, Proceedings and Transactions, v. 1b, p. 84 - 86.

Coastal Engineering Research Centre
1973:   Shore Protection Manual; Publication of U.S. Army Coastal Engineering Research Centre.

Courtois, G. and Hours, R.
1965:   Propositions concernant les conditions particu-lières d'emplois des radioisotopes pour étudier les mouvements des sédiments; Canadian Infor-mation, v. 8, p. 441 - 480.

Courtois, G. and Sauzay, G.
1966:   Count rate balance methods using radioactive tracers for measuring sediment mass flow; La Houille Blanch, v. 3, p. 279 - 290.

Crickmore, M.J. and Lean, G.H.
1962:   The measurement of sand transport by the time integration method with radioactive tracer; Royal Society, London, Proceedings, v. 1340, p. 27 - 47.

Crosby, D.G.
1962:   Wolfville map-area, Nova Scotia; Geological Survey of Canada Memoir 325.

Daborn, G. (editor)
1977:   Fundy Tidal Power and the Environment; Proceedings of a Workshop on the Environmental Implications of Fundy Tidal Power, held at Wolfville, Nova Scotia, November 4 - 5, 1976, G. Daborn, ed.; Acadia University Press, v. 28, p. 304.

Dalrymple, R.W.
1972:   Preliminary investigation of an intertidal sand body, Cobequid Bay, Bay of Fundy; McMaster University, Hamilton, Technical Memorandum 72-1, unpubl. MS.
1973:   Field studies of intertidal sand bars, north shore of Minas Basin, Bay of Fundy, Nova Scotia; McMaster University, Hamilton, Technical Mem-orandum 73-5, unpubl. MS.
1977:   Sediment dynamics of macrotidal sand bars, Bay of Fundy; unpubl. Ph.D. thesis, McMaster University, Hamilton, p. 634.

Dalrymple, R.W., Knight, R.J. and Middleton, G.V.
1975:   Intertidal sand bars in Cobequid Bay (Bay of Fundy); in Estuarine Research, v. 2, p. 293 - 307.

Dames and Moore Ltd.
1968:   Report marine surveys proposed tidal power project, Bay of Fundy, New Brunswick and Nova Scotia; unpubl. MS.

Dawson, W.
1917:   Tides at the head of the Bay of Fundy; Canada Department of Naval Service, Ottawa, p. 34.

Fader, G.B., King, L.H. and MacLean, B.
1977:   Surficial geology of the eastern Gulf of Maine and Bay of Fundy; Geological Survey of Canada, Paper 76-17, p. 23.

Forgeron, F.C.
1962:   Bay of Fundy bottom sediments; unpubl. M.Sc. thesis, Carleton University, Ottawa.

Goldthwait, J.W.
1924:   Physiography of Nova Scotia; Geological Survey of Canada Memoir 140, p. 179.

Graf, W.H.
1971:   Hydraulics of Sediment Transport; McGraw-Hill, p. 513.

Grant, D.R.
1970a: Recent coastal submergence of the Maritime Provinces, Canada; unpubl. Ph.D. thesis, Cornell University, Ithaca, New York, p. 109.
1970b: Recent coastal submergence of the Maritime Provinces, Canada; Canadian Journal of Earth Sciences, v. 7, p. 676 - 689.

Greenberg, D.
1977:   Effects of tidal power development on the physical oceanography of the Bay of Fundy and Gulf of Maine; in Fundy Tidal Power and the Environment, G. Daborn, ed.; Acadia University Press, p. 200 - 232.

Groen, P.
1967:   On the residual transport of suspended matter by an alternating tidal current; Netherlands Journal of Sea Research, v.3, p. 564 - 574.

Huntec Ltd.
1966:   Report on geological-geophysical study Minas Basin, Bay of Fundy, Nova Scotia; unpubl. MS, p. 127.

Johns, B.
1976:   A note on the boundary layer at the floor of a tidal channel; Dynamics of Atmospheres and Oceans, v.1, p. 91 - 98.

Klein, G. de V.
1963:   Bay of Fundy intertidal zone sediments; Journal of Sedimentary Petrology, v.33, p. 844 - 854.
1970:   Depositional and dispersal dynamics of intertidal sand bars; Journal of Sedimentary Petrology, v. 40, p. 1095 - 1127.

Knight, R.J.
1977:   Sediments, bedforms and hydraulics in a macrotidal environment, Cobequid Bay (Bay of Fundy), Nova Scotia; unpubl. Ph.D. thesis, McMaster University, Hamilton, p. 693.

Komar, P.D.
1976:   Beach Processes and Sedimentation; Prentice-Hall, 429 p.

Lambiase, J.J.
1977:   Sediment dynamics in the macrotidal Avon River estuary, Nova Scotia; unpubl. Ph.D. thesis, McMaster University, Hamilton, p. 415.

Long, B.F.N.
1977: Determination of sediment transport rate in the Minas Basin, Nova Scotia: Preliminary results of the first tracer experiment using radioisotope; in Report of Activities, Part B, Geological Survey of Canada, Paper 77-1B, p. 85 - 92.

Long, B.F.N. and Belanger, J.R.
1978: Bed form movement studies by remote sensing balloon technique in Minas Basin, Bay of Fundy; in Current Research, Part A, Geological Survey of Canada, Paper 78-1A, p. 503 - 508.

Marine Environmental Data Service
1977: Waves recorded off Minas Basin, Nova Scotia, June 30, 1975 to November 23, 1976; unpubl. MS.

McMullen, R.M. and Swift, D.J.P.
1967: An occurrence of large scale rhomboid ripples, Minas Basin, Nova Scotia; Journal of Sedimentary Petrology, v. 27, p. 705, 706.

Middleton, G.V.
1972: Brief field guide to intertidal sediments, Minas Basin, Nova Scotia; Maritime Sediments, v.8, p. 114 - 122.
1977: The sediment regime of the Bay of Fundy; in Fundy Tidal Power and the Environment, G. Daborn, ed.; Acadia University Press, p. 125 - 130.

Middleton, G.V. and Davis, P.M.
1979: Surface textures and rounding of quartz sand grains on intertidal sand bars, Bay of Fundy; Canadian Journal of Earth Sciences (in press).

Middleton, G.V., Knight, R.J. and Dalrymple, R.W.
1976: Facies model for macrotidal environments, Cobequid Bay, Nova Scotia; American Association of Petroleum Geology Bulletin, v. 60, p. 697, 698.

Miller, J.A.
1966: The suspended sediment system in the Bay of Fundy; unpubl. M.Sc. thesis, Dalhousie University, Halifax, p. 100.

NASA
1976: LANDSAT Data Users Handbook; Goddard Space Flight Center.

Owens, E.H.
1977: Coastal environments, oil spills and clean-up programmes in the Bay of Fundy; Economic and Technical Review Report, EPS-3-EC-77-9, p. 175.

Pelletier, B.R.
1974: Sedimentary textures and relative entropy and their relationship to the hydrodynamic environment, Bay of Fundy system; Geological Survey of Canada, Paper 74-30, v.1, p. 77 - 95.

Pelletier, B.R. and McMullen, R.M.
1972: Sedimentation patterns in the Bay of Fundy and Minas Basin; in Tidal Power, T.J. Gray and O.K. Gashus, ed.; Plenum Publishing Co., p. 153 - 187.

Risk, M.J., Yeo, R.K. and Craig, H.D.
1977: Aspects of the marine ecology of the Minas Basin relevant to tidal power development; in Fundy Tidal Power and the Environment, G. Daborn, ed.; Acadia University Press, p. 164 - 179.

Sauzay, G.
1968: Méthode du bilan des taux de comptage d'indicateurs radioactifs pour la détermination du débit de charriage des lits sableux; Ph.D. thesis, Toulouse University, France.

Spiegel, M.R.
1961: Theory and problems of statistics; Schaums Outline Series, p. 359.

Stephens, G.R.
1977: Geology and tectonic framework of the Bay of Fundy - Gulf of Maine region; in Fundy Tidal Power and the Environment, G. Daborn, ed.; Acadia University Press, p. 82 - 100.

Swift, D.J.P. and Borns, H.W.
1967: A raised fluvial outwash terrace, north shore of the Minas Basin, Nova Scotia; Journal of Geology, v. 75, p. 693 - 710.

Swift, D.J.P., Cok, A.E. and Lyall, A.K.
1966: A subtidal sandbody in the Minas Channel, eastern Bay of Fundy; Maritime Sediments, v.2, p. 175 - 180.

Swift, D.J.P. and Lyall, A.K.
1968: Origin of the Bay of Fundy, an interpretation from sub-bottom profiles; Maritime Geology, v.6, p. 331 - 343.

Swift, D.J.P. and McMullen, R.M.
1968: Preliminary studies of intertidal sand bodies in the Minas Basin, Bay of Fundy, Nova Scotia; Canadian Journal of Earth Sciences, v. 5, p. 175 - 183.

Swift, D.J.P., McMullen, R.M. and Lyall, A.K.
1967: A tidal delta with an ebb-flood channel system in the Minas Basin, Bay of Fundy; Preliminary report; Maritime Sediments, v. 3, p. 12 - 16.

Swift, D.J.P., Pelletier, B.R., Lyall, A.K. and Miller, J.A.
1973: Quaternary sedimentation in the Bay of Fundy; Geological Survey of Canada, Paper 71-23, p. 113 - 151.

Tee, K.T.
1975: Tide induced residual current in Minas Channel and Minas Basin; unpubl. Ph.D. thesis, Dalhousie University, Halifax, p. 142.
1976: Tide-induced residual current, a 2-D nonlinear numerical tidal model; Journal of Maritime Research, v. 34, p. 603 - 628.
1977: Tide-induced residual current-verification of a numerical model; Journal of Physical Oceanography, v. 7, p. 396 - 402.

Welsted, J.
1976: Post-glacial emergence of the Fundy Coast: An analysis of the evidence; Canadian Geographer, v. 20, p. 367 - 383.

10.

LINEAR SAND BAR DEVELOPMENT AND TIDAL CURRENT FLOW IN COBEQUID BAY (BAY OF FUNDY), NOVA SCOTIA

R. John Knight
Geological Research, Petro-Canada, Calgary, Alberta

Knight, R. John, Linear sand bar development and tidal current flow in Cobequid Bay (Bay of Fundy), Nova Scotia; in The Coastline of Canada, S.B. McCann, editor; Geological Survey of Canada, Paper 80-10, p. 123-152, 1980.

Abstract

Cobequid Bay, at the eastern end of the Bay of Fundy, is renowned for its large tides which have a mean range of 11.6 m near the entrance. The semidiurnal, reversing tidal currents, with speeds as high as 2.0 m/s, dominate the sedimentary environment. No major rivers enter the bay and most of the strongest wave energy is expended on bedrock headlands and at the seaward end of the sand bar complex. Sand deposition is concentrated primarily in the centre of the bay as an extensive intertidal to subtidal channel-bar complex, 5 to 15 m thick, underlain by local accumulations (up to 10 m) of premodern (possibly Pleistocene) sediments and bedrock. The sand bars are elongate features, 1 to 5 km long, aligned roughly parallel with the tidal currents. They are asymmetrical in transverse and longitudinal section, tapered towards their seaward ends, and covered with megaripples (length 1-12 m) and sand waves (length 5-30 m). The sand bar complex evolved during the past 4000 years as sea level rose and as the large tidal range was established. During this period, sediments were supplied from the erosion and reworking of Pleistocene and Triassic sources in and around the bay, and from the input of glaciofluvial sediments from the margin of the bay. The distribution of ebb and flood dominant areas indicates that the general pattern of sediment circulation in the bay resembles an ebb delta. The observed geometry and morphology of the sand bars is maintained by the time-velocity asymmetry of the tidal currents, the opposing ebb and flood cross-bar components of flow that develop during the high-water sheet-flow phases of the tide (while the bar crests are submergent), and the low-water channel-flow phases of the tide (while the bar crests are emergent).

Résumé

La baie Cobequid à l'extrémité est de la baie de Fundy est réputée pour ses grandes marées dont l'amplitude moyenne est de 11,6 m près de l'entrée. Les courants de marée inversés et semi-diurnes atteignant des vitesses de 2,0 m/s dominent le milieu de sédimentation. Aucun grand cours d'eau n'entre dans la baie et la plus grande partie de la plus forte énergie due aux vagues se déploie sur les promontoires rocheux et sur l'extrémité marine du complexe de cordons. La sédimentation sableuse se concentre surtout au centre de la baie où elle forme un vaste complexe de cordons et de chenaux intertidaux à subtidaux, de 5 à 15 m d'épaisseur, reposant sur des accumulations intermittentes (qui atteignent 10 m) de sédiments et de roches en place d'âge récent (probablement du Pléistocène). Les cordons sont des accidents de forme allongée, d'une longueur de 1 à 5 km, dont l'alignement est plus ou moins parallèle aux courants de marée. Elles sont asymétriques et appartiennent à des sections transversales et longitudinales, effilées vers leur extrémité qui avance dans la mer et recouvertes d'énormes rides de plage (d'une longueur de 1-12 m) et des ondulations de sable (d'une longueur de 5-30 m). Le complexe de cordons a évolué au cours des 4 000 dernières années à mesure que le niveau de la mer s'est élevé et que la grande amplitude de marée s'est établie. Au cours de cette période, les matériaux ont été fournis par l'érosion et le remaniement de sources pléistocènes et triasiques dans la baie et autour de celle-ci, et à partir de l'apport de matériaux fluvioglaciaires provenant de la bordure de la baie. La répartition des ondes de jusant et de flot indique que l'organisation générale de la circulation des matériaux dans la baie ressemble à celle d'un delta de jusant. La géométrie et la morphologie des cordons sont entretenues par l'asymétrie temps-vitesse des courants de marée, les composantes opposées de cordons transversals de jusant et de flot qui se développent pendant les phases d'écoulement en nappe au moment des hautes eaux de la marée (tandis que les crêtes de cordons sont submergées), et les phases d'écoulement en chenal au moment des basses eaux de la marée lorsque les crêtes de cordons émergent).

INTRODUCTION

Tidal current ridges characterize many areas of the world's coastal ocean (Off, 1963; Swift, 1975; Swift and Ludwick, 1976). Their depositional morphology results from the interaction of many dynamic factors including tidal action, wave energy, fluvial regime, climate, sediment sources and yields, basin geometry and tectonics. The ridges are basically elongate accumulations of sand or gravel, which are oriented parallel to the tidal currents. They may be either symmetrical or asymmetrical in transverse section, and typically are found in groups in relatively shallow seas (less than 60 m; Off, 1963) along continental margins in areas with strong tidal currents (up to 2.3 m/s; Allen, 1968, p.49). Since the early observations by Van Veen (1935, 1937, 1950), tidal current ridges have received increasing attention, but many questions remain unanswered. For example, many workers do not distinguish between ridges that are 'tide-formed' and those that are 'tide-maintained'.

Swift (1975) recognized three types of tidal current ridge occurrence: (i) ridges in or at the mouth of estuaries and embayments (e.g., Allen et al., 1972; Green, 1975; Hayes and Kana, 1976; Klein, 1970; Ludwick, 1972, 1974; Off, 1963; Meckel, 1975; Oomkens and Terwindt,1960; Reineck, 1963; Robinson, 1960; Smith, 1968, 1969; Swift and McMullen, 1968; Terwindt et al., 1963; Wright et al., 1973, 1975; Van Veen, 1950); (ii) ridges off capes and promontories (e.g., Cloet, 1954; Off, 1963; Robinson, 1966; Swift, 1975; Swift and Ludwick, 1976; Van Veen, 1937; and (iii) ridges on open shelves and shelf edges (e.g., Caston, 1972; Caston and Stride, 1970; Houbolt, 1968; Huthnance, 1973; James and Stanley, 1968; Jordan, 1962; Stewart and Jordan, 1965; Stride et al., 1972; Van Veen, 1935, 1937). The ridges in estuaries and embayments are generally elongate in a perpendicular or slightly oblique direction relative to the regional trend of the shoreline. Ridges found further offshore, off promontories and capes, and on the shelves and shelf edges, commonly develop parallel to the shoreline or

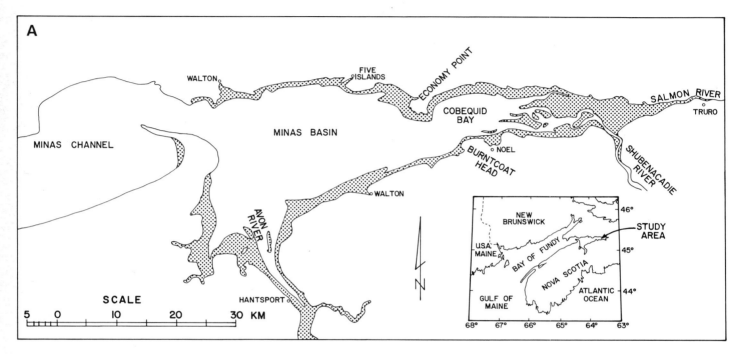

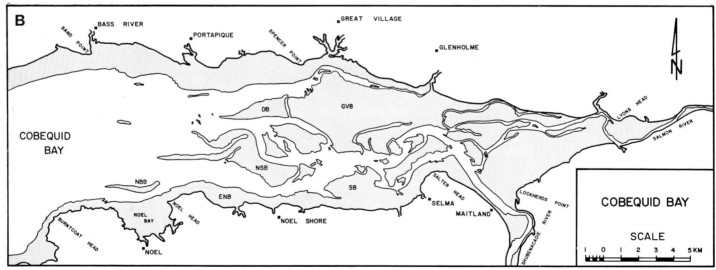

NBB – Noel Bay Barr   NSB – Noel Shore Bar

DB – Diamond Bar   ENB – East Noel Bar

SB – Selmah Bar   GVB – Great Village Bar

Figure 10.1.   *Location map of A) Minas Basin and Cobequid Bay at the head of the Bay of Fundy, and B) Cobequid Bay. Intertidal zone is stippled.*

edge of the continental shelf. At first glance, the morphological similarities of the tidal current ridges from different settings suggest that all ridges belong to a single generic group. There are, however, significant differences in the dynamic factors responsible for the formation and maintenance of tidal current ridges between different settings, as well as significant differences between the various settings themselves. These differences support the argument that individual groups of tidal current ridges should be treated as separate genetic types.

To gain a better understanding of some of the specific processes and mechanics involved in the formation and maintenance of one type of tidal current ridge, a field study was conducted on some elongate, intertidal to subtidal sand bars (ridges) located in Cobequid Bay, a tide-dominated estuary at the head of the Bay of Fundy. This paper will deal primarily with the dynamic factors responsible for the maintenance of the sand bars in Cobequid Bay (Fig. 10.1) because this aspect is easier to document than speculations about the possible origins of the sand bars. The results reported here are part of a larger study (Knight, 1977) concerned with the sedimentary dynamics of the sediments, bedforms and hydraulics in a macrotidal setting.

THE STUDY AREA

Environmental factors

Cobequid Bay is at the eastern end of the Bay of Fundy, an area renowned for its large semidiurnal tides, which are believed to be the result of resonant amplification of the tide's lunar component (Garrett, 1972) as it moves across the continental shelf southwest of Nova Scotia and into the Bay of Fundy. The amplitude of the tide developed largely within the last 6000 years (Grant, 1970) as the Bay of Fundy system reached resonant dimensions through the combined effects of the eustatic rise of sea level, the sinking of the land as a result of excessive isotatic rebound, and erosion of the shoreline and seabed.

The present tides have a mean range of 11.7 m. The mean spring range is approximately 12.3 m at lunal apogee and 15.4 m at lunar perigee. The maximum measured tidal range is 16.3 m (Dawson, 1917) from the west side of Burntcoat Head at the entrance to Cobequid Bay. The mean speed of the reversing tidal currents associated with the large rise and fall of the tides varies greatly during the tidal cycle, between neap and spring phase of the lunar cycle, and from place to place within the bay. In general, maximum near-bottom (0.5 m) currents attain speeds of up to 2.0 m/s. The average tidal prism has an approximate discharge of 2.94 billion m^3 into and out of Minas Basin-Cobequid Bay every 6.2 hours (Atlantic Tidal Power Engineering and Management Committee, 1969 (ATPEMC).

The westerly prevailing winds have an average speed of 15.7 km/h. Although this direction coincides with the major axis of Minas Basin-Cobequid Bay (Fig. 10.1), wave development is limited because the study area is isolated from the main Bay of Fundy and the fetch is relatively short (about 50 km). Waves generated within the bay are dissipated largely on the bedrock headlands and broad intertidal foreshores around the margins of the bay, and at the seaward edge of the intertidal to subtidal sand body in the centre of Cobequid Bay. Most waves observed during the summer (May through September) had average heights of less than 0.5 m.

The climate of the area is strongly influenced by the easterly passage of air masses from the continental interior. Although proximity to the ocean modifies annual temperatures to some extent, the mean annual temperature is only about 6.3°C. From December to March (or early April), the mean monthly temperatures fall below freezing. Annual precipitation averages about 1.18 m and is distributed uniformly throughout the year. During the winter, much of the study area is covered with drift ice, the intertidal zone is covered with a frozen (ice-sediment) crust, and the shoreline is bordered with an ice foot. Each of these affects the nature of sedimentation during the winter (Knight and Dalrymple, 1976). The presence of drift ice dampens wave activity while the shorefast ice foot protects the shoreline from erosion. The frozen crust covering the intertidal zone almost completely immobilizes the intertidal sediments, preventing normal bedload transport and the development of large bedforms.

Most of the rivers entering the bay are small and are not contributing large volumes of either water or sediment. The fluvial regime was likely of much greater importance during the post-Pleistocene retreat of the continental ice sheets from the area. The rivers discharging into the bay have an average watershed area of less than 250 km^2 and Stichling (1974) reported that sediment concentrations were less than 50 mg/L. The Salmon River, which is the largest river entering the bay (Fig. 10.1), has a watershed area of about 360 km^2 (Hennigar, 1972; J.E. Peters, pers. com.), a mean daily discharge of approximately 11 m^3/s and a mean annual discharge of about 4.38 x 10^{8}m^3. Its mean suspended sediment concentration is about 9.5 mg/L.

Although freshwater input into the bay is relatively small, it is sufficient to lower salinities in the bay to 29 to 30 per thousand. The large tidal range, however, causes thorough mixing of the fresh and salt water, preventing the development of any vertical stratification in the water column. Mean water temperatures ranged from 10 to 20°C during the summer months and as low as -0.5°C during periods of winter observations. Temperatures of the flooding tide are about 2 to 3° colder and salinities are about 1 to 2 per thousand higher than those measured during the ebb (ATPEMC, 1969; Knight, 1977). These differences reflect the influx of colder, more saline ocean water during the flood, and the discharge of warmer, freshwater diluted seawater during the ebb. The extensive intertidal zone in Cobequid Bay plays an important role in controlling water temperatures, tending to cool temperatures during the winter and warm them during the summer.

The amount of suspended sediment in the bay is much higher than that found in the rivers above any tidal influence. Concentrations range up to 2700 mg/L (Knight, 1977), but are generally about 20 to 200 mg/L. They vary up to an order of magnitude during a single tidal cycle and from place to place in the bay. The highest concentrations occur during the late ebb and early flood and commonly lag the time of maximum current speeds by 15 to 30 minutes. Suspended sediment concentrations during the flood are often as much as 50 per cent greater than those measured during the late ebb. The large amount of suspended sediment in the water likely is related to the resuspension of mud from the intertidal mudflats by wave and current activity. Examination under a binocular microscope of the suspended sediments collected 0.5 m from the bottom indicates that most are silt and clay sized particles, not sand sized sediments.

Holocene sediments

There are wide variety of sediments and sedimentary facies in Cobequid Bay (Fig. 10.2) and Minas Basin (Dalrymple, 1977; Klein, 1964, 1968, 1970; Knight, 1977; Lambiase, 1977). The distribution of sediment types, particularly in the intertidal zone, is closely related to the lithology and proximity to source materials in and around the bay (Figs. 10.3a, 10.3b). The Holocene sediments in the bay were derived from the erosion of Triassic sandstones, and Pleistocene glaciofluvial and till sediments found exposed in the shoreline and bottom of the bay. Although rivers are not presently contributing much sediment, they were likely important sediment sources during the post-Pleistocene period.

The importance of shoreline sediment sources is readily evident from the broad wave- and current-eroded platform (Fig. 10.3a) around the margins of the bay, the lithological similarities between the shoreline source materials and the sediments in the bay (Balazs and Klein, 1972; Dalrymple, 1977; Klein, 1964, 1968, 1970; Knight, 1977), and the reported rapid rates of shoreline erosion (up to 2 m/y; Amos and Joice, 1977; ATPEMC, 1969; Churchill, 1924; Klein, 1968). Submarine sources of sediment are difficult to document, but the seabed is still considered to be an important source. King and MacLean (1974) reported that the lithology of materials comprising the seabed was similar to that found in the shoreline. Amos and Joice (1977) made a comparison of an 1858 British Admiralty Chart of Cobequid Bay and the results from their 1976 hydrographic survey to delineate areas of net accretion or erosion on the seabed. Their mapped results are, however, somewhat inconclusive.

The bay is bordered largely by cliffs of Triassic sandstone (Fig. 10.3a), which reach up to 30 m in height, and low bluffs of Pleistocene and post-Pleistocene sediments (Fig. 10.3b), which range up to 10 m. The intertidal zone is characterized by a bedrock platform that is either scoured (Fig. 10.3a) or covered with a veneer of sediments (Figs. 10.3c, 10.3d). Mud accumulates only in areas that are sheltered (Figs. 10.3e, 10.3f) from strong wave and current activity. These areas are restricted to the margins of the bay in estuaries and small embayments. The mudflats are generally backed by supratidal saltmarshes. More complete descriptions of the intertidal zone sediments can be found in Dalrymple (1977) and Knight (1977).

As in tide dominated estuaries and embayments found elsewhere, sand deposition is concentrated primarily in the centre of the bay (Fig. 10.2), away from shore (Knight, 1977; Pelletier and McMullen, 1972; Swift and McMullen, 1968). The sand in Cobequid Bay has been moulded into an extensive intertidal to subtidal sandbar complex about 10 by 25 km.

THE SAND BODY

There are many similarities between the morphology of the sand body in Cobequid Bay and the morphological model proposed by Hayes (1975, p.17) for a macrotidal estuary. Some of the similarities include dominance of tidal processes, a broad-mouthed, funnel-shaped estuarine geometry, and sand deposition in the centre of the estuary in the form of elongate bodies oriented parallel with the tidal currents. Hayes suggested further that the intertidal foreshore is commonly dominated by broad tidal mudflats. Cobequid Bay does not, however, conform to this latter aspect. From a preliminary examination of the literature and hydrographic charts from other macrotidal estuaries, it seems that Cobequid Bay is not an exception to the model and that Hayes's model is a little overgeneralized. Previous studies of the sandbars in Cobequid Bay and Minas Basin include those of Balazs and Klein (1972), Dalrymple (1973a, b, 1974a, b, 1975, 1976, 1977), Dalrymple et al. (1975, 1978), Klein (1968, 1970), Klein and Whaley (1972), Knight (1971, 1972, 1973, and 1977), Knight and Dalrymple (1975, 1976), Lambiase (1977), Middleton (1972) Middleton et al. (1975 and 1976) and Swift and McMullen (1968).

As a result of the large tidal range, an extensive intertidal zone (Fig. 10.1b) is exposed around the margins of the bay and on the upper parts of the sand body in the centre of the bay. The sand body comprises two principal subfacies: (i) broad intertidal sand flats with a braidlike channel pattern (Figs. 10.4a, 10.4b) located at the head of the bay, which are composed chiefly of fine-grained sand and which are covered with ripples and relatively few large bedforms, and (ii) elongate intertidal to subtidal sandbars (Figs. 10.4c, 10.4d) separated by relatively few, but deep, channels located in the outer part of the bay (west of Salter Head), which are composed of medium- to coarse-grained sands and are covered with megaripples and sand waves. It is this subfacies that is of particular interest to this study.

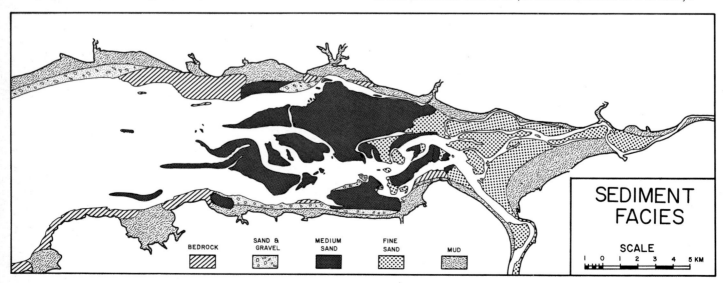

Figure 10.2. Distribution of the intertidal sediment facies in Cobequid Bay.

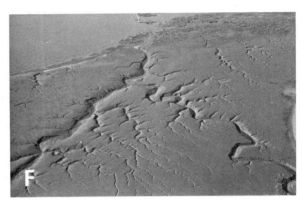

A. *Oblique air photo of erosional bedrock plat-form at Burntcoat Head. Seacliffs are composed of Triassic sandstone and are approximately 15 m in height.*

B. *View of Pleistocene tills exposed in the shoreline near Selmah Bar. Note the sandy-gravel and boulder-strewn intertidal fores-hore. Bluffs in background are about 5 m in height.*

C. *View of Noel Head showing the presence of a sand veneer overlying the erosional platform at the base of the bedrock cliffs. Note the occurrence of lag gravel near the high water mark and the figure for scale.*

D. *View of intertidal zone sediments near Selmah Bar. Note Selmah Bar in the background.*

E. *Oblique air photo of Noel Bay (Noel bay Bar to left centre) showing the development of mudflats in sheltered embayments of the coastline. Note occurrence of saltmarsh around the margins of the bay.*

F. *Oblique air photo of the mudflats located to the east of Selmah Bar showing the dendritic drainage pattern.*

Figure 10.3. *Sediment sources in the shoreline and sedimentary facies in the intertidal foreshore around Cobequid Bay.*

Emergence of the upper parts of the sandbars at low tide provides an opportunity, seldom found in other tide dominated estuaries, to examine directly many sedimentary features (e.g., bedforms, sedimentary structures, sandbar geometry). Several sandbars were selected from Cobequid Bay (Fig. 10.1b) for detailed study. These included: Noel Bay Bar and Noel Shore Bar from the outer, relatively higher energy part of the sand body away from the shoreline; East Noel Bar in the flood lee of Noel Head in a relatively lower energy part of the bay adjacent to the shoreline; and Selmah Bar in the ebb lee of Salter Head in a low- to medium-energy part of the sand body relatively close to the shoreline. The detailed studies of these sandbars included description and mapping of the bar morphology and geometry, the bedforms (more than 600 measurement sites), the sediments (more than 250 samples) and the tidal current flow at representative locations (Knight, 1977). The results of the detailed studies were then extrapolated to other sandbars in the bay with the aid of spot studies. Supplementary data were collected from Great Village Bar and several of the major interbar channels, and from detailed studies carried out by Dalrymple (1977) on Diamond Bar.

Bathymetry and structure

Thirteen transects of the sand body in Cobequid Bay (Fig. 10.5a), totalling about 110 km of survey line, and numerous individual surveys of the four bars selected for detailed study were obtained using a Raytheon Fathometer (model DE-719) and a Huntec 'sparker', in order to ascertain the bathymetric configuration and three-dimensional structure of the sand body and the sandbars.

The sandbars (Fig. 10.2) vary considerably in size, geometry and morphological complexity. The dimensions of the emergent parts of the bars range from 1 to 10 km, in length and 0.2 to 4.2 km in width. The average relief, from the adjacent channel bottoms (Figs. 10.5b, 10.9), decreases from more than 15 m near the dominantly subtidal, seaward edge of the sand body to less than 5 m near Salter Head. At high tide, the bars are covered by 5 to more than 20 m of water, depending upon their location in the bay. The surface elevation of the sand body and the individual sandbars increases towards the head of the bay.

A. Oblique air photo looking into the estuary of the Salmon River. Note zonation from saltmarsh to mudflat to sandflat (left to right) and meandering channel from the estuary.

B. Oblique air photo of sand flats northeast of Salter Head. Note the braided nature of the channel patterns and the relatively few large bedforms.

C. Oblique air photo of sand bars. Great Village Bar is in the foreground, Noel Shore Bar in the middle and Noel Bay in the middle background. The tide level is about one hour before low water.

D. Oblique air photo from the south side of the bay looking towards Selmah Bar. Note Salter Head in the upper right corner and Great Village Bar off to the upper left.

Figure 10.4. Intertidal sand flats and sand bars in Cobequid Bay.

In plan, the seaward ends of the sandbars are tapered compared to their eastern extremities. In transverse section, the bars are asymmetrical (Figs. 10.8, 10.9), generally with their steeply sloping sides inclined (4 to 12 degrees) towards the central axis of the bay and with their gently sloping sides inclined (3 to 5 degrees) towards the margins of the sand body. There are, however, numerous exceptions to this generalization, dependent upon the morphological complexity of the individual sandbars.

It is difficult to determine from a comparison of old hydrographic charts and airphotos whether the sand body and the individual sandbars have significantly changed their configuration and size. A preliminary examination (Figs. 10.2, 10.6) suggests that little change in the size of the sand body has occurred, but there have been some changes in the low tide outline and surface morphology of individual sandbars. These conclusions are, however, somewhat misleading because each airphoto set was taken at different times relative to the time and elevation of low water. Furthermore, since the sand body has developed largely within the last 4000 years as tidal amplitude increased (Grant, 1970), one could question whether a change in the size of the sand body could realistically be detected for the past 100 years (i.e., a change of about 1/40 of its size).

In general, the individual sandbars have maintained their positions in the sand body, but there have been some significant changes in their low tide configuration and surface morphology. Sandbars near or adjacent to the shoreline have changed least. Bars farther away from shore, and particularly towards the seaward edge of the sand body,

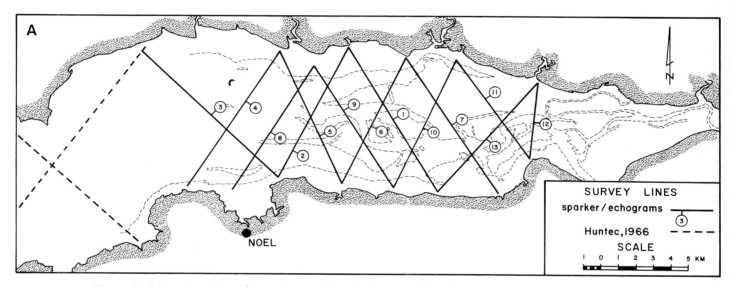

Figure 10.5A. *Location of sounding and 'sparker' survey lines in Cobequid Bay. The weak dashed line represents the outline of the intertidal zone.*

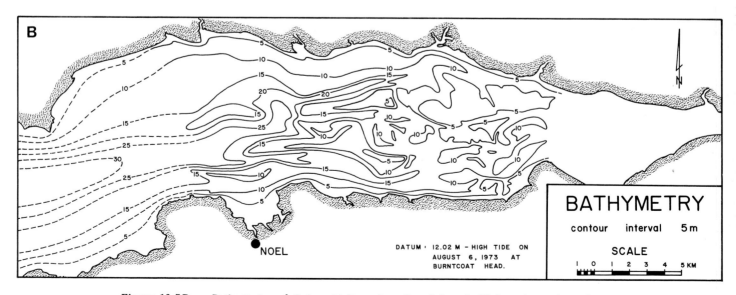

Figure 10.5B. *Bathymetry of Cobequid Bay. Sounding datum is 12.4 m above chart datum.*

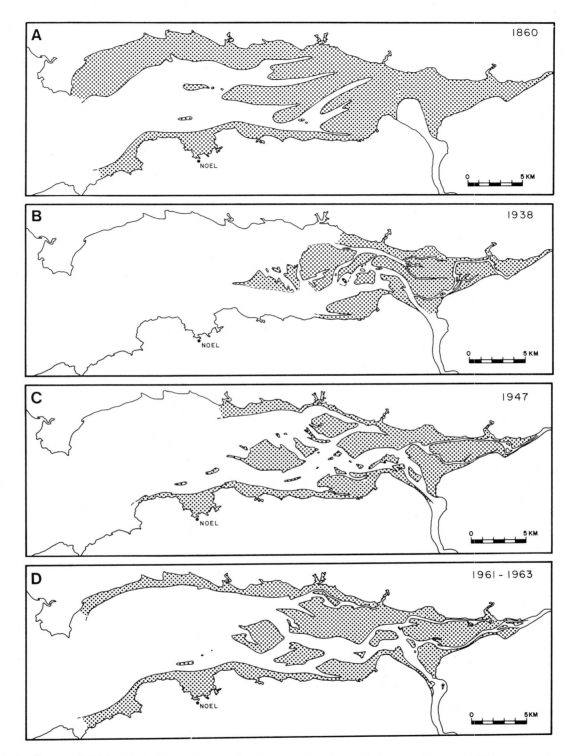

A. *From a British Admiralty hydrographic chart surveyed in 1860.*

B. *From airphotos taken in 1938 (photographed about 1.5 hours before low water).*

C. *From airphotos taken in 1947 (photographed about 1.0 hour before low water).*

D. *From airphotos taken in 1961 and 1963 (photographed about 1.0 hour before low water).*

Figure 10.6. *Historical variation of the intertidal zone outline in Cobequid Bay. For a comparison with the 1973 outline, refer to Figure 10.2.*

have undergone more substantial changes, possibly as a result of lateral migration or avulsion of crossbar swatchways and interbar channels. Channel avulsion is of particular importance at the head of the bay where the interbar channels have changed position rather frequently and quickly. Lateral migration of these channels would not account for the changes because an average migration rate of about 180 m/a* would be required.

The surfaces of the sandbars are covered with a variety of bedforms (Fig. 10.7), including: (i) ripples, with spacings generally less than 0.15 m and heights less than 0.05 m; (ii) megaripples (or dunes), with spacings ranging from 1 to 12 m and heights from 0.10 to 0.70 m; and (iii) sand waves, with spacings ranging from 10 to 30 m and heights from 0.40 to 1.50 m. The bedforms form as a result of the movement of bed material by traction and intermittent suspension close to the bed. At low tide the bedforms are either ebb-oriented or ebb-modified flood features with their crestlines generally oriented at an oblique angle to the longitudinal axis of the sandbars. Bedform scale and type varied primarily as a function of flow strength and sediment size (Dalrymple et al., 1978); depth was of only secondary importance.

During the winter, the frozen crust on the sandbars caused almost complete immobilization of the intertidal sediment surface, preventing the development of large bedforms (Knight and Dalrymple, 1976). The combined effects of grounding drift ice and the formation of the frozen crust either subdued or completely obliterated pre-existing bedforms. Further modification of the bar surfaces resulted from the increased amount of surface runoff across the frozen crust. The increased volume of late-stage ebb runoff caused erosion of the frozen crust, exposing the underlying unfrozen bar sediments. Localized removal of the frozen crust also occurred as a result of current scour and the freezing of drift ice to the frozen crust.

The sand body is underlain by Triassic bedrock (Figs. 10.8, 10.9; Amos and Joice, 1977; ATPEMC, 1969; Huntec, 1966; King and MacLean, 1974; Knight, 1977; Swift and McMullen, 1968). Contours on this erosional surface indicate a relatively broad, longitudinal depression extending along the central axis of the bay, both shallowing and converging towards the head of the bay. The bedrock surface is overlain by up to 25 m of sediment or more. The sediment occurs as either isolated or tabular accumulations elongate to the major axis of the bay and separated by

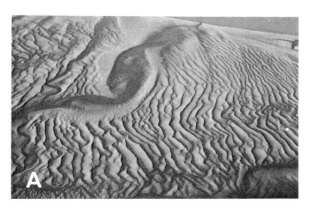

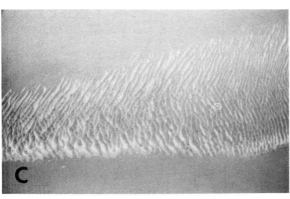

A. Oblique airphoto over the central part of Selmah Bar showing the occurrence of flood oriented sand waves and a swatchway across the bar.

B. Large sand waves on Selmah Bar with obliquely superimposed megaripples. Scale in figures hand is 1 m long.

C. Oblique airphoto of the surface of Noel Bay Bar showing the occurrence of megaripples and their oblique crestline orientation relative to the bar crest.

D. Sinuous crested megaripples on the north side of Selmah Bar. Note figures for scale.

Figure 10.7. Bedforms on the surface of the sand bars.

---

*a is the SI abbreviation for year.

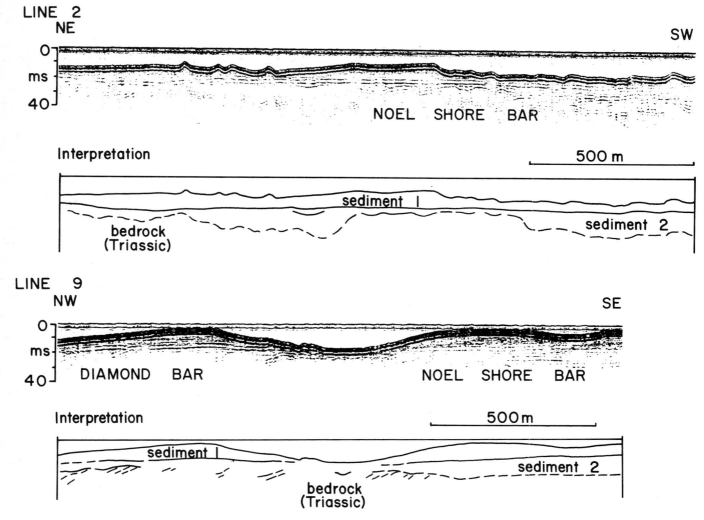

Figure 10.8. *Two representative segments of 'sparker' profiles from Cobequid Bay. See Figure 10.5 A for the location of the lines.*

channels commonly scoured down to the bedrock surface. The sediments comprise a lower premodern (up to 10 m thick) and upper modern (up to 15 m thick) accumulation, both of which thin towards the head of the bay (Fig. 10.9). From the nature of the premodern sediments, traced laterally to intertidal exposures, they appear to represent either Pleistocene tills or post-Pleistocene glaciofluvial sands and gravels, or both, rather than a multistory stacking of Holocene sand bodies developed in response to the post-glacial rise of sea level and growth of the tidal range. Further evidence to support this conclusion follows from tracing the thick accumulation of premodern sediments found immediately west of Economy Point (Fig. 10.9, line 4) to glaciofluvial sediments found in the Bass and Portapique river valleys along the north shore of the bay.

The modern sediments constitute the present day sand body in Cobequid Bay. In samples collected from bedform crests on the sandbars, the average sediment size is a medium sand (about 0.34 mm) and the sediments are moderately well sorted. Areal variations of grain size and sorting tend to parallel the major axis of the sandbars. The coarsest and most poorly sorted sediments were on the side of the bars closest to the shoreline. Grain size decreased and sorting improved fairly regularly away from the shore, towards the crestline of the bars and towards the head of the bay. The intervening channels between the bars were either scoured to bedrock (Figs. 10.8, 10.9) or floored with thin accumulations of lag gravel or sand. The sediments in the channels were typically coarser and somewhat more poorly sorted.

There are many similarities between the sandbars found in Cobequid Bay and those examined by Klein (1970) and Dalrymple (1977) at Economy Point and Five Islands, by Swift and McMullen (1968) near Walton, and by Lambiase (1977) in the Avon River estuary. The sandbars located off Economy Point and near Walton are, however, probably exposed to the strongest wave activity in Cobequid Bay and Minas Basin, while those located at Five Islands are sheltered by several bedrock islands. The sandbars found in the Avon River estuary are also well sheltered from strong waves. Thus the sandbars in Cobequid Bay may not be directly comparable to other bars found within Minas Basin, because of differences in setting and environmental factors.

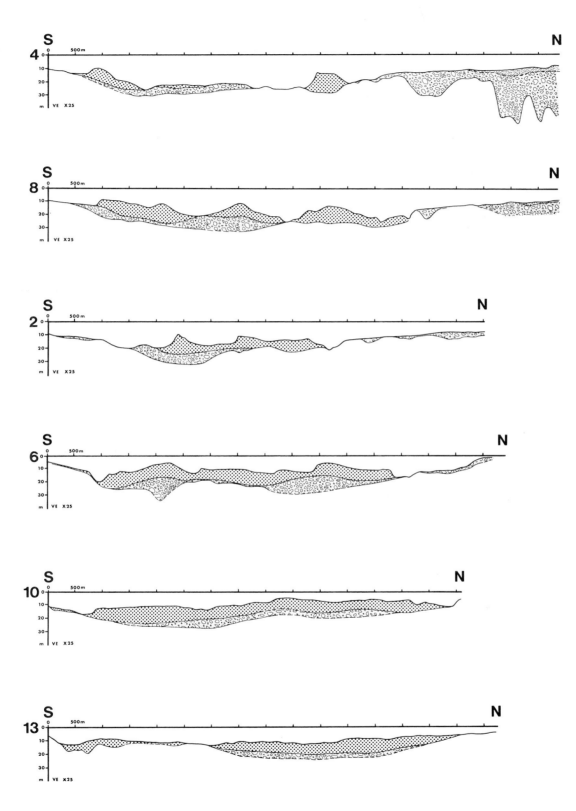

Figure 10.9. *Representative interpreted structural cross-sections of intertidal to subtidal sand body in Cobequid Bay from the entrance to the head. See Figure 10.5A for the location of the lines.*

TIDAL CURRENT FLOW

A fundamental problem in understanding the dynamics of sediment movement is that the exact form of the relationship between the fluid and the sediment in either laboratory flumes or natural flows is not fully understood. A major problem, therefore, is the choice of the appropriate hydraulic variables. Experience from flumes and rivers suggests that the two most important variables are water depth and mean speed (Brooks, 1958; Colby, 1964; Southard, 1971; Vanoni, 1974). In tidal environments, flow direction is also of particular importance. Both water depth and flow direction can be determined relatively reliably from field measurements, and mean speed can be easily calculated from the measured vertical velocity profiles, and these are the principal variables to be discussed in the following sections.

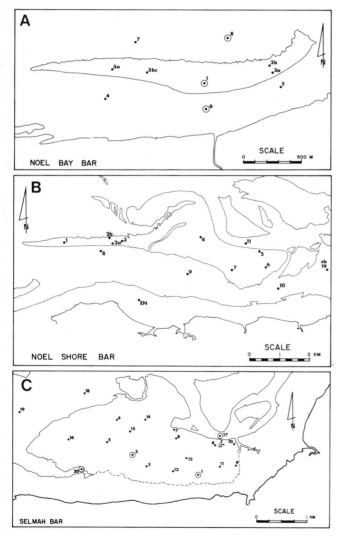

Figure 10.10. *Location of the current flow measurement locations on A) Noel Bay Bar, B) Noel Shore Bar and C) Selmah Bar. Circled locations refer to sites where automatic recording current meters were used. All locations indicate sites of vertical veolocity profile measurements.*

Considerable effort was made to obtain current measurements from as many of the studied areas as possible (Fig. 10.10; Knight, 1977), and to select representative measurement sites from different parts of the sandbars and from different bed configurations. During the summer of 1971 through to 1973, current measurements were made at more than 40 locations in Cobequid Bay with a Kelvin-Hughes 'direct-reading' current meter. These measurements involved recording more than 1200 vertical velocity profiles of current speed and direction relative to water depth during as much of a tidal cycle as possible. Many locations were occupied several times during the lunar month in order to ascertain the variation of current speed with tidal range. Further current data were obtained with several automatic recording current meters moored 0.5 m from the bottom over a total of about 150 days.

Water depth

Water depths in Cobequid Bay change rapidly during the semidiurnal tidal cycle (Figs. 10.11, 10.12). The mean rates of ebb and flood water level change (Table 10.1; standardized to a mean tidal range of 11.7 m) are about 2.3 m/h and 3.0 m/h, respectively. The flood rises at a greater rate than the ebb falls, because of the distortion of the tidal wave as it enters shallow water depths. Wright et al. (1973) reported similar findings from the Ord River. The result is also consistent with the findings of Swift and McMullen (1968), who found that the flow during the ebb lasted about one hour longer than during the flood for channels in the central part of the bay.

This particular characteristic of water levels and flow durations, plus the lag time of up to 1.5 hours between the low water times towards the head of the bay (Dalrymple, 1977; Knight, 1977), suggests that the tide in Cobequid Bay conforms to the properties of a progressive wave. The time of high water, however, is at almost the same time throughout the bay (within five minutes), and tidal range decreases slightly towards the head of the bay (Knight, 1977). This is consistent with the properties of a standing wave. The existence of a standing wave is further supported by current observations, which indicate that the tidal currents are slack at high and low water. Thus the tide in Cobequid Bay exhibits the characteristics of both a progressive wave and a standing wave, a situation which is apparently not uncommon in tidal estuaries elsewhere (Hunt, 1964; Wright et al., 1973). However, the properties consistent for a standing wave seem to dominate.

The rapid change of water levels during the tidal cycle and the emergence of the intertidal sandbars during periods of low water suggest that both ebb and flood should be divided into two phases. During ebb, prior to emergence of the sandbars, and during the flood, after submergence of the sandbars, the tidal currents move essentially as a sheet-flow. During the late ebb and early flood, while the sandbars are emergent, current flow is confined to the channels between the bars.

Current speed

The temporal variation of current speed at different locations in Cobequid Bay is complex and varied (Figs. 10.11, 10.12; Table 10.1), and dependent upon several factors. Current observations support the existence of a standing tidal wave. Speeds are maximum near midebb and midflood, and zero during high and low slack water. Following high slack water, flow speed increases steadily and rapidly to a maximum within 1 to 2 hours after high water. The rate of increase is related to the progressive, asymmetrical distortion of the tidal wave as it encounters shallower water depths towards the head of the bay. After reaching a maximum, current speeds remain relatively constant for approximately 1 to 2 hours during midebb. Following this interval, current speeds may suddenly increase a little more for a very short period, reflecting the emergence of the sandbars and confinement of the flow into the interbar channels which have relatively small cross-sectional areas. Current speeds then decline steadily towards low slack water, beginning about 1 hour before low tide.

Low slack water in Cobequid Bay tends to be very short (Fig. 10.12). In fact, the tide may still be ebbing while water levels are beginning to rise. During the ensuing flood, current speeds once again increase both steadily and rapidly to a maximum, generally shortly after the submergence of the bar crest (about 1 or 2 hours after low water). In this manner, maximum speeds occur closer to low water during the ebb than during the flood. Once maximum speeds are attained, they remain fairly uniform for less than 1 hour, then steadily decrease to zero at high slack water, beginning about 1.5 to 2 hours before high tide.

The inequality between the shorter duration of the rising flood and the longer duration of the falling ebb, characteristic of a progressive tidal wave in a shallow estuary, should produce greater flood current speeds than those during the ebb and increased tidal asymmetry towards the head of the estuary for flow continuity to be maintained (Wright et al., 1973). Although tidal asymmetry increases slightly towards the head of the bay (Figs. 10.11, 10.12; Table 10.1), maximum flood speeds are not always consistently greater than maximum ebb speeds. This suggests that the characteristics of a progressive tidal wave do not totally dominate the estuarine flow regime of Cobequid Bay.

Table 10.1. Selected hydraulic parameters from some representative locations in Cobequid Bay

Location	Rates of water level change		Average maximum mean speed		Mean bottom flow direction		Ebb/flood dominance
	ebb	flood	ebb	flood	ebb	flood	
	(m/h*)		(m/s**)		(degrees†)		
Noel Bay Bar							
1d	2.3	2.5	.86	.67	292	123	E
2a	2.0	2.6	.94	.87	272	123	E
3a	2.5	2.7	.64	.55	223	118	E
6a	2.4	3.4	.88	.85	274	98	E
7	2.2	3.0	.98	1.02	279	112	F
Noel Shore Bar							
1	2.5	3.6	1.02	1.19	284	124	F
2a	2.3	3.0	1.04	1.07	272	118	F
2b	2.3	3.5	.96	1.15	275	115	F
4	2.3	3.3	.93	1.20	262	74	F
5	2.1	3.1	.58	.78	281	97	F
6	2.3	3.1	1.10	.70	267	94	E
7	2.4	3.1	1.27	1.50	279	100	F
9	2.2	3.0	1.93	1.29	292	104	E
10	2.0	2.7	1.37	1.64	254	87	F
11	2.1	3.2	1.20	.93	300	103	E
Selmah Bar							
1d	2.2	3.0	.46	.75	245	81	F
2e	2.3	3.1	.72	1.07	276	93	F
4a	2.1	2.3	.41	.54	275	75	F
5c	2.4	3.1	.80	1.07	277	86	F
6f	2.3	2.8	1.11	1.09	269	78	E
9	2.1	3.3	.36	.74	248	75	F
16	2.8	3.9	.48	.91	268	83	F
17	1.9	3.0	1.02	.59	308	96	E
18	1.7	3.3	1.14	1.36	277	86	F
19b	1.8	2.8	1.30	1.21	246	67	E
20b	2.1	2.7	.76	.94	289	118	F

* Standardized to mean tidal range of 11.7 m.
** Average of 3 maximum mean speeds per ebb and flood standardized as above.
† Measured 1.0 m from the bottom.

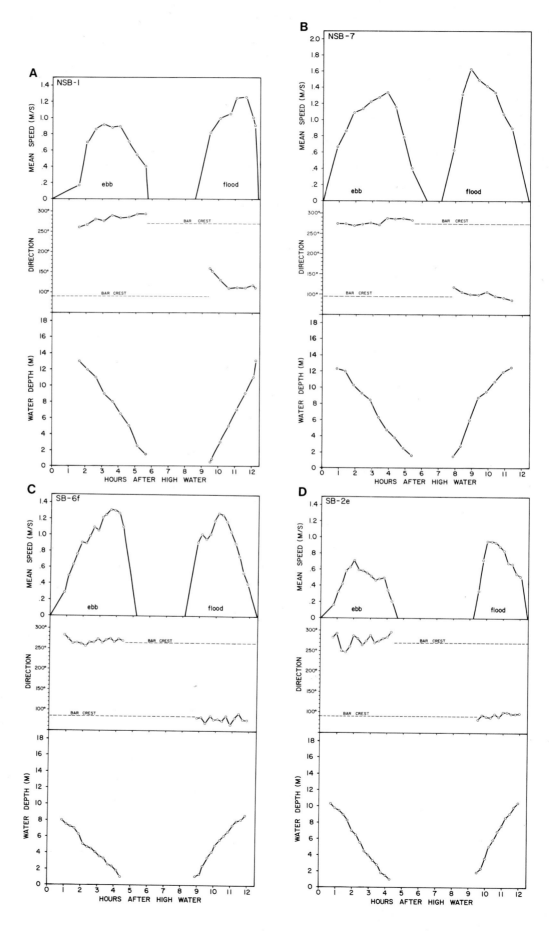

Figure 10.11. *Time-mean speed-near-bottom direction −(1.0 m) depth relationships for four representative bar locations.*

A. *Noel Shore Bar 1*

B. *Noel Shore Bar 7*

C. *Selmah Bar 2e*

D. *Selmah Bar 6f*

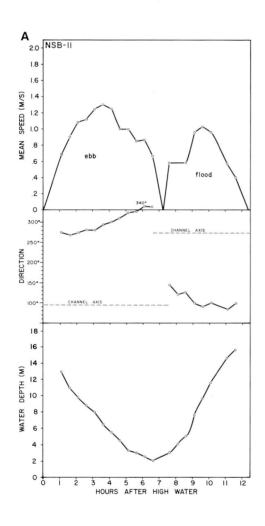

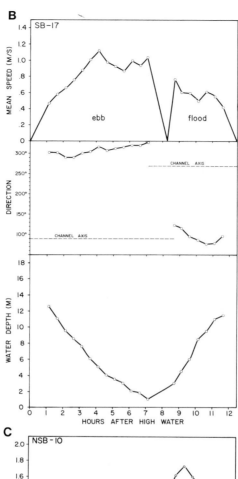

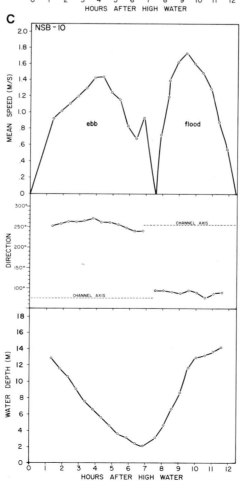

Figure 10.12. *Time-mean speed–near-bottom direction –(1.0 m) depth relationships for three channel locations.*

A. *Noel Shore Bar 11*

B. *Selmah Bar 17*

C. *Noel Shore Bar 10*

As long as current flow remains in the high-water channel phase, its behaviour is dependent upon the tide in the open bay. As soon as the current flow is confined to the interbar channels, after the emergence or before the submergence of the sandbars after low tide, flow operates almost independently of the tide in the open bay. During the low-water channel phase of the ebb, current flow is confined to the interbar channels and its discharge characteristics are dependent on the hypsometry of the intertidal areas being gravitationally drained and the cross-sectional area of the interbar channels. The rise of water levels during the flood depends somewhat more on the tide in the open bay, but also on the hydraulic gradient of the ebb drain and the hypsometry of the intertidal area being flooded. As a result of these complexities of the current flow, particularly the confinement of the ebb, it is possible to attain current speeds greater than otherwise expected for a situation which has many properties of a progressive tidal wave.

The inequality of the ebb and flood, expressed by the duration of the rise and fall of the tide and the difference between maximum ebb and flood speeds, is commonly referred to as time-velocity asymmetry. Differences in time-velocity asymmetry result from real dissimilarities between the ebb and flood, and not from different ranges of the tide between each phase. Maximum ebb and flood speeds varied from 10 to 20 per cent. Such differences provide one means of determining ebb or flood dominance at a given location.

The variation of tidal range during a lunar month does, however, affect the magnitude of the maximum mean current speeds (Fig. 10.13) and the relative duration of the ebb and flood. There is a difference of about 6.5 m between the neap and spring tidal ranges at Burntcoat Head. This represents about 42 per cent of the range of a large tide. During neap tides, the tidal range is smaller and water levels do not rise as high or fall as low. The tidal prism is larger during spring tides because the range is greater between high and low water. With the increased size of the tidal prism during spring tides and the finite length of the

semidiurnal cycle (12.42 h), maximum current speeds are consequently higher and flow durations are somewhat shorter over the sandbars because water levels fall to a lower elevation. The effect is opposite during neap tides. Current measurements at most locations reflected a positive relationship with increasing tidal range. Maximum mean current speeds varied by about 0.1 to 0.2 m/s per metre change in the tidal range. The rate of change of the maximum mean ebb and flood current speeds with tidal range did not follow any consistent pattern.

Differences in the time-velocity asymmetry of the tidal currents are also attributable to topographic effects of the bathymetry in Cobequid Bay. Various workers have previously noted this relationship (e.g., Boothroyd, 1969; Boothroyd and Hubbard, 1975; Daboll, 1969; Farrell, 1970; Hartwell, 1970; Klein, 1970; Ludwick, 1974; Robinson, 1960; Salsman et al., 1966; Swift and McMullen, 1968). The topographic features (Figs. 10.8, 10.9) produce ebb and flood shields which control the exposure of different parts of the intertidal and subtidal system to strong ebb and flood currents, thus affecting the development of maximum current speeds. The degree to which a topographic shield affects current speeds and the time-velocity asymmetry of the tidal currents depends upon the orientation of the shield relative to flow directions and its lateral size, as well as its extension into the intertidal zone. On the south side of Selmah Bar (Fig. 10.15), for example, the bar is protected from strong ebb currents (Figs. 10.11c, 10.12b) by Salter Head and the topographic crestline of the bar along its northern margins. In contrast, the south and west end of the bar are exposed to strong flood currents (Fig. 10.11c) while the northern and eastern parts of the bar are flood shielded by the bar crestline (Fig. 10.12b). This shielding results in higher flood current speeds along the south side of the bar and higher ebb speeds along the north side of the crestline. In some parts of the bar, ebb and flood current speeds are almost equal (Fig. 10.11d).

Current direction

The tidal currents in Cobequid Bay reverse their mean direction of flow by almost 180° (Figs. 10.11, 10.12, 10.15) with each ebb and flood phase of the tide. Flow directions reverse abruptly during the high- and low-water slack periods separating the ebb and the flood.

During the ebb and flood phases of the tide, current directions do not remain constant nor do they parallel the major axis of the sandbars in Cobequid Bay. Even during the early ebb and late flood sheet-flow phases, when water depths are relatively great, current directions are not totally independent of bathymetry, and flow is directed upslope at a small angle across the bathymetric contours. As water depths become progressively shallower during the ebb sheet-flow phase, the effect of bottom friction is stronger and flow is gradually deflected at a greater oblique angle across the bathymetric contours in an upslope direction towards the crest of the sandbars. As a result, current flow tends to accelerate obliquely up the upstream slope towards the crest of the sandbars as streamlines converge. On the other side of the bar crest, the currents diverge obliquely along the downstream side. During the flood the opposite effect occurs. An analysis of the mean, near-bottom (1.0 m) current directions (Fig. 10.15) indicates that the currents generally flow obliquely up the steep side of the sandbars during the ebb and obliquely up the gentle side of the bars in the opposite direction during the flood. This characteristic was also noted by Dalrymple (1977) on Diamond Bar.

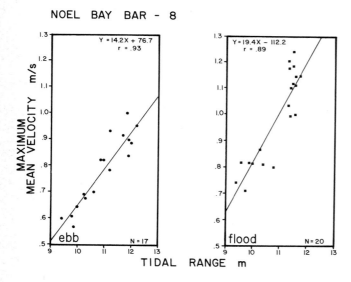

NOEL BAY BAR - 8

Y = 14.2X + 76.7
r = .93

Y = 19.4X - 112.2
r = .89

MAXIMUM MEAN VELOCITY m/s

TIDAL RANGE m

ebb   N = 17

flood   N = 20

Figure 10.13. *Maximum mean velocity as a function of tidal range (Burntcoat Head) at location 8 adjacent to Noel Bay Bar.*

The vertical variation of current directions during the ebb and flood phases of a tidal cycle (Fig. 10.14) indicates that bottom and surface flow directions are not the same and that the bottom-to-surface differences increase in a fairly regular fashion towards low water and decrease towards high water. This reflects the increased effects of bottom friction and the deflection of current flow across the sandbars during the ebb as water levels fall. Although more irregular, the opposite situation occurs during the flood. Further analysis shows the development of secondary flow patterns in the water column, which appear to vary during the tidal cycle. In nearly every case the sense of secondary flow is opposite to that required to support a helical flow pattern. Dalrymple's (1977) observations on Diamond Bar are again consistent with this finding.

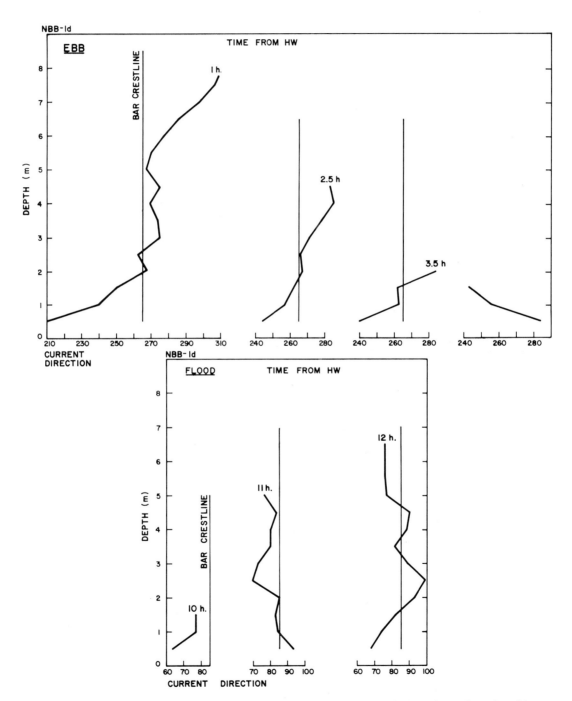

Figure 10.14. *Vertical variation of current directions during a tidal cycle at location 1d on Noel Bay Bar.*

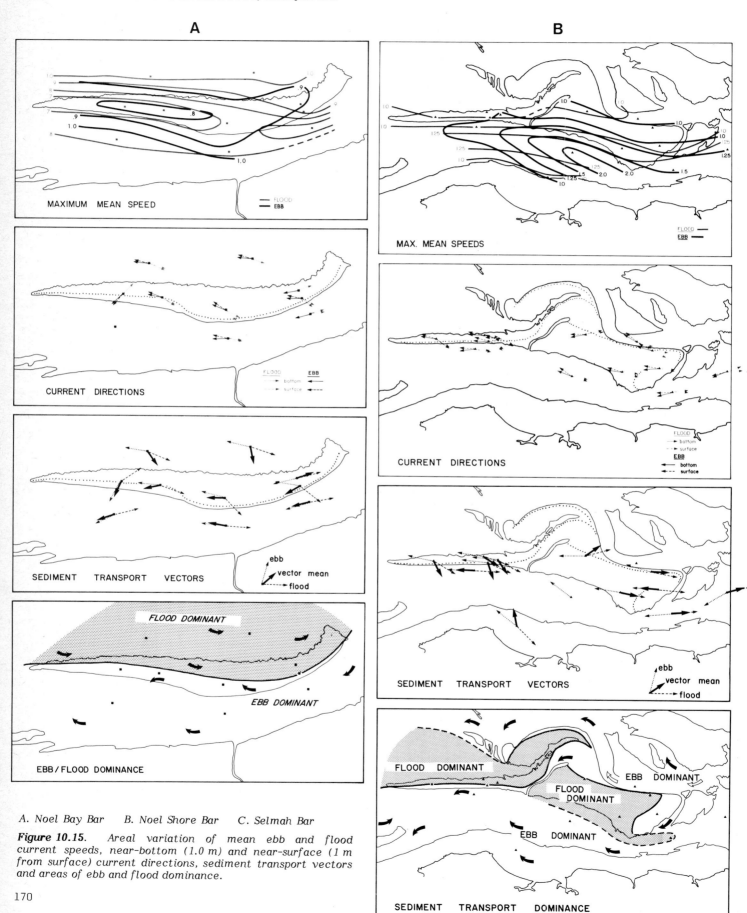

A. Noel Bay Bar   B. Noel Shore Bar   C. Selmah Bar

Figure 10.15.   Areal variation of mean ebb and flood current speeds, near-bottom (1.0 m) and near-surface (1 m from surface) current directions, sediment transport vectors and areas of ebb and flood dominance.

C

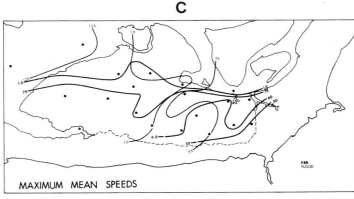

MAXIMUM MEAN SPEEDS

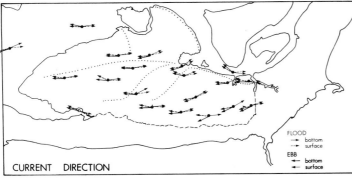

CURRENT DIRECTION

FLOOD
→ bottom
-→ surface
EBB
← bottom
←-- surface

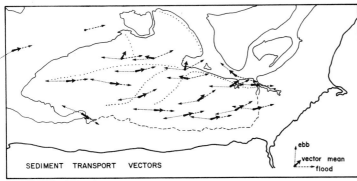

SEDIMENT TRANSPORT VECTORS

↑ ebb
| vector mean
↓ flood

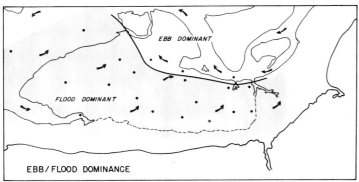

EBB DOMINANT

FLOOD DOMINANT

EBB/FLOOD DOMINANCE

Areal variations

The characteristics of the tidal current flow for a particular location are only of significance for an understanding of different bed configurations and grain size distributions. To understand the nature of tidal flow throughout the sand body in Cobequid Bay, the areal variations of the pertinent hydraulic variables must be mapped. This requires some standardization of the variables, particularly current speed, which varies significantly with tidal range. The average of the three maximum mean current speeds per ebb and flood at a given location was selected as the representative parameter for flow strength to ensure that any random fluctuations of a single velocity measurement would be averaged out. This value of current speed was then standardized against a mean tidal range of 11.7 m.

The areal variation of the standardized maximum mean current speeds for both ebb and flood (Fig. 10.15) shows that different parts of the sandbars are dominated by different phases of the tide. Dominance of the ebb or flood at a given location is, in fact, a common characteristic of tidal current flow in Cobequid Bay and results in areas of opposing asymmetries on opposite sides of the bar crest. The patterns of ebb and flood dominance, combined with bedforms observations at low tide (Fig. 10.7) and with mean current directions which flow obliquely up the steep side of the bars during the ebb and obliquely up the gentle side in the opposite direction during the flood, result in sediment being transported in the opposite direction on either side of the sandbar crest. As a consequence, residual sand circulation occurs around individual sandbars or parts of sandbars in closed or nearly closed elliptical loops. Similar examples of this pattern of circulation were reported by Allen (1968), Balazs and Klein (1972), Caston (1972), Caston and Stride (1970), Houbolt (1968), James and Stanley (1968), Jones et al. (1965), Klein (1970), Reineck (1963), Stride (1963), Smith (1969), Swift (1975) and Van Veen (1950).

This pattern of sand circulation around the sandbars is further confirmed by using an empirical relationship (Ackers and White, 1973) to determine sediment transport (Fig. 10.15) and sediment dispersal studies (Dalrymple, 1977) on several sandbars in Cobequid Bay. Sediment transport, estimated by the empirical total-load equation indicated that rates of movement varied considerably over the sandbars and in the channels. Net transport rates along the steep side of the sandbars were generally an order of magnitude greater than net rates up the gentle sides. Typical transport rates on the gentle side of the bars were usually less than 5.0×10^2 kg/m during the ebb and ranged from about 3.5×10^3 to 7.5×10^3 g/m during the flood. Along the steep side of the bars and their adjacent channels, typical transport rates ranged between 4.0×10^3 and 1.5×10^4 kg/m during the ebb and generally less than 3.0×10^2 g/m during the flood. These rates imply that there is a considerable volume of sediment leaving the sand body in Cobequid Bay, but since it does not appear to be either increasing or decreasing in size and there are no large accumulations of sand reported in the Minas Basin (Amos and Joice, 1977), then much of the sand must be circulated around the ends of the sandbars.

During the winter, the relative importance of this residual circulation in the transport of sediments around the sandbars is decreased. Although the relative zones of ebb and flood dominance persist through both summer and winter, the frozen crust on the intertidal surface of the sandbars significantly reduces the amount of sediment available for transport during the winter (Knight and Dalrymple, 1976).

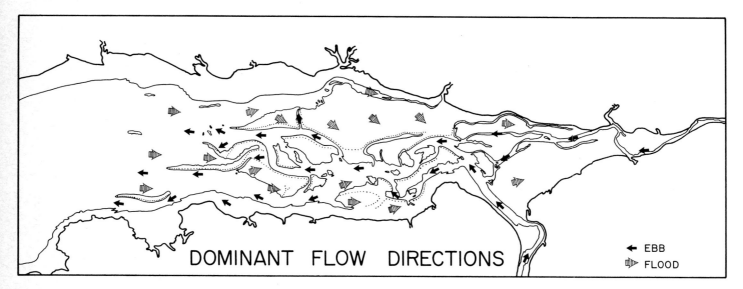

DOMINANT FLOW DIRECTIONS

← EBB
▷ FLOOD

Figure 10.16. *Directions of dominant tidal current circulation and sediment transport in the Cobequid Bay sand body.*

The areal variation of ebb- and flood-dominant areas throughout the entire sand body in Cobequid Bay (Fig. 10.16) shows that while the gentle sides of the sandbars are dominated by the flood and the steep sides dominated by the ebb, the interbar channel down the centre of the sand body is dominated by ebb currents and the two channels along the northern and southern margins of the sand body tend to be dominated by flood currents. Sediment is circulated predominantly counterclockwise on the bars located in the southern part of the bay (e.g., Selmah Bar and east end of Noel Shore Bar), and clockwise in the northern part of the bay (e.g., Great Village Bar and Diamond Bar, Dalrymple, 1977). In fact, the general circulation pattern in Cobequid Bay appears to resemble that of a large ebb-tidal delta, similar in many respects to the ebb-tidal delta model proposed by Hayes's (1975) mesotidal inlets. The areal patterns of suspended sediment concentrations and the position of foam lines in the bay (Fig. 10.17) determined from air photographs taken during the early flood after the tide has begun to turn at the seaward end of the sand body, clearly show the partitioning of the ebb and flood currents by the sandbars, and the continued ebb-drain from the bay while the tide is flooding along the margins of the sand body. There is no evidence from tidal current flow in Cobequid Bay to support the existence of a Coriolis circulation pattern as proposed by Pelletier and McMullen (1972).

DISCUSSION AND CONCLUSIONS

Three hydraulic mechanisms frequently are used to explain the tidal sand ridges on shallow continental shelves: (i) the development of double helical flow cells in the intervening channels between the ridges (Allen, 1968; Caston and Stride, 1970; Houbolt, 1968; Off, 1963); (ii) the interdigitation of ebb- and flood-dominant areas by ridge systems (Caston, 1972; Ludwick, 1974; Robinson, 1960; Van Veen, 1935); and (iii) the development of a reversing cross-ridge component of flow (Huthnance, 1973; Smith, 1968, 1969).

These mechanisms for the maintenance of tidal current ridges may have some application to those ridges found in

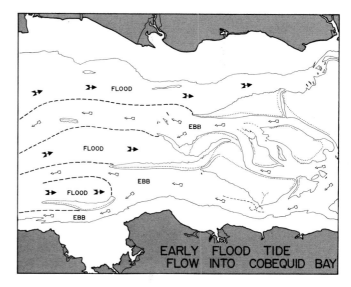

EARLY FLOOD TIDE FLOW INTO COBEQUID BAY

Figure 10.17. *Early flood tide flow into Cobequid Bay (based on airphoto interpretation) showing the partitioning of the ebb and flood by the sand bars and the dynamic diversion of the flood tide by the ebb towards the margins of the sand body.*

estuaries and embayments, either individually or in combination. The tidal flow in estuaries and embayments is, however, reversing in nature and not rotary as in the open oceans. Thus some other mechanism or combination of mechanisms may be responsible for the maintenance of tidal current ridges in settings such as Cobequid Bay. Similar patterns of estuarine deposition can be found in meso- and macrotidal estuaries elsewhere (e.g., Table 10.2; Off, 1963); hence the sand body in Cobequid Bay is not a unique depositional pattern.

Tidal maintenance of the sandbars

The tides are the dominant dynamic factor affecting the depositional morphology of the sand body in Cobequid Bay. The sandbars are 'tide maintained'. Wave activity and river processes are of only secondary importance.

Tidal flow in Cobequid Bay is controlled by several factors: (i) the characteristics of the tidal wave in shallow water; (ii) the hypsometry of the intertidal areas being drained and flooded; and (iii) the interaction of the sandbars with the flow. Figure 10.18 summarizes the complex interaction between these factors in maintaining the present morphology of the sandbars.

The ebb tide in Cobequid Bay is basically a 'tidal drain' (Price, 1963) or gravitational fall of water levels that is initiated by the relatively rapid withdrawal of the tidal wave from the bay. The rate of the ebb fall is controlled by the degree of asymmetrical distortion of the tidal wave in shallow water. During the early ebb (Fig. 10.18a), water

Table 10.2. Selected tidal estuaries with tidal current ridges

Location	Tidal range*	
	Mean	Maximum
	(m)	(m)
Argentina		
Puerto Gallegos	10.4	13.2
Australia		
Ord River	4.3	5.9
Darwin	5.5	7.8
Burma		
Rangoon River	5.8	7.4
Canada		
Cobequid Bay	11.7	15.4
Avon River	11.8	15.3
England		
Thames River	6.6	7.9
Humber River	6.5	8.4
Mersey River	8.4	10.5
Severn River	8.4 - 12.4	--
Avon River	11.0 - 12.3	14.5
France		
Le Havre	6.8	8.0
India		
Gulf of Cambay	8.8	11.9
Hooghly River	5.0	5.7
Mozambique		
Beira	5.6	6.9
U.S.A.		
Cook Inlet	8.6 - 9.0	--
Nushagak Bay		
Kuichak River		
Colorado River	9.0	--

*Tidal range taken from British Admiralty Tide Tables.

depths are relatively large so that relative roughness is small and bottom topography has little effect on the ebb-tidal flow. As a result, flow directions tend to parallel the sandbars at a very slight angle to the bathymetric contours and secondary flow development is very weak. The progressive withdrawal of the tidal wave causes a draw-down of the water surface towards the continental shelf. With the cross-sectional area of the flow still fairly large, the surface energy gradient is small and consequently current speeds are relatively low.

With the continued drawdown of the water surface, the surface energy gradient of the ebb increases to a limit during midebb (Fig. 10.18b) and current speeds reach a maximum. During this period of the tidal cycle, water depths are considerably shallower, particularly over the bar crest, and the relative roughness of the bottom topography is significantly larger. The increased bottom friction and the orientation of the sandbars (or parts of them) at small angles to the flow cause the flow streamlines to converge towards the bar crests and diverge on the downflow side, producing a hydraulic pressure gradient across the bar crests at an oblique angle to the crestline (Smith, 1969). As a result, the currents accelerate obliquely up the steep side and across the bar crests, then decelerate down the gentle side where they are deflected along the length of the bar. The angular difference between the bathymetric contours and the flow direction on the upflow side of the bars is dependent upon the relative roughness of the flow, the steepness of the bar side, and the orientation of the bar relative to the flow. This pattern of flow over and around the bars is further confirmed by the orientation of the bedform crestlines seen at low tide on the surface of the bars. Midebb represents the period of maximum secondary flow development across the bar crests.

The maximum speed of the ebb currents typically occurs just before the bar crests become emergent. After the crests become emergent, flow is confined to the interbar channels and current speeds higher than expected are produced as a result of the increased gradient of the hydraulic head. The channel phase of the ebb (Fig. 10.18c) is essentially independent of the tide in the outer bay, but is dependent upon the hypsometry of the intertidal area being drained by the channel and upon the hydraulic geometry of the channel. As soon as the upflow head of water is decreased, current speeds decrease rapidly.

The configuration of the channels and the character of the tidal flow are interrelated. The ebb-dominated channels located roughly down the centre of the sand body are maintained by the higher current speeds that result from the effective confinement of the flow between the sandbars at low tide. During this phase of the ebb, secondary currents are expected to develop as they would in a fluvial open-channel flow.

The ebb continues to flow from the sand body after the theoretical time of low water because there is a time lag between the fall of water levels and the discharge capacity of the interbar channels. It enters the relatively deeper water at the seaward edge of the sand body as a 'spreading jet'. Using Wright's (1977) criteria to describe sediment transport and deposition at estuary mouths, the sandbar morphology at the seaward edge of the sand body resembles some of the features for both a friction-dominated and a buoyant type of outflow. The seaward ends of both Noel Shore Bar and Diamond Bar resemble the channel-margin linear bars in Hayes's (1975) model and the intertidal to subtidal channel levees of Wright (1977). If this analogy is correct, it may explain the reason for the tapered seaward ends of the sandbars in Cobequid Bay.

Figure 10.18.

Cartoon summary depicting the areal and cross-sectional variations of current circulation, secondary current flow, sediment transport and water levels during a tidal cycle in Cobequid Bay. Note that the morphology of the bay and the sand bars have been greatly simplified.

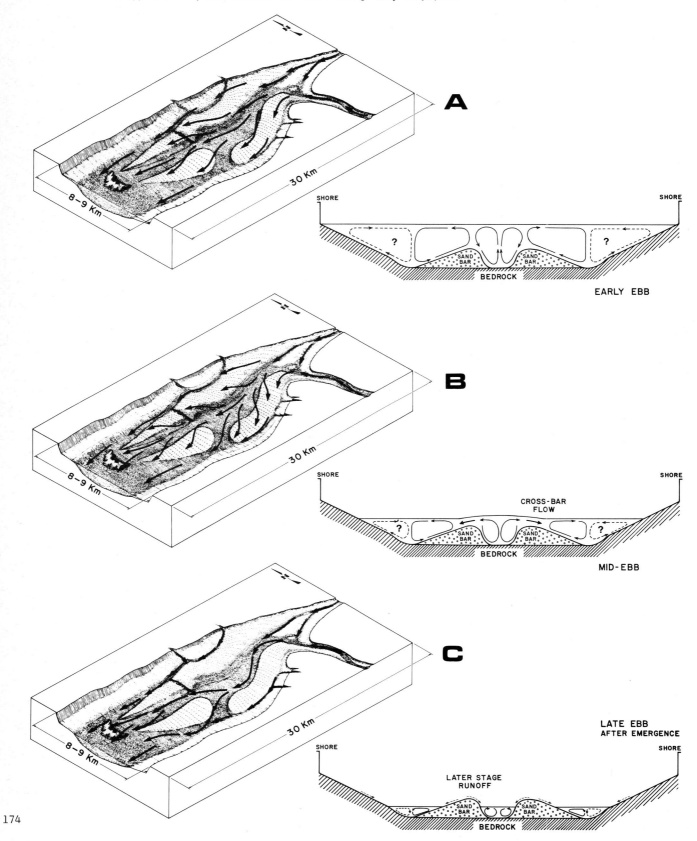

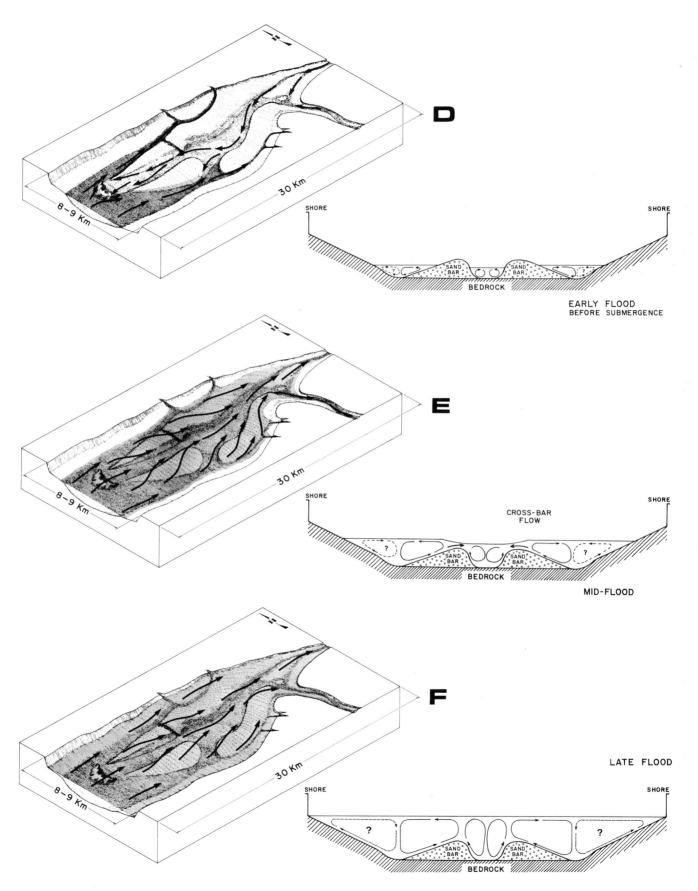

D

30 Km

8–9 Km

SHORE   SHORE

SAND
BAR   SAND
                        BAR   ?

BEDROCK

EARLY FLOOD
BEFORE SUBMERGENCE

E

30 Km

8–9 Km

SHORE   SHORE

CROSS-BAR
FLOW

?   ?

SAND
BAR   SAND
                        BAR

BEDROCK

MID-FLOOD

F

30 Km

8–9 Km

LATE FLOOD

SHORE   SHORE

?   ?

SAND
BAR   SAND
                        BAR

BEDROCK

As the tide begins to flood (Fig. 10.18d), it is impeded by friction due to the shallow water depths, the hydraulic gradient of the continued ebb drain and the hypsometry of the intertidal area being flooded. When the flooding tide encounters the ebb outflow, it is deflected to either side of the ebb by a process that Todd (1968) referred to as 'dynamic diversion'. As a result, the flood enters the sand body along its margins. Some interdigitation of the ebb and flood occurs near the seaward edge of the sand body owing to the morphological complexity of the sandbars and the interbar channels. The rate of flood rise is controlled by the distortion of the tidal wave as it enters shallow water (Wright et al., 1973). Without a strong or large ebb drain to overcome in the marginal channels of the sand body, the flood rises more rapidly over the gentle side of the sandbars (which generally face the shorelines of the bay) than up the central ebb-dominated channels adjacent to the steep side of the bars. Current speeds during the early flood remain relatively low because only a comparatively small volume of water is required to raise water levels enough to satisfy the rate of advance of the tidal wave.

According to Robinson (1960), the flood tide should have more erosive potential because it is more saline and colder (i.e., denser) than the ebb. The flood-dominated channels along the margins of the sand body are, however, about as deep as the ebb-dominated channels located down the centre of the bay. It appears that the effective confinement and extended duration of the ebb within the interbar channels sufficiently makes up for any density differences between the ebb and flood with respect to erosion competence. A further factor to consider is that the Triassic sandstones underlying the sand body possibly limit any differential downcutting between the ebb and flood.

Once the bar crests are submerged by the flood tide (Fig. 10.18e), a relatively larger volume of water is required to raise water levels because the cross-sectional area of the flow is suddenly increased. Flow is now in the opposite direction to the ebb, moving obliquely up the gentle side and across the bar crests. The angle between the bathymetric contours and the flow direction is smaller than that during the ebb, because the slope of the flood dominated side of the bars is smaller. Speeds are maximum shortly after the submergence of the bar crests. As long as water depths are relatively shallow and the relative roughness is large, the direction of flow continues across the bar crests. As water depths increase, the cross-sectional area of the flow becomes progressively larger, current speeds decline and flow directions are affected less by bottom topography (Fig. 10.18f).

Because tidal currents are time-velocity asymmetrical, one phase of the tide tends to dominate the other, resulting in residual transport patterns. The sandbars appear to be maintained by the lateral convergence of ebb- and flood-dominated sediment transport towards the bar crests, by the residual transport around the bars and by the effective confinement of the relatively strong ebb currents in the intertidal channels between the sandbars during the low-water period (i.e., an ebb delta).

The surface level of the sandbars is controlled by the base level of strong wave activity. Because the largest waves approach Cobequid Bay from the west and most wave energy is dissipated at the seaward edge of the sand body, the surface elevation of the sandbars increases towards the head of the bay, in the direction of decreasing effectiveness of wave activity. Thus the bars are able to build farther into the intertidal zone at the head of the bay than those at the seaward edge of the sand body.

Evolution of the sandbars

The modern tidal regime in Cobequid Bay explains the maintenance of the observed morphology of the sandbars, but it does not account for the sources of sand in the bars, or for the localization and growth of the sand body at the head of the bay. Although there is little question that the Triassic sandstones around the margins of the bay were and continue to be an important source of sand for the bars (Amos and Joice, 1977; Churchill, 1924), the glacial and glaciofluvial sediments beneath the modern tidal sand body (Figs. 10.8, 10.9) and exposed in the shoreline and river valleys entering the bay imply that these materials were perhaps important sources in the past, particularly during the retreat of the continental ice sheets from the Bay of Fundy.

According to Prest and Grant (1969) and Grant (1970), the sea invaded the Bay of Fundy about 13 200 years B.P. with the retreat of the Wisconsin ice sheets to the highlands surrounding the bay. Emergent banks at the entrance effectively separated the Gulf of Maine and the Bay of Fundy system from the tidal dynamics of the Atlantic Ocean until about 8000 years B.P. As a result, the proto - Bay of Fundy was a tideless sea which did not begin to reach resonant dimensions until about 6000 years B.P., and only since that time has the tidal range been amplified. Most of the tidal growth occurred during the past 3000 to 4000 years (Grant, 1970). Grant's (1970, Fig. 15) projections for the rate of 'inferred tidal amplification' during the Holocene indicated that the rate has decreased substantially during the last 500 years.

Swift and McMullen (1968) and several others believed that the Holocene sand body originated from the erosion of materials, primarily Triassic sandstones, in the shoreline during the post-Pleistocene marine transgression into the Bay of Fundy and the growth of the tides. They described the early sand body in Cobequid Bay as a tabular 'sand-sheet', which had developed in response to the 'dominant sheet-flood phase' of the tide.

However, given that considerable volumes of glaciofluvial sediments were deposited into the proto - Cobequid Bay during and after the Wisconsin ice retreat, and that further sediments were supplied through the erosion of materials in and around the bay as sea level rose, there must already have been a significant volume of sediment present before any appreciable tidal influence developed (i.e., before 8000 years B.P.). It thus seems more likely that the pre-modern sand body consisted of several glaciofluvial outwash and delta accumulations (e.g., Swift and Borns, 1967; Wightman, 1975, 1976), dissected with numerous drainage channels. Only with the evolution of the large tides were these deposits later reworked.

Considering these factors, the following sequence of events is postulated for the evolution of the sandbars in Cobequid Bay:

1. The Bay of Fundy became tidal during the post-Pleistocene marine transgression. As sea level continued to rise, tidal range grew in response to the changing dimensions of the Bay of Fundy and its approach to resonant conditions. These premodern tides were asymmetrically distorted by shallow water depths towards the head of the bay, causing flood dominance of the tide and further accumulation of sediment at the head of the bay.

2. As the tides continued to grow, the morphology of the sand body changed to accommodate the increasing tidal prism. Since the ebb is essentially a gravitational drain

from the head of the bay, it followed pre-existing fluvial drainage channels. The location of the major ebb-dominated channels down the centre of the bay reflects the importance of the gravitational drain of the ebb and its selection of the most direct seaward route through the unconsolidated sediments in the bay. The seaward-dipping bedrock surface underlying the Holocene sediments played some role in the initial positioning of the ebb channels, and limited the amount of channel downcutting as the tidal amplitude increased. The flood-dominated marginal channels developed as a result of dynamic diversion (Todd, 1968) by the ebb outflow from the sand body.

3. With the decreased importance of fluvial processes and the increased importance of the tides, the sediment dynamics in the sand body eventually became tide-dominated. Wave activity from the west enhanced the concentration of sediment at the head of the bay and controlled the vertical growth of the sandbars into the intertidal zone (assuming a continuous supply of sediment). Once the major ebb and flood channel systems were developed, the processes of the modern tidal regime were able to continue the development of and maintain the present morphology of the sand body in Cobequid Bay.

Acknowledgments

This study was carried out while I was a graduate student at McMaster University under the supervision of Dr. G.V. Middleton, to whom I am indebted for his advice and interest throughout the study, and for his willingness to wet his feet in the Fundy tides.

The research was supported by grants from the Department of Energy, Mines and Resources, and a Penrose Bequest Grant from the Geological Society of America. Further financial assistance was provided by a McMaster University graduate fellowship. Field support by Bedford Institute of Oceanography is acknowledged.

Special thanks go to the people who helped in the field, and the many kind people from the study area. Numerous discussions with R.W. Dalrymple and J.J. Lambiase, two fellow graduate students, were greatly appreciated.

Finally, thanks go to Petro-Canada for their help with the preparation of the figures.

References

Ackers, P. and White, W.R.
1973: Sediment transport: new approach and analysis; Proceedings of the American Society of Civil Engineers, v. 99 (HY11), p. 2041 - 2060.

Allen, G.P., Castaing, P. and Klingebiel, A.
1972: Distinction of elementary sand populations in the Gironde estuary (France) by R-mode factor analysis of grain size data; Sedimentology, v. 19, p. 21 - 35.

Allen, J.R.L.
1968: Current ripples; North-Holland Amsterdam, 433 p.

Amos, C.L. and Joice, G.H.E.
1977: The sediment budget of Minas Basin, Bay of Fundy, Nova Scotia; Bedford Institute of Oceanography, Data Series/BI-D-77-3, 411 p.

Atlantic Tidal Power Engineering and Management Committee
1969: Report to Atlantic Tidal Power Programming Board on feasibility of tidal power development in the Bay of Fundy; Atlantic Tidal Power Engineering and Management Committee, Halifax, Nova Scotia, 189 p. plus 11 appendices.

Balazs, R.J. and Klein, G. de Vries
1972: Roundness-mineralogical relations of some intertidal sands; Journal of Sedimentary Petrology, v. 42(2), p. 425 - 433.

Boothroyd, J.C.
1969: Hydraulic conditions controlling the formation of estuarine bedforms; in Coastal environments of northeastern Massachusetts and New Hampshire, M.O. Hayes, ed; Society of Economic Paleontologists and Mineralogists (Eastern Section) Guidebook, p. 417 - 427.

Boothroyd, J.C. and Hubbard, D.K.
1975: Genesis of bedforms in mesotidal estuaries; in Estuarine Research, Vol. II, J.E. Cronin, ed.; Academic Press, New York, p. 217 - 234.

Brooks, N.H.
1958: Mechanics of streams with movable beds of fine sand (with discussions); Transactions of the American Society of Civil Engineers, v. 123, p. 526 - 594.

Caston, V.N.D.
1972: Linear sand banks in the southern North Sea; Sedimentology, v. 18, p. 63 - 78.

Caston, V.N.D. and Stride, A.H.
1970: Tidal sand movement between some linear sand banks in the North Sea off northeast Norfolk; Marine Geology, v. 9, p. M38 - M42.

Churchill, F.J.
1924: Recent changes in the coastline in the county of Kings; Proceedings and Transactions, Nova Scotia Institute of Science, v. 16, p. 84 - 86.

Cloet, R.L.
1954: Hydrographic analysis of the Goodwin Sands and the Brake Bank; Geographical Journal, v. 120, p. 202 - 215.

Colby, B.R.
1964: Discharge of sands and mean velocity relationships in sand-bed streams, U.S. Geological Survey, Professional Paper 462-A, 47 p.

Daboll, J.M.
1969: Holocene sediments of the Parker River Estuary, Massachusetts; Department of Geology, University of Massachusetts, Amherst, Coastal Research Group Contribution No. 3-CRG, 138 p.

Dalrymple, R.W.
1973a: Preliminary study of an intertidal sand body, Cobequid Bay, Bay of Fundy, Nova Scotia; Maritime Sediments, v. 9, no. 1, p. 21 - 28.

Dalrymple, R.W. (cont.)

1973b: Sediment texture and transport studies in an intertidal environment: a progress report; Maritime Sediments, v. 9, no. 2, p. 45 - 58.

1974a: Factor analyses of grain-size data from Cobequid Bay, Bay of Fundy, Nova Scotia; Geological Society of America, Abstracts, v. 5, no. 1, p. 17.

1974b: Field studies on intertidal sand bars (1973), north shore of Minas Basin, Bay of Fundy, Nova Scotia; Department of Geology, McMaster University, Hamilton, unpubl. Technical Memorandum 73-5, 21 p.

1975: Sediment transport in Cobequid Bay with special reference to sediment tracer experiments; Proceedings, Mathematical Aspects of Fundy Tidal Power, Canadian Mathematic Congress Summer Research Institute, Halifax, Nova Scotia, p. 3, 4.

1976: Sediment transport in a macro-tidal environment (Bay of Fundy); American Geophysical Union, Transactions, v. 57, no. 4, p. 268.

1977: Sediment dynamics of macrotidal sandbars; unpubl. Ph.D thesis, McMaster University, Hamilton, 635 p.

Dalrymple, R. W., Knight, R.J. and Lambiase, J.J.
1978: Bedforms and their hydraulic stability relationships in a tidal environment, Bay of Fundy, Canada; Nature, v. 75, no. 5676, p. 100 - 104.

Dalrymple, R.W., Knight, R.J. and Middleton, G.V.
1975: Intertidal sand bars in Cobequid Bay (Bay of Fundy); in Estuarine Research, Vol. II, L.E. Cronin, ed.; Academic Press, New York, p. 293 - 307.

Dawson, W.B.
1917: Tides at the head of the Bay of Fundy; Department of Naval Service, Ottawa, 34 p.

Farrell, S. C.
1970: Sediment distribution and hydrodynamics: Saco River and Scarboro estuaries; Department of Geology, University of Massachusetts, Amherst, Coastal Research Group Contribution No. 6-CRG, 129 p.

Garrett, C.
1972: Tidal resonance in the Bay of Fundy and Gulf of Maine; Nature, v. 238, p. 441 - 443.

Grant, D.R.
1970: Recent coastal submergence of the Maritime Provinces, Canada; Canadian Journal of Earth Sciences, v. 7, no. 3, p. 676 - 689.

Green, C.D.
1975: A study of hydraulics and bedforms at the mouth of the Tay Estuary, Scotland; in Estuarine Research, Volume II, L.E. Cronin, ed.; Academic Press, New York, 587 p.

Hartwell, A. D.
1970: Hydrography and holocene sedimentation of the Merrimack River estuary, Massachusetts; Department of Geology, University of Massachusetts, Amherst, Coastal Research Group Contribution No. 5-CRG, 166 p.

Hayes, M.O.
1975: Morphology of sand accumulation in estuaries: An introduction to the symposium; in Estuarine Research, Volume II, L.E. Cronin, ed.; Academic Press, New York, 587 p.

Hayes, M.O. and Kana, T. W., eds.
1976: Terrigenous clastic depositional environments: some modern examples; Coastal Research Division, Department of Geology, University of South Carolina, Technical Report No. 11-CRD, 295 p.

Hennigar, T.W.
1972: Hydrogeology of the Truro area, Nova Scotia; Department of Mines, Groundwater Section, Report 72-1, 127 p.

Houbolt, J.J.H.C.
1968: Recent sediments in the Southern Bight of the North Sea; Geologie en Mijnbouw, v. 47, no. 4, p. 245 - 273.

Hunt, J.N.
1964: Tidal oscillations in estuaries; Royal Astronomical Society, Geophysical Journal, v. 8, p. 440 - 455.

Huntec Ltd.
1966: Report on geological-geophysical study of Minas Basin, Bay of Fundy, N.S.; unpubl. report to Atlantic Development Board of Canada, Huntec Ltd., Toronto, 58 p.

Huthnance, J.M.
1973: Tidal current asymmetries over the Norfold Sandbanks; Estuarine Coastal Marine Science, v. 1, p. 89 - 99.

James, N.P. and Stanley, D.J.
1968: Sable Island Bank off Nova Scotia: sediment dispersal and recent history; American Association of Petroleum Geologists, Bulletin, v. 52, p. 2208 - 2230.

Jones, N.S., Kain, J.M. and Stride, A.H.
1965: The movement of sand waves on Warts Bank, Isle of Man; Marine Geology, v. 3, p. 329 - 336.

Jordan, G.F.
1962: Large submarine sand waves; Science, v. 136, p. 839 - 848.

King, L.H. and MacLean, B.
1974: Geology of the Scotian Shelf and adjacent areas, Map 812H; Geological Survey of Canada, Paper 74-31, Ottawa.

Klein, G. de V.
1964: Sedimentary facies in the Bay of Fundy intertidal zone, Nova Scotia; Deltaic and Shallow Marine Deposits, Developments in Sedimentology, Vol. I, J.M.J.U. van Stroaten, ed.; Elsevier, Amsterdam, 464 p.

1968: Intertidal zone sedimentation, Minas Basin, northshore, Bay of Fundy, Nova Scotia; National Symposium on Ocean Science and Engineering of the Atlantic Shelf, A.E. Margulies and R.C. Steere, eds.; Marine Technology Society, Transactions, p. 91 - 107.

Klein, G. de V. (cont.)
1970: Depositional and dispersal dynamics of intertidal sand bars; Journal of Sedimentary Petrology, v. 40, no. 4, p. 1095 - 1127.

Klein, G. de V. and Whaley, M.L.
1972: Hydraulic parameters controlling bedform migration on an intertidal sand body; Geological Society of America, Bulletin, v. 83, p. 3465 - 3470.

Knight, R.J.
1971: Cobequid Bay sedimentology project. A progress report; Maritime Sediments, v. 7, no. 1, p. 1 - 18.
1972: Cobequid Bay sedimentology project. A progress report; Maritime Sediments, v. 8, no. 2, p. 45 - 60.
1973: Intertidal sedimentation in Cobequid Bay, Nova Scotia; Fluvial Processes and Sedimentation Proceedings - Hydrology Symposium, University of Alberta, Edmonton, p. 639 - 650.
1977: Sediments, bedforms and hydraulics in a macrotidal environment, Cobequid Bay (Bay of Fundy), Nova Scotia; unpubl. Ph.D. thesis, McMaster University, Hamilton, 693 p.

Knight, R. J. and Dalrymple, R. W.
1975: Intertidal sediments from the south shore of Cobequid Bay, Bay of Fundy, Nova Scotia, Canada; Tidal Deposits, A Casebook of Recent Examples and Fossil Counterparts, R.N. Ginsburg, ed.; Springer-Verlag, New York, 428 p.
1976: Winter conditions in a macrotidal environment, Cobequid Bay, Nova Scotia; La Revue de Géographie de Montréal, v. XXX, no. 1, 2, p. 65 - 86.

Lambiase, J.J.
1977: Sediment dynamics in the macrotidal Avon River Estuary, Nova Scotia; unpubl. Ph.D. thesis, McMaster University, Hamilton, 415 p.

Ludwick, J.C.
1972: Migration of tidal sand waves in Chesapeake Bay entrance; in Shelf Sediment Transport, D.J.P. Swift, D.B. Duane and O.H. Pilbey, eds.; Dowden, Hutchinson and Ross, 756 p.
1974: Tidal currents and zig-zag sand shoals in a wide estuary entrance; Geological Society of American Bulletin, v. 85, p. 717 - 726.

Meckel, L.D.
1975: Holocene sand bodies in the Colorado Delta area, northern Gulf of California; Deltas: models for Exploration, M.L. Broussard, ed.; Houston Geological Society, p. 237 - 265.

Middleton, G.V.
1972: Brief field guide to intertidal sediments, Minas Basin, Nova Scotia; Maritime Sediments, v. 8, no. 3, p. 114 - 122.

Middleton, G.V., Knight, R.J. and Dalrymple, R. W.
1976: A facies model for a macrotidal environment - Cobequid Bay, Nova Scotia; American Association of Petroleum Geologists, v. 60, p. 697, 698.

Middleton, G.V., Knight, R.J., Dalrymple, R.W. and Lambiase, J.J.
1975: Intertidal sand bodies in the Minas Basin, Bay of Fundy; Geological Society of America, Abstract, v. 7, no. 6, p. 82.

Off, T.
1963: Rhythmic linear sand bodies caused by tidal currents; American Association of Petroleum Geologists, Bulletin, v. 47, p. 324 - 341.

Oomkens, E. And Terwindt, J.H.J.
1960: Inshore estuarine sediments in the Haringoliet (Netherlands); Geologie en Mijnbouw, v. 39, p. 701 - 710.

Pelletier, B.R. and McMullen, R. M.
1972: Sedimentation patterns in the Bay of Fundy and Minas Basin; in Tidal Power, T. J. Gray and O.K. Gashus, eds.; Plenum Publishing, New York, 630 p.

Prest, V.K. and Grant, D.R.
1969: Retreat of the last ice sheet from the Maritime Provinces - Gulf of St. Lawrence Region; Geological Servey of Canada Paper 69-33, 15 p.

Price, W. A.
1963: Patterns of flow and channeling in tidal inlets; Journal of Sedimentary Petrology, v. 33, no. 2, p. 279 - 290.

Reineck, H.I.
1963: Sedimentgefuge im Bereich der Sudlichen Nordsee. Senckenbergischen Naturforschende Gesellschaft, Abhandlungen, v. 505, p. 1 - 138.

Robinson, A.H.W.
1960: Ebb-flood channel systems in sandy bays and estuaries; Geography, v. 45, p. 183 - 199.
1966: Residual currents in relation to shoreline evolution of the East Anglian Coast; Marine Geology, v. 4, p. 57 - 84.

Salsman, G.G., Tolbert, W. H. and Villars, R.G.
1966: Sand-ridge migration in St. Andrew Bay, Florida; Marine Geology, v. 4, p. 11 - 19.

Smith, J.D.
1968: The dynamics of sand waves and sand ridges; University of Chicago Photoduplication Thesis No. T16801, 78 p.
1969: Geomorphology of a sand ridge; Journal of Geology, v. 77, p. 39 - 55.

Southard, J.B.
1971: Representation of bed configurations in depth-velocity-size diagrams; Journal of Sedimentary Petrology, v. 41, no. 4, p. 903 - 915.

Stewart, H.B. and Jordan, G.F.
1965: Underwater sand ridges on Georges Shoal; in Papers in Marine Geology, R. L. Miller, ed.; MacMillan, New York, 531 p.

Stichling, W.
1974: Sediment loads in Canadian Rivers; Inland Waters Directorate, Environment Canada, Technical Bulletin, 74, 27 p.

Stride, A.H.
1963: Current-swept sea floors near the southern half of Great Britain; Quarterly Journal, Geological Society of London, v. 119, p. 175 - 200.

Stride, A.H., Belderson, R.H. and Kenyon, N.H.
1972: Longitudinal furrows and depositional sand bodies of the English Channel; Memoires du Bureau de recherches Géologiques et Minières, v. 79, p. 233 - 240.

Swift, D.J.P.
1975: Tidal sand ridges and shoal-retreat massifs; Marine Geology, v. 18, p. 105 - 134.

Swift, D.J.P. and Borns, H.W. Jr.
1967: A raised fluviomarine outwash terrace north shore of Minas basin, N.S.; Journal of Geology, v. 75, p. 633 - 711.

Swift, D.J.P. and Ludwick, J.C.
1976: Substrate response to hydraulic processes: grain size frequency distributions and bedforms; in Marine Sediment Transport and Environmental Management, D.J. Stanley and D.J.P. Swift, eds.; Wiley, p. 159 - 196.

Swift, D.J.P. and McMullen, R.M.
1968: Preliminary studies of intertidal sand bodies in the Minas Basin, Bay of Fundy, N.S.; Canadian Journal of Earth Sciences, v. 5, p. 175 - 183.

Terwindt, J.H.J., de Jong, J.D. and van der Wilk, E.
1963: Sediment movement and sediment properties in the tidal area of the Lower Rhine; Koninklijk Nederlands Geologisch Mijnbouwkundig Genootschap, Geol. Serie, v. 2, no. 2, p. 243 - 258.

Todd, T.W.
1968: Dynamic Diversion: influence of longshore current-tidal flow interaction on Chenier and Barrier Island Plains; Journal of Sedimentary Petrology, v. 38, no. 3, p. 734 - 746.

Vanoni, V.A.
1974: Factors determining bed forms of alluvial streams; Proceedings of the American Society of Civil Engineers, v. 100(HY3), p. 363 - 377.

Van Veen, J.
1935: Sand waves in the North Sea; Hydrographic Review, v. 12, p. 21 - 28.
1937: Korte beschrijuing der uitkomsten van onderzoekingen in de Hoofden en langs de Nederlandsche kust; Tijdschrift van het K. Nederlandsch aardrijkskundig genootschap Ser. 2, v. 54, p. 155 - 195.
1950: Eb- en vloedschaarsystemen in de Nederlandse getijwateren; Wadden-symposium Tijdschrift van het K. Nederlandsch aardrijkskundig genootschap v. 67, p. 45 - 65.

Wightman, D.M.
1975: Paleotidal range and Pleistocene sea-level changes at Cape d'Or, Bay of Fundy, N.S., Geological society of America, Abstract v. 7, no. 6, p. 880, 881.
1976: The sedimentology and paleotidal significance of a late Pleistocene raised beach, Advocate Harbour, Nova Scotia; unpubl. M.Sc. thesis, Dalhousie University, Halifax, 156 p.

Wright, L.D.
1977: Sediment transport and deposition at river mouths: a synthesis; Geological Society of America Bulletin, v. 88, p. 856 - 968.

Wright, L.D., Coleman, J.M. and Thom., B.G.
1973: Processes of channel development in high-tide-range environment: Cambridge Gulf - Ord River Delta, western Australia; Journal of Geology, v. 81, p. 15 - 41.
1975: Sediment transport and deposition in a macrotidal river channel: Ord River, Australia; in Estuarine Research, Volume II, L.E. Cronin, ed.; Academic Press, New York, p. 309 - 321.

11.

TOPOGRAPHIC CONTROL OF SEDIMENT DISTRIBUTION
ON AN INTERTIDAL SAND BAR: A CASE STUDY

Joseph J. Lambiase

Department of Geological Sciences, Virginia Polytechnic Institute and State University, Blacksburg, Virginia

Lambiase, Joseph J., *Topographic control of sediment distribution on an intertidal sand bar: a case study; in The Coastline of Canada, S.B. McCann, editor; Geological Survey of Canada, Paper 80-10, p. 181-187, 1980.*

Abstract

Sediment distribution on an intertidal sand bar in the Avon River estuary, Bay of Fundy, indicates that topography has a strong influence on sediments. The sand bar has a bedrock core that modifies the local hydraulic environment by decreasing current speeds over the bar and altering flow patterns around the bar. The hydraulics dictate sediment distribution so that sediments reflect the presence of the bedrock core.

Most aspects of the sediment distribution are affected by the core. Sediment transport paths and the overall morphology of the bar and the position of its crest reflect flow around the core. Bedform flow regime and mean grain size increase away from the centre of the bar in response to an increase in current speed in that direction caused by the core.

The patterns of sediment distribution caused by the bedrock core are only subtly different from patterns on other Bay of Fundy intertidal sand bars. However, these small differences are enough to produce a distribution that allows definition of the shape, position and size of the bedrock core by analysis of sedimentological data.

Résumé

La répartition des matériaux sur un cordon intertidal dans l'estuaire de la rivière Avon (baie de Fundy) indique que la topographie possède une forte influence sur les matériaux. Le cordon possède un noyau de roche en place qui modifie le milieu hydraulique local en réduisant la vitesse du courant au-dessus du cordon et en modifiant les modes d'écoulement autour du cordon. Les lois de l'hydraulique commandent la répartition des matériaux de telle sorte que celui-ci reflète la présence du noyau rocheux.

La plupart des aspects de la répartition des matériaux sont affectés par le noyau. Les tracés de transport des matériaux et la morphologie d'ensemble du cordon ainsi que la position de sa crête reflètent l'écoulement qui existe autour du noyau. Le régime d'écoulement suivant la forme du lit et la taille moyenne des grains augmente à mesure qu'on s'éloigne du centre du cordon par suite d'un accroissement de la vitesse du courant dans cette direction à cause du noyau.

Les modes de répartition des matériaux provoquées par le noyau de roche ne sont que légèrement différents des modes observés sur les autres cordons intertidals de la baie de Fundy. Toutefois, ces petites différences sont suffisantes pour entraîner une répartition qui demande une définition de la forme, de la position et de la taille du noyau rocheux au moyen d'analyses de données sédimentologiques.

INTRODUCTION

Hydraulics is generally recognized to govern sediment distribution in the intertidal environment. Tidal range has been credited as the major control on the morphology of sediment accumulations in the intertidal zone (Hayes et al., 1973), and bedform stability and grain size distribution have been related to current speed and hydraulic process (Boothroyd and Hubbard, 1975; Green, 1975; Kumar and Sanders, 1975; Visher and Howard, 1974).

This paper aims to relate the morphology, bedforms and grain size distribution of one intertidal estuarine sandbar to its hydraulic environment. The sandbar is affected by unusual topography in that it is cored by bedrock, and this study is primarily concerned with delineating the interactions between topography, hydraulics and sediment distribution. Detailed discussion of other sandbars, bedforms and grain size distribution in the same estuary is available elsewhere (Lambiase, 1977, 1980a, b).

The sandbar examined in this study was named Middle Ground by the Canadian Hydrographic Service (1972). It is at the seaward end of the Avon River estuary in central Nova Scotia and is one of the six major intertidal sandbars in that system (Fig. 11.1). The Avon River empties into Minas Basin, the northeastern arm of the Bay of Fundy.

There have been several studies of sediment distribution in Minas Basin, including Dalrymple (1977), Dalrymple et al. (1975), Knight (1977), Knight and Dalrymple (1975), Lambiase (1977, 1980a, b), Klein (1970), Swift and McMullen (1968) and Swift et al. (1967). These authors have described virtually all the major intertidal sandbars in the basin without finding any other with a bedrock core. Thus it appears that Middle Ground may be the only sandbar in Minas Basin with a bedrock core.

Swift et al. (1967) and Swift and McMullen (1968) studied grain size distribution and current velocities on Middle Ground. Neither paper related hydraulics or grain size to the bedrock core because the existence of the core was unknown prior to a 1975 seismic profile that was run by Bedford Institute of Oceanography.

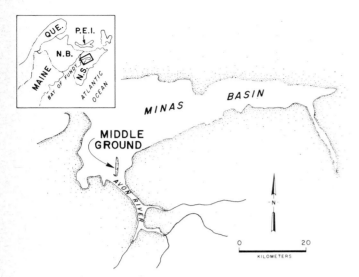

Figure 11.1. *Location of Middle Ground at the seaward end of the Avon River estuary within Minas Basin.*

HYDRAULICS

The Bay of Fundy is renowned for its large tidal ranges. The Avon River estuary has a mean tidal range of 12.0 m and a maximum range of 15.6 m at lunar perigee (Canadian Hydrographic Service, 1976). The tidal ranges generate strong currents, which are the only important hydraulic process operating in the system (Lambiase, 1977, 1980a).

Tidal current speed has a characteristic relationship with the tidal curve. Current speeds are lowest at high and low tide and greatest near the half-tides during both flood and ebb flow. The current speeds are highest just prior to emergence (and just after submergence) of the intertidal sandbars. This relationship holds essentially everywhere in Minas Basin (Knight, 1977; Dalrymple, 1977; Lambiase, 1977).

Middle Ground is an exception to this relationship. Current speeds measured at several stations over and near Middle Ground indicate that maximum speeds are greatest away from the centre of the sandbar and that they decrease markedly towards the bar centre (Fig. 11.2). This pattern is not as pronounced over other sandbars in the Avon River estuary, and current speeds recorded over the centre of Middle Ground are lower than those measured over all other bars in the Avon (Lambiase, 1977). The bedrock core raises the bar's surface elevation above that of other sandbars so that the higher parts of the bar are emergent during the segments of the tidal cycle that are associated with the strongest currents.

The bedrock core also affects flow pattern at the site of Middle Ground. It acts as an obstacle that flow must diverge around; this produces a different flow pattern from patterns associated with other sandbars in the Avon River estuary (Lambiase, 1977, 1980a). Thus Middle Ground's bedrock core influences the hydraulic environment over the sandbar by producing maximum current speeds and flow patterns that are distributed differently from those associated with other sandbars in the Avon River estuary.

SEDIMENT DISTRIBUTION

Three aspects of the sediment distribution on Middle Ground were examined; each is controlled by the local hydraulics and thus influenced by the bedrock core. The aspects are sandbar morphology, bedforms and grain size distribution; each will be treated separately.

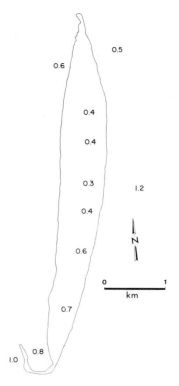

Figure 11.2. *Maximum current speeds over and near Middle Ground. Speeds are in m/s and are the maximum value of mean velocity during a complete tidal cycle.*

Sandbar morphology

The intertidal portion of Middle Ground is 5.6 km long and 0.9 km wide near the centre, tapering to a point at both ends (Fig. 11.3). There is a large ebb spit at the southern end of the bar.

A well developed crest trends parallel to the long axis of the bar. The bar is asymmetrical in cross-section with a steep slope on one side of the crest and a gentle slope on the other side (Fig. 11.4). Figure 11.4 also depicts bar surface elevations; elevations decrease rapidly away from the bedrock core.

The outline of the bedrock core on Figure 11.4 was interpreted from surficial features (this interpretation is discussed later) rather than seismic evidence because only one seismic profile was run across Middle Ground during Bedford Institute's program (C. Amos, 1975, pers. com.). The core appears to be block-faulted bedrock, the surface of which is 1 to 2 m below the surface elevation of the sandbar (C. Amos, 1975, pers. com.).

Much of the morphology of Middle Ground is the product of its bedrock core. The elongate shape of the sandbar, in an orientation roughly parallel to current direction, is typical of sandbars in Minas Basin (Knight, 1977; Dalrymple, 1977). However, the shape is the product of three sediment transport zones the direction and orientation of which are influenced by the bedrock core.

Tidal current flow is deflected around the bedrock core so that low-velocity areas, which resemble 'half-bodies' (Streeter, 1971), form in the lee of the core and sediment accumulates in the low-velocity areas (Fig. 11.5). This happens during both the ebb and flood stages of the tide and the shape of the bar approximates that of two overlapping half-bodies (Fig. 11.5).

Figure 11.3

Aerial photograph of Middle Ground. The area of poor drainage is relatively dark and near the centre of the bar.

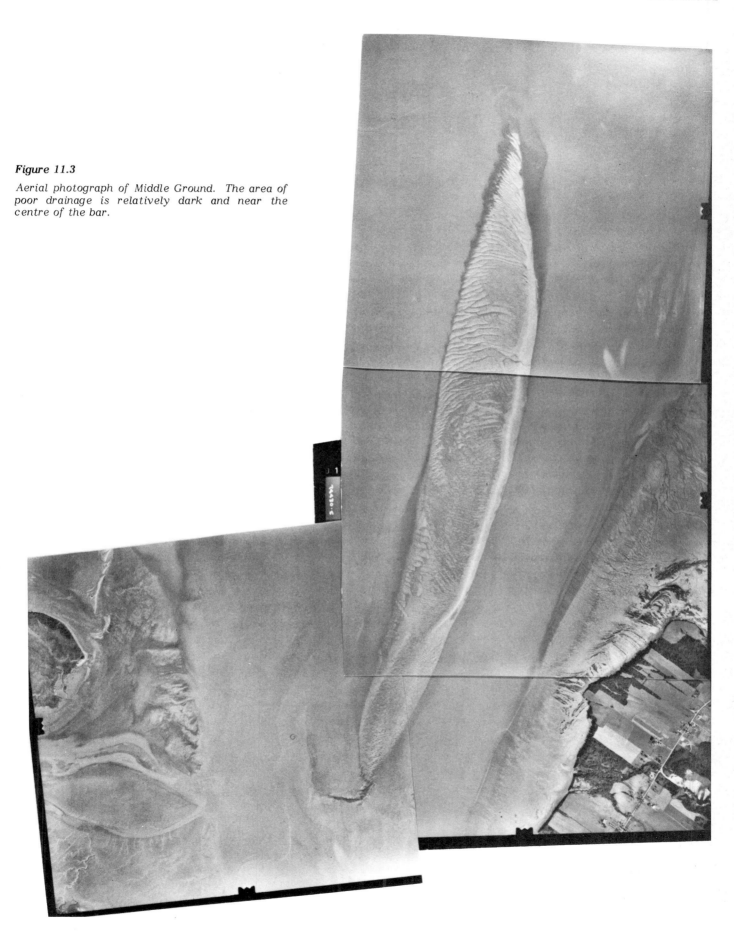

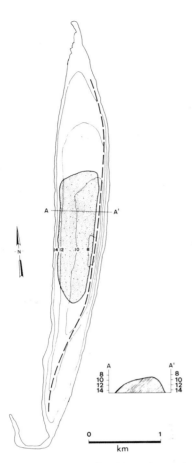

Figure 11.4. *Contour map of Middle Ground; contours are in metres below higher high water. The position of the sand bar crest is illustrated with a slashed line and the area underlain by the bedrock core is stippled. Also, a cross-section of the bar is depicted.*

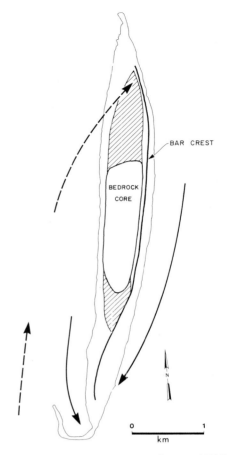

Figure 11.5. *Sediment transport paths on Middle Ground. Ebb dominant zones have slashed arrows and flood dominant zones have solid arrows. The positions of the "shadow zones" behind the bedrock core are hatched.*

The origin of Middle Ground is not linked exclusively to its bedrock core. Middle Ground is a channel-margin linear bar in an ebb-tidal delta (Swift et al., 1967; Lambiase, 1977, 1980a); the channel east of the bar is a marginal flood channel and the one west of the bar is the central ebb channel in the tidal delta. Thus, a sandbar probably would exist where Middle Ground lies even if the bedrock were absent, but its morphology would be different.

The effects of the core and the influence of the ebb-tidal delta combine to control the relative size of the sediment transport zones on Middle Ground, and the position and orientation of its crest. The southern half of the bar has two flood sediment transport zones (Fig. 11.5). The easternmost is large because it is the 'constructive' result of the marginal flood channel and flow around the bedrock core, whereas the westerly flood transport zone is small because it owes its existence solely to flow around the core and it actually runs counter to the ebb transport direction that would be expected if the ebb-tidal delta were the only influence. The relative size of these flood zones causes the crest to lie along the western side of the bar with its steep slope to the west near the southern end of Middle Ground (Fig. 11.5). The large ebb spit also is the result of interaction between the small flood transport zone and the central ebb channel of the ebb-tidal delta (Fig. 11.5).

The situation is similar north of the bedrock core. There is a large westerly ebb transport zone because it is a constructive system between flow around the core and the central channel (Fig. 11.5). There is no easterly ebb transport zone because flow around the core is destructive with respect to the marginal flood channel. This causes the crest to lie along the eastern margin of the bar with the steep side to the east (Fig. 11.5).

On the south end of Middle Ground, destructive interaction between ebb-tidal delta effects and flow around the bedrock core results in a sediment transport zone that reflects the influence of flow around the core (Fig. 11.5). This suggests that the morphology of Middle Ground is controlled as strongly by its bedrock core as by its role in the ebb-tidal delta.

Bedforms

Recent work on the hydraulic criteria for bedforms in Minas Basin reveals that mean grain size and current speed are the most important controls on bedform distribution, and that water depth is of secondary importance (Dalrymple et al., 1978). At any location, it is the maximum local current speed that governs bed configuration.

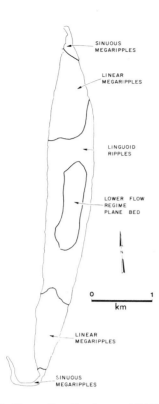

Figure 11.6.   *Bedform distribution on Middle Ground.*

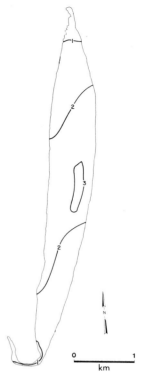

Figure 11.7.   *Mean grain size on Middle Ground.   Contours are in phi values.*

There are four bed configurations on Middle Ground, including lower flow regime plane bed, linguoid ripples, linear megaripples and sinuous megaripples (terminology of Dalrymple et al., 1978). Linguoid ripples are up to 0.3 m long and 0.05 m high while lower flow regime plane bed is a flat surface. Linear and sinuous megaripples have similar dimensions with heights up to 0.5 m and wavelengths up to 10.0 m but sinuous megaripples have relatively short sinuous crests so that they are three-dimensional, whereas linear megaripples are straight-crested and therefore two-dimensional. Sinuous megaripples also have scours associated with their troughs but linear megaripples do not.

Each of the four bed configurations can form at any of the mean grain sizes on Middle Ground (grain size distribution is discussed later) so that maximum current speed should control bedform distribution. The maximum current speeds illustrated in Figure 11.2 suggest that successively higher flow strength bedforms will occur progressively farther from the bedrock core. Bedform distribution on Middle Ground verifies this prediction as there are successive transitions from lower flow regime plane bed to linguoid ripples, then to linear megaripples and finally to sinuous megaripples progressively farther from the core (Fig. 11.6); this is the exact sequence that occurs with increasing flow strength throughout Minas Basin (Dalrymple et al., 1978).

The area of lower flow regime plane bed is colonized heavily by the tube-building polychaete *Spiophanes wigleyii* with recorded tube densities of up to 300 000 per m^2 (V. Tunnicliffe, 1975, pers. com.). The high concentration of worm tubes suggests that the sediment in this area is not very mobile; this supports the generally accepted idea that lower flow regime plane bed implies zero mobility.

Thus Middle Ground's bedrock core influences bedform distribution because it influences maximum current speeds over the bar and maximum speed is the most important control on bed configuration.

Grain Size Distribution

Surficial sediment samples were collected from 112 locations on Middle Ground. All samples were sieved at 0.25 phi intervals and moment measure textural parameters were computed. Cumulative frequency curves also were examined.

Mean grain size is finest near the centre of the sandbar and gets increasingly coarser towards each end (Fig. 11.7). Middle Ground is the only sandbar in the Avon River estuary with this pattern, and the central part of the bar is the only area at the seaward end of the estuary with mean grain sizes finer than 2.75 phi (Lambiase, 1977, 1980a). This pattern is expected from the current speed pattern illustrated in Figure 11.2; mean grain size is related directly to maximum current speed. Again, the bedrock core is instrumental in establishing the current speed pattern so that the core influences mean grain size.

The areal distribution of cumulative curve shapes suggests that there are differences in the relative importance of different sediment transport mechanisms on different parts of Middle Ground. Three different cumulative curve shapes were found in sediment samples from the Avon River estuary as a result of differing proportions of three grain populations; each grain population is related to a different sediment transport mechanism (Lambiase, 1980b). One type of cumulative curve has a large fine tail and essentially no coarse tail, and is found only at the shoreward end of the estuary and near the centre of Middle Ground. This curve shape is indicative of a large fine-grain population that was deposited from suspension with very little transport by traction (Lambiase, 1980b).

At the shoreward end of the estuary, this curve shape is produced by a hydraulic sorting process that eliminates the traction population (Lambiase, 1980b), but on Middle Ground it probably is related to the very low current velocities over the central area. Because the surface of the bedrock core is shielded from strong currents, coarse sediments cannot be transported into the area and the coarse tail is small. The large fine tail probably results from deposition of fine sediment from suspension by waning currents near high tide. These sediments were suspended by stronger currents away from the bedrock core and, once deposited, cannot be transported by the weak currents over the core. This supports the contention that the lower flow regime plane bed in this area is an area of zero mobility.

Cumulative curves from the rest of Middle Ground suggest that traction and intermittent suspension are important transport mechanisms away from the bedrock core, just as on all other sandbars at the seaward end of the Avon River estuary (Lambiase, 1980b). Transport mechanism is apparently an important control on grain size distribution on Middle Ground, and the relative importance of each mechanism is influenced by the bedrock core.

DISCUSSION

It is apparent from the preceding paragraphs that the bedrock core has a strong influence on the sediment distribution of Middle Ground: sediment transport paths, sandbar morphology, bedforms and grain size distribution all are affected by the core. However, the influence does not produce any sedimentological features that are not found on other sandbars in the Avon estuary or elsewhere in Minas Basin (Klein, 1970; Knight, 1977; Dalrymple, 1977; Lambiase, 1977, 1980a). Instead, the bedrock core causes a particular pattern of 'typical' Minas Basin sedimentological features.

The boundary of the bedrock core depicted in Figure 11.9 is not based on seismic evidence but was constructed from the evidence provided by the patterns of sediment distribution, because only one seismic profile has been run across the cored section of Middle Ground.

The position of the sandbar crest helps to define the southern and eastern extent of the bedrock core. The south edge of the core must be as far or farther north than the north end of the two southern flood transport zones (Fig. 11.5) because these zones form behind the core during flood flow. Thus the southern limit of the bedrock core must be farther north than the area where the bar crest crosses from the east to the west side of the sandbar (Fig. 11.4). The bar crest also delineates the east edge of the core because sediment transport zone morphology indicates that flood currents sweep around the east side of the core (Fig. 11.5).

The positions of the north and west margins of Middle Ground's bedrock core were defined from the drainage pattern on the sandbar surface. Drainage from the central part of Middle Ground is much poorer than from the remainder of the bar. At low tide, surface sediments on the central part of the bar are very wet and the water table remains within a few centimetres of the sediment surface. Elsewhere on the bar, surface sediments are well drained by small runoff channels and the water table is deeper than 0.5 m in most areas.

The poor drainage in the centre of Middle Ground probably results from relatively impermeable bedrock underlying fine sediments that also are less permeable than most sediment on the bar. Pore waters sit on top of the shallowly buried bedrock with minimal lateral mobility. Poor drainage should be confined to the area overlying bedrock, since other areas have coarser sediment and more lateral and vertical pore water mobility.

The transition from poorly drained to well drained is rapid at all margins of the poorly drained area. The different drainage patterns can be detected, although not easily, on aerial photographs (Fig. 11.3). The extent of the poorly drained area corresponds closely to the boundaries of the core that were inferred from sandbar morphology; multiple lines of evidence suggest the position and size limits of Middle Ground's bedrock core. The boundary of the core also corresponds closely to the boundary of the lower flow regime plane bed configuration (Fig. 11.6).

Before the seismic profile was run in 1975, it was apparent that there was something anomalous about Middle Ground, but even without seismic data the sedimentological patterns on the sandbar should have allowed inference that a bedrock core exists because it controls so much of the sediment distribution. Thus, the aspects of sediment distribution that reflect the bedrock core in Middle Ground, while subtly different from sediment distribution on other intertidal sandbars in Minas Basin, are distinct and are related to the hydraulic environment the core produces. As well, they could be used to detect the presence, position and size of the bedrock core without *a priori* knowledge of its existence.

CONCLUSIONS

Several conclusions can be drawn about the influence of topography on sediment distribution on Middle Ground. Topography, in this case a bedrock core, modifies the hydraulic environment by altering flow paths and local current speeds. It is the modified hydraulic environment that produces the sedimentological features that are related to the bedrock core. Thus the core actually has a second-order effect on the sediment distribution.

Middle Ground's bedrock core has a relatively subtle influence on sediment distribution. No unique sedimentological features result from the core and sediments generally are similar in character to the rest of Minas Basin. However, the influence is sufficient to affect virtually every aspect of the sediment distribution. Sediment transport paths, sandbar morphology, bedforms and grain size distribution reflect the presence of the core.

Sediment distribution on Middle Ground can be used to define the position, shape and size of the bedrock core. The various aspects of sediment distribution are consistent with the available seismic data so that the existence of a bedrock core could be predicted from sedimentological data alone.

Acknowledgments

This study was part of a Ph.D. program at McMaster University, Hamilton, and was supervised by G.V. Middleton whose suggestions and criticisms constitute a valuable contribution to the results. R.J. Knight and R.W. Dalrymple also made numerous helpful suggestions. C.L. Amos provided information about Bedford Institute's 1975 seismic profile.

Maureen Dickson aided in processing sediment samples, Dave Brown drafted the figures and Sue Bruce provided photographic assistance. The study was supported by the Department of Energy, Mines and Resources, and Imperial Oil Limited.

References

Boothroyd, J.C. and Hubbard, D.K.
  1975: Genesis of bedforms in mesotidal estuaries; in Estuarine Research, L.E. Cronin, ed.; v. 2, p. 217 - 234.

Canadian Hydrographic Service
  1972: Avon River and approaches; Chart 4140.
  1976: Canadian tide and current tables; v. 1, Atlantic Coast and Bay of Fundy.

Dalrymple, R.W.
  1977: Sediment dynamics of macrotidal sand bars, Bay of Fundy; unpubl. Ph.D. thesis, McMaster University, Hamilton, 635 p.

Dalrymple, R.W., Knight, R.J. and Middleton, G.V.
  1975: Intertidal sand bars in Cobequid Bay (Bay of Fundy); in Estuarine Research, L.E. Cronin, ed.; v. 2, p. 293 - 307.

Dalrymple, R.W., Knight, R.J. and Lambiase, J.J.
  1978: Bedforms and their hydraulic stability relationships in a tidal environment, Bay of Fundy, Canada; Nature, v. 275, p. 100 - 104.

Green, C.D.
  1975: A study of hydraulics and bedforms at the mouth of the Tay estuary, Scotland; in Estuarine Research, L.E. Cronin, ed.; v. 2, p. 323 - 344.

Hayes, M.O., Owens, E.H., Hubbard, D.K. and Abele, R.W.
  1973: Investigation of form and processes in the coastal zone; in Coastal Geomorphology, Proceedings of 3rd Annual Geomorphology Symposium Series, Binghamton, New York, D.R. Coates, ed.; p. 11 - 41.

Klein, G. de Vries
  1970: Depositional and dispersal dynamics of intertidal sand bars; Journal of Sedimentary Petrology, v. 40, p. 1095 - 1127.

Knight, R.J.
  1977: Sediments, bedforms, and hydraulics in a macrotidal environment, Cobequid Bay (Bay of Fundy), Nova Scotia; unpubl. Ph.D. thesis, McMaster University, Hamilton, 693 p.

Knight, R.J. and Dalrymple, R.W.
  1975: Intertidal sediments from the south of Cobequid Bay, Bay of Fundy, Nova Scotia, Canada; in Tidal Deposits, R.N. Ginsburg, ed.; Springer-Verlag, New York, p. 47 - 55.

Kumar, N. and Sanders, J.E.
  1975: Inlet sequence formed by the migration of Fire Island Inlet, Long Island, New York; in Tidal Deposits, R.N. Ginsburg, ed.; Springer-Verlag, New York, p. 75 - 83.

Lambiase, J.J.
  1977: Sediment dynamics in the macrotidal Avon River estuary, Bay of Fundy, Nova Scotia. Unpub. Ph.D. thesis, McMaster University, 415 p.
  1980a: Sediment dynamics in the macrotidal Avon River estuary, Bay of Fundy, Nova Scotia; Canadian Journal of Earth Sciences, (in press).
  1980b: Hydraulic control of grain size distributions in a macrotidal estuary; Sedimentology, v. 27, p. 433-446.

Streeter, V.L.
  1971: Fluid mechanics; McGraw-Hill, New York, 755 p.

Swift, D.J.P. and McMullen, R.M.
  1968: Preliminary studies of intertidal sand bodies in Minas Basin, Bay of Fundy, Nova Scotia; Canadian Journal of Earth Sciences, v. 5, p. 175 - 183.

Swift, D.J.P., McMullen, R.M. and Lyall, A.K.
  1967: A tidal delta with an ebb-flood channel system in the Minas Basin, Bay of Fundy: preliminary report; Maritime Sediments; v. 3, p. 12 - 16.

Visher, G.S. and Howard, J.D.
  1974: Dynamic relationship between hydraulics and sedimentation in the Altamaha estuary; Journal of Sedimentary Petrology, v. 44, p. 502 - 521.

12.

ANIMAL-SEDIMENT RELATIONSHIPS IN THE MINAS BASIN, BAY OF FUNDY

Michael J. Risk and Ross K. Yeo
Department of Geology, McMaster University, Hamilton, Ontario

Risk, Michael J., and Yeo, Ross K., Animal-sediment relationships in the Minas Basin, Bay of Fundy; in The Coastline of Canada, S.B. McCann, editor; Geological Survey of Canada, Paper 80-10, p. 189-194, 1980.

Abstract

Organisms living in the intertidal sediments of the Minas Basin influence geochemical cycles by controlling the thickness of the oxidized layer and by mobilizing and recirculating sediment and organic matter. Sediment mobilization is produced largely through the activities of deposit feeders. Sediment stabilization is produced by the sediment-binding activities of bacteria and algae, and through physical baffling by marsh grasses and worm tubes.

Rapidly-accreting areas support organisms adapted to high water contents and low shear strengths. As algal carbon is accumulating in rapidly-accreting areas, it is possible that potential hydrocarbon source rocks could be identified by their trace fossil content.

Résumé

Les auteurs ont constaté que certains organismes vivants dans les sédiments intertidaux du bassin Minas influencent les cycles géochimiques en commandant l'épaisseur de la couche oxydée et en mobilisant et en faisant recirculer les sédiments et la matière organique. La mobilisation de sédiment résulte surtout de l'action des sources d'alimentation en matériaux. La stabilisation de sédiment est produite par l'action liante des bactéries et des algues sur les sédiments, et par l'effet de chicane des hautes herbes et des trous de vers des marais.

Les zones à engraissement rapides font vivre des organismes adaptés aux hautes eaux et à de faibles résistances au cisaillement. Comme le carbone algal s'accumule dans des zones à engraissement rapide, il est possible que les roches susceptibles de produire de l'hydrocarbone puissent être identifiées par leur teneur en fossiles en traces.

INTRODUCTION

Recent work on animal-sediment relationships owes a tremendous debt to earlier research in the North Sea and on the northwestern coast of Europe, notably by the Dutch and by Germans working out of the Senckenberg Institute. North American interest in this area of marine research began to accelerate in the 1960s, with particularly important work being done by Ralph Gordon Johnson, of the University of Chicago and his student, Donald C. Rhoads (now at Yale University) and by Howard Sanders, at Woods Hole. Recent years have seen a flurry of activity, with centres of excellence on both coasts of the United States.

We are now aware that the influence of the benthos can be profound, in some cases controlling nutrient cycling and sediment properties and influencing water chemistry. Canada lags in the study of animal-sediment relationships: realization of the fundamental importance of this field of study has not yet percolated north across the border.

BIOLOGICAL CHARACTERISTICS OF THE MINAS BASIN

Previous work in the Minas Basin has demonstrated the unique nature of the animal communities on the intertidal flats (Craig, 1977; Risk et al., 1977; Yeo, 1978). Organism densities and biomass values are some of the highest ever recorded (Table 12.1), while the species diversity is extremely low. These high organism densities are supported in sediments with relatively low carbon values, suggesting rapid overturning rates driven by tidal flushing (Table 12.2).

Table 12.1. Densities and biomass of major species from Minas Basin versus other areas

Location	Macoma		Corophium	Mya
	Maximum	Average	Maximum	Maximum
			Density	
Waddensea	212	48 (1)	100 (2)	500 (3)
U.K.	6000	112 (4)	63000 (5)	500 (4)
Minas Basin	3500	670	63000	419
Cumberland-Shepody	4400	1900	7600	0
			Biomass	
Waddensea	2.2 (6)	--	0.3 (6)	167 (3)
U.K.	0.34 (1)	--	--	5.5(1)
Minas Basin	105.6	47	19.5	183
Cumberland-Shepody	18.1	5.6	6.7	0

Densities expressed in no./m^2. Biomass expressed in gm dry weight/m^2.

Table 12.2. Values of organic carbon from surface sediments of intertidal flats of the Minas Basin

	April	June	July
	(%)	(%)	(%)
Muds	0.34	0.38	0.31
Muddy sands	0.23	0.26	0.20
Sands	0.16	0.20	0.19
Averages of several hundred analyses.			

Typical sediment profiles begin with a gravel lag just below a peat horizon near maximum high tide. This gravel quickly grades into an upper mudflat, with very high water contents and moderate organism densities. The highest organism densities are found in the lower mudflat, in which water contents are also lower. ('Mudflat' is used here as a field term. The flats are, technically, muddy sandy silt-flats.) The lower mudflat coarsens fairly quickly to sands, frequently megarippled, near the low-tide mark. The differing water contents of the upper and lower mudflats (Fig. 12.1) are partly due to more efficient drainage of the lower flats, and partly to differing conditions of deposition, resuspension and bioturbation. The vertical profile of water content in the sediment is largely controlled by the burrowing activities of *Corophium volutator* and *Macoma balthica*.

Immediately after spring breakup, the whole of the intertidal zone is frequently covered with a layer of fine sand, a remnant of winter storms and ice-rafted sediment. During winter and early in spring, the reducing layer in the sediments is very close to the surface, and small-scale ripple marks are frequently on the lower mudflats.

As the water warms, biological activity accelerates. The layer of fine sand is buried by bioturbation by late May. The oxidized layer increases in thickness through the summer, generally averaging 10 - 15 cm by August. Formation of small ripples on the lower mudflats is inhibited by *Macoma balthica*; in control plots where *Macoma* is removed, ripples reappear (Craig, 1977). In general, the upper part of the mudflats is completely bioturbated. Although traces are found in the sands (Craig, 1977; Risk and Tunnicliffe, 1978) bioturbation is much less pronounced.

On this seasonal picture of the alternating importance of physical and biological processes is overprinted the effect of catastrophic events: storms, hurricanes, high tides. Storms and hurricanes have been observed to remove large amounts of sediment off the flats, and to cause catastrophic mortalities among the benthos (Yeo, 1978). The effect of storms is likely preserved in the sediments as buried coarser layers, and as sedimentary couplets showing characteristic trace fossil suites.

INFLUENCE OF ORGANISMS ON GEOCHEMICAL CYCLES

Thickness and distribution of the oxidized layer in fine sediments in the Minas Basin is controlled by burrowing. Organisms inhabiting semipermanent feeding and dwelling burrows, such as *Macoma* and *Corophium*, respire by continually pumping oxygenated water through their burrows. At the same time, burrows produced by the foraging activities

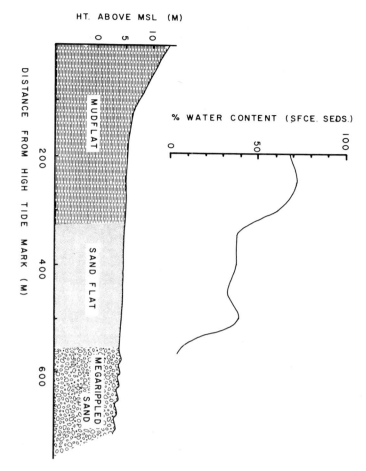

Figure 12.1. *Profile across a typical intertidal flat in the Minas Basin, showing sediment types and water contents.*

of carnivores, such as some of the nereid polychaetes, become conduits through which oxygen may penetrate into the sediments. Empty burrows made by *Nereis diversicolor* are frequently found oxidized to more that 15 cm in depth. Salt marsh sediments have a thin oxidized surface layer, because of a lack of burrowing organisms.

Deposit feeding organisms produce large amounts of excreta (feces and pseudofeces), most of which is high in water content and hence easily transported. Resuspension of these biodeposits is believed to contribute significantly to the turbidity of the water; Risk and Moffat (1977) have described the tremendous contribution made by *Macoma balthica*. Such recycling of fine material is believed to be an important feedback process increasing the efficiency of food utilization. Much of the detritus available to deposit feeders has a very high C:N ratio, and consists of relatively refractory plant debris. Deposit feeders ingest the sediment and eat the bacteria growing on the detritus. The process therefore involves conversion of low-protein plant detritus to high-protein bacterial biomass. The voided detritus contains a few viable bacteria, which immediately begin to multiply, preparing the sediment to be eaten again, as it were. Obviously, the longer this cycle runs the more complete will be the utilization of the carbon in the system. (This concept is discussed in Newell, 1970, and an example from the Minas Basin is given in Tunnicliffe and Risk, 1977.)

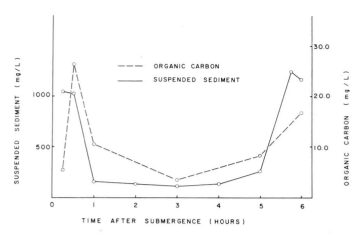

Figure 12.2. *Values of suspended sediment concentration and organic carbon content over a tidal cycle, for water samples pumped from 1 cm above the sediment surface.*

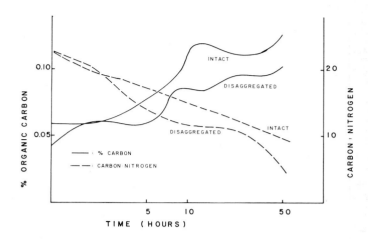

Figure 12.3. *Organic carbon content and Carbon-Nitrogen ratios for* **Macoma** *pellets taken in the field and maintained in sea water tanks. Half the sample was mechanically disaggregated prior to commencement of the experiment.*

Suspended sediment concentrations are very high immediately above the mudflats. The sediment itself consists of plant detritus, fecal pellets and a large number of organically bound aggregates; values of organic carbon in this lower turbid layer are higher than the organic carbon values on the flats themselves, and the C:N ratio is lower (Yeo, 1978). This intermittently resuspended material, therefore, is the food that supports the high benthic productivities, and is in turn largely produced by the feeding activities of the organisms themselves (see Risk and Moffat, 1977, Fig. 8, for a summary of the process).

In an experiment performed in the summer of 1976, water samples from three different heights above a mudflat (1, 5, and 20 cm off the bottom) were pumped up to a stationary moored boat. Analysis of the suspended sediments showed that the organic carbon content parallels the suspended sediment concentration throughout a tidal cycle (Fig. 12.2), suggesting that the organic matter is transported at the same rates and velocities as the average suspended sediment grain. The C:N ratio is lower both just after submergence and just before emergence (roughly 9 or 10 to 1), again suggesting that the high-protein bacterial biomass is being transported on the surface of that grain of aggregate size which is most readily moved across the flats---fine sand, or fecal pellets somewhat larger. Following voiding of feces, subsequent pellet breakdown in the turbulent conditions of the Minas Basin is undoubtedly largely through physical abrasion and collision. The necessary bacterial bloom takes place very rapidly, however, on either intact or disaggregated pellets. Laboratory study of *Macoma balthica* pellets showed carbon increases and C:N ratio decreases occurring almost immediately after voiding (Fig. 12.3). The C:N ratios of disaggregated pellets drop below 10:1 less than a day later; these pellets can survive at least one tidal cycle, but are unlikely to last more than a few days before breaking down into mucus-bound organic aggregates.

SEDIMENT STABILIZATION BY ORGANISMS

Although movement of coarse particles in high-energy environments (such as the offshore bars in the Minas Basin) is a physical process, transport processes of sand-size and smaller particles across the intertidal flats cannot adequately be understood without an understanding of biological influences.

At the bottom of the taxonomic scale, bacteria and blue-green algae both secrete a gelatinous sheath. In the bacteria, the sheath is believed to be a defence mechanism; many modern antibiotics operate by destroying the slime sheath, thereby allowing the bacterium to be attacked by the body's own defences. The sheath in blue-green algae also is believed to function as a repellent to grazing organisms and as a deterrent to competing algae (Monty, 1967). Naturally, these sheaths serve to bind sediment grains together; both bacteria and blue-green algae are capable of producing stromatolites. Blue-green algae are not common in Minas Basin sediments but bacteria are abundant.

Diatoms also secrete a mucopolysaccharide layer when moving through sediment. Diatoms are plentiful in sediments of the Minas Basin and frequently form surface slicks or patches.

Finally, some of the invertebrates stabilize the surface layer, either directly or indirectly. *Nassarius obsoletus* (a scavenging snail), the nereid polychaetes and the nemertean worms all move through or on the sediment utilizing mucous secretions. *Corophium* does not secrete a binding agent, but instead lines its burrows with fine sediment and compacts the walls.

In an attempt to evaluate the relative amount of organic binding contributed by bacteria, encaryotic algae, and the total of all organisms, an informal experiment was performed in the summer of 1975. Spray dispensers were used to write a word upon the mudflats three times, with a tetracycline solution (a wide-spectrum antibiotic effective on most bacteria), an algicide, and a formaldehyde solution of sufficient strength to kill all life. After one tidal cycle, each of the three words was outlined in negative relief, indicating significant erosion had taken place. No relative comparisons were possible regarding the degree of binding by each of the three groups of organisms.

Physical stabilization of sediments is also produced by baffling and current retardation. Patches of lower salt marsh are often an area of deposition of fine sediment, particularly following storm erosion elsewhere. After a severe storm in 1974, *Corophium* carcasses were deposited in salt marshes, in solid layers several centimetres thick. In addition, on some of the extensive sand flats (especially off Cambridge) large populations occur of the tubeworms *Spiophanes wigleyi* and *Clymenella torquata*. The tubes of these worms are believed to suppress formation and migration of ripples, both because of the current retardation produced by the tubes elevated above the sediment-water interface, and also because of the large amounts of sediment physically bound into the tubes at any one time. At maximum *Spiophanes* densities, for example, half the sand grains on the flat are bound into worm tubes (Featherstone and Risk, 1977). Small-scale ripples would potentially form on many of the lower mud flats, but are suppressed by feeding activities of *Macoma*.

SEDIMENT MOVEMENT BY ORGANISMS

Much of the influence of organisms on sediment mobilization has already been covered in the discussion on geochemical cycles. Newly exposed sand and mudflats are frequently covered by a thin veneer of flocculent, organically bound fine sediment. In *Macoma* zones this layer is quickly cleaned off by feeding, exposing the characteristic feeding pits. In rippled areas this material accumulates in the ripple troughs as flasers. In high density *Macoma* zones, removal of sediment by feeding amounts to about 30 cm per year (Risk and Moffat, 1977), much of which, of course, is immediately redeposited.

There is also a certain amount of sediment movement produced by the feeding activities of birds and fishes, but this process is quantitatively unimportant. Flatfish feeding pits are abundant on the flats (Risk and Craig, 1976), and pits attributed to sturgeon (which must have been >2 m long!) have been observed in the Cumberland Basin. Rays sometimes come in to feed on the tubeworms on Cambridge Flats, using their wings to excavate holes up to 1 m across and 0.5 m deep.

RELATIONSHIP BETWEEN ORGANISMS AND SEDIMENT TYPE

It is now recognized that, while size-distribution curves are important to sedimentologists, the organisms actually living in the sediment also respond to the mass properties of the sediment, particularly the water content and shear strength. That mass properties and size distribution can, in turn, be controlled by organisms has been demonstrated off Canada's Atlantic coastline (Pemberton, 1976). Two mud-flats can, for example, have identical size distribution parameters. One flat may be a normal result of slow or intermittent rates of deposition, and will have surface water contents of perhaps 20 per cent, and surface shear strengths of perhaps $4-5$ kilopascals/cm^2. The other flat may have been rapidly deposited, and may have water contents up to 80 per cent, and essentially no shear strength. Naturally, these flats will each support different assemblages of organisms.

The normal mudflat fauna will contain the semipermanent feeding burrows of *Macoma* and *Corophium*, the branching burrows of nereid polychaetes, and will be completely bioturbated. This situation represents the maximum utilization of the available carbon.

In areas of rapid deposition, a completely different set of adaptations is found. To support themselves in sediments with low shear strengths, *Macoma* reduce their bulk density, by secreting thinner shells and increasing their aspect ratio (Hirtle, unpubl. data). In order to get at the organic matter which has been buried by the high sedimentation rate, some organisms (mostly in sands) adopt a strategy of systematic horizontal mining (Risk and Tunnicliffe, 1978). In both sands and muds, upside-down deposit feeding is common: in sands the species is *Clymenella torquata*, while rapidly deposited finer sediments are frequently dominated by *Heteromastus*

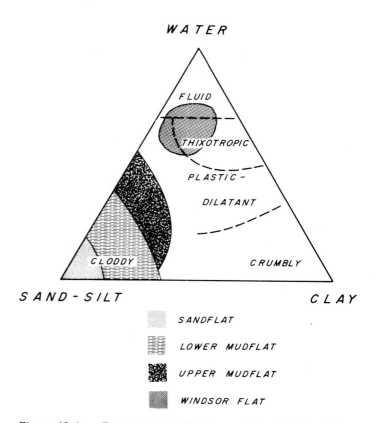

Figure 12.4. *Ternary classification of intertidal Minas Basin sediments. The Windsor Flat is notably different.*

filiformis. It is interesting to note that, in the trace fossil genus *Skolithos*, larger diameter species seems to occur in coarser sediments. Both *Clymenella* and *Heteromastus* tubes would fossilize as *Skolithos*. The decrease in diameter in finer sediments may reflect an adaptation to lowered shear strengths; the weight of a worm is a function of the square of the radius, while the bearing area is a function of the circumference. Larger diameter worms may simply sink into worm oblivion. Food on rapidly deposited flats should therefore not be as efficiently assimilated; bioturbation should be less intense and carbon values higher.

In our attempt to evaluate the impact of the sedimentation bound to follow construction of tidal power barrages, we have for some years now been considering the newly created mudflat at Windsor, Nova Scotia, as an analogue (this is well described in Amos, 1977). Organism densities on the Windsor flat are greatly reduced over normal flats (Yeo, 1978; Hirtle, unpubl. data), and the organisms themselves are representative of what we have termed our siltation-tolerant suite; small *Macoma*, some *Corophium*, nereid polychaetes, nemerteans, and many *Heteromastus filiformis*. *Mya arenaria*, the softshell clam, is absent. Sediments on this flat are similar in grain size content to those on other flats, but the water contents are very high (Fig. 12.4). The controlling factor on the invertebrate populations on the Windsor flat is probably the shear strength, which is essentially zero to a depth of 15 cm (Fig. 12.5). On the other hand, values of sedimentary Chlorophyll A on the Windsor Flat are comparable to control flats (Burns, 1978), and sedimentary organic carbon contents are considerably higher (Hirtle, unpubl. data). Food is being produced on the Windsor flat, but it is not being utilized.

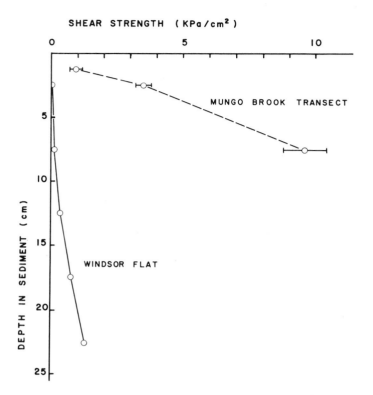

SHEAR STRENGTH (KPa/cm²)

Figure 12.5. *Shear strength values with depth for the Windsor Flat and a control flat, the Mungo Brook transect. (Values determined with a Pilcon Shear Vane, and were comparable to values determined using several other methods.)*

TRACE FOSSILS, SEDIMENTATION RATES AND HYDROCARBON SOURCE ROCKS

The normal Minas Basin mudflat, completely bioturbated and containing large numbers of semipermanent feeding burrows, has low organic carbon contents, and little or no carbon is accumulating at depth. Most of the carbon on the flats may be algal in origin, as suggested by a series of stable carbon isotope analyses $\delta^{13}C$ of four composite samples, East Noel transect, was - 21.08, standard deviation 0.57). Burial of algal carbon under reducing conditions is believed to produce high-quality crude oil (Tissot et al., 1974). On the Windsor flat, algal carbon is being buried under reducing conditions. It therefore seems possible that potential hydrocarbon source beds could be differentiated from nonsource beds, on the basis of their trace fossil content.

Nonsource beds would be bioturbated, and would contain well developed semipermanent feeding burrows often with protrusive spreiten. Because of the lower water contents and higher shear strengths, horizontal burrows would not be greatly compressed. Source beds would retain horizontal lamination, and would contain escape structures, burrows with retrusive spreiten, and small-diameter *Skolithos*. Horizontal feeding burrows would be greatly compressed. Although there is considerable controversy over the timing of expulsion of crude oil from source rocks, some 'proto-oil' is believed to be expelled at relatively shallow depths (Sabins, 1963). Dewatering of a Windsor-type flat along horizontal bedding planes could conceivably drive out the trapped organic matter, perhaps in the form of proto-oil. This hypothetical process is summarized in Figure 12.6.

SUMMARY

Organisms on the intertidal flats of the Minas Basin respond to sediment type, and in turn control some of the properties of the sediments themselves. In comparison with other coastal areas, for example, the North Sea and the Georgia coast, the direct effect of organisms on the coarser sediments is not great. Their effect on the finer sediments is, however, profound. The ability of organisms to recycle the sediment through their feeding activities undoubtedly is one of the prime factors accounting for the extraordinarily high densities and productivities recorded for the area.

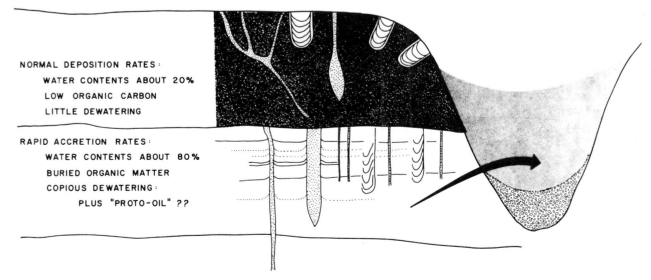

NORMAL DEPOSITION RATES:
  WATER CONTENTS ABOUT 20%
  LOW ORGANIC CARBON
  LITTLE DEWATERING

RAPID ACCRETION RATES:
  WATER CONTENTS ABOUT 80%
  BURIED ORGANIC MATTER
  COPIOUS DEWATERING:
    PLUS "PROTO-OIL" ??

Figure 12.6. *Sketch of the hypothetical characteristics of nonsource sediments (upper bed) and source sediments (lower bed), adjacent to a gravel-floored drainage channel.*

Acknowledgments

We thank Paulette Burns, Cathy Capell and Verena Tunnicliffe for help in the field. The study was supported by the Department of Energy, Mines and Resources, via research subventions with Atlantic Geoscience Centre, whose staff (particularly Dale Buckley and Kevin Robertson) we thank for their infinite patience, enthusiastic cooperation, and scientific acumen in early realizing the importance of biological research in this area.

We thank the people of Hants County, Nova Scotia, for their interest and hospitality.

References

Amos, C.L.
1977: The effects of tidal power structures on the sediment transport and loading in the Bay of Fundy - Gulf of Maine system; Workshop on Environmental Implications of Fundy Tidal Power, Acadia University Institute, No. 28, p. 233 - 253.

Burns, P.
1978: Photosynthetic pigment concentrations in inter- tidal sediments of the Minas Basin, Bay of Fundy; unpubl. B.Sc. thesis, Department of Geology, McMaster University, Hamilton.

Craig, H.D.
1977: Intertidal animal and trace zonations in a macrotidal environment, Minas Basin, Bay of Fundy; unpubl. M.Sc. thesis, Department of Geology, McMaster University, Hamilton.

Featherstone, R.P. and Risk, M.J.
1977: Effect of tube-building polychaetes on intertidal sediments of the Minas Basin, Bay of Fundy; Journal of Sedimentary Petrology, v. 47, p. 446 - 450.

Monty, C.L.
1967: Distribution and structure of recent stromatolitic algal mats, eastern Andros Island, Bahamas; Societé Géologique de Belgique, Annales, v. 90, p. 55 - 110.

Newell, R.C.
1970: Biology of intertidal animals; Elsevier, New York, 555p.

Pemberton, S.G.
1976: Deep bioturbation by *Axius serratus* in the Strait of Canso, Nova Scotia; unpubl. M.Sc. thesis, Department of Geology, McMaster University, Hamilton.

Risk, M.J. and Craig, H.D.
1976: Flatfish feeding traces in the Minas Basin; Journal of Sedimentary Petrology, v. 46, p. 411 - 413.

Risk, M.J. and Moffat, J.S.
1977: Sedimentological significance of fecal pellets of *Macoma balthica* in the Minas Basin, Bay of Fundy; Journal of Sedimentary Petrology, v. 47, p. 1425 - 1436.

Risk, M.J. and Tunnicliffe, V.J.
1978: Intertidal spiral burrows: *Paraonis fulgens* and *Spiophanes wigleyi* in the Minas Basin, Bay of Fundy; Journal of Sedimentary Petrology, v. 48, p. 1287 - 1292.

Risk, M.J., Yeo, R.K. and Craig, H.D.
1977: Aspects of the marine ecology of the Minas Basin relevant to tidal power development; Workshop on Environmental Implications of Fundy Tidal Power, Acadia University Institute, No. 28, p. 164 - 179.

Sabins, F.F., Jr.
1963: Anatomy of stratigraphic trap, Bisti, New Mexico; Bulletin, American Association of Petroleum Geologists, v. 47, p. 193 - 228.

Tissot, B., Durand, B., Espitalié, J. and Combas, A.
1974: Influence of nature and diagenesis of organic matter in the formation of petroleum; Bulletin, American Association of Petroleum Geologists, v. 58, p. 499 - 506.

Tunnicliffe, V.J. and Risk, M.J.
1977: Relationships between *Macoma balthica* and bacteria in intertidal sediments: Minas Basin, Bay of Fundy; Journal of Marine Research, v. 35, p. 499 - 507.

Yeo, R.K.
1978: Animal-sediment relationships and the ecology of the intertidal mudflat environment, Minas Basin, Bay of Fundy, N.S.; unpubl. M.Sc. thesis, Department of Geology, McMaster University, Hamilton.

13. HOLOCENE COASTAL ZONE SAND BUDGET, SOUTH SHORE, NOVA SCOTIA

David J.W. Piper

Departments of Geology and Oceanography, Dalhousie University, Halifax, Nova Scotia

Piper, David J.W., Holocene coastal zone sand budget, South Shore, Nova Scotia; in The Coastline of Canada, S.B. McCann, editor; Geological Survey of Canada, Paper 80-10, p. 195-198, 1980.

Abstract

The South Shore of Nova Scotia, from St. Margaret's Bay to Port Mouton, is a submerging rocky coastline. Sand occurs in a few large barrier beaches, and in shallow basins on the inner shelf in water depths up to 70 m. Erosion of till cliffs is the principal sediment source. Sediment budget calculations show that this source can account for observed sand only in silled coastal bays. Elsewhere, sand is much more abundant than would be expected. This sand must have entered the coastal zone during deglaciation, and have been transported landwards during the Holocene transgression.

Résumé

Sur la côte sud de la Nouvelle-Ecosse, de la baie St. Margaret à Port Mouton, le littoral est rocheux et submergé. On trouve du sable dans quelques grandes plages-barrières et dans certains bassins peu profonds sur la plate-forme intérieure dans des eaux atteignant une profondeur de 70 m. L'érosion des falaises de till est le principal facteur d'alimentation en matériaux. Le calcul du bilan sédimentaire démontre que cette érosion ne donne que le sable observé dans les baies côtières à seuils rocheux. Ailleurs, le sable est beaucoup plus abondant qu'on le croirait. Ce sable doit avoir pris naissance dans la zone littorale ou au cours de la déglaciation et a probablement été transporté à l'intérieur des terres au cours de la transgression à l'Holocène.

INTRODUCTION

The South Shore of Nova Scotia is a low rocky coastline of submergence. Its first-order morphology is controlled by the seaward-dipping Cretaceous peneplane developed on Meguma Group metasediments and Devonian granites of South Mountain (Goldthwait, 1924). This surface has been modified by glacial erosion, including excavation of silled basins and glacial deposition of drumlins, sheet till and fluvioglacial outwash. Late Wisconsinan glacial ice retreated 12-13 000 B.P. (Prest and Grant, 1969), and apparent sea level has probably risen ever since that time. The rate of sea level rise over the last 7000 years has been determined as around 1.7 mm per year (Scott, 1977), and preliminary results of modelling of ice loading (G. Quinlan, pers. com., 1978) suggest relative sea level 10 000 years ago was about 20 m below its present position. The present coastline is highly indented, with many islands of both bedrock and drumlins. The larger bays are glacially overdeepened basins.

A wide range of geological studies has been made in the coastal zone of the South Shore from St. Margaret's Bay to Port Mouton (Fig. 13.1) and some preliminary results from St. Margaret's and Mahone bays are reported by Keen and Piper (1976), Piper and Keen (1976), and Barnes and Piper (1978). Further work is described in theses by Barnes (1976), Kepkay (1977) and Letson (1980). Studies of beaches have been made by Bowen (1975), Piper and Bowen (1976) and Urquhart (1977). A general account of the nearshore geology of the South Shore is in preparation.

Occasional large sandy barrier beaches occur along the rocky coastline of the South Shore (Fig. 13.1). An earlier study of the environmental consequences of sand removal from beaches (Bowen, 1975) suggested there was little source for the sand on these beaches, other than from nearshore sand bodies. At that time little was known of the distribution and character of sands on the inner shelf and nearshore in this region. This paper outlines the distribution of sand in the coastal zone and considers its source and movements in the light of sediment budget estimates. Some of the data used are based only on preliminary interpretations and should be treated with caution.

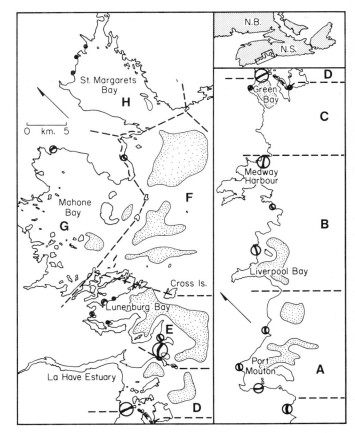

Figure 13.1. *South Shore of Nova Scotia, showing nearshore sand bodies (stippled) and major beaches (circles). Coastal segments A to H referred to in Table 13.1.*

Table 13.1. Nearshore sand budget

Coastal Segment*	Sources					Sinks			
	Area of eroding drumlin face	Annual sand supply** from drumlin erosion	Total supply over 10^4 years	Area of eroded drumlin platform	Total supply over 10^4 years	Volume of sand in beaches, dunes and lagoons	Volume of sand in nearshore muddy sediments	Submarine sand bodies area	Submarine sand bodies volume[†]
	$(10^4 m^2)$	$(10^3 m^3/a)$	$(10^6 m^3)$	(km^2)	$(10^6 m^3)$	$(10^6 m^3)$	$(10^6 m^3)$	(km^2)	$(10^6 m^3)$
A	<0.5	<0.5	<5	<1	<3	10	–	33	66
B	<0.5	<0.5	<5	<1	<3	5	–	20	40
C	<0.1	<0.1	<1	<0.3	<1	6	–	15	30
D	3	5	50	15	45	<0.5	2	12	24
E	2	5	50	18	54	5	2	61	122
F	<0.1	<0.3	3	?5	?15	<0.5	–	85	170
G	5	5	30 [††]	10	30	1.5	6	8	16
H	1	1	10	5	15	1	6	2	4

* See Figure 13.1.
** Assume retreat rates 0.3 m/a for coastal bays and bouldery till with bedrock footings southwest of Cape La Have; 1 m/a for exposed coastline northeast of Cape La Have.
[†] Assume average thickness of 2 m. This is very conservative for all segments except G and H.
[††] This rate of erosion for only 6000 years after incursion of sea.

PRESENT SAND DISTRIBUTION

Surficial sediment distribution has been mapped between St. Margaret's Bay and Port Mouton from the shoreline to 8 km offshore. Three principal sediment types are recognized:

(1) Muds, in places sandy or gravelly, occur in sheltered waters and in the deep basins of the coastal bays.

(2) Sands, in places gravelly, are found in shallow basins seaward of the coastal bays; lesser amounts are found on beaches and near the entrances to coastal bays (Fig. 13.1).

(3) Bedrock or till, with a patchy veneer of gravel or boulders, outcrops over large areas of seafloor exposed to waves. In the coastal bays, protected from the open ocean by shoals and in some cases by shallow sills, such outcrops are found only in depths less than 10 m. Seaward, as exposure to long periods and large storm waves increases, outcrops occur in areas of positive relief in depths as great as 70 m.

The surface distribution of sand can be determined by bottom sampling and its distinctive reflectivity in 14 kHz sounder profiles. Thickness of sand is determined from 3.5 kHz sounder lines, augmented by piston cores and deep-towed high-resolution sparker lines. Sand basins on the open shelf typically have 2 - 5 m of sand overlying early Holocene

or late Pleistocene sediment, till or bedrock. Thicknesses in excess of 10 m occur in deeper depressions. The volumes given in Table 13.1 are very conservative, as they are based on an assumed average thickness of only 2 m.

The volumes of sand in beach systems can be crudely estimated by projecting observed bedrock surfaces beneath beach accumulations for which profiles are available. The estimates in Table 13.1 suggest that beaches, dunes and lagoons are of minor importance as sand sinks. Muddy areas of coastal bays contain some sand: volumes in Table 13.1 are estimated from known surface distribution, thickness and grain size distribution of muddy sediments.

PRESENT SOURCES OF SAND

Rivers contribute almost no sand at present to the South Shore nearshore zone, and the predominant source of sediment is from the erosion of till cliffs (Piper and Keen, 1976). These contain 20 to 40 per cent sand-size material. Rates of cliff retreat (and hence of sediment supply) are dependent on exposure to waves and on whether the cliffs have a bedrock footing (Bowen, 1975). Rates of erosion have been determined for about 10 cliffs from ground survey and historical data. This has been supplemented with the data in Bowen (1975) and examination of old air photographs. Retreat rates are from 1 to 2.5 m/year on exposed coasts, whereas rates of 20 - 40 cm/year are found on the more exposed cliffs within coastal bays. Most of the drumlins southwest of Cape La Have are low and bouldery and many have a bedrock footing; retreat rates here appear to be less than 1 m/year. Estimates in Table 13.1 of annual supply rates of sand from drumlin erosion are based on observed lengths and heights of eroding cliffs and application of a retreat rate based on degree of exposure, assuming that the till contains 30 per cent sand. Some sand may also move inshore from the open continental shelf (this point is considered later).

SOURCES OF SAND OVER THE LAST 10 000 YEARS

There is no reason to suppose that over the last 10 000 years the predominance of till-derived sediment was much lower than at present. Rising sea level would progressively have exposed more landward drumlins to wave erosion. Spring river discharges may have been slightly higher in the early Holocene, but thalweg irregularities would have trapped most bedload.

The former distribution of drumlins out to the 20 m isobath (10 000 B.P. sea level) can be estimated in two ways. One is to assume a density of drumlins similar to that on the adjacent land: effectively then, the present rate of drumlin erosion is assumed to have prevailed over the last 10 000 years.

Where drumlins have not been eroded away completely down to bedrock, their submerged eroded remnants can be recognized both on seismic reflection profiles and from their characteristic boulder armour. Making assumptions as to average original drumlin height allows the total sediment supplied by erosion to be calculated.

SAND BUDGET

Both St. Margaret's and Mahone bays have shallow bedrock sills separating them from the open shelf. The lack of sand in deep basins behind the sills suggests little exchange of sand between the bays and the open shelf. St. Margaret's Bay had only a very narrow channel linking it with the sea at 10 000 B.P., and would have been completely protected from open shelf waves (Piper and Keen, 1976). The Mahone Bay sill was breached about 6000 B.P. (Barnes and Piper, 1978). The observed volume of sand in these bays (11 x 10^6 m^3 in St. Margaret's, 23.5 x 10^6 m^3 in Mahone) is approximately balanced by the estimated supply over the last 10 000 years (10 - 15 x 10^6 m^3 and 30 x 10^6 m^3, respectively). The volume calculations are too imprecise for any significance to be attached to the slight excess of supply over observed sinks.

The La Have estuary appears from Table 13.1 to have a sand supply double that of the observed sinks; however, the assumed 2 m thickness for the shelf basin sand bodies off La Have is highly conservative, and 5 or even 10 m is more realistic. All other coastal segments have a substantial excess of observed sand over inferred supply for the last 10 000 years. The abundance of beach sand appears unrelated to total rates of sand supply from till erosion. Indeed, 10 000 years of till erosion appears inadequate even to supply the observed beach sand southwest of Cape La Have.

The excess sand must either have been introduced into the system more than 10 000 years ago, or have been brought in by longshore transport processes. Variation in heavy mineral assemblages along the coast (unpubl. data; Nolan, 1963) closely follows that found in tills on land, suggesting that longshore transport is of minor importance. The excess sand must have been derived from fluvioglacial and moraine sediments immediately following deglaciation, and have been moved landwards with the Holocene transgression.

Seismic reflection profiles and coring show common fluvioglacial material in bedrock depressions, probably associated with downwasting of the South Mountain ice sheet after the sea broke into the Bay of Fundy around 14 000 B.P. Some open shelf basins contain sand resting on muds. These muds accumulated in the depressions which were more sheltered when sea level was lower, and were then covered by transgressive sand.

This type of study does not establish how sand is moved landwards. In the nearshore, sand is presumably transported landwards by shoaling waves. In Bowen (1975) the role of storm washover and tidal delta deposition into lagoons in the landward movement of beach sands in this area has been demonstrated. During transgression, neither process allows much sand transport from the inner shelf into bays with deep basins behind the sills.

Acknowledgments

This study was funded by Energy, Mines and Resources research agreements and a National Research Council strategic grant. The assistance of the staff from Bedford Institute of Oceanography and the Nova Scotia Research Foundation is acknowledged.

References

Barnes, N.E.
  1976:   The areal geology and Holocene history of the eastern half of Mahone Bay, Nova Scotia; unpubl. M.Sc. thesis, Dalhousie University, Halifax, 125 p.

Barnes, N.E. and Piper, D.J.W.
  1978:   Late Quaternary geological history of Mahone Bay, Nova Scotia; Canadian Journal of Earth Sciences, v. 15, p. 586 - 593.

Bowen, A.J.
  1975:   Maintenance of beaches: technical report; Institute for Environmental Studies, Dalhousie University, Halifax, 582 p.

Goldthwait, J.W.
  1924:   Physiography of Nova Scotia; Geological Survey of Canada, Memoir 140, 179 p.

Keen, M.J. and Piper, D.J.W.
  1976:   Kelp, methane and an impenetrable reflector in a temperate bay; Canadian Journal of Earth Sciences, v. 13, p. 312 - 318.

Kepkay, P.E.
  1977:   Preliminary investigation of free gas associated with a sub-bottom acoustic reflector in the fine grained sediments of Halifax Harbour and St. Margaret's Bay, Nova Scotia; unpubl. M.Sc. thesis, Dalhousie University, Halifax.

Letson, J.R.J.
  1980:   Contemporary sedimentation in south-western Mahone Bay, Nova Scotia; unpubl. M.Sc. thesis, Dalhousie University, Halifax.

Nolan, F.J.
  1963:   Heavy mineral analysis of the beach sands of Nova Scotia; unpubl. M.Sc. thesis, Dalhousie University, Halifax.

Piper, D.J.W. and Bowen, A.J.
1976:   Beach maintenance and removal of sand and gravel; Institute for Environmental Studies, Dalhousie University, Halifax, 69 p.

Piper, D.J.W. and Keen, M.J.
1976:   Geological studies in St. Margaret's Bay, Nova Scotia; Geological Survey of Canada, Paper 76-18, 18 p.

Prest, V.K. and Grant, D.R.
1969:   Retreat of the last ice sheet from the Maritime Provinces - Gulf of St. Lawrence region; Geological Survey of Canada, Paper 69-33, 15 p.

Scott, D.B.
1977:   Distributions and population dynamics of marsh-estuarine foraminifera with applications to relocating Holocene sea levels; unpubl. Ph.D. thesis, Dalhousie University, Halifax, 252 p.

Urquhart, E.F.
1977:   Holocene history of Kings and Hartling Bays, Atlantic Coast of Nova Scotia; unpubl. B.Sc. (hons) thesis, Dalhousie University, Halifax, 112 p.

14.

MORPHOLOGICAL CHANGES IN AN ESTUARY:
A HISTORICAL AND STRATIGRAPHICAL COMPARISON

David B. Scott

Department of Geology, Dalhousie University, Halifax, Nova Scotia

Scott, David B., Morphological changes in an estuary: a historical and stratigraphical comparison; in The Coastline of Canada, S.B. McCann, editor; Geological Survey of Canada, Paper 80-10, p. 199-205, 1980.

Abstract

Maps and air photos of Chezzetcook Inlet, Nova Scotia, dating back to 1766 are used to reconstruct morphological changes that have occurred during the last 200 years. This information is compared with a detailed stratigraphic record for the last 6000 years. Although the 1766 map lacks detail it appears that there was significant infilling of Chezzetcook Inlet and an adjoining inlet, Three Fathom Harbour, between 1766 and 1854. Between 1854 and 1945 little morphological change took place in Chezzetcook, but between 1945 and 1974 significant changes again occurred and the salt marsh area dramatically increased in this period. The stratigraphic record shows a long sequence of stable mudflat or shallow subtidal conditions until the last 200 years when a large area was simultaneously covered by salt marsh.

The area appears outwardly to be emergent with surfaces rising relative to sea level. However, relative sea-level is rising faster now than in the past and increased sedimentation rates are masking the effects of rising sea level. Several mechanisms may be responsible for the increased sedimentation but it is probably associated with early European settlement 200-300 years ago.

Résumé

Pour reconstituer l'évolution morphologique qui s'est produite au cours des 200 dernières années, les auteurs se sont servis de cartes et de photographies aériennes de l'inlet Chezzetcook (Nouvelle-Écosse) qui remontent à 1766. Ils ont comparé les renseignements obtenus avec des relevés stratigraphiques détaillés concernant les 6000 dernières années. Bien que la carte de 1766 manque de détails, il semble qu'il existait un engraissement appréciable dans l'inlet Chezzetcook et un inlet voisin, le havre Three Fathom, entre 1766 et 1854. Entre 1854 et 1945, Chezzetcook n'a connu qu'une faible évolution morphologique, mais entre 1945 et 1974 des changements appréciables se sont produits de nouveau et la zone de marais salants a pris une grande ampleur au cours de cette période. Les relevés stratigraphiques montrent une longue suite de conditions favorables à la formation de platières stables et d'un régime subtidal peu profond jusqu'à ces 200 dernières années, époque où une vaste zone a été simultanément recouverte par un marais salant.

La zone semble émerger vers l'extérieur et sa surface semble s'élever par rapport au niveau de la mer. Toutefois, le niveau relatif de la mer s'élève plus rapidement maintenant qu'autrefois et les vitesses de sédimentation accrues masquent les effets du niveau de la mer de plus en plus élevé. On peut attribuer à plusieurs mécanismes cette sédimentation accrue mais en réalité, elle est probablement liée à l'existence d'établissements européens il y a 200 à 300 ans.

INTRODUCTION

When studying the morphological changes of an inlet or estuary most workers either centre on short-term historical documents, such as maps or air photos, or examine the long-term stratigraphical changes, basically ignoring recent changes. In Chezzetcook Inlet, Nova Scotia (Fig. 14.1) there was an opportunity to examine both recent changes (the last 200 years) and changes over a longer term (the last 6000 years). The former were examined by comparing a series of maps and airphotos and the latter from drillholes from one area in Chezzetcook Inlet.

Combining these data allows the comparison and assessment of recent changes versus the longer term changes observed in the stratigraphic record. This type of comparison aids in differentiating episodic and gradual changes as well as determining whether the event was induced naturally or artificially.

PHYSIOGRAPHY OF THE PRESENT INLET

The mouth of the inlet is characterized by large sand spits, having westerly and northerly extensions at Cape Entry and extending both north and east from Story Head (Fig. 14.2). Red Island is primarily a sandbar. The largest features inside the inlet are the extensive intertidal mudflats and salt marshes. The intertidal areas are drained by a network of channels that dissects the mudflats. The channels begin at the head of the estuary as one large channel originating from the East Head, which bifurcates just west of Labreque Island. A small channel from the West Head enters the main channel just above the bifurcation point and both continue down the estuary and empty into a large central area just south of Conrad Island. The upper part of the channel system in the East Head appears to be the remnant of a river channel but the channels in the open part of the inlet appear to be formed by tidal currents.

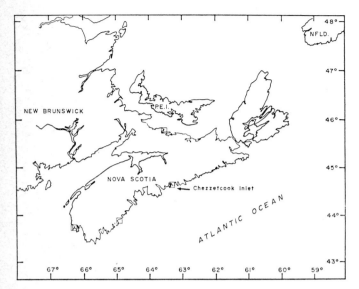

Figure 14.1 *Location map showing the position of Chezzetcook Inlet on the Atlantic coast of Nova Scotia.*

The inlet can be subdivided into three general areas: the nearshore area south of Conrad Island where the channels disappear into a large turbulent, shallow zone that is no longer intertidal; a large central region containing large mudflats and many drumlin islands; and an upper region which has comparatively narrow channels and a well developed marsh area (East and West heads). The oceanographic characteristics (i.e., salinity-temperature profiles) are described elsewhere (Scott, 1977a).

PHYSICAL CHANGES IN CHEZZETCOOK INLET IN HISTORICAL TIMES

Data sources

The basic sources of information are a map of Halifax Harbour, which also shows Chezzetcook, prepared by Capt. James Cook in 1766; a British Admiralty Chart (no. 2439) prepared in 1854; a set of 1945 airphotos and a set of 1974 airphotos. Supplementary information was obtained from a 1927 topographic map.

Comparison of the 1766 and 1854 maps

The distortion of the 1766 map (Fig. 14.3) is high compared to the excellent map produced in 1854 (Fig. 14.4). This may be the result of Cook's inability to navigate past the entrance of the inlet with a large sailing ship, because the major features (near the entrance) appear to be mapped accurately. The 1766 map shows a spit extending from Story Head and Cape Entry and a deep channel between the end of the Cape Entry spit and the small drumlin just west of Conrad Island. By 1854 this deep channel was shallow and almost closed. The entrance to the inlet was also substantially shallower. The shallowing of the main channel also occurred in Three Fathom Harbour in the same period (Figs. 14.3, 14.4). A large mudflat is shown on the east side of Chezzetcook in 1766 and by 1854 mudflats covered most of the inlet. The large marsh shown behind the Cape Entry spit in 1854 may not have been present in 1766. It is difficult to determine if the change in the size of the mudflat is real since the detail on the 1766 map is not reliable landward of Conrad Island.

Figure 14.2. *1974 map (prepared from air photos) of Chezzetcook Inlet.*

The most interesting and puzzling piece of information on the 1766 map is in the legend, where the tidal range at Cape Sambro (just outside Halifax Harbour) is given as follows: neap tides 6 to 7 feet, and spring tides 10 to 11 feet. On the 1854 map tidal ranges are the same as those today: neap tides 4 to 5 feet, spring tides 6.5 to 7 feet. The tidal range given for 1766 is open to question. Tidal measurements at Brest, France, measured with reliable accuracy since 1711, indicate that tides in the North Atlantic since then have changed less than 5 per cent (Cartwright, 1972a, b), whereas the apparent change at Cape Sambro between 1766 and 1854 is about 50 per cent. As it is

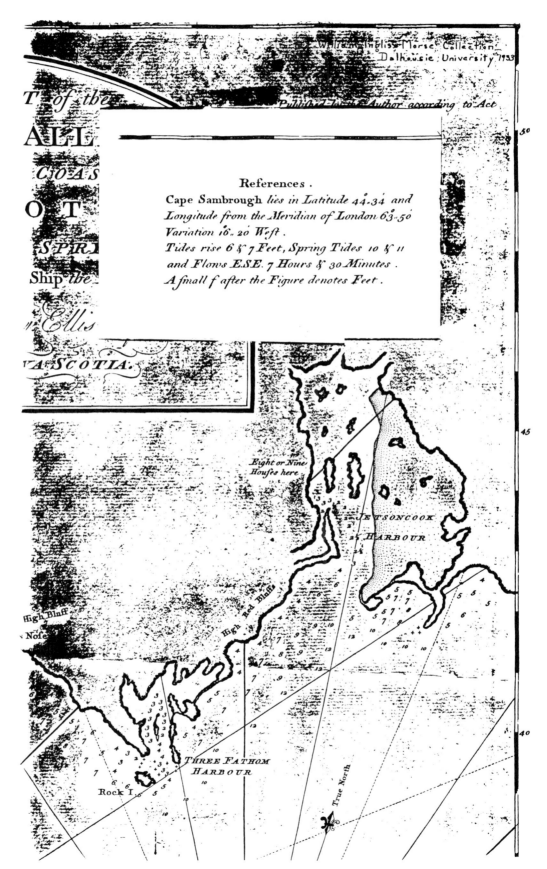

References .

Cape Sambrough *lies in Latitude* 44.34 *and*
Longitude from the Meridian of London 63.50
Variation 16. 20 *West* .
Tides rise 6 & 7 *Feet, Spring Tides* 10 & 11
and Flows E.S.E. 7 *Hours* & 30 *Minutes* .
A small f after the Figure denotes Feet .

Figure 14.3. *1766 map of Chezzetcook Inlet by James Cook. The inlet was on the edge of a Halifax Harbour map. Note that the tidal range is given for Cape Sambrough which is near the mouth of Halifax Harbour.*

201

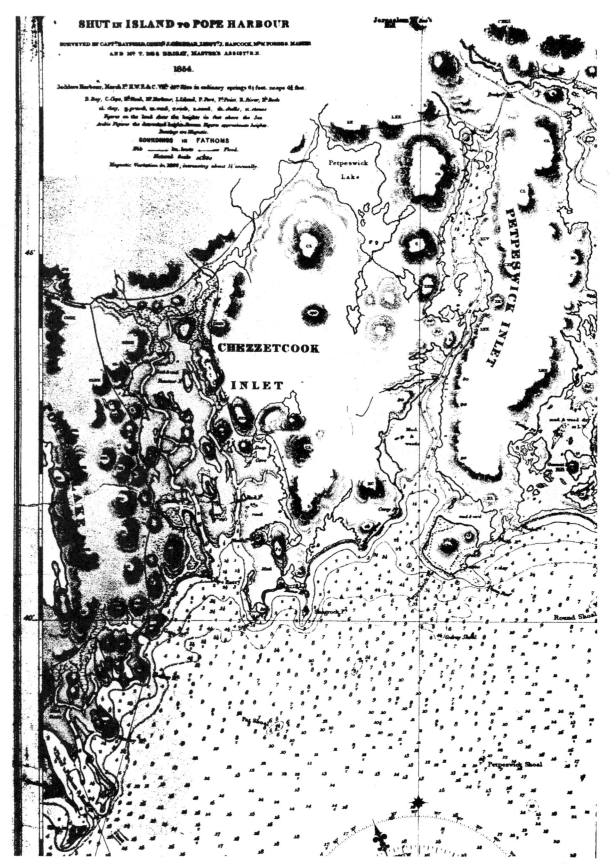

Figure 14.4. *1854 map (admiralty chart) of Chezzetcook Inlet. Note tidal range given on this map.*

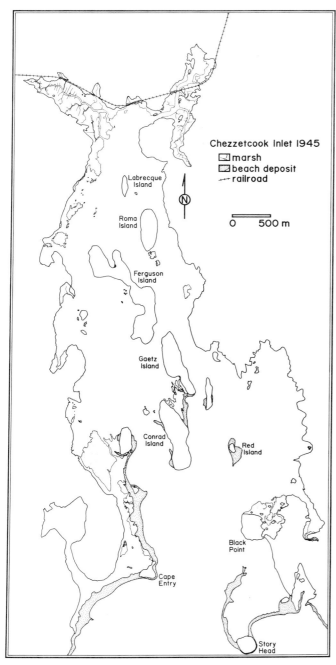

Figure 14.5. *1945 map (prepared from air photos) of Chezzetcook Inlet. Channels are not shown but are the same as those shown in Figure 14.2.*

show no noticeable expansion of the marsh areas. There was a new spit between Conrad and Gaetz islands, which apparently formed after 1927, since it is not shown on the 1927 map. The opening in the northern extension of Cape Entry spit was closed by 1927, and the houses on the small drumlin just west of Conrad Island suggest that the closure may have been artificial. Some breakwaters that exist today are shown near the 1927 entrance and the present channel system was in existence. The channel system has changed little since 1854; one new channel is shown on the 1945 air photos in the area between Ferguson and Roma islands. The 'pond' is shown as a swamp in 1854, but as open water in 1927 and 1945. The extent of marshes behind the Cape Entry spit (westerly extension) in 1854 appears greatly reduced by 1945. All islands appear to have remained the same size and shape between 1854 and 1945.

Comparison of the 1945 and 1974 maps

Changes between 1945 and 1974 (Fig. 14.2) are more pronounced than those between 1854 and 1945. Large movements of sand occurred near the entrance to the inlet. The spit on the west side of Conrad Island lengthened considerably between 1945 and 1974, further constricting the main channel, which feeds the western part of the inlet. The small island just southeast of Gaetz Island became connected by a sandbar to the main spit between Conrad and Gaetz islands. The most pronounced change was in the vicinity of Red Island. It was a small, rounded island up until 1945; by 1974 it had an elongated, half-moon shape. The spits at both Story Head and Cape Entry moved landward significantly between 1945 and 1974. This apparently had little effect at Story Head, but the Cape Entry spit has overridden existing marsh and isolated a small pond that had been open to tidal influence in 1945. North of the entrance to the inlet, mostly in its western part, much new marsh has formed since 1945. The large open mudflat north of Roma Island now apparently is being rapidly colonized by marsh plants.

STRATIGRAPHY OF THE WEST HEAD OF CHEZZETCOOK

Drillholes in the West Head (Figs. 14.6, 14.7) cover a period of over 6000 years (^{14}C date at the base of Drillhole V) and make it possible to compare changes over the last 200 years with those of the last 6000 years.

At the base of Drillhole V there is a gradational marsh sequence which is quickly overridden by an open-marine mudflat sequence and a long brackish mudflat sequence. At the 1.5 m mark, the mudflat sequence turns into a salt marsh deposit, which extends to the surface. The lower part of the marsh deposit is low marsh whereas the upper part is middle marsh, as determined using marsh foraminifera (Scott, 1977b; Scott and Medioli, 1978). This 1.5 m marsh deposit evidently started forming over most of the West Head almost simultaneously and represents a major change in the environment.

A relative sea level curve was determined for this area using ^{14}C dates from basal marsh deposits in drillholes from the West Head of Chezzetcook. This curve shows a relative sea level rise of 14 cm/ century between 6000 B.P. and 2000 B.P. with an increased rate of sea level rise of 30 cm/century from 2000 B.P. to the present (Scott, 1977b).

The present marsh surface over most of the West Head is approximately 80 cm above mean sea level (Scott, 1977b). Therefore, the lower part of the deposit is 70 cm below mean sea level. Lowest marsh begins to colonize mudflats at or slightly below (-30 cm) mean sea level; hence sea level must have been 40 - 70 cm lower at the time this deposit

not in an area of extreme tides, as in the Bay of Fundy, the changes in tidal range might be expected to be similar to those elsewhere in the North Atlantic. The accuracy of the 1766 measurements cannot be determined and the tidal information must be substantiated from another independent source before it can be considered seriously.

Comparison of 1854 and 1945 maps

There were few major changes in the configuration of the inlet between 1854 and 1945. The 1945 photos (Fig. 14.5)

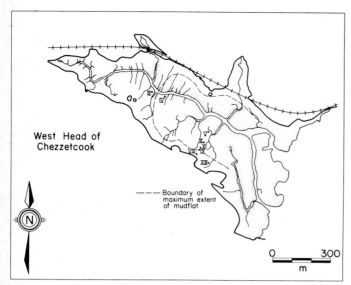

Figure 14.6. *Enlargement of the West Head at Chezzetcook showing the position of the drill holes. The dashed line represents an approximation of the maximum mud flat extent.*

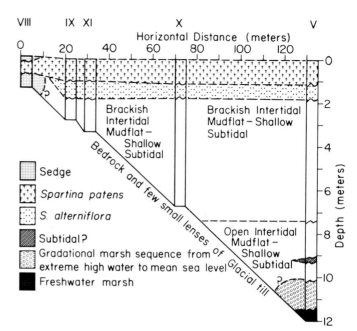

Figure 14.7. *Drill hole stratigraphy from the West Head based on foraminiferal content in the sediments (from Scott, 1977b).*

began to form. If a 30 cm/century rate of sea level rise is assumed for the last 200 years, then 200 years ago the relative sea level was 60 cm lower than present, and this coincides closely with the interval between 1766 and 1854. Hence the marsh area in the West Head was probably not present or just beginning to form in 1766.

DISCUSSION

Two major episodes of sedimentological and morphological change appear to have taken place in Chezzetcook Inlet: a poorly documented but dramatic episode between 1766 and 1854, and a well documented period between 1945 and 1974. The first episode was apparently a more regional event with effects in at least two separate harbours (Three Fathom and Chezzetcook), whereas the second episode was more localized to Chezzetcook.

The localized event between 1945 and 1974 was associated with the growth of sand spits near the inlet entrance. It is suggested that the enlargement of sand spits near major channels, such as the spit on western Conrad Island, caused significant changes in current speeds and sedimentation rates, with the result in Chezzetcook that much new salt marsh formed between 1945 and 1974. Further evidence that this was strictly a local event is that no significant new areas of marsh have formed in Petpeswick Inlet (just east of Chezzetcook) since 1854.

The regional episode between 1766 and 1854 is more difficult to account for. Since sea level has been rising faster in the last 2000 years than previously, the apparent emergence (i.e., formation of marsh and shallowing of channels) must be the result of increased sedimentation on a regional scale due to either an increase in the sediment supply or a reduction in coastal tidal current velocities. The most likely explanation is an increase in the amount of terrestrial sediment supplied to the inlet as a result of farming practices and logging introduced by early European settlers 200 to 300 years ago. There is now only a small contribution of sediment from terrestrial sources, but even small changes in land use could alter this situation. Without

further documentation of the 1766 tidal information, a reduction in tidal currents associated with reduced tidal ranges cannot be advanced as an explanation.

The morphological changes in Chezzetcook Inlet over the last 200 years appear at first to be the result of an emergent coastline, especially the formation of new marsh areas over a relatively lower intertidal mudflat. However, the opposite is the case and this demonstrates that high rates of sedimentation can mask the effects of rising sea level. Hence, attempts to classify coastlines, particularly estuarine areas, as emerging or submerging should not be based solely on recent geomorphological changes.

This study is intended to provide a model for studying recent changes in inlets along the Atlantic coast of Nova Scotia. It is important to combine recent data (i.e., maps, airphotos) with stratigraphical data to determine if the recent changes represent long-term trends or a departure from the previous events. In the case of Chezzetcook, at least in the West Head, there was a long period (probably 5000 years) where only mudflats were forming, and only in the last 200 years have extensive marshes formed. This is interesting not only geologically but also environmentally, since the coming of the European settlers has indirectly caused wide-reaching changes to a previously stable marine environment, changes which the Europeans probably assumed were a natural occurrence. The recognition that the changes were caused by human activities rather than naturally may aid in the planning of future developments along the coastal zone.

Acknowledgments

Franco Medioli and David J.W. Piper provided many helpful comments, both scientific and editorial, on this report. Maps were obtained from the Killiam Library at Dalhousie and from the Nova Scotia Archives. Airphotos were obtained through the Nova Scotia Department of Lands and Forests. This work was funded by a National Research Council grant to Medioli.

References

Cartwright, D.E.
 1972a: Some ocean tide measurements of the eighteenth century and their relevance today; Proceedings of the Royal Society, England, Challenger Centenary Congress, v. 72, no. 32, p. 331 - 339.
 1972b: Secular changes in the oceanic tides at Brest, 1711 - 1936.

Scott, D.B.
 1977a: Physiographic and oceanographic characteristics of Chezzetcook Inlet, Nova Scotia; Maritime Sediments, v. 13, no. 3.
 1977b: Distribution and population dynamics of marsh-estuarine foraminifera with applications to relocating Holocene sea-levels; unpubl. Ph.D. dissertation, Dalhousie University, Halifax, 252 p.

Scott, D.B. and Medioli, F.S.
 1978: Vertical zonations of marsh foraminifera as accurate indicators of former sea levels; Nature, v. 272, no. 5653, p. 528 - 531.

15.

SHORE PLATFORM MORPHOLOGY AND TIDAL-DURATION DISTRIBUTIONS IN STORM WAVE ENVIRONMENTS

A.S. Trenhaile and M.G.J. Layzell
Geography Department, University of Windsor, Windsor, Ontario

Trenhaile, A.S. and Layzell, M.G.J., Shore platform morphology and tidal-duration distributions in storm wave environments; in The Coastline of Canada, S.B. McCann, editor; Geological Survey of Canada, Paper 80-10, p. 207-214, 1980.

Abstract

A mathematically simple model was used to simulate the development of shore platform profiles in Gaspé, Québec and in the Vale of Glamorgan in south Wales. Intertidal erosion at any point on a platform profile was determined by the slope immediately below, by an erodibility factor related to wave intensity and rock hardness, and by the frequency-duration distribution of still water level within the tidal range. Model runs showed that platform gradient at each elevation eventually assumes a value which causes the erosion rate to be equal at all points across the platform. The shape of simulated equilibrium profiles is very similar to shore platform profiles in each study area. Other aspects of platform morphology, such as the strong relationship between gradient and tidal range, and the presence and form of ramps and low tide cliffs, may also be explained by this model. It appears that the sea may have been at its present level long enough to account for the present dimensions of shore platforms without recourse to inheritance from a period when sea level was similar to today's. The model suggests that the presence of shore platforms may be governed by the occurrence of a narrow range of suitable geological and morphogenic conditions.

Résumé

Un modèle mathématique simple a servi à simuler l'évolution des profils de plate-forme littorale en Gaspésie (Québec) et dans le vallon de Glamorgan en Galles du sud. L'érosion intertidale en un point quelconque du profile de la plate-forme a été déterminée par la pente immédiatement en contrebas, par un facteur d'érodibilité lié à l'intersité de la vague et à la dureté des roches ainsi que par la répartition de la durée-fréquence du niveau des eaux calmes dans les limites de l'amplitude de la marée. Les essais du modèle ont montré que le gradient de la plate forme à chaque niveau d'élévation prend éventuellement une valeur qui fait que la vitesse d'érosion est égale en tous points de la plate-forme. La forme des profils d'équilibre simulée est très semblable aux profils de plate-forme littorale dans chaque zone étudiée. D'autres aspects de la morphologie de la plate-forme, comme la forte relation entre le gradient et l'amplitude de la marée, ainsi que la présence et la forme des rampes et des falaises de basses eaux, peuvent aussi être expliquées par ce modèle. Il semble que la mer puisse avoir été à son niveau actuel pendant assez longtemps pour qu'on lui attribue les dimensions actuelles des plates-formes littorales sans avoir à recourir aux vestiges d'une période où le niveau était analogue à celui d'aujourd'hui. Le modèle permet de penser que la présence de plates-formes littorales peut être commandée par l'existence d'une gamme étroite de conditions géologiques et morphologiques appropriées.

INTRODUCTION

Morphogenic environments largely determine the width, mean elevation, gradient and shape of shore platforms, although differences in exposure or rock resistance are responsible for local variations (Bartrum, 1926; Edwards, 1941; Wright, 1967). A number of structural and lithological factors determine surface roughness and may be responsible for more severe modification of platform geometry (Bird and Dent, 1966; Trenhaile, 1971). Good correlations between platform gradients and tidal ranges (Trenhaile, 1972, 1974a, 1978), however, and between the elevation of cliff-platform junctions and high tide levels (Wright, 1970; Trenhaile, 1972) suggest that geological factors are largely responsible for local deviations about morphological means that are determined by morphogenic environments. Until recently, differences in the morphogenic environments of southern and northern hemisphere coastlines have not been fully recognized (Davies, 1964). Because the interest of Australasian workers did not begin to be reciprocated by

their counterparts in the northern hemisphere until the mid-1960's, most texts had assumed that the morphology of shore platforms in northern Europe and northern North America is essentially compatible with those around the Pacific rim.

Davies (1964) contended that morphogenic factors, such as wave and tidal regimes, are responsible for the global diversity of coastal environments. Trenhaile (1974b) proposed that the morphology of quasihorizontal platforms, which terminate abruptly seawards in a low-tide cliff in the southern hemisphere, is governed by a smaller tidal range, weaker swell wave activity, and greater chemical weathering than in the storm wave environments of the north. Although northern hemisphere shore platforms usually slope seawards with gradients between one and three degrees, and continue below low tide level without abrupt termini, significant differences do occur within the storm wave environment. It is the purpose of this paper to discuss and explain marked differences in the morphology of shore platforms in two storm wave environments.

THE STUDY AREAS

Shore platforms have been examined along about 120 km of coastline between Rivière à Claude and Rivière au Renard in northern Gaspé, Québec, and for about 50 km in the Vale of Glamorgan in Wales (Fig. 15.1). Platforms are formed in middle Ordovician flysch, consisting of generally steeply dipping shales, argillites and graywackes in Gaspé, and in quasihorizontal beds of lower Liassic limestones and shales, and Triassic marls and limestones in Glamorgan. The shore platforms of the Vale of Glamorgan, which are generally between 150 and 250 m wide, slope gently seawards with gradients between two and three degrees, and pass below the level of the low neap tides without abrupt termini. Gaspésian platforms, however, are quasihorizontal surfaces that are usually narrower than those in Glamorgan (60 - 120 m) and often terminate abruptly seawards in a low tide cliff. The areas and their platforms have been described elsewhere, and will not be, discussed at length here (Trenhaile, 1971, 1972, 1978).

TIDAL DURATION AND PLATFORM MORPHOMETRY

In view of the processes responsible for their development, the greater similarity between the morphology of storm wave Gaspésian and swell wave Australasian platforms, rather than between Gaspésian and British platforms, is surprising. Chemical weathering probably plays a less significant role in Gaspé than in Australasia, partly because of lower temperatures, but also because of the greater prominence of wave erosion in Gaspé. The significance of frost weathering associated with saline solutions in Gaspé may account for some morphological disparity with the Vale of Glamorgan, although it can hardly account for its similarity to Australasia, where frost action is generally insignificant. It appears, therefore, that similarities between Gaspésian and Australasian platforms must be related to their meso-to microtidal environments, which contrast with the macrotidal environment of Glamorgan. It has been suggested that platform width is determined by tidal range (Edwards, 1941; Flemming, 1965), but recent work has shown that width is largely a function of the erosion rate, whereas platform gradient is highly correlated with tidal range (Trenhaile, 1972, 1974a, 1978). Other aspects of platform geometry, such as mean elevation, the elevation of the cliff-platform junction, profile shape, and the presence, height, and slope of the low tide cliff, are also intimately associated with tidal parameters (Trenhaile, 1978). If the tide is the chief architect of platform construction, however, then storm waves represent the workforce. In a storm wave environment, rock hardness and the amount of wave energy determine the size of platforms, but the tidal distribution of wave activity is responsible for sculpturing their shape.

Several attempts to assess the role of tides in shore platform formation have considered the elevation-frequency of the extremes of tidal cycles (Takahashi, 1974a). This approach produces a biomodal frequency curve, which ignores or grossly under-represents the proportion of wave activity experienced at intermediate points on the tidal cycle. Other analyses of the contribution of tides to a number of erosive processes have considered the period of water cover experienced at various intertidal elevations (Robinson, 1977a; Kirk, 1977). To determine the tidal role in directing the expenditure of wave energy within the tidal range, it is necessary to consider the fluctuation of still water level. So (1965) suggested that slight flattening of platforms near midtide level, a feature which has been noted in Glamorgan (Trenhaile, 1972), may be related to the maximum frequency of storm wave attack at this elevation. The distribution of storm wave activity is determined by the distribution of still water level.

The still water level occupies a particular intertidal level in two time components: one when high or low tides coincide with this elevation, and the other when the level is briefly but frequently occupied at the ebb and flow stages at intermediate points on tidal cycles. The duration of still water level (F), therefore, at an elevation (n) is given by

$$F_n = (D_e \cdot N_e) + (2D_i \cdot N_i) \qquad (1)$$

where D_e is the duration and N_e the number of high or low tides coinciding with that level; D_i is the duration of the tide at that level when it is an intermediate point on the tidal cycle; and N_i is the number of tidal extremes above or below this level. The computation of tidal duration curves has been discussed elsewhere, and will not be repeated here (Trenhaile, 1978).

The tidal duration curves for Gaspé (Pointe Saint-Pierre) and the Vale of Glamorgan (Cardiff) succinctly express the multifarious nature of storm wave environments (Fig. 15.2). Tides in the Vale of Glamorgan distribute storm wave energy over a vertical range of more than 11 m, compared with less than 2 m in Gaspé. In contrast with Glamorgan, however, wave energy is concentrated into a very narrow range of elevations in Gaspé. These differences in the distribution of wave energy have important ramifications for the development of shore platforms in these areas, and are vital considerations for the interpretation of their morphology.

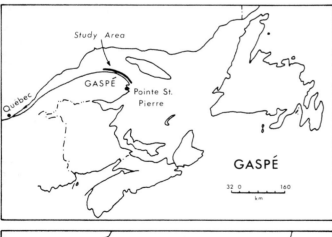

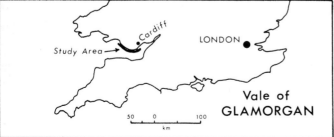

Figure 15.1.   *The study areas.*

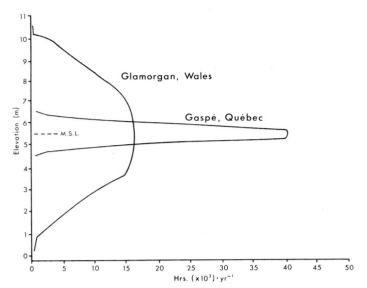

Figure 15.2. *Tidal duration curves for the study areas.*

THE MODEL

Previous attempts to model shore platform development theoretically (Johnson, 1919; Flemming, 1965; Scheidegger, 1970) or experimentally (Sanders, 1968; Sunamura, 1973) have failed to consider the role of tidal duration. Robinson (1977b) and Kirk (1977) have considered models of platform development as logical extensions of detailed investigations of the processes and rates of erosion operating on shore platforms. Reliable modelling should be cognizant of the contemporary rate of erosion and its variation across platform profiles. Unfortunately, however, whereas there are increasing data on processes and rates of downwearing on shore platforms, less is known of the processes and rates of backcutting, involving joint-block removal and the retreat of scarps. Field examination of platforms in quasihorizontal strata in southern Britain and in a few places in Gaspé (Trenhaile, 1972, 1974a, 1978), has demonstrated that downwearing processes are rarely able to penetrate more than a few centimeters into a rock surface before landward retreat of the scarps completely removes the strata. Hydraulic action and joint block quarrying also appear to dominate platform development in steeply dipping strata in Gaspé.

If the development of shore platform profiles in Gaspé and the Vale of Glamorgan is determined primarily by hydraulic action (quarrying) related to storm wave attack, then the amount of erosion at any level is proportional to the quantity of wave energy expended at that level, and the strength of the rock. Deep-water wave energy is a function of the morphogenic environment, but in shallow water, wave energy declines according to the slope of the bottom (Putnam and Johnson, 1949; Cooper and Longuet-Higgins, 1951). Furthermore, the wave energy expended at a specific intertidal elevation is dependent on the frequency with which still water level coincides with that elevation. The amount of erosion (E) which occurs at an intertidal level (n) in a time t_1 (years), therefore, is approximated by

$$E_{n, t_1} = t_1 A F_n \tan\alpha_{n-1, t_0} \qquad (2)$$

where A is a constant related to the energy of the waves in

deep water and the strength of rocks (the erodibility factor); F_n is the amount of time still water level is at elevation level n each year, as given by Equation 1; and α_{n-1, t_0} is the slope of the platform extending downwards from level n to level n-1 before erosion.

Consideration of the effect of bottom gradient on incoming wave energy is limited in the model to slopes at depths down to only 91.4 cm below each level. Although the effect in nature is exerted over much greater depths, for the relatively short, locally derived waves which are primarily responsible for erosion in the study areas, only relatively shallow depths cause much adjustment in wave length and height, and this effect is strongest in very shallow water. Modifying the simple model to consider slopes at much greater depths did not significantly affect the results, but added considerably to the computational complexity, and most importantly, to the assumptions inherent in the model.

The model is also dependent on the rate of submarine erosion immediately below the level of the lowest tides. Submarine erosion may (a) decline significantly as the submarine slope declines; (b) be so slow that little change could have occurred in the roughly 2500 years since the sea reached its present level; or (c) remain essentially constant, dependent only on water depth.

The destruction of rock on the submarine slope is a function of bottom wave energy, which may be taken to be proportional to the square of maximum orbital velocity on the bottom (Zenkovitch, 1967)

$$\text{i.e., } E = kV^2 \qquad (3)$$

where E is the bedrock erosion rate; k is a constant related to, amongst other things, rock hardness; and V is the maximum orbital velocity on the bottom. If water depth is greater than half the wavelength, or if wave height is greater than 0.04 to 0.06 water depth, waves consist of isolated crests with flat intervening troughs. Isolated wave theory indicates that (Bagnold, 1963)

$$V = H\sqrt{gh} / 2h \qquad (4)$$

where H is wave height; g is the force due to gravity; and h is the water depth. Substituting in Equation 3:

$$E = CH^2 / h \qquad (5)$$

where C = kg/4. When a wave first encounters shallow water, wave height declines, its height in deep water being regained only when the ratio of water depth to wavelength is about 0.06. Although wave height may increase rapidly towards the breakpoint, the effect is greatest for long flat waves, and may be relatively small for very steep storm waves (Bigelow and Edmonson, 1947). For a wavelength of 15 m, the deep water height is regained when water depth declines to 0.9 m. Although strictly incorrect therefore, it may be acceptable to assume that wave height is independent of the changing water depth or slope below low tide level which may occur as the model progresses. If, however, wave height does change significantly with relatively small changes in water depth and submarine slope, the effect is probably quite small, since the rate of submarine erosion in shallow areas close to hardrock coastlines appears to be very low. The rate of lowering of a linear profile is given by $V\tan\alpha$, where V is the cliff recession rate and α is the submarine gradient (Zenkovitch, 1967). Applied to the shore platform coastlines of southern Britain, this suggests that submarine downwearing is less than 1 mm per annum, and only 0.06 mm in the Vale of Glamorgan. Although Zenkovitch's formula is valid only for the cliff base, a related expression of somewhat greater complexity (the derivation of which is outside the scope of this paper), which considers submarine erosion immediately below the level of the lowest tides, confirms that erosion rates are very low. These low values are similar to rates of downwearing of only a few tenths of a millimetre per annum in the calcareous rocks of the Black Sea, where abrasion is reported to be active and pronounced (Zenkovitch, 1967). Cliff recession rates have not been assessed for eastern Gaspé, but consideration of the morphogenic environment and the structure and lithology of the rocks suggest that rates of submarine downwearing are probably similar to those in Britain. Wave height at low tide level, therefore, is unlikely to have varied significantly in response to changes in water depth or slope related to submarine erosion, since the sea reached its present level. Accordingly, for modelling purposes, the submarine erosion rate immediately below low tide level was assumed to be constant through time.

Simulated platform profiles for Gaspé and the Vale of Glamorgan consisted of linear segments connecting levels 91.4 cm apart (Fig. 15.3). The number of levels in each case, therefore, was determined by the tidal range. Model runs were initiated by calculating the amount of erosion at each level, on a surface which is assumed to have been inherited by the postglacial rise in sea level. Short but variable time intervals, determined by the rates of erosion, were used to prevent large changes in slope, and therefore in incoming wave energy, during runs. The angle of the platform segment connecting levels n and n-1 after time t_1 is given by

$$\alpha_{n-1,t_1} = \tan^{-1}\left[(91.44)/(E_{n,t_1} - E_{n-1,t_1}) + 91.44\ \cot\alpha_{n-1,t_0}\right] \quad (6)$$

where E_{n,t_1} and E_{n-1,t_1} are the amounts of erosion at levels n and n-1, respectively, in time t_1, as given by Equation 2; and α_{n-1,t_0} is the initial slope at that level. These new angular values were then used to calculate the next stage in the model run.

RESULTS

The tidal duration (F) values are initially responsible for great differences in erosion rates across the platform profiles. Steep slopes permit high rates of erosion, providing rapid changes in the width and gradient of each platform segment. Gradients decline quickly in most cases, but when relatively high rates of low tide erosion are combined with low erodibility, slopes near high and low tide level decline more slowly than those at midtide, or even increase once the steep, inherited surface has been reduced. As the simulated profiles progress through time, platform segments attempt to attain gradients which compensate for the differences in the F-values across the profiles. The erosion rates at each level, in response to changes in platform slope, slowly converge towards equality. If sufficient time is available, a state of dynamic equilibrium is attained, in which the erosion rate at each level is equal to the constant rate occurring below low tide level. Once equilibrium has been achieved, platform slope, shape and size remain constant, although the slow landward shift of the platform continues. Platform gradients have now adjusted to the intertidal distribution of wave energy (Fig. 15.4).

Comparison of actual and simulated platform profiles is difficult, since segment gradient and width are dependent on the erodibility and submarine erosion constants. In a broad sense, most simulated equilibrium profiles are similar to their real counterparts, whatever values are used for the constants. The simulated Gaspésian profiles consist of very

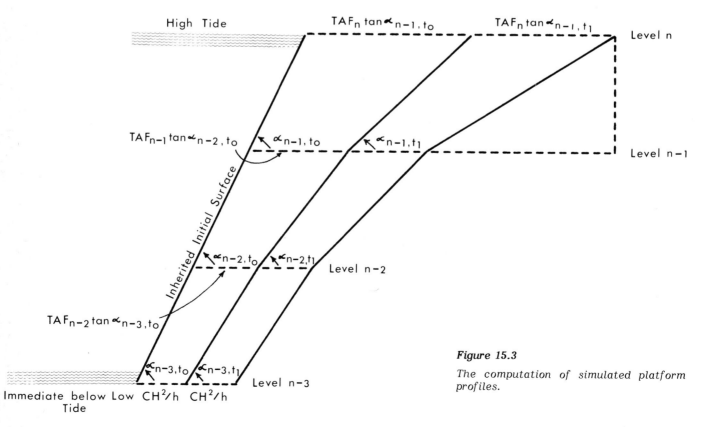

Figure 15.3

The computation of simulated platform profiles.

low gradients and a marked break of slope at their seaward termini, whereas those in Glamorgan are generally steeper, with a long linear segment extending for some distance above and below midtide level (Fig. 15.4). Simulated equilibrium profiles were closest to their real counterparts when the ratio of the submarine erosion rate to the erodibility value (E_L/A) was between 12 to 6 in Glamorgan, producing platforms between 132 to 264 m wide, and between 10 to 5 in Gaspé with associated widths between 69 and 138 m, respectively. Optimum values $E_L/A = 8$ for Glamorgan produced a platform 198 m wide with a generally linear slope

of about 2°, with one ramp of about 5° at the cliff base, and another of about 8° at absolute low tide level. When E_L/A is between 5 and 10, simulated profiles that are very similar to those in Gaspé were produced, with gradients between 24 and 48 minutes and low tide cliffs with slopes between 8 and 16 degrees.

The equilibrium form of platforms may be calculated without recourse to their intermediate stages. Equilibrium is attained at a time T when the rate of erosion at each level is equal to that immediately below low tide level. Thus

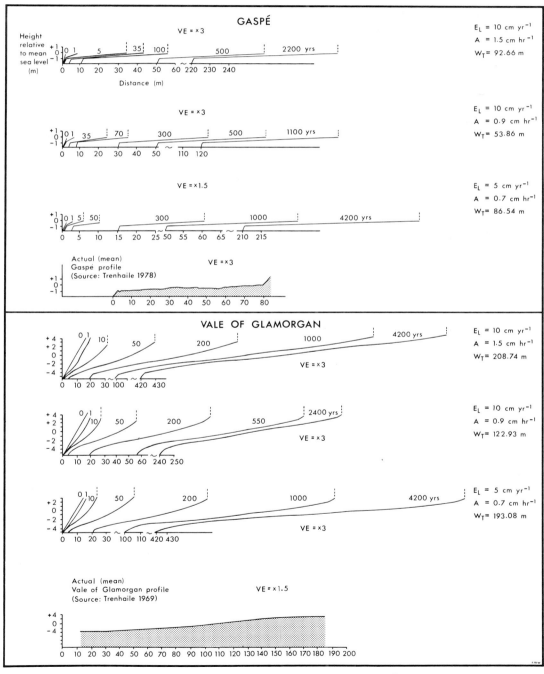

Figure 15.4. *Examples of some simulated profiles.*

$$TAF_n \tan\alpha_{n-1,T} = TAF_{n-1} \tan\alpha_{n-2,T} = TE_L$$

$$\therefore \tan\alpha_{n-1,T} = E_L/AF_n \qquad (7)$$

Platform width is also constant at equilibrium and may be calculated from the gradient values. A comparison of actual and theoretical platform width in the two study areas, however, will be discussed elsewhere, and will not be dealt with at length here.

It has been shown that the equilibrium gradient of each platform segment increases with the submarine erosion rate and decreases with erodibility and tidal duration. The slope of the inherited surface, however, does not influence the equilibrium form, but does exert a minor influence on the time needed to achieve equilibrium. These conclusions have important implications. The decline in equilibrium gradient with tidal duration accounts for the slight flattening found at midtide level in southern Britain (So, 1965; Trenhaile, 1972). The role of the erodibility constant may account for the steeper slopes of platforms in areas with resistant rock (Trenhaile, 1969, 1972), or in embayments (So, 1965; Wood, 1968); although the general association of hard rock with high exposure on headlands, and the reverse in embayments, makes any explanation complex.

Whereas equilibrium width and gradient are influenced by submarine erosion rates and the erodibility constant, profile shape is independent of these factors, since

$$\tan\alpha_{n-1,T} = E_L/AF_n,$$

$$\text{and } \tan\alpha_{n-2,T} = E_L/AF_{n-1} \qquad (8)$$

$$\therefore \tan\alpha_{n-1,T}/\tan\alpha_{n-2,T} = F_{n-1}/F_n$$

Therefore, whatever erodibility and submarine erosion values are considered, the ratio of the gradients of one platform segment to that of the segment below is constant. This indicates that, irrespective of the tidal range, declining tidal duration values about the midtide maximum causes platforms to be concave near high tide, linear over much of their length and convex at their seaward termini. In actuality, however, several factors may serve to obscure this ideal form. The gradient of the concave ramp at the cliff base or the convex low tide 'cliff' depends upon the value of E_L/AF_n, as derived in Equation 7. If the rate of submarine erosion is low and erodibility high, then both slopes may be so gentle that they grade almost imperceptibly into the main platform slope. Variation of the erodibility value caused by structural and lithological factors may also serve to emphasize or obscure these nonlinear elements. If weak strata overlie more resistant beds, platforms may develop that have much lower gradients than those in more homogeneous outcrops in the same morphogenic environment. These platforms will have imperceptible ramps at the cliff base and a steep low tide cliff at their seaward termini. These platforms are typified by Breaksea Point in Glamorgan, where the erosion of weak upper *bucklandi* shales has exhumed a platform cut in more resistant lower *bucklandi* limestones (Trenhaile, 1969). Breaksea Point is more than 550 m wide, has a gradient of less than one degree, and the only abrupt seaward terminus in Glamorgan. Alternatively, resistant strata overlying weaker beds provide steeper platforms than their neighbours, and gentler seaward termini. This explains platform gradients of more than a degree, and an ill defined low tide break of slope near Grande Vallée, Gaspé (Trenhaile, 1978). The occurrence of ramps is often related to beds of resistant

strata at the cliff base (Trenhaile, 1978), or to sheltered environments (Trenhaile, 1969; Hills, 1972), where erodibility is also low. Ramps, therefore, may be associated with narrow, steep platforms in sheltered locations where erodibility is low across the platform, or may be the expression of low erodibility values at the cliff base, related to geological factors. In the latter case, prominent ramps may be found on profiles which lack the marked convex slopes of the seaward termini. In Gaspé, where steeply dipping strata determine that low tide erosion must eventually encounter relatively resistant beds of rock, low tide cliffs are common, in contrast to areas where strata are quasihorizontal, as at Rivière à Claude, Gaspé, or throughout the Vale of Glamorgan.

The strong empirical relationship between platform gradient and tidal range appears to be the most fundamental morphological characteristic of shore platforms (Trenhaile, 1978). Tidal duration analysis can now provide an explanation of this relationship. Actual platform gradient is largely determined by the long quasilinear segment extending from the base of the ramp at the cliff foot to the top of the convex slope at its seaward terminus. The slope of this segment corresponds with the high tidal duration values around midtide level. According to Equation 7, the slope of this linear segment is equal to E_L/AF_n. Plotting the reciprocal of F_n maximum at midtide level against tidal range for seven ports in the northern and southern hemisphere showed that there is a linear relationship between the two factors. The very slight deviations from a straight line were so small that they were probably derived from inaccuracies in the calculation of the tidal duration values. The relationship between platform gradient and tidal range, therefore, may be restated as a relationship between platform gradient and the concentration of wave energy within the tidal range. When tidal range is small, wave energy is concentrated about midtide level, producing quasihorizontal platforms, whereas when tidal ranges are greater, wave energy is better distributed among a range of elevations, producing platforms with steeper gradients.

It has often been suggested that shore platforms are, at least in part, inherited from a period when sea level was similar to today's (Stephens, 1957; Orme, 1962; Phillips, 1970). Absolute time predicted in the model cannot be accepted, if only because of the uncertainty regarding the values of the constants. The model may, however, be capable of suggesting the approximate time necessary to reach equilibrium. The relationship between equilibrium time and the erodibility and submarine erosion values is complex. The time required to reach equilibrium increases with these values. High rates of submarine erosion cause the platform to steepen, thereby frustrating its efforts to reach a low gradient equilibrium state. Although rapid rates of erosion are associated with high erodibility, the equilibrium profiles are lower than those with low erodibility. Inspection of model runs demonstrated that slope reduction is much more rapid when erodibility is high, but most time is expended, in any run, in reducing profiles which already have low gradients, by the one or two degrees necessary to finally attain equilibrium. Despite their rapid erosion rates, therefore, high erodibility platforms require more time to achieve their gentle equilibrium gradients than do platforms with low erodibility, where equilibrium gradients are steeper. Although the time necessary for equilibrium varies according to the constant values, simulated platforms achieved comparable gradients and widths to those in the field within 2500 years in most cases, and within 5000 years for all but those with the highest erodibility and submarine erosion rate values. This suggests that sufficient time has been available since the sea reached its present level for platforms to have attained their present dimensions, without recourse to inheritance.

CONCLUSIONS

The model described here is essentially a very simple attempt to simulate the development of platform profiles. The simplicity of the model design is deliberate, since it is suggested that platform development and form bear a relatively simple relationship to the tidal distribution of wave energy. Nevertheless, several potential sources of error may be noted. The model is concerned with the distribution of still water level within the tidal range, but storm waves operate some distance above this level. Although this discrepancy should be considered when examining the relationship between the elevation of platform features and specific tidal levels, it is largely irrelevant to investigations of platform slope and width. Although submarine erosion rates were considered to be low and constant through time, if submarine gradients do decline significantly within the life of a model run, the submarine erosion rate, and consequently the erosion rate at each intertidal level, may also decline. Equilibrium profiles therefore, may decline slowly in slope while increasing in width in a continual attempt to adjust to the decline in the submarine gradient. Similar adjustments in platform gradient would be necessary in response to isostatic or eustatic land-sea level changes. Such changes may have occurred in both study areas (Trenhaile, 1972, 1978). Other adjustments may be associated with increasing cliff height or rocks of variable resistance to erosion. Although concerned with erosion related directly to incoming wave energy, a more sophisticated model should also consider the role of a number of other processes. This model might possibly consider the effect of submarine erosion in the intertidal zone, which is related to the duration of tidal inundation at each level (Robinson, 1977a; Kirk, 1977). It is doubtful, however, whether a more sophisticated model, designed to consider some of the factors mentioned above, could improve significantly on the much simpler model described here. The validity of any theoretical model is best assessed by reference to comparisons with the real world. Despite a number of assumptions and implications inherent in this model, its results bear close similarity to the morphology of shore platforms in storm wave environments.

This paper is mainly concerned with the equilibrium form of shore platform profiles. Standard texts, and some of more recent vintage, would maintain that the topic is esoteric, that platform geometry is constantly changing, (Johnson, 1919; Flemming, 1965; Scheidegger, 1970), that they contain elements inherited from a period when sea level was similar to today's, or that sufficient time has not been available for equilibrium to be attained since the sea reached its present level. Strong correlations between a number of morphological and morphogenic factors, however, deny these claims, suggesting that platforms have already achieved a high degree of adjustment to the forces acting on them. The thesis presented in this paper has now provided an explanation for these empirical relationships.

The values of E_L/A which produce simulated profiles that are most like those in the field are very similar for Gaspé and the Vale of Glamorgan. This, and the apparently small effect of variation in either E_L or A other than on the local level, as evidenced by the very close relationship between platform gradient and the reciprocal of maximum (midtide) tidal duration, suggest that very restrictive conditions govern the occurrence of shore platforms. This provides support for the general observation that platforms are absent where rocks are particularly resistant, or where wave activity is comparatively weak, but suggests that the range of suitable conditions for platform development is much narrower than has been previously assumed. These restrictive conditions appear to be satisfied in the storm wave environments of the northern hemisphere by outcrops of sedimentary rocks consisting of alternations of beds of variable resistance to erosion. The occurrence of platforms as far west as Trois-Pistoles on the St. Lawrence estuary, in sheltered sites on the eastern British coast, and on the Inland Sea coast of Japan, suggests that exposure in storm wave environments plays a subordinate role to geology in determining the occurrence of platforms, although they are generally wider in areas of high exposure (Takahashi, 1974b).

Acknowledgments

Model runs were made using a computer program written by Mr. Richard Dumala. Study of the Gaspésian platforms was financed by the National Research Council of Canada.

References

Bagnold, R.A.
1963:   Beach and nearshore processes; in The sea, mechanics of marine sedimentation, M.N. Hill, ed.; Interscience, New York; v. 3, pt.1, p. 507 - 528.

Bartrum, J.A.
1926:   Abnormal shore platforms; Journal of Geology, v. 34, p. 793 - 807.

Bigelow, H.B. and Edmonson, W.T.
1947:   Wind waves at sea, breakers and surf; Hydrographic Office, U.S. Navy, Publication 602.

Bird, E.C.F. and Dent, O.F.
1966:   Shore platforms on the south shore of New South Wales; Australian Geographer, v. 10, p. 71 - 80.

Cooper, R.I.B. and Longuet-Higgins, M.S.
1951:   An experimental study of the pressure variations in standing water waves; Proceedings, Royal Society of Australia, v. 206., p. 424 - 435.

Davies, J.L.
1964:   A morphogenic approach to world shorelines; Zeitschrift fur Geomorphologie, v. 8, p. 127 - 142.

Edwards, A.B.
1941:   Storm wave platforms; Journal of Geomorphology, v. 4, p. 223 - 236.

Flemming, N.C.
1965:   Form and relation to present sea level of Pleistocene marine erosion features; Journal of Geology, v. 73, p. 799 - 811.

Hills, E.S.
1972:   Shore platforms and wave ramps; Geological Magazine, v. 109, p. 81 - 88.

Johnson, D.W.
1919:   Shore processes and shoreline development; Facsimile edition, 1965, Hafner, New York, 584 p.

Kirk, R.M.
1977:   Rates and forms of erosion on intertidal platforms at Kaikoura Peninsula, South Island, New Zealand; New Zealand Journal of Geology and Geophysics, v. 20, p. 571 - 613.

Orme, A.R.
1962:   Abandoned and composite seacliffs in Britain and Ireland; Irish Geographer, v. 4, p. 279 - 291.

Phillips, B.A.M.
1970:   Effective levels of marine planation on raised and present rock platforms; Revue de Géographie de Montréal, v. 14, p. 227 - 240.

Putnam, J.A. and Johnson, J.W.
1949:   The dissipation of wave energy by bottom friction; Transactions, American Geophysical Union, v. 30, p. 67 - 74.

Robinson, L.A.
1977a: Marine erosive processes at the cliff foot; Marine Geology, v. 23, p. 257 - 271.
1977b: The morphology and development of the northeast Yorkshire shore platform; Marine Geology, v. 23, p. 237 - 255.

Sanders, N.K.
1968:   The development of Tasmanian shore platforms; unpubl. Ph.D. dissertation, University of Tasmania.

Scheidegger, A.E.
1970:   Theoretical geomorphology; New York.

So, C.L.
1965:   Coastal platforms of the Isle of Thanet, Kent; Transactions, Institute of British Geographers, v. 37, p. 147 - 156.

Stephens, N.
1957:   Some observations on the interglacial platform and early post-glacial raised beach on the east coast of Ireland; Proceedings, Royal Irish Academy, v. 58B, p. 129 - 149.

Sunamura, T.
1973:   Coastal erosion due to waves---field investigations and laboratory experiments; Journal, Faculty of Engineering, University of Tokyo, v. 32, p. 1 - 86.

Takahashi, T.
1974a: Level and age of the planation of emerged platforms near Cape Muroto, Shikoku; Scientific Reports, Tohoku University, 7th series, v. 24, p. 47 - 58.
1974b: Distribution of shore platforms in southwestern Japan; Scientific Reports, Tohoku University, 7th series, v. 24, p. 33 - 45.

Trenhaile, A.S.
1969:   A geomorphological investigation of shore platforms and high water rock ledges in the Vale of Glamorgan; unpubl. Ph.D. dissertation, University of Wales.
1971:   Lithological control of high water rock ledges in the Vale of Glamorgan, Wales; Geografiska Annaler, v. 53A, p. 59 - 69.
1972:   The shore platforms of the Vale of Glamorgan, Wales; Transactions, Institute of British Geographers, v. 56, p. 127 - 144.
1974a: The geometry of shore platforms in England and Wales; Transactions, Institute of British Geographers, v. 62, p. 129 - 142.
1947b: The morphology and classification of shore platforms in England and Wales; Geografiska Annaler, v. 56A, p. 103 - 110.
1978:   The shore platforms of Gaspé, Quebec; Annals, Association of American Geographers, v. 68, p. 95 - 114.

Wood, A.
1968:   Beach platforms in the chalk of Kent, England; Zeitschrift für Geomorphologie, v. 11, p. 36 - 46.

Wright, L.R.
1967:   Some characteristics of the shore platforms of the English Channel coast and the northern part of the North Island, New Zealand; Zeitschrift fur Geomorphologie, v. 11, p. 26 - 46.
1970:   Variation in the level of the cliff-shore platform junction along the south coast of Great Britain; Marine Geology, v. 9, p. 347 - 353.

Zenkovitch, V.P.
1967:   Processes of coastal development; Oliver and Boyd, Edinburgh, 738 p.

16.

GÉOMORPHOLOGIE DU LITTORAL DE LA CÔTE NORD
DU SAINT-LAURENT: ANALYSE SOMMAIRE

J.M.M. Dubois
Département de géographie, Université de Sherbrooke, Sherbrooke, Québec

Dubois, J.M.M., Géomorphologie du littoral de la Côte Nord du Saint-Laurent: analyse sommaire; in The Coastline of Canada, S.B. McCann, editor; Geological Survey of Canada, Paper 80-10, p. 215-238, 1980.

Résumé

Les 5200 km de côtes (incluant les îles) entre Baie-Comeau et Blanc-Sablon ont été cartographiées, principalement par photo-interprétation, à l'aide d'un minimum de travaux de terrain entre 1972 et 1976. Des critères de classification de l'énergie du relief, de la géomorphologie et de la lithologie, tant pour la côte et l'arrière-côte, la ligne de rivage, la plage et l'estran, que pour la plate-forme marine ont permis d'identifier 27 zones homogènes. Ces zones ont par la suite été regroupées sous neuf environnements côtiers distincts. L'auteur déduit des relations entre la longueur de côtes insulaires et la longueur de côtes de terre ferme et entre le trait de côte et la tectonique. Il donne aussi un aperçu de la répartition, de l'origine et de la mobilité des sédiments et il introduit la notion d'unité physiographique de côte.

Abstract

The 5200 km of coast (including the islands) between Baie-Comeau and Blanc-Sablon were mapped mainly by air photo interpretation, with additional field work at selected locations, between 1972 and 1976. The identification of 27 homogeneous zones was carried out by a classification of the coast and the hinterland, the coast line, the shore and backshore, and the marine platform, using relief, geomorphological and lithological criteria. These zones were subsequently organized into nine coastal environments. The relationships between the length of island coasts and the length of mainland coasts, and also between the tectonic features and the coastal outline are discussed. The distribution, origin and mobility of the sediments in the various physiographic units is considered.

INTRODUCTION

Une des régions les plus mal connues du Québec, la Côte Nord du Saint-Laurent, s'étend sur environ 5500 km (incluant les îles) entre le Saguenay et Blanc-Sablon, à la frontière du Labrador. Elle se subdivise en trois parties: la Haute Côte Nord du Saguenay à la Moisie, la Moyenne Côte Nord de la Moisie à l'Aguanus et la Basse Côte Nord de l'Aguanus au Labrador (fig. 16.1).

Des levés au 1: 250 000 et au 1: 50 000 de la zone côtière (fig. 16.2) ont été faits, principalement par photo-interprétation, sur environ 5200 km à l'est de la rivière aux Outardes par Dubois (1973a) et Desmarais (1976). Des levés plus précis au 1: 25 000 entre la Moisie et la Mingan sont en voie d'être terminés par Dubois (1980). Même si Jacques Cartier (Biggar, 1924) avait déjà commencé à décrire toute cette côte lors de ses voyages de 1534, 1535 et 1536, il faudra attendre Faessler en 1942 pour avoir une première description de la côte entre la Betsiamites et la Moisie, Robitaille en 1954 pour les îles de Mingan, Grenier en 1957 entre la Romaine et l'Aguanus et Bussières en 1962 pour l'ensemble. D'autres travaux spécifiques ou localisés méritent notre attention, ce sont ceux de Laverdière (1954), de Roquefeuil (1965) et Dredge (1971) sur le delta de la Moisie, Welsted (1960) sur le delta de la Natashquan, le ministère des Travaux publics du Canada (1972, 1973) dans la région des Sept-Îles, de Mingan, d'Havre-Saint-Pierre et de quelques autres localités de la Basse Côte Nord, Landry (1975) sur les îles de Mingan, Lévesque (1976) à Blanc-Sablon et Moign (1972) qui a décrit la plage entre les Sept-Îles et la Moisie.

Notre travail essaiera donc de faire une mise à jour des connaissances sur le littoral de la Côte Nord en faisant ressortir les zones homogènes à partir d'une classification de la zone côtière mise au point par Dubois (1973a). Cette classification, dont nous présentons une version simplifiée (fig. 16.3), a été établie à partir d'une rétrospective des principales classifications des côtes et du rivage. Elle a l'avantage d'être multiscalaire, c'est-à-dire de se cartographier à n'importe quelle échelle de travail, elle est descriptive, génétique et dynamique en plus d'être applicable à l'aide de documents usuels avec un minimum de travaux de terrain.

LE CADRE PHYSIQUE GÉNÉRAL

La physiographie

La presque totalité de la Côte Nord se situe dans la région laurentidienne. Celle-ci se subdivise en deux sous-régions à partir de la rivière Romaine: le plateau de Mécatina à l'est et les hautes-terres laurentidiennes à l'ouest (Bostock, 1970). Ces deux sous-régions sont généralement caractérisées de la côte vers l'intérieur par trois secteurs altimétriques: (1) une plaine côtière généralement de dépôts meubles, de 5 à 10 km de largeur, de moins de 30 m d'énergie de relief (dénivellation thalweg---ligne de faîte) et dépassant rarement 150 m d'altitude; (2) un piémont généralement rocheux de 15 à 25 km de largeur, de 30 à 75 m d'énergie de relief et variant entre 150 et 300 m d'altitude; (3) on atteint enfin le plateau lui-même formé de collines rocheuses dont l'énergie de relief varie entre 75 et 150 m et dont l'altitude atteint en moyenne 450 à 600 m.

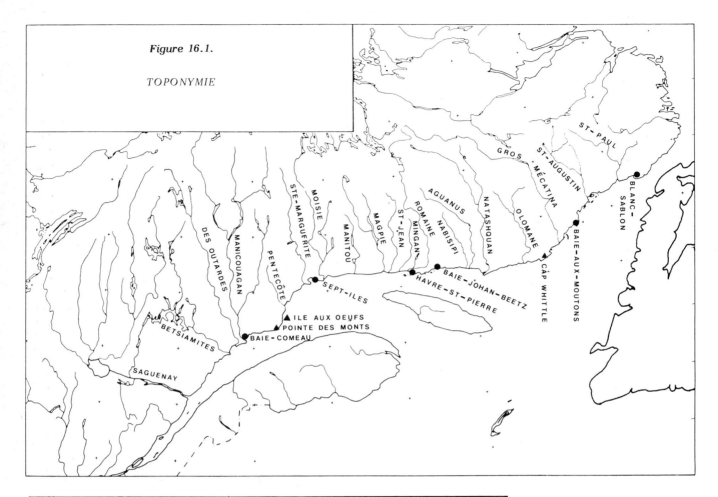

Figure 16.1.

TOPONYMIE

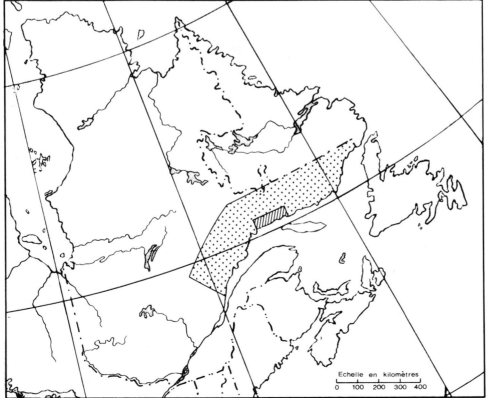

Figure 16.2. Zone d'étude.

Zone d'étude extensive

Zone d'étude intensive

Echelle en kilomètres
0 100 200 300 400

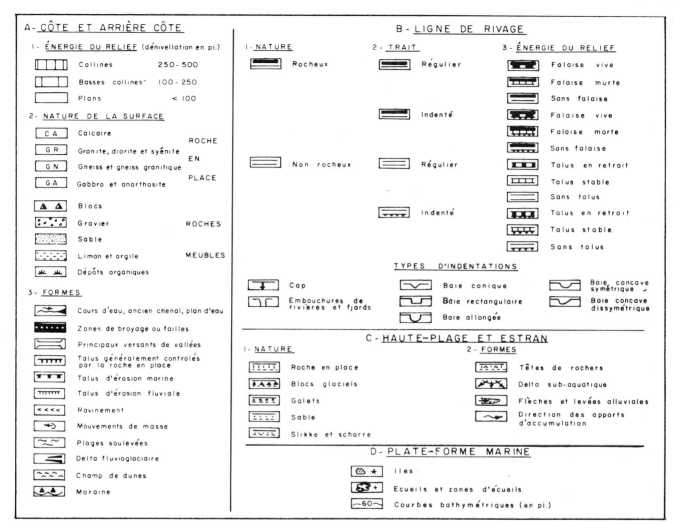

Figure 16.3. *Classification de la zone côtière.*

Il y a cependant deux exceptions à cette règle générale. Dans le premier cas, la plaine côtière envahit le piémont sur 15 à 35 km; ce sont les zones de vastes deltas tels que ceux de Manicouagan-aux Outardes, Moisie, Romaine, Natashquan, Olomane et Mécatina. Dans le deuxième cas, le piémont a empêché la plaine côtière de se former; ce sont les secteurs entre Baie-des-Moutons et Blanc-Sablon à l'est ainsi qu'entre Baie-Comeau et pointe des Monts à l'ouest.

La deuxième région physiographique est représentée par la partie est des basses-terres du Saint-Laurent (Bostock, 1970) dont la majeure partie est ennoyée et forme toute une série de plate-formes le long de la côte jusqu'à 200 m de profondeur. La morphologie et la largeur de ces plates-formes sont variables de sorte qu'on peut distinguer trois secteurs différents.

Le premier secteur, qui va du Saguenay aux Sept-Îles, comprend deux plans inclinés réguliers et étroits, de moins de 20 km de largeur, et séparés par le chenal Laurentien qui vient les annihiler à pointe des Monts: à l'ouest la plate-forme des Escoumins (Loring et Nota, 1973) et à l'est, la plate-forme de Pentecôte. Le deuxième secteur, qui va des

Sept-Îles à la Mécatina, est extrêmement large et formé de trois rangées de cuestas dont quelques unes émergent sur la côte entre Mingan et Baie-Johan-Beetz ou forment l'archipel de Mingan et même l'île d'Anticosti, séparée des autres par le chenal de Mingan à l'ouest et le chenal d'Anticosti à l'est. Mis à part les plates-formes associées à cette troisième rangée de cuestas, qui comprend aussi le banc Parent à l'ouest d'Anticosti et probablement le banc Beaugé au large du cap Whittle, la plate-forme de la Côte Nord (Loring et Nota, 1973) est très disséquée et varie entre 20 et 50 km de largeur. Le troisième secteur, qui va de la Mécatina à Blanc-Sablon, est aussi très disséqué et varie entre 50 et 70 km de largeur. Cette plate-forme est composite puisqu'elle s'est formée autant dans la région laurentidienne près de la côte, la plate-forme interne du Québec-Labrador, que dans les basses-terres du Saint-Laurent au large, la plate-forme externe du Québec-Labrador (Loring et Nota, 1973). Ces deux plates-formes sont séparées par une fosse, la tranchée de Mécatina, et la plate-forme externe est formée d'une rangée de cuestas jusqu'à Terre-Neuve (Haworth et Sanford, 1976).

La géologie

Aux deux régions physiographiques de la Côte Nord correspondent deux provinces structurales: la province de Grenville et la plate-forme du Saint-Laurent.

La province de Grenville est représentée par deux subdivisions à partir de la Moisie: la partie orientale de la province de Grenville à l'est et le segment de Baie-Comeau à l'ouest (Stockwell et al., 1970), le contact étant constitué par le passage entre des roches de métamorphisme homogène à l'ouest et non homogène à l'est (Wynne-Edwards, 1972). La Côte Nord est essentiellement formée du rebord de ce bouclier cristallin précambrien dont les roches métasédimentaires et ignées forment l'assise sur laquelle reposent en discordance les strates sédimentaires subhorizontales de la plate-forme du Saint-Laurent, d'âge Paléozoïque.

Les strates sédimentaires n'accusent qu'un léger pendage vers le sud et le sud-est et elles ont été érodées de la fin du Mésozoïque jusqu'au Cénozoïque jusqu'à sa configuration actuelle (Jones, 1962) selon un système reflétant le réseau actuel de vallées et dont le plancher du collecteur, le Saint-Laurent, se trouve à plus de 300 m sous le niveau actuel des eaux (Loring et Nota, 1973).

Les axes exploités par l'érosion sont les failles, les fractures, les foliations ou certaines roches plus tendres tels les quartzites et les schistes précambriens ou les schistes paléozoïques. Demeurent en relief, les roches massives ou plus résistantes tels les gabbros, granites ou syénites précambriennes ou les dolomies et calcaires paléozoïques.

Le Quaternaire

L'entière Côte Nord a été envahie par le dernier inlandsis wisconsinien qui s'est généralement écoulé franc sud avant d'être canalisé par le système du chenal Laurentien au moins dans l'estuaire. De nouvelles hypothèses voudraient que cet englacement n'ait pas débordé de beaucoup la Côte Nord du golfe et n'ait même pas englacé Anticosti (Grant, 1977).

La récession glaciaire aurait commencé à libérer la côte au moins vers 11 500 BP à Baie-Comeau et Blanc-Sablon, vers 10 500 BP entre Sept-Îles et Havre-Saint-Pierre, et, s'il y a lieu, avant 13 000 BP à Anticosti. Cette récession s'est effectuée sur la côte immédiate par vêlage d'icebergs, ce qui semble être la raison du peu de matériaux glaciaires délaissés sous la limite marine sur la côte, ce qu'avait déjà observé Hind en 1864.

La transgression de la mer de Goldthwait a donc talonné le glacier jusque vers 150 m d'altitude à Tadoussac (Dionne, 1970), probablement 140 m à Baie-Comeau (Low, 1897; Conlon, 1966), 131 m aux Sept-Îles et à Mingan (Tremblay, 1975; Dubois, 1977), au moins 122 m à Natashquan (Towsend, 1913) et 152 m à Blanc-Sablon (Grant, 1969a). Cette phase transgressive a laissé de grandes épaisseurs de silts et d'argiles principalement dans les dépressions de grandes vallées; il y aurait ainsi plus de 100 m de dépôts marins à l'embouchure de la Moisie et un sondage en a même révélé 238 m (Tremblay, 1975). Cette phase transgressive se serait terminée vers 9500 BP au moins sur la Moyenne Côte Nord (Dubois, 1977).

La régression marine due au relèvement isostatique aurait été très rapide dès le début avec des taux annuels d'au moins 38 mm à Baie-Comeau, 56 mm aux Sept-Îles et 44 mm à Mingan (Dubois, 1980). Ce taux n'est plus que d'environ 3 mm/an en moyenne depuis 5500 à 6000 BP (Dubois, 1980). C'est cette phase régressive qui a le plus marqué la Côte Nord puisque c'est elle qui a permis l'édification des vastes deltas sableux de 30 à 50 m de puissance (incluant les lits basaux ou les sédiments estuariens) et dont les terrasses

s'étalent de la limite marine maximale jusque vers 6 à 10 m d'altitude. Ces terrasses de dépôts meubles de 6 à 10 m se retrouvent presque partout sur la Côte Nord et forment souvent la côte actuelle. Cette côte, qui daterait de 2000 à 4000 BP selon les endroits, serait donc une côte jeune en émersion décélérée.

Depuis le début de cette régression les cours d'eau ont réentaillé leurs propres alluvions fluviales ou deltaïques de sorte que ces sédiments sont venus s'ajouter aux sédiments fluvioglaciaires au début et aux sédiments érodés aux bassins-versants par la suite. La décélération du relèvement isostatique a cependant passablement ralenti ce processus de nos jours.

La mer

Comme le pied de glace persiste sur les plages pendant au moins 5 mois, soit de décembre à avril (Moign, 1972), la circulation générale qui intéresse est celle de l'été. Selon Trites (1971) cette circulation de surface se fait d'est en ouest de Blanc-Sablon à pointe des Monts, mais d'ouest en est dans l'estuaire jusqu'à pointe des Monts où les courants sont tous les deux déviés vers la Gaspésie.

Ce mouvement en sens antihoraire dans le golfe, est le même que celui de la propagation des marées et ceci semble influencer plusieurs courants de dérive littorale si l'on tient compte des tendances générales que démontrent les formes littorales de la Côte Nord. Les courants de marée connus dans l'estuaire à l'ouest de pointe des Monts, dans la région de l'île aux Oeufs et dans les archipels des Sept-Îles et de Mingan indiquent tous ce flot vers l'ouest et le reflux vers l'est. L'amplitude des marées moyennes décroît rapidement de 2,8 m à Baie-Comeau, à 0,9 m à Baie-Johan-Beetz et se maintient entre 1,0 et 1,4 m jusqu'à Blanc-Sablon.

Selon Ploeg (1971), les hauteurs de vagues sont de 0,6 à 0,8 m aux Sept-Îles avec une possibilité extrême annuelle de 4,9 m et de 1,1 à 1,4 m au cap Whittle et avec une possibilité extrême annuelle de 5,8 m.

LES ZONES HOMOGÈNES

Les critères d'identification

Chaque zone est d'abord définie à partir de caractéristiques de la côte et de l'arrière-côte, de la ligne de rivage, de la haute-plage et de l'estran ainsi que de la plate-forme marine (fig. 16.3).

Les caractéristiques de la côte et de l'arrière-côte sont l'énergie du relief (plans de moins de 30 m, basses collines de 30 à 75 m et collines de 75 à 150 m) et la nature de la surface (roches meubles ou consolidées). Les caractéristiques de la ligne de rivage sont l'énergie du relief (falaise ou sans falaise), la nature de la surface (roches meubles ou consolidées) et le trait (régulier, échancré, échancré avec fjärds). Les caractéristiques de la haute-plage et de l'estran sont la nature de la surface (sédiments vaseux, sableux, graveleux, blocs ou roc), tandis que celles de la plate-forme littorale sont la largeur de la plate-forme immédiate de moins de 36 m, le degré de dissection et la présence ou non d'îles ou d'écueils. Dans ce dernier cas, les données sur la nature de la surface sont très fragmentaires.

Les sources de sédiments à la côte sont identifiées pour chaque zone et, lorsque c'est possible, les modalités de mouvements des sédiments sont indiquées.

La description des zones homogènes

Le delta Manicouagan - aux Outardes

Cette zone de 70 km, qui va de Ragueneau à l'embouchure de la rivière à la Chasse, est essentiellement formée des deltas conjoints des rivières Manicouagan et aux Outardes dont l'énergie de relief est moins de 30 m (fig. 16.4). La ligne de rivage est régulière et formée de falaises souvent actives dans les sédiments meubles. La haute-plage et l'estran sont sablonneux avec des vases à l'extrême ouest, près de Ragueneau. La plate-forme marine, formée des sédiments sableux des deux rivières, est un plan de 2 à 9 km de largeur. Outre les sédiments fluviaux, les falaises sont affectées par le ravinement et les glissements de terrain et la dérive littorale se fait d'ouest en est, dans le sens du courant principal de l'estuaire, excepté à la pointe ouest du delta où elle est en sens contraire. Cette divergence dans les courants est due à une divergence des fronts de vagues.

La côte accore rocheuse de Baie-Comeau/Godbout

Cette zone de 86 km, qui va de la rivière à la Chasse à l'anse Saint-Augustin, est formée d'une côte et d'une arrière côte de basses collines rocheuses à l'exception des deltas de Mistassini, de Franquelin et de Godbout. La ligne de rivage est régulière et formée de falaises accentuées par des fractures dans les gneiss et les paragneiss (Franconi et al., 1975). Quelques fjärds commandés par des axes de fracture,

viennent découper cette monotonie, tels ceux de Baie-Comeau, de baie des Anglais, de l'anse Saint-Pancrace et de baie Saint-Nicolas. La haute-plage et l'estran sont rocheux ou à blocs, locaux ou glaciels, avec présence de sable principalement à l'ouest du cap Saint-Nicolas où les apports sableux des rivières Manicouagan, Mistassini et Franquelin sont dispersés sur la côte ainsi que dans le secteur de la rivière Godbout. La plate-forme marine, qui a généralement moins de 100-150 m, peut atteindre 1 à 1,5 km au large des zones deltaïques. La dérive littorale est divergente à partir du cap Saint-Nicolas et la partie ouest est affectée aussi par une dérive à partir du delta de Manicouagan - aux Outardes.

La côte à tombolos de Baie-Trinité

Cette zone de 30 km, dont 7 km d'îles, qui va de l'anse Saint-Augustin à Islets-Caribou, est essentiellement formée des sédiments sableux des deltas des rivières de la Trinité et de la petite Trinité. La ligne de rivage est échancrée, à part les 4 km de plage régulière de Baie-Trinité. Il n'y a pas de falaise et les secteurs de dépôts meubles alternent avec les secteurs de roches gneissiques (Franconi et al., 1975) autant sur la ligne de rivage que sur la haute-plage et l'estran. La plate-forme marine de 0,5 à 2 km de largeur est assez régulière mais elle est parsemée de petites îles et d'écueils rocheux. La côte évolue par tombolos et remplissage de fond de baies entre les petits caps à partir d'une dérive littorale probablement vers le sud-ouest.

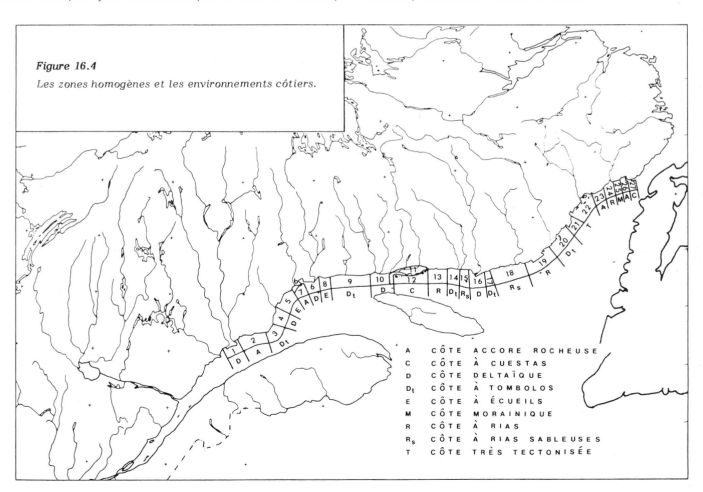

Figure 16.4
Les zones homogènes et les environnements côtiers.

A	CÔTE ACCORE ROCHEUSE
C	CÔTE À CUESTAS
D	CÔTE DELTAÏQUE
Dt	CÔTE À TOMBOLOS
E	CÔTE À ÉCUEILS
M	CÔTE MORAINIQUE
R	CÔTE À RIAS
Rs	CÔTE À RIAS SABLEUSES
T	CÔTE TRÈS TECTONISÉE

Figure 16.5. *Exemple d'une côte à écueils: région de Pointe Jambon au sud de Port-Cartier. La topographie émergée et immergée ainsi que le trait de côte sont contrôlés par la structure gneissique du substratum rocheux. (Photo E.M.R. A-17945-100).*

Les plages de Pointe-aux-Anglais

Cette zone de 36 km, dont 3 km d'îles, qui va d'Islets-Caribou à la rivière Pentecôte, est formée des sédiments sableux des deltas de la petite rivière de la Trinité et de la Pentecôte. Excepté les îles qui sont rocheuses, la ligne de rivage de dépôts meubles est régulière et sans falaise au sud de l'île aux Oeufs. La haute-plage et l'estran sont sableux et la plate-forme marine de 1,5 à 2,5 km de largeur est régulière excepté dans la zone des îles et écueils de l'île aux Oeufs. De gros blocs glaciels se terrent d'ailleurs entre ces îles et la côte. Les sédiments sableux apportés par les rivières et ruisseaux, comme en témoignent plusieurs petits deltas sous-aquatiques, sont dispersés par une dérive convergente vers l'embouchure de la rivière du Calumet entre Islets-Caribou et l'île aux Oeufs, et une dérive divergente entre l'île aux Oeufs et la Pentecôte.

La côte à écueils de rivière aux Rochers

Cette zone de 120 km, dont 40 km d'îles, qui va de la Pentecôte à la pointe Sainte-Marguerite, ressemble un peu à la côte à tombolos de Baie-Trinité mais elle est moins échancrée puisque la quantité de sédiments à la côte est moindre (fig. 16.5). L'énergie du relief est moins de 30 m et à part la zone de mangérite entre Port-Cartier et la pointe Sainte-Marguerite, la côte et l'arrière côte sont formées des sédiments sableux des deltas des rivières Pentecôte, Vachon et aux Rochers. La ligne de rivage est échancrée et commandée par des axes de fractures évidents à Port-Cartier. Elle est habituellement sans falaise importante et découpée dans les gneiss, les anorthosites et les mangérites (Franconi et al., 1975) à part les fonds de baies. La haute-plage et l'estran aussi sont rocheux mais les fonds de baies sont sablonneux à l'exception de la baie des Homards où s'est développée une slikke à blocs glaciels dont les matériaux sont dérivés de l'érosion et du ravinement de falaises dans les sédiments fins. La plate-forme marine est parsemée d'écueils de largeur variable; de 2 à 5 km entre Pentecôte et Port-Cartier, elle s'amenuise à peine à 200 m passé la pointe Sainte-Marguerite. Le sens de la dérive littorale est inconnu pour la majeure partie de la zone. Mais une dérive vers le nord-est semble cependant disperser les alluvions de la Pentecôte sur une courte distance.

Les deltas Moisie/Sainte-Marguerite

Cette zone de 85 km, qui va de la pointe Sainte-Marguerite à la rivière Matamec, est formée des deltas sableux juxtaposés des rivières Moisie et Sainte-Marguerite (fig. 16.6). La ligne de rivage est régulière dans le détail mais l'ensemble forme quatre grandes baies qui sont de l'ouest à l'est, les baies de Sainte-Marguerite, des Sept-Îles, de la Boule et de Moisie. Cette ligne de rivage est inscrite dans les sédiments meubles et est habituellement sans falaise dans les zones d'accumulation (sud de Gallix, embouchure de la Sainte-Marguerite, fond de la baie des Sept-Îles, de l'embouchure de la Moisie à Matamec) et avec falaises dans les autres secteurs stables ou d'érosion. La haute-plage et l'estran sont toujours sableux excepté dans la baie des Sept-Îles où un grand nombre de ruisseaux et de rivières érodent sable et argile marine qui viennent s'accumuler sous forme de slikke et éventuellement combler cette baie; une dérive littorale et un important apport de blocs glaciels vers cette baie y contribuent aussi. Selon Dredge (1976, p. 126) des blocs de gneiss viendraient de l'est de la Moisie. Une plate-forme marine sablonneuse de 1 à 3 km de largeur se maintient dans toute cette zone excepté dans l'archipel des Sept-Îles qui forme une autre zone côtière décrite plus bas.

Dans la baie de Sainte-Marguerite, la dérive se fait vers l'embouchure de la rivière mais au nord de cette dernière, elle est cependant complexe au sud. Dans les baies de Moisie et de la Boule, la dérive littorale est généralisée vers l'ouest (Laverdière, 1954; Thom et Moign, 1970) et des zones de courants de déchirure près de Maliotenam transfèrent des sédiments vers le large (Moign, 1972).

La côte accore rocheuse de l'archipel des Sept-Îles

En incluant les 28 km de la presqu'île de la pointe Noire, cette zone de 73 km comprend 7 îles rocheuses importantes et une multitude d'écueils. Ces collines de gabbro (Franconi et al., 1975) émergent de 100 à 200 m des eaux du Saint-Laurent. Une ligne de rivage relativement régulière est souvent formée d'une falaise rocheuse qui débouche sur un estran rocheux et une plate-forme marine étroite, de 200 à 1000 m de largeur. Ces traits structuraux sont dérivés des failles suborthogonales qui ont permis aux îles de s'ériger en horsts et aux chenaux d'être formés par des grabens. Les seules plages de sable se retrouvent sur la péninsule de la pointe Noire: quelques petites plages de fond de baie au sud et à l'est ainsi qu'une grande plage qui couvre la partie nord et dont les matériaux viennent de la baie des Sept-Îles par une dérive littorale qui vient d'accomplir son mouvement giratoire antihoraire.

La côte à écueils de la pointe Saint-Charles

Cette zone de 86 km, dont 23 km d'îles, qui va de la Matamec au cap du Cormoran, est rocheuse et possède moins de 30 m d'énergie de relief. La ligne de rivage est échancrée et sans falaise. Les baies se sont inscrites (Sharma et Franconi, 1975) dans les axes de faiblesse des gneiss où des granites gneissiques comme le démontre en particulier le havre Saint-Charles. La haute-plage et l'estran sont rocheux, excepté dans quelques baies où des sables et des silts ont été érodés à quelques petits deltas tels ceux des rivières Matamec, aux Loups Marins et Pigou. On y trouve plusieurs petites slikkes dans l'anse Amory, dans la baie au Cormoran, dans l'estuaire de la rivière aux Loups Marins et derrière l'île du Cormoran. Le peu de sédiments à la côte est dû au fait que les rivières de cette zone drainent de très petits bassins. La plate-forme marine de 1 à 3 km de largeur et parsemée de petits écueils poursuit la topographie terrestre sous l'eau. Il est probable que la dérive littorale est divergente à partir de la pointe Saint-Charles, mais cette dernière n'a pas beaucoup d'influence sur les mouvements de sédiments qui demeurent emprisonnés entre les caps.

La côte à tombolos de Manitou-Magpie

Cette zone de 100 km dont 15 km d'îles, qui va du cap du Cormoran à Magpie, est très composite (fig. 16.7). La côte et l'arrière côte, d'une énergie de relief de moins de 30 m, sont formées de granites, de granites gneissiques et de mangérites (Sharma et Franconi, 1975) sur les interfluves et de sédiments marins et deltaïques dans les vallées comme celles des rivières au Bouleau, Tortue, grande Manitou, à la Chaloupe, Sheldrake, au Tonnerre et Jupitagon. La ligne de rivage, où alternent aussi des secteurs rocheux et non rocheux, est peu échancrée et non rocheux, est peu échancrée et généralement formée de falaises. Sur la haute-plage et l'estran de la zone de mangérites à l'est de Sheldrake alternent les secteurs de roc et de sable et gravier avec un peu de sable près des grandes rivières. Entre les rivières Sheldrake et Tortue, la haute-plage et l'estran sont plus rocheux et les sables et graviers n'existent que dans les baies abritées et à

Figure 16.6. *Exemple d'une côte deltaïque: la partie ouest du delta de la Sainte-Marguerite en contact avec le rebord du socle précambrien, comme tous les deltas de la Côte Nord, celui-ci a été remanié en terrasses étagées par l'action marine et incisé par les cours d'eau. La dérive littorale se fait vers l'est. (Photo E.M.R. A-17945-110).*

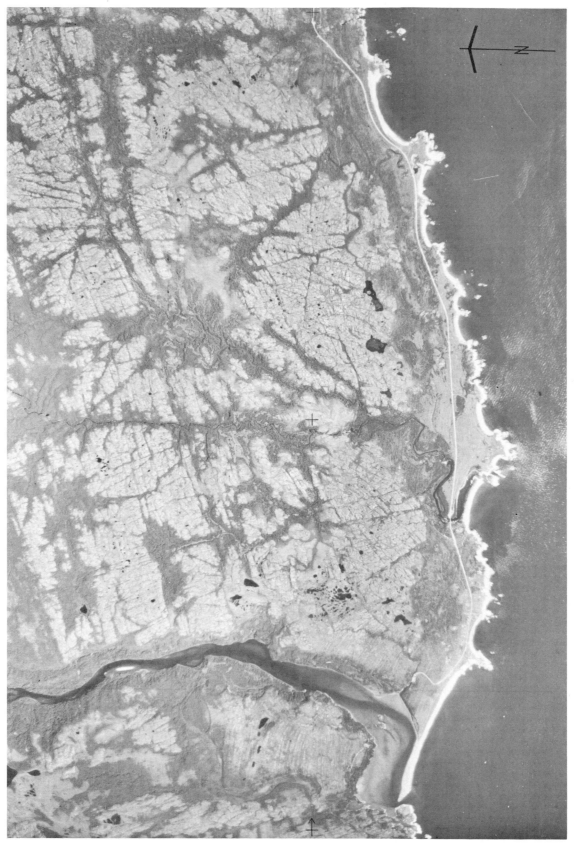

Figure 16.7.   *Exemple d'une côte à tombolos associée à des complexes deltaïques: région de Sheldrake. Cette côte tend à se régulariser par accumulation de sédiments entre les tombolos. Les cours d'eau se sont mis en place dans des axes de fractures dont on peut d'ailleurs remarquer tout le réseau dans les anorthosites et les gabbros. (Photo E.M.R. A-11700-325).*

l'embouchure des grandes rivières. Quant au secteur du cap du Cormoran à la Tortue, la ligne de rivage très abrupte et régulière dans les granites et la haute-plage et l'estran sont formés en majeure partie d'un pavage de blocs locaux et glaciels. Dans cette zone des falaises rocheuses ont été striées par la glace jusqu'au littoral actuel. La plate-forme marine, de 1 à 4 km de largeur, poursuit sous l'eau un relief terrestre assez calme. La dérive littorale de cette zone est complexe; elle diverge généralement de part et d'autre de caps importants, telle la pointe à Canot à l'ouest de la Manitou, mais elle présente un sens général vers l'ouest. Presque toute cette côte, principalement entre la pointe à Canot et la rivière à la Chaloupe ainsi qu'entre Sheldrake et Magpie, évolue par comblement des baies entre les tombolos.

Les deltas de Magpie/Saint-Jean/Mingan

Cette zone de 40 km, qui va de Magpie à la rivière Mingan, est formée des deltas sableux juxtaposés des rivières Magpie, Saint-Jean et Mingan; la côte et l'arrière-côte possèdent donc une énergie de relief inférieure à 30 m. La ligne de rivage est régulière et entièrement dans les dépôts meubles; elle présente des falaises actives dans sa partie ouest à partir de la région de la Saint-Jean et l'on y remarque aussi nombre de glissements de terrain. La haute-plage et l'estran sont sableux et quelque peu graveleux. La plate-forme marine est régulière, large de 1 à 8 km, et probablement composée en majeure partie de sable dérivé des deltas; la Mingan nourrit encore un vaste delta sous-aquatique. La dérive littorale est généralisée vers l'est à part quelques petits courants de retour notamment à l'est de l'embouchure des rivières.

Le delta de la Romaine

Cette zone de 78 km, qui va de la Mingan à la baie Saint-Laurent, est essentiellement formée du delta de la Romaine et d'une partie de celui de la Mingan. Ces deltas ont ennoyé sous leurs sédiments sableux plusieurs cuestas paléozoïques parmi celles qui forment les deux rangées de l'archipel de Mingan (Twenhofel, 1938). La côte et l'arrière-côte possèdent donc une énergie de relief de moins de 30 m. La ligne de rivage forme de grandes baies entre les affleurements de calcaire ou de dolomie et, dans le détail, les zones d'affleurements rocheux possèdent des falaises et échancrent le trait de côte tandis que les fonds de baies en dépôts meubles sont rectilignes et à falaise. Quelques cas s'écartent de la règle, ce sont le cap rocheux sans falaise de la pointe aux Morts et les rivages de dépôts meubles sans falaise du fond des baies Saint-Laurent, des Trilobites et celle qui est à l'est de la Mingan; un autre cas sans falaise est la zone d'accumulation à l'est de Havre-Saint-Pierre. La haute-plage et l'estran sont généralement sableux. On rencontre cependant des fonds de baies assez vaseux comme les baies Saint-Laurent et des Trilobites de même que la baie à l'est de l'embouchure de la Romaine. La présence de ces sédiments fins est liée aux nombreux ravinements, glissements de terrain et ruisseaux qui drainent les vastes tourbières contenues au sommet du delta par une cuirasse ferrugineuse imperméable. Ceux-ci finissent par crever la cuirasse, forment de petits deltas dans le fond des baies et les courants de dérive étendent le matériel. Tout comme la Mingan, la Romaine nourrit encore un delta sous-aquatique dont la matériel tend à ennoyer les îles Moutange et Moniac. Dans le reste de la zone, l'interférence des îles rend hasardeux l'interprétation des courants de dérive mais il semble au moins que les sédiments de la baie Saint-Laurent et de la baie des Trilobites soient dirigés vers l'ouest. La plate-forme marine est commune à l'archipel de Mingan.

L'archipel de Mingan

Cette zone est formée uniquement d'une trentaine d'îles et de nombreux récifs dont le périmètre est d'environ 210 km. Ces îles, en majeure partie rocheuses, ne dépassent pas 46 m d'altitude sur la Grande Île. Elles forment deux rangées de cuestas à revers de calcaire ou de calcaire dolomitique ordovicien sur l'assise gréseuse de la formation de Romaine et dont le pendage est d'à peine 1,3 à 1,5 pour cent vers le sud (Twenhofel, 1938). La rangée sud, qui va des Perroquets à l'ouest à l'île Sainte-Geneviève à l'est, se maintient entre 50°11' et 50°15'; elle comprend aussi le secteur de terre ferme entre le cap à l'Eau Claire et la pointe Tête de Perdrix. La rangée nord, qui comprend les îles du Havre de Mingan (Harbour), de Grande Romaine (Moutange) et de Petite Romaine (Momiac), ainsi que les secteurs de terre ferme de pointe aux Morts et du mont Sainte-Geneviève, se maintient entre 50°15' et 50°18'. Selon l'allure des courbes bathymétriques il est évident que les cuestas se prolongent vers l'ouest jusqu'à l'archipel des Sept-Îles et vers l'est au moins jusqu'à Natashquan. La plate-forme marine est très large au sud, généralement entre 8 et 10 km, mais elle est étroite de quelques centaines de mètres au nord si elle n'est pas rattachée à la côte ou à une autre rangée de cuestas; dans un tel cas, elle peut atteindre 3 km.

Le trait de rivage est généralement régulier mais il peut être échancré dans le cas de l'île à la Chasse. Des falaises rocheuses pouvant atteindre 10 m de hauteur marquent au nord le front des cuestas. Ces falaises évoluent par sapement basal et écroulements à un rythme relativement rapide pour du roc mais certainement pas au rythme estimé à plus de 3m/an à Anticosti par Twenhofel et Conine (1921). Au pied des falaises, la haute-plage et l'estran sont rocheux, étroits et encombrés de débris allant des blocs aux quartiers de roc. On y rencontre aussi de très beaux monolithes d'érosion ainsi que de petites plages de fond de baie formées de gravier calcaire local ou de sable transporté de la côte. Sur le côté sud, il n'y a pas de falaise; la ligne de rivage est rocheuse excepté sur l'île Nue de Mingan, la Grande Île et l'île à la Proie à l'ouest. La plage et la haute-plage sont généralement rocheuses excepté sur les îles mentionnées ci-haut où elles peuvent être formées de gravier et de galets calcaires gélifractés. L'estran est rocheux, très large au sud mais étroit au nord et il est soumis à l'abrasion littorale, à l'altération chimique et surtout à la gélifraction en accentuant un réseau orthogonal de diaclases. Il se dégage alors des formes trapézoïdales ou coniques aux sommets arrondis (Landry, 1975). L'estran est parfois façonné par d'importantes cannelures glaciaires d'orientation sud (±5°) au nord-est de l'île à la Chasse (Landry, 1975), au sud de la Petite Romaine (Twenhofel, 1938), de l'île du Havre (Landry, 1975) et de l'île du Havre de Mingan; on en rencontre aussi de 6 m de largeur et de 1 à 2 m de profondeur sur la côte dans le havre de Betchouane, dans la baie des Trilobites et au cap à l'Eau Claire (Twenhofel, 1938). Nous avons aussi observé à l'instar de Twenhofel et Conine (1921) sur Anticosti et de Landry (1975) des erratiques ou des blocs glaciels cristallins (généralement des anorthosites) au sud des îles surtout. Fait assez curieux, nous avons aussi trouvé sur les plages de la petite île au Marteau des débris de forme 'corallienne' et quelques pêcheurs nous ont dit que la roche 'poussait' entre certaines îles!

La côte à rias de Baie-Johan-Beetz

La longueur de la côte est difficile à évaluer mais elle est d'au moins 446 km, dont exactement la moitié est insulaire (fig. 16.8). Cette zone de moins de 30 m d'énergie de relief

Figure 16.8. *Exemple d'une côte à rias: région de la baie Pontbriand à l'est de Baie-Johan-Beetz.*
Les échancrures de la côte sont dues au rubanement des gneiss. (Photo E.M.R. A-11700-154).

est complètement rocheuse et va de la baie Saint-Laurent à la baie Pashashibou. À part la colline Sainte-Geneviève formée de calcaire dolomitique cambrien, elle se compose de roches cristallines: gneiss, granite gneissique, granite quartzite, schistes, gabbro et pegmatites (Grenier, 1957). La ligne de rivage est sans falaise et extrêmement échancrée; elle est rocheuse partout excepté au fond de très rares baies. Cette topographie tourmentée se prolonge d'ailleurs régulièrement sous les eaux du golfe en une plate-forme marine de 4 à 8 km de largeur et ponctuée d'une infinité d'îles et d'écueils. Les orientations dans le découpage du trait de côte sont dues principalement à l'exploitation des axes structuraux par l'érosion mais aussi de certaines différences de résistance dans la lithologie; d'une façon générale, les granites et les gabbros forment des massifs ou des crêtes tandis que les roches métasédimentaires tels les quartzites et surtout les schistes sont en dépression (Cooper, 1951; Dépatie, 1967; Grenier, 1957). On peut donc distinguer jusqu'à quatre traits de rivage différents dans cette zone.

Entre la baie Saint-Laurent et la rivière Corneille, le rivage plus régulier est dû à la structure massive du granite et aussi à la présence de plus de sédiments à la côte. Entre ce secteur et la baie Johan-Beetz, le rivage moins régulier est dû à l'érosion des diaclases et des foliations des granites gneissiques. Entre la baie Johan-Beetz et la rivière Watshishou, les baies sont longues, étroites et alignées vers le sud-ouest; elles sont parallèles aux stratifications ou aux foliations de la roche et sont formées dans des quartzites en dépression entre des caps de gabbro ou de pegmatite. Enfin, entre la rivière Watshishou et la baie Pashashibou, l'évasement des baies est dû aux directions plus variables des diaclases et des foliations dans les gneiss et les zones échancrées sont dues au rubanement de ces gneiss.

La haute-plage et l'estran sont aussi rocheux excepté au fond des baies qui reçoivent des apports de sable sous forme de deltas; les principales sont de l'ouest à l'est, la baie Saint-Laurent, les baies Victor et de la Grande Hermine, la baie Quetachou et la baie Jalobert. Il n'y a pas de transfert littoral de sédiments d'une baie à l'autre.

La côte à tombolos du delta Nabisipi-Aguanus

Cette zone de 23 km, dont 3 km d'îles, est principalement constituée des deltas conjoints des rivières Nabisipi et Aguanus entre les baies Pashashibou et Aguanish; elle a donc moins de 30 m d'énergie de relief. Le rivage est régulier, sans falaise et principalement sableux à part quelques anciennes îles rocheuses jointes à la côte par le phénomène de tombolo. On retrouve d'ailleurs quelques unes de ces îles où des pointements rocheux sous moins de 5 m d'eau sur une plate-forme marine de 4 à 5 km de largeur. La haute-plage et l'estran sont formés de sable que la dérive littorale transporte de façon divergente à partir du cap Nabisipi au centre de la zone.

La côte à rias sableux de Natashquan

Cette zone de 100 km de longueur dont près de la moitié, soit 41 km, est insulaire, va d'Aguanish à Natashquan. La côte et l'arrière-côte ont moins de 30 m d'énergie de relief et sont principalement formées par l'ennoyage des reliefs gneissiques par les sédiments deltaïques de l'Aguanus. Ces reliefs se retrouvent d'ailleurs sur une plate-forme marine de 4 à 5 km de largeur. Le rivage est sans falaise, très échancré et rocheux excepté au fond des baies où il est sableux; il en va de même de la haute-plage et de l'estran. Les baies ont tendance à se combler des sédiments apportés par les ruisseaux ainsi que par la petite rivière Natashquan.

Là où les sédiments sont plus abondants, ils débordent les baies et la côte tend à se régulariser par le phénomène de tombolo. La dérive littorale semble assez complexe à cause de l'interférence des nombreuses îles mais un mouvement général vers l'est peut être observé aux deux extrémités à partir d'Aguanish et de l'embouchure de la petite rivière Natashquan.

Le delta de la Natashquan

Cette zone de 40 km de longueur, qui va de Natashquan à la rivière Kégashka, est constituée par la surface sablonneuse et de moins de 30 m d'énergie du delta de la Natashquan. La ligne de rivage régulière est formée de falaises dans les dépôts meubles à l'est de la rivière; à l'ouest de la rivière par contre, principale zone d'accumulation sableuse, le rivage est plat. La haute-plage et l'estran sont aussi sableux; ce sable semble provenir en grande partie du ravinement du delta de la rivière elle-même et aussi de la déflation. Selon les travaux de Welsted (1960), on peut déduire que les houles proviennent de trois directions, de l'WNW et du SSE principalement ainsi qu'une houle mineure provenant du SW; c'est ce qui détermine la forme de trapèze déversé du delta. Les observations de dérives littorales concordent avec les observations de Welsted (1960). Elles sont convergentes vers l'embouchure de la rivière et aussi vers la pointe de Natashquan. Dans le secteur est, une petite dérive vers l'est transporte les sédiments vers la rivière Kégashka. La plate-forme marine, probablement en majeure partie sableuse, est étroite vers l'embouchure de la rivière et s'élargit vers les deux extrémités puisqu'elle passe de 2 km à 5 km de largeur.

La côte à tombolos de Kégashka

Cette zone de 44 km, dont 24 km d'îles, qui va de la rivière Kégashka à pointe Curlew, possède une énergie de relief à moins de 30 m et sa surface est en partie formée de gneiss et de granites (Bassaget, 1970) et en partie des sables deltaïques de la rivière Kégashka, qui ont comblé les dépressions entre les aspérités du substratum rocheux. La ligne de rivage est aussi mi-rocheuse, mi-sableuse, elle est légèrement échancrée et possède des falaises seulement vers l'ouest, vers le delta de la Natashquan. Elle évolue par tombolos et sa haute-plage et son estran sont presqu'entièrement sableux. La dérive littorale semble être convergente vers le grand tombolo de la pointe de Kégashka. La plate-forme marine qui varie de 4,5 à 8 km de largeur, reflète le relief émergé.

La côte à rias sableux de Gethsémani

La longueur de la côte est difficile à évaluer mais elle est d'au moins 580 km dont la moitié est insulaire; c'est exactement la constatation qui avait été faite dans la zone à rias de Baie-Johan-Beetz. Cette zone de moins de 30 m d'énergie de relief est en majeure partie rocheuse et s'étend entre les baies de Kégashka et Coacoachou. Des accumulations de dépôts meubles peuvent être observées le long de la majorité des grandes vallées et spécialement dans celle de l'Olomane. La ligne de rivage sans falaise est extrêmement échancrée de baies profondes et assez étroites qui dénotent un relief tourmenté qui se prolonge sous les eaux en une large plate-forme marine très disséquée de 7 à 12 km de largeur. Les orientations dans le découpage du trait de côte sont dues principalement à l'exploitation des axes structuraux tels les diaclases, les foliations et le litage des gneiss et des gneiss granitiques (Claveau, 1950). La ligne de rivage ainsi que la haute-plage et l'estran sont rocheux excepté les fonds de baies qui sont sablonneux. Le grand nombre de deltas sous-aquatiques est un trait caractéristique de cette zone, tout spécialement celui de l'Olomane. Le fort découpage de la côte ne permet cependant pas le transfert de sédiments d'une grande baie à l'autre.

La côte à rias d'Étamamiou

La longueur de cette côte, qui s'étend de la baie Coacoachou à 6 km à l'ouest de la rivière Nétagamiou, est aussi difficile à préciser mais elle est d'au moins 775 km, dont 420 km est insulaire. Cette côte rocheuse est formée de méta-arkose à l'ouest et de charnockite à l'est (Boorne, 1978) et a moins de 30 m d'énergie de relief. La ligne de rivage est généralement sans falaise, complètement rocheuse et extrêmement échancrée. La dissection du relief s'est faite selon les axes de fracture et les foliations dans les roches. La haute-plage et l'estran sont aussi rocheux excepté le fond de quelques baies où des ruisseaux ont édifié de petits deltas. Le relief très tourmenté se prolonge en une plate-forme marine très large de 10 à 15 km, très disséquée et truffée d'îles. Il y a donc pratiquement pas de sédiments à la côte et ces derniers ne peuvent être transférés d'une baie à l'autre. La raison de cette pénurie de sédiments est certainement le fait qu'étant un immense cap, cette zone ne possède pas de grands bassins-versants d'autant plus qu'elle est encadrée de deux grandes rivières qui ont certainement drainé tous les sédiments fluvioglaciaires: l'Olomane et la Mécatina.

La côte à tombolos du delta Nétagamiou - Petit Mécatina

Cette zone de 78 km de côtes sur la terre ferme possède aussi au moins 440 km de côtes insulaires. Cette côte, qui s'étend de la rivière Nétagamiou à l'île du Grand Rigolet, possède moins de 30 m d'énergie de relief et est formée du delta des rivières Nétagamiou et du Petit Mécatina qui a en partie ennoyé un archipel d'îles rocheuses. Les îles seraient en grande partie gneissiques et syénitiques d'après Davies (1965). Près de la côte, quelques îles presqu'entièrement formées de dépôts meubles, font partie du delta lui-même. Elles sont sises sur une très large plate-forme marine de 5 à 14 km dont le rebord rectiligne, orienté environ N45°E, suggère la présence d'une grande fracture.

La ligne de rivage sans falaise est presque régulière, inscrite dans le substratum rocheux vers les caps et dans les dépôts meubles dans les baies et près de l'embouchure des cours d'eau principaux. La haute-plage et l'estran sont presque toujours sablonneux excepté sur les caps plus avancés où ils sont rocheux. Le trait de côte est presque régularisé par le phénomène de tombolos dans le secteur de la Nétagamiou où il y a très peu d'îles; ailleurs, malgré les nombreux ravinements et surtout l'apport considérable de sédiments du Petit Mécatina, la multitude d'îles empêche cette régularisation. Le delta sous-aquatique de la Mécatina est impressionnant puisqu'il recouvre la plate-forme marine dans un rayon de 9 km. La dérive littorale est complexe vers l'est à cause de l'interférence des îles, mais les sédiments semblent très mobiles. Vers l'ouest, la dérive littorale semble être convergente vers l'embouchure de la Nétagamiou.

La côte tectonique échancrée du Gros Mécatina

Cette zone d'environ 215 km de longueur, dont au moins 165 km insulaire, va de l'île du Grand Rigolet à la baie des Ha! Ha! (fig. 16.9). Tout est rocheux sur ce grand cap car les sédiments que pourrait transporter la seule grande rivière qui s'y jette, la rivière du Gros Mécatina, sont trappés tout au long de son cours. Le découpage de la côte est essentiellement dû à des axes de fractures et de failles d'orientation N30°-45°-60°E ainsi que N-S. Deux secteurs différents peuvent cependant être distingués: les collines de Mécatina à l'est et les basses-terres du Gros Mécatina à l'ouest. Le premier est un massif de 30 à 75 m d'énergie de relief dans les syénites résistantes (Davies, 1965). Le trait de rivage est moins échancré et une plate-forme marine étroite de moins de 2 km ne laisse émerger que peu d'îles. Par contre, cette dernière reprend à 5 km au large principalement dans la région de l'île du Gros Mécatina. Le deuxième secteur de moins de 30 m d'énergie de relief et très échancré est constitué de gneiss dont les foliations, le litage et les fractures ont été exploités par l'érosion (Davies, 1965) de sorte qu'on retrouve un relief très tourmenté qui se prolonge par une large plate-forme marine de 7 à 10 km et parsemée d'îles.

La côte tectonique à fjärds de Saint-Augustin

La longueur du littoral de cette zone est des plus difficiles à évaluer à cause du grand nombre de bras de mer, des fjärds de plus de 36 m de profondeur, qui s'y trouvent et qui morcellent un relief entièrement rocheux et de 30 à 75 m d'énergie en une multitude de grandes îles. Cette zone de gneiss ou de granites gneissiques (Davies, 1963, 1965), qui s'étend entre les baies des Ha! Ha! et de Jacques-Cartier, est longue d'au moins 965 km, dont 650 km d'îles. Le trait de côte, les fjärds et tous les grands alignements de baies sont dûs à des failles ou à de grands axes de fracture d'orientation N30°-35°-40°-60°E qui en joignent d'autres moins importants d'orientation franc N±10°. La plate-forme marine, de relief tout aussi tourmenté, a toujours environ 4 km de largeur et son rebord est rectiligne et d'orientation N45°E avec un décrochement entre les îles de la Grande Passe et Wakeham. Selon Davies (1963) les échancrures mineures de la côte suivent la foliation des gneiss. Les seuls dépôts meubles de ce secteur, le delta de la Saint-Augustin, sont emprisonnés dans la baie du même nom derrière 12 ou 13 km d'îles et il n'y a pas possibilité de transfert de sédiments.

La côte accore à fjärds de Port-Saint-Servan

Cette zone de 115 km de longueur, dont 18 km insulaire, est régulière, entièrement rocheuse (la carte géologique n'est pas levée), de 30 à 75 m d'énergie de relief et s'étend de la baie Jacques-Cartier aux îles aux Chiens. Le trait de côte se présente sous forme de falaises de direction N80°E à l'ouest de Port-Saint-Servan et N40°E à l'est. Ces axes de fracture recoupent d'autres axes de direction N5° à 20°E dans lesquels sont installés des fjärds de plus de 36 m de profondeur. Une plate-forme marine de 6 à 7 km de largeur, morcelée par ces fractures, ressemble à un graben abaissé d'une centaine de mètres et duquel à peine quelques îles percent la surface des eaux. Des ruisseaux ont édifié des deltas au fond de quelques petites baies mais il ne peut certainement pas y avoir de transfert de sédiments de l'une à l'autre.

La côte à rias du Vieux Fort

Cette zone d'au moins 245 km, dont 175 km insulaire, s'étend des îles aux Chiens à la baie Bonne-Espérance. Les reliefs de 30 à 75 m d'énergie, sont entièrement rocheux (la carte géologique n'est pas encore levée) excepté de rares plages de dépôts meubles sur quelques îles et au fond de quelques petites baies, dont les plus importantes sont celles en face de Vieux-Fort et de Rivière-Saint-Paul. La ligne de rivage est sans falaise excepté, dans le secteur ouest, la falaise sise

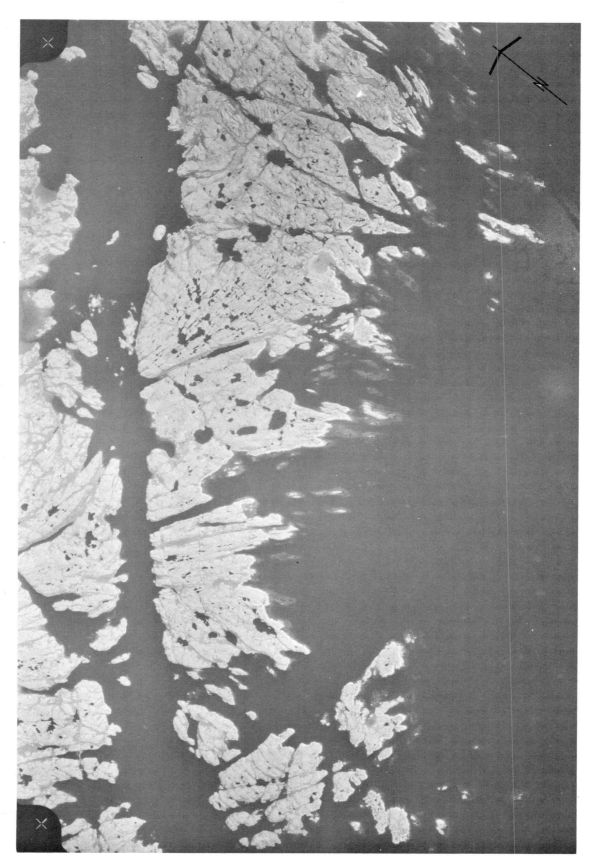

Figure 16.9.   *Exemple d'une côte fortement tectonisée: la Grande Passe au sud-ouest de la baie de Saint-Augustin.   Cette Côte est extrêmement échancrée par de grands fjärds dans toutes les directions des axes de fractures.   (Photo E.M.R.   A-18933-27).*

sur le prolongement de l'axe de fracture d'orientation N40ºE de la zone précédente. Le trait du rivage est extrêmement échancré et ce relief se poursuit sur une plate-forme marine de 6 à 10 km de largeur littéralement truffée d'îles. A part quelques rares ruisseaux surtout vers l'ouest il ne semble pas y avoir d'apport de sédiments à la côte, même pas de la rivière Saint-Paul car tous ses sédiments sont trappés avant l'embouchure.

La côte morainique de la baie du Milieu

Cette zone de 80 km de longueur, dont 15 km insulaire, s'étend entre les baies de Bonne-Espérance et de Brador. D'une énergie de relief de 30 à 75 m en général, la côte et l'arrière-côte sont en majorité rocheuses (la carte géologique n'est pas levée) excepté la côte immédiate. La ligne de rivage sans falaise est échancrée et généralement en dépôts meubles de même que la haute-plage et l'estran. La plate-forme marine, qui varie de 0,5 à 3,5 km de largeur, est irrégulière mais son rebord rectiligne avec un décrochement à la baie du Milieu suit probablement une fracture de direction N55º à 60ºE. Le littoral évolue par phénomène de tombolos selon une dérive littorale complexe. Cependant la présence de ces importants sédiments n'est certainement pas liée à des apports fluviaux puisque le seul cours d'eau qui en serait susceptible est le ruisseau au Saumon à l'extrême ouest et au fond de la baie du même nom. La seule explication plausible serait un dépôt glaciaire lié au système morainique de Brador (Grant, 1969a, b; Dubois, 1977).

La côte accore rocheuse de la faille de Brador

Cette zone rectiligne de 10 km de longueur (fig. 16.10) est formée à partir d'une côte entièrement rocheuse de 30 à 75 m d'énergie de relief et dont le rebord constitue une falaise d'environ 100 m de hauteur dans les gneiss granitiques et les granites massifs: c'est la faille de Brador de direction N76ºE. Une plate-forme marine d'environ 3 à 4 km de largeur et probablement disséquée dans les micaschistes, est surbaissée d'environ 125 à 150 m par rapport au rebord du plateau.

La côte à cuestas de Blanc-Sablon

Cette dernière zone de 80 km de longueur (fig. 16.10), dont 45 km insulaire, s'étend de l'anse aux Moustiques au fond de la baie de Brador à la frontière du Labrador à l'est de la baie de Blanc-Sablon. La côte et l'arrière-côte, de moins de 30 m d'énergie de relief, sont en majeure partie rocheuses à part les sédiments littoraux et marins qui tapissent les dépressions. Le sommet des collines tabulaires est formé des calcaires et des schistes de la formation de Forteau surmontant les grès de la formation de Brador. Ces roches paléozoïques reposent en discordance sur les granites, les gneiss granitiques et les micaschistes précambriens (De Boutray et Hillaire-Marcel, 1977). La ligne de rivage est en majeure partie rocheuse et à falaise, à part les baies qui sont de dépôts meubles et sans falaise. Le trait du rivage est échancré dans les roches précambriennes au nord de Bradore Bay, au sud de Lourdes-de-Blanc-Sablon et sur les îles de la baie de Brador, ceci étant dû aux foliations; par contre, il est régulier dans les zones de dépôts meubles et dans les roches gréseuses.

La haute-plage et l'estran sont généralement constitués de sédiments meubles en grande partie sableux excepté sur les caps où ils sont rocheux. Il n'est pas possible ici de déduire les données de dérive littorale mais il est fort probable qu'il n'y a pas de transfert de sédiments hors des principales baies. La plate-forme marine dans les roches précambriennes à l'ouest et dans les roches paléozoïques au sud varie de 1 à 8 km de largeur.

Conclusion

La description de la zone côtière de la Côte Nord permet donc de diviser les quelques 5200 km de littoral en 27 zones homogènes. L'examen de ces données permet de déduire des enseignements généraux et des constantes importantes qui permettent une meilleure schématisation de l'organisation du littoral et du zonage des plages sableuses.

L'ANALYSE SYNTHÈSE DE LA ZONE CÔTIÈRE

La classification des environnements côtiers

De l'analyse des 27 zones homogènes, on peut définir 9 environnements côtiers distincts (fig. 16.4): deltaïque, à tombolos associé à un delta, morainique, à écueils, à rias sableuses à rias, fortement tectonisée, accore rocheux et à cuestas.

La côte deltaïque (D)

Cet environnement (fig. 16.6), qui correspond à 7 pour cent de la Côte Nord (349 km), est essentiellement constitué des grands deltas des rivières Manicouagan et aux Outardes (zone 1), de la petite Trinité, du Calumet et Pentecôte (zone 4), Sainte-Marguerite et Moisie (zone 6), Magpie, Saint-Jean et Mingan (zone 10), Romaine (zone 11) et Natashquan (zone 16). La côte et l'arrière-côte sont sableuses, parfois légèrement graveleuses comme à Magpie par exemple, et l'énergie du relief est de moins de 30 m.

La ligne de rivage est toujours sableuse, régulière et généralement à falaise excepté les plus fortes zones d'accumulation. La haute-plage et l'estran sont sableux excepté dans le secteur de Magpie à Mingan, où ils sont très légèrement graveleux, et la baie des Sept-Îles et quelques baies du delta de la Romaine qui sont vaseuses avec présence de nombreux blocs glaciels. Les graviers du premier secteur sont dérivés des formations graveleuses sommitales des deltas tandis que les vases à blocs du deuxième secteur sont dues à l'érosion des sédiments fins marins à la base des deltas; ces sédiments sont déposés dans des baies abritées où viennent s'échouer les glaces flottantes qui y délestent leur charge. La plate-forme marine, régulière et certainement sableuse, varie en moyenne de 2 à 5 km de largeur et la sédimentation y est toujours active comme on le voit particulièrement bien par les deltas sous-aquatiques des rivières Manicouagan, aux Outardes et Mingan (fig. 16.5) ou par les grandes flèches d'embouchure des rivières qui s'allongent la plupart du temps vers l'ouest. Par contre, l'érosion a fait son oeuvre récemment comme en témoignent les nombreuses falaises mortes qui correspondent à la ligne de rivage actuelle et quelques unes sont très actives en plus d'être affectées par le ravinement ou les glissements de terrain principalement dans le secteur de la Saint-Jean.

La côte à tombolos associée à un delta (Dt)

Cet environnement, qui correspond à 13 pour cent de la Côte Nord (675 km) est en fait sur-représenté à cause des 400 km de côtes insulaires du secteur des deltas de Nétagamiou - Petit Mécatina (fig. 16.7). Il est constitué des secteurs limitrophes à quelques grands deltas mentionnés plus haut ou de secteurs deltaïques fortement insulaires: secteurs de Baie-Trinité (zone 3), de Manitou-Magpie (zone 9), de Nabisipi-Aguanus (zone 14), de Kégashka (zone 17) et de Nétagamiou - Petit Mécatina (zone 20). La côte et l'arrière-côte, d'une énergie de relief de moins de 30 m, sont en majeure partie sableuses excepté dans le secteur de Manitou-Magpie où elles sont plutôt rocheuses (fig. 16.6). Ceci est dû à la présence dans ce secteur de très petits bassins-versants de cours d'eau qui trappent leurs sédiments sur leur parcours.

Figure 16.10.   Exemple de côte accore rocheuse au nord de la photographie et de côte à cuestas à l'est: région de la baie de Brador. La côte accore est modelée sur le tracé de la faille de Brador de direction N 76° E.   Quant à la côte de la région de Blanc-Sablon à l'est, les cuestas gréseuses surplombent l'assise cristalline précambrienne qui a parfois été mise à jour par l'érosion de la couverture paléozoique. Le trait de côte régulier marque des roches sédimentaires tandis que le trait de côte échancré marque des roches cristallines. (Photo E.M.R. A-20178-6).

La ligne de rivage est échancrée excepté là où il y a une plus forte influence deltaïque comme dans les secteurs des deltas de la Trinité, de Nabisipi-Aquanus et de Nétagamiou-Petit Mécatina où elle est légèrement échancrée et même régulière. À part la zone de Manitou-Magpie et le secteur ouest de la zone Kégashka il n'y a pas de falaise.

La ligne de rivage ainsi que la haute-plage et l'estran sont sableux entre les caps et rocheux sur ces derniers; le rapport varie cependant selon la quantité de sédiments à la côte de sorte qu'ils peuvent passer d'une majorité rocheuse dans une zone comme celle de Manitou-Magpie à une majorité sableuse dans une zone comme celle des deltas de Nabisipi-Magpie à une majorité sableuse dans une zone comme celle des deltas de Nabisipi-Aquanus où une grande quantité de sédiments a permis une régularisation efficace du littoral par remplissage des baies entre les tombolos. Il y a cependant une exception à cette règle quant à la nature des sédiments: c'est la section du cap du Cormoran à la rivière Tortue, à l'ouest de la zone de Manitou-Magpie, où on retrouve une plage de blocs locaux ou glaciels de 9 km de longueur, parfois sous forme de pavage (becevnik), et qui sont dérivés en majeure partie des falaises rocheuses ou des anciennes plages de cette côte.

La plate-forme marine de 2 à 10 km de largeur en moyenne est légèrement disséquée et reflète le relief émergé. Elle est certainement en majeure partie rocheuse et elle n'est ponctuée de nombreuses îles que dans la zone plus fortement tectonisée de Nétagamiou-Petit Mécatina. Des petits deltas sous-aquatiques peuvent être observés à l'embouchure de la rivière au Bouleau à l'ouest de la zone de Manitou-Magpie et à l'embouchure de petits ruisseaux à l'ouest de la zone de Kégashka et de grands deltas à l'embouchure des rivières Nétagamiou et du Petit Mécatina.

La côte morainique (M)

Cet environnment de 80 km à peine ne comprend que la côte de la baie du Milieu (zone 25). Cette côte qui évolue par tombolos à partir de la moraine de Brador mise en place sur le littoral, est déjà décrite dans les zones homogènes.

La côte à écueils (E)

Cet environnment, qui correspond à environ 4 pour cent de la Côte Nord (206 km), est représenté par les secteurs de la rivière aux Rochers (zone 5) et de la pointe Saint-Charles (zone 8) (fig. 16.5). La côte et l'arrière-côte ont moins de 30 m d'énergie de relief mais dans le premier cas elles sont formées en majorité de dépôts meubles alors que dans l'autre, elles sont entièrement rocheuses. Par contre, la ligne de rivage est rocheuse, échancrée et sans falaise. La haute-plage et l'estran sont rocheux excepté le fond des baies qui est sablonneux ou vaseux à blocs glaciels dans les cas de la baie des Homards (zone de Baie-Trinité) et de l'anse Amory (zone de pointe Saint-Charles); les sédiments fins qui constituent la vase proviennent des sédiments marins au fond de chacune des baies. La plate-forme marine de 2 à 3 km de largeur, est disséquée, certainement rocheuse, et reflète un relief émergé qui est commandé par des axes de fractures (fig. 16.7). Les côtes insulaires représentent dans les deux cas près de 50 pour cent des côtes de terre ferme.

La côte à rias sableuses (Rs)

Cet environnement, qui correspond à 13 pour cent de la Côte Nord, est constitué des secteurs qui s'étendent d'Aguanish à Natashquan (zone 15) et de la baie de Kégashka à la baie de Coacoachou (zone 18). La côte et l'arrière-côte ont une

énergie de relief de moins de 30 m et sont formées soit en majorité de dépôts meubles lorsque les reliefs rocheux sont ennoyés par des sédiments deltaïques, c'est le cas de la première zone, soit de larges interfluves rocheuses avec des dépôts meubles le long des principales vallées, c'est le cas de la deuxième zone.

La ligne de rivage est très échancrée et sans falaise; tout comme la haute-plage et l'estran, elle est rocheuse excepté les fonds de baies qui sont sablonneux. Ces dernières sont alimentées en sédiments par de nombreux deltas sous-aquatiques. Une plate-forme marine de 4 à 8 km de largeur est très disséquée, certainement rocheuse et reflète un relief émergé qui est commandé par des axes de fractures. Les côtes insulaires représentent toujours une longueur à peu près égale à celle des côtes de terre ferme.

La côte à rias (R)

Cet environnement (fig. 16.8), qui correspond à 28 pour cent de la Côte Nord (1466 km), est constitué des secteurs de Baie-Johan-Beetz (zone 13), l'Étamamiou (zone 19) et du Vieux-Fort (zone 24). La côte et l'arrière-côte sont rocheuses et de moins de 30 m d'énergie de relief excepté la zone du Vieux-Fort qui possède une énergie de relief de 30 à 75 m.

La ligne de rivage est très échancrée, sans falaise, excepté dans le secteur ouest de la zone du Vieux-Fort, et entièrement rocheuse sauf de très rares fonds de baies sablonneux. La haute-plage et l'estran sont rocheux aussi sauf quelques fonds de baies sablonneux qui sont alimentés par de petits deltas sous-aquatiques (fig. 16.8). Une plate-forme marine de 5 à 12 km de largeur en moyenne est très disséquée, certainement rocheuse et reflète un relief émergé commandé par de nombreux axes de fractures surtout dans les zones du Vieux Fort et d'Étamamiou. Dans ces zones d'ailleurs la longueur de côte insulaire surpasse parfois de beaucoup la longueur de côtes de terre ferme.

La côte fortement tectonisée (T)

Cet environnement (fig. 16.9), qui correspond à 23 pour cent de la Côte Nord (1180 km), est constitué des secteurs du Gros Mécatina (zone 21) et de Saint-Augustin (zone 22). La côte et l'arrière-côte sont entièrement rocheuses et l'énergie de leur relief est de 30 à 75 m excepté le secteur des basses-terres du Gros Mécatina à l'ouest de la zone 21. La ligne de rivage est généralement sans falaise et extrêmement échancrée souvent en de longs fjärds. Tout comme la haute-plage et l'estran, elle est entièrement rocheuse à part le delta de la Saint-Augustin dans un fond de baie. Le découpage de cette côte est fortement commandé par de grands axes de fractures ou de failles en tous sens (fig. 16.9) qui se prolongent sur une plate-forme marine de 2 à 4 km de largeur mais qui ressort au large dans le premier cas ou qui débute réellement devant une très forte densité de grandes îles dans le deuxième cas. Dans ces zones, la longueur de côtes insulaires est toujours plus du double de la longueur des côtes de terre ferme.

La côte accore rocheuse (A)

Cet environnement (fig. 16.10), qui correspond à 5 pour cent de la Côte Nord (284 km), est constitué des secteurs de Baie-Comeau/Godbout (zone 2), de l'archipel des Sept-Îles (zone 7), de Port-Saint-Servan (zone 23) et de la faille de Brador (zone 26). La côte et l'arrière-côte sont généralement rocheuses et de 30 à 75 m d'énergie de relief. La ligne de rivage est régulière (excepté quelques fjärds des zones de Baie-Comeau/Godbout mais principalement de Port-Saint-Servan), à falaise et rocheuse à part quelques petits deltas comme celui de la Godbout. La haute-plage et l'estran sont généralement rocheux aussi à part quelques secteurs de blocs locaux ou glaciels et de sable dérivés des petits deltas dans le secteur de Baie-Comeau/Godbout ainsi que quelques fonds de baies sableux dans les zones de l'archipel des Sept-Îles et de Port-Saint-Servan. Ce type de côte est sis sur un ou plusieurs axes de fractures ou de failles de sorte que leur plate-forme marine est très étroite (0,2 km en moyenne) si le graben est très abaissé, comme c'est le cas de la zone de Baie-Comeau/Godbout, ou assez large (4 à 6 km en moyenne) s'il n'est pas tellement abaissé, comme c'est le cas des zones de Port-Saint-Servan ou de la faille de Brador (fig. 16.10). Les îles sont à peu près inexistantes dans cet environnement.

La côte à cuestas (C)

Cet environnement (fig. 16.10), qui correspond aussi à 5 pour cent de la Côte Nord (290 km), est représenté par les deux seules zones de roches sédimentaires, l'archipel de Mingan (zone 12) et la région de Blanc-Sablon (zone 27). La côte et l'arrière-côte sont en majorité rocheuses et de moins de 30 m d'énergie de relief. La ligne de rivage est généralement régulière à part les zones de substratum précambrien qui apparaissent dans la zone de Blanc-Sablon (fig. 16.10). Elle est généralement à falaise sur le coté nord des îles de Mingan et dans la majorité de la zone de Blanc-Sablon à part les vastes estrans rocheux au sud des îles de la première zone (fig. 16.5) et les secteurs de baies dans les dépôts

meubles de la seconde zone. La ligne de rivage, de même que la haute-plage et l'estran, sont habituellement rocheux excepté les grandes baies sableuses de la zone de Blanc-Sablon, les plages graveleuses et à galets de l'île Nue de Mingan et de la Grande Île (archipel de Mingan) et les plages de blocs et de quartiers de roc basculés du nord des îles de Mingan. La plate-forme marine, qui poursuit le relief émergé sous l'eau, est de 4 à 5 km de largeur en moyenne, quoique dans la zone de cuestas typiques des îles de Mingan elle soit généralement de moins de quelques kilomètres de largeur au nord, dans ce secteur de front, et de 8 à 10 km de largeur au sud sur le revers formé de formations résistantes à pendage de 1,3 à 1,5 pour cent.

La relation entre les côtes insulaires et les côtes de terre ferme

D'une façon générale, la Côte Nord possède un peu plus de côtes insulaires (2812 km) que de côtes de terre ferme (2388 km). Ce fait, doublé des correspondances entre la dissection et l'énergie des reliefs terrestres et sous-marins en fait un exemple type de côtes ennoyées.

De plus, il y a une relation évidente entre l'augmentation de la longueur de côtes insulaires et l'augmentation de la dissection du relief ou de la largeur de la plate-forme marine, qui elle-même est fonction de la pente. A l'exception des côtes deltaïques et accores la plate-forme a toujours plus de 4 km de largeur en moyenne lorsque la longueur des côtes insulaires égale ou dépasse la longueur des

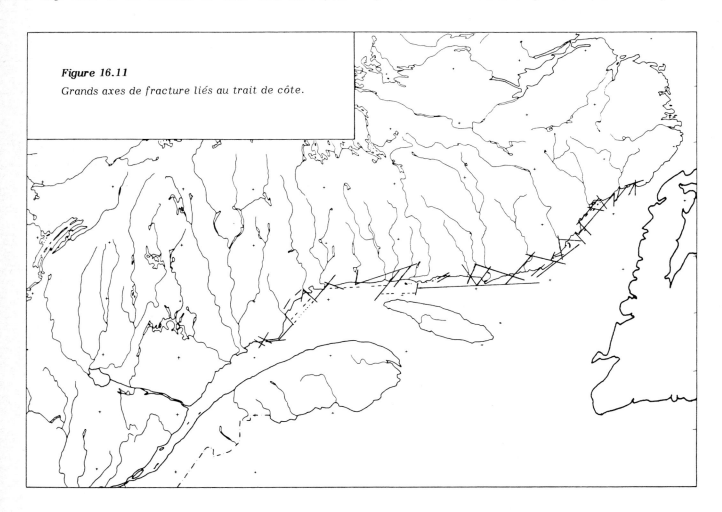

Figure 16.11
Grands axes de fracture liés au trait de côte.

côtes de terre ferme. Cette relation peut aller jusqu'à 5/1 dans le cas de plates-formes très larges comme celle de la zone de Nétagamiou - Petit Mécatina. On peut même établir des rapports significatifs croissants entre la longueur de côtes insulaires et la longueur des côtes de terre ferme pour les cinq principaux environnements côtiers où il y a présence d'îles. Pour les côtes à tombolos les îles forment habituellement moins de 25 pour cent de la longueur de côtes excepté dans le cas des zones plus évidemment tectonisées à l'est de Natashquan. Pour les côtes à écueils les îles forment environ 33 pour cent de la longueur de côtes tandis qu'elles forment la moitié des côtes à rias sableuses. Dans le cas des rias, où les fonds de baies ne sont pas comblés de sédiments, le pourcentage varie de 50 à 75 pour cent tandis que dans le cas des côtes fortement tectonisées la longueur des côtes insulaires dépasse les 75 pour cent.

La relation entre le trait de côte et la tectonique

Plusieurs chercheurs, dont plus récemment Kumarapeli et Saull (1966) et Lasserre (1973), en sont arrivés à la conclusion que la vallée du Saint-Laurent était fondamentalement un fossé d'effondrement à multiples phases de rejeu tectonique depuis le Précambrien; les phases d'érosion fluviales à l'origine des rivières de la Côte Nord entre la fin du Mésozoïque et du Cénozoïque (Jones, 1962) ainsi que les glaciers quaternaires n'auraient que modifié ce fossé.

Cette conception se trouve renforcée lorsque l'on compare la localisation et l'orientation des grands axes linéaires de faille ou tout au moins de fracture sur la Côte Nord (fig. 16.11). On s'aperçoit que de très grands axes de fracture commandent les grandes orientations de la côte et que des axes secondaires commandent pratiquement chaque grande échancrure principalement dans la zone fortement tectonisée à l'est de Natashquan.

La présence et la mobilité des sédiments sableux sur la côte

Origine des sédiments

La presque totalité des sédiments forment, ou sont dérivés des deltas post-glaciaires (fig. 16.12). Au fur et à mesure du relèvement isostatique les cours d'eau se sont incisés dans leur propre delta et ont en grande partie remobilisé ces sédiments pour les redéposer et faire ainsi progresser le delta. On s'aperçoit aussi que les plus grands deltas ont été formés à l'exutoire des plus grands bassins-versants, principalement ceux dont le cours d'eau présente moins de trappes à sédiments ou dont les trappes à sédiments sont éloignées du rivage; c'est le cas des rivières aux Outardes, Manicouagan, Moisie, Romaine, Natashquan et Gros Mécatina. Les zones de très petits bassins-versants ou de bassins dont les trappes à sédiments sont près de la côte présentent très peu de sédiments à la côte, comme c'est le cas de la côte à tombolos de Manitou-Magpie, et même pas du tout, comme c'est le cas de la côte à rias d'Étamamiou.

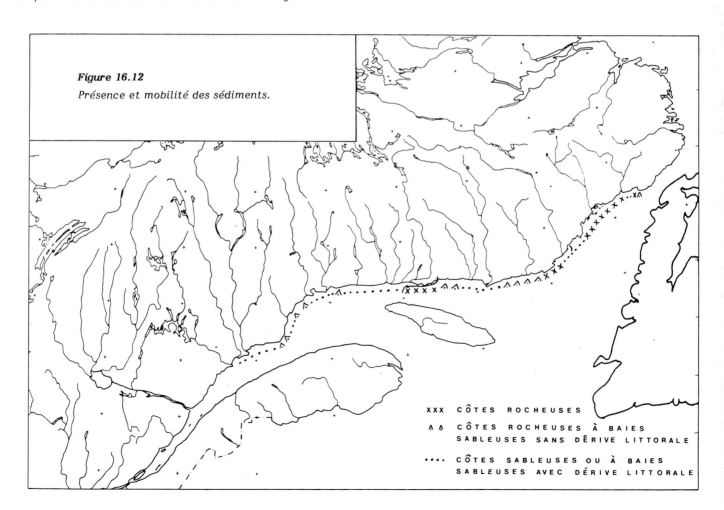

Figure 16.12
Présence et mobilité des sédiments.

XXX CÔTES ROCHEUSES

ΛΛ CÔTES ROCHEUSES À BAIES SABLEUSES SANS DÉRIVE LITTORALE

.... CÔTES SABLEUSES OU À BAIES SABLEUSES AVEC DÉRIVE LITTORALE

La deuxième plus grande source de sédiments, aussi représentée par des sédiments fluviaux, forme les deltas récents de fonds de baies souvent sous-aquatiques comme c'est le cas de la côte à rias sableuses de Gethsémani.

La troisième source de sédiments est l'érosion littorale des falaises de dépôts meubles, comme dans la région de Rivière-Saint-Jean, et des falaises rocheuses des cuestas (sédiments grossiers).

La quatrième source est représentée par les sédiments morainiques comme ceux de la moraine de Brador dans la zone de la baie du Milieu.

Enfin, l'apport éolien est quasi nul et il n'y a aucune preuve d'apport de sédiments venant de la plate-forme marine.

Répartition et mobilité des sédiments

Les côtes rocheuses (zones 7, 12, 19, 21, 22, 23, 24 et 26) ne présentent pratiquement pas de sédiments à la côte et, lorsqu'il y en a, ils sont confinés sur des îles ou au fond de profondes baies. Elles représentent 2608 km de longueur, soit exactement la moitié de la Côte Nord.

Sur les côtes rocheuses à baies sableuses (zones 3, 5, 8, 13, 18 et 28) les sédiments sont peu mobiles, même si leur quantité est relativement importante, puisque ces sédiments sont confinés dans des compartiments bordés de caps empêchant le transfert littoral. Elles représentent 1342 km de longueur, soit un peu plus du quart de la Côte Nord.

Il n'y a donc que le dernier quart de la Côte Nord qui soit affecté par les transferts de sédiments par dérive littorale, soit un total de 1250 km de côtes (zones 1, 2, 4, 6, 9, 10, 11, 14, 15, 16, 17, 20 et 25).

Les unités physiographiques des côtes affectées par la dérive littorale

La notion d'unité physiographique de côte a été définie par Mason (1950) comme étant "... a shore area so limited that the shore phenomena within the area are not affected by the physical condition in adjacent area." Cette notion, appliquée aux mouvements de sédiments, devient donc une unité de bilan sédimentologique quasi nul face aux unités avoisinantes et où il n'y a aucun apport étranger de sédiments littoraux et aucune sortie de sédiments, abstraction faite des mouvements internes des sédiments.

L'unité physiographique est donc principalement délimitée par des caps rocheux, de grandes zones de littoral rocheux et les secteurs d'eau très profonde comme les canyons où se perdent les sédiments. On peut ainsi établir une hiérarchie d'unités physiographiques allant des grandes unités très certaines aux petites qui sont plus contestables et qui sont souvent délimitées par des formes tels les tombolos (Dubois, 1973b).

Cette notion appliquée aux côtes sableuses ou à baies sableuses affectées par la dérive littorale donne le résultat qui suit, en ne tenant compte que des évidences géomorphologiques de dérive littorale: forme et orientation des flèches littorales et d'embouchures, déviation des embouchures des petits cours d'eau (Sunamura et Horikawa, 1971, 1972), présence et dissymétrie de tombolos, de pointes triangulaires, de zones importantes de courants de déchirure et de cordons pré-littoraux, ensablement des structures côtières, forme et courbure des fonds de baies, et enfin, sur le terrain, décroissance granulométrique (Sunamura et Horikawa, 1971, 1972).

La zone du delta Manicouagan - aux Outardes.
Les sédiments dérivés des deux rivières et aussi du ravinement et des glissements affectant le delta sont en majeure partie dispersés vers l'est et affectent le rivage de la baie des Anglais jusqu'à la pointe Saint-Pancrace. Une partie cependant est dirigée vers l'ouest à partir de la Pointe-aux-Outardes et affecte la côte jusqu'au cap de Papinachois.

La zone de Baie-Comeau/Godbout.
Trois unités physiographiques bien définies s'y dessinent. La première, qui comprend les deltas des rivières Mistassini et Franquelin, est affectée par une dérive littorale qui part du cap Saint-Nicolas à l'est et qui affecte le rivage jusqu'à la pointe Mistassini à l'ouest. La deuxième, qui comprend les sédiments de la baie Saint-Nicolas et ceux de l'ancien delta de la Godbout, est affectée par le dérive littorale qui part du cap Saint-Nicolas à l'ouest et qui affecte le rivage jusqu'au cap Rouge à l'est. La troisième, qui est essentiellement formée du delta de la rivière Godbout, est affectée par une dérive convergente vers l'embouchure de la Godbout à partir du cap Rouge à l'ouest et du cap du ruisseau Blanc à l'est.

La zone de Pointe-aux-Anglais.
Cette zone doit être prise à priori comme une seule unité physiographique bornée au sud par la pointe aux Morts et au nord par la pointe Sproule. Apportés par les rivières et les ruisseaux, comme en témoignent plusieurs petits deltas sous-aquatiques, les sédiments sont dispersés entre ces deux caps par une dérive convergente vers l'embouchure de la rivière du Calumet, où les sédiments semblent se perdre vers le large, et par une dérive divergente entre l'île aux Oeufs et la Pentecôte à cause de fronts de vagues divergentes. On se retrouve donc avec une possibilité de trois unités physiographiques à la limite.

La zone des deltas Moisie/Sainte-Marguerite.
Cette zone peut être divisée en deux unités physiographiques bien délimitées. La première est celle du delta de la Moisie entre la côte rocheuse de Matamek et la pointe Noire et dont les sédiments, qui proviennent presque tous de la Moisie, sont affectés par une dérive littorale vers l'ouest jusque dans la baie des Sept-Îles. Cependant une zone de courants de déchirure transfère les sédiments vers le large à Maliotenam. L'étude de Moign (1972), au moyen de traceurs fluorescents, vient confirmer ces observations. De plus, Thom et Moign (1970), avaient déjà émis l'hypothèse de cette dérive vers l'ouest de même que Laverdière (1954) qui avait remarqué l'ensablement du vieux quai des Sept-Îles vers l'est et l'érosion de la plage vers l'ouest. La deuxième est celle du delta de la Sainte-Marguerite où une dérive venant de la pointe Sainte-Marguerite à l'ouest et de la pointe Noire à l'est converge vers le centre de la baie pour former une pointe triangulaire qui indique qu'à cet endroit les sédiments se dirigent vers le large comme en témoignent d'ailleurs les courbes bathymétriques.

La zone de Manitou-Magpie.
Cette vaste zone de rivage quasi rectiligne et faiblement échancrée peut être divisée en 12 petites unités physiographiques. La première, essentiellement composée de plages de blocs et qui comprend le delta de la rivière au Bouleau, semble être affectée d'une dérive littorale vers l'ouest du rivage rocheux des Mornes Rouges à l'est au cap du Cormoran à l'ouest. La deuxième unité, composée de plusieurs plages, est probablement affectée par une dérive convergente à partir des Mornes Rouges à l'ouest et de la pointe à Canot (Buchan Point) à l'est. La troisième unité est affectée d'une dérive vers l'est de la pointe à Canot à la pointe de l'anse à Bibi. La quatrième unité, composée du delta de la Manitou, est affectée par une dérive convergente entre la pointe de l'anse à Bibi et la Tête de Manitou avec une prédominance vers

l'est. La dérive de la cinquième unité est difficile à déterminer entre la Tête de Manitou et le cap de l'anse à l'Ours à cause du morcellement du trait de côte mais la déviation de l'embouchure de petits cours d'eau indique une prédominance vers l'ouest; l'érosion des falaises de dépôts meubles alimente cette dérive. Dans la sixième unité, entre le cap de l'anse à l'Ours et la pointe à la Baleine et la septième unité, entre la pointe à la Baleine et la Tête de Sheldrake, des dérives convergentes sont suggérées par la déviation des embouchures de cours d'eau ainsi que par l'orientation de la flèche d'embouchure de la Sheldrake. Dans la huitième unité, entre la Tête de Sheldrake et la pointe Couture, la flèche d'embouchure de la Couture suggère une dérive vers l'est tandis que la neuvième unité, entre la pointe Couture et le cap de la rivière Moiac, est affectée d'une dérive vers l'ouest suggérée par une décroissance granulométrique des matériaux de plage et la déviation d'une embouchure de cours d'eau. La dixième unité, composée du delta de la rivière au Tonnerre, entre le cap de la Moiac et la pointe au Tonnerre, est affectée d'une dérive vers l'est suggérée par une décroissance granulométrique des matériaux de plage et la sédimentation à l'ouest du quai de Rivière-au-Tonnerre. La onzième unité, entre la pointe au Tonnerre et Ridge Point - Est, et la douzième unité, entre Ridge Point - Est et la pointe de Magpie, sont toutes deux affectées d'une dérive vers l'ouest suggérée par la déviation des embouchures de petits cours d'eau.

Les zones des deltas Magpie/Saint-Jean/Mingan et Romaine. Ces deux zones peuvent difficilement être traitées séparément et on peut y distinguer 6 grandes unités. Une première grande unité physiographique, comprenant les deltas de la Magpie, de la Saint-Jean, de la Mingan et l'embouchure de la Romaine, est délimitée à l'ouest par la pointe de Magpie et à l'est par la pointe aux Morts; les dérives littorales y sont généralisées vers l'est, quoique plusieurs sous-unités peuvent être délimitées à partir de fronts de vagues divergentes et de zones de pertes de sédiments vers le large. Les principales sources de sédiments sont les rivières, l'érosion des falaises de sédiments meubles et les glissements de terrain de Magpie jusque vers 5 km à l'est de la Saint-Jean. La deuxième unité physiographique, probablement affectée par une dérive littorale vers l'ouest, est délimitée par la pointe aux Morts à l'ouest et la pointe à l'Eau Claire à l'est. La troisième unité, qui semble affectée par une dérive littorale vers l'ouest aussi, est délimitée par la pointe à l'Eau Claire à l'ouest et Ragg Point à l'est. La quatrième, cinquième et sixième unité sont formées des baies Ragg, Betchouane et Saint-Laurent, séparées de l'ouest à l'est par la pointe Ragg, la pointe Betchouane, la Tête de Perdrix et Indian Point. La dérive littorale semble être vers l'ouest dans les trois cas.

La zone du delta Nabisipi-Aguanus. Cette zone peut être subdivisée en deux unités à partir de la pointe Nabisipi. Une dérive littorale vers l'ouest affecte une première unité jusqu'à la pointe Pashashibou tandis qu'une dérive vers l'est affecte une deuxième unité jusqu'au cap à l'ouest de la baie Washtawouka; une dérive secondaire vers l'ouest affecte cependant la partie ouest de la deuxième unité.

La zone à rias sableuses de Natashquan. Cette zone de baies en partie remblayées ou à deltas sous-aquatiques relativement étendus est affectée par une dérive littorale complexe à cause de l'interférence des nombreuses îles.

Les zones du delta de la Natashquan et de Kégashka. Ces deux zones peuvent être subdivisées en trois unités. La première comprend le delta de la Natashquan entre la pointe Noire et le cap à l'ouest de l'embouchure de la Kégashka. La dérive littorale est convergente vers l'embouchure de la rivière et aussi vers la pointe de Natashquan, tandis qu'une autre

dérive littorale vers l'est transporte les sédiments vers la Kégashka. La flèche d'embouchure de la Natashquan aurait peut être commencé à se former vers 1900 et elle se serait allongée de 90 m par année selon Welsted (1960). De plus, il semblerait qu'il y aurait eu un changement dans les dérives littorales il y a une centaine d'années. En effet, Dumont (1952), rapporte qu'aux dires des pêcheurs de la région, l'île Sainte-Hélène, à l'embouchure de la rivière, faisait partie d'une flèche qui progressait vers l'est et qui était rattachée à la rive nord vers 1875; ceci est confirmé par Welsted (1960), qui y a remarqué les mêmes levées de plages que sur la rive nord.

La deuxième unité semble être affectée par une dérive qui part du cap de la rivière Kégashka à l'ouest et se dirige vers la pointe de Kégashka à l'est. La troisième unité semble être affectée par une dérive qui part de la Curlew Point à l'est vers la pointe de Kégashka à l'ouest.

La zone du delta Nétagamiou - Petit Mécatina. Cette zone peut à peine se subdiviser en deux unités physiographiques à cause de l'ampleur des deltas sous-aquatiques dont le principal est celui du Petit Mécatina. La première unité est limitée de part et d'autre de l'embouchure de la Nétagamiou; la dérive littorale est convergente vers l'embouchure comme en témoignent les flèches orientées vers le large. La deuxième vaste unité est délimitée à l'ouest par le cap à l'est de la Nétagamiou et le cap de l'île du Grand Rigolet à l'est. La dérive littorale y est complexe à cause de l'interférence de nombreuses îles.

La zone de la baie du Milieu. Outre l'île de la Demoiselle et la baie au Saumon qui forment en soi chacune une unité physiographique, le reste de la zone, entre le cap de Baie-au-Saumon et la vaste zone rocheuse de la faille de Brador, peut difficilement être subdivisé en plus de deux unités de part et d'autre de la pointe Blanche. La dérive littorale y est complexe.

CONCLUSION

Dans un premier temps, cette méthode montre que même si environ le dixième de la Côte Nord a été visité, il est possible, principalement par photo-interprétation, d'en tirer assez d'éléments géomorphologiques pour classifier adéquatement les neuf autres dixièmes de la zone côtière.

Dans un deuxième temps, les travaux de terrain entrepris sur le vingtième du territoire, permettent d'acquérir assez de connaissances sur les formes associées aux dérives littorales pour pouvoir délimiter de grandes unités physiographiques de côte et diagnostiquer les grands mouvements des sédiments.

Il est évident que dans le détail, ou pour implanter des aménagements côtiers, des études de dérive par traceurs combinées à des études de l'hydrodynamique et des patrons de réfraction sont nécessaires. Cependant notre méthode permet non seulement de cerner les problèmes mais aussi de délimiter les grandes zones d'influence.

Une prochaine étape de cette étude consistera à l'examen de diverses séquences de photographies aériennes entre 1930 et 1976 dans le but de montrer les variations récentes des côtes sableuses.

Remerciements

Le début de ces travaux a été financé en 1972 et 1973 par le Ministère des Travaux publics du Canada dans le cadre de l'Étude des Rives du Saint-Laurent et, de 1974 à 1977, la Commission géologique du Canada et la Woods Hole Oceanographic Institution ont défrayé les coûts de l'étude intensive de la Moyenne Côte Nord. Je remercie les étudiants gradués de Sherbrooke pour leur aide précieuse sur le terrain et spécialement Guy Desmarais dans le région de Baie-Comeau à pointe des Monts.

Références

Bassaget, J.P.
1970: Géologie de la région de Natashquan, comté de Duplessis; Ministère des Richesses Naturelles du Québec, R.P.-582, 14 p., Carte 1712, 1 mi/po.

Biggar, H.P.
1924: The voyages of Jacques Cartier. F.A. Acland, imprimeur au roi, Ottawa; les Archives publiques du Canada, Publication n⁰ 11, 330 p.

Boorne, J.
1978: Communication orale sur les travaux de cartographie géologique des cartes 12J et 12K; Commission géologique du Canada, Ottawa.

Bostock, H.S.
1970: Subdivisions physiographiques du Canada; dans Géologie et ressources minérales du Canada, Commission géologique du Canada, R.J.W. Douglas, réd.; Série de la géologie économique, n⁰ 1, carte 1254A.

Bussières, P.
1962: Aspects de géographie de la Côte Nord et de son arrière-pays; thèse de D.E.S., Université Laval, 365 p.

Claveau, J.
1950: North Shore of the Saint-Lawrence from Aguanish to Washicoutai Bay, Saguenay County; Ministère des Richesses Naturelles du Québec, Geol. Rept. 43, 40 p., Carte 819, 1 mi/po.

Conlon, R.J.
1966: Landslide on the Toulnustouc river, Quebec. Canadian Journal of Sciences, v. 3, n⁰ 3, p. 113 - 144.

Cooper, G.E.
1951: Preliminary report on Johan Beetz Area (Eastern half), Drucourt and Johan Beetz Townships, Saguenay County; Ministère des Mines du Québec, R.P.-263, 8 p., Carte 935, 1 mi/po.

Davies, R.
1963: Geology of the St. Augustin Area, Duplessis County; Ministère des Richesses Naturelles du Québec, R.P.-506, 9 p., Carte 1506, 1 mi/po.
1965: Geology of Baie-des-Moutons Area, Duplessis County; Ministère des Richesses Naturelles du Québec, R.P.-543, 13 p., Carte 1594, 1 mi/po.

De Boutray, B., and Hillaire-Marcel, C.
1977: Aperçu géologique du substratum et des dépôts meubles dans la région de Blanc-Sablon, Québec; Géographie Physique et Quaternaire, v. 31, n⁰ 3, 4, p. 207 - 215.

Dépatie, J.
1967: Géologie de la région du lac de l'Ours, comté de Duplessis; Ministère des Richesses Naturelles du Québec, R.P.-559, 13 p., Carte 1644, 1 mi/po.

De Roquefeuil, R.
1965: Rapport sur un déménagement éventuel du village de Moisie, comté de Duplessis; ARDA-Québec, 17 p.

Desmarais, G.
1976: Contribution à l'étude du Quaternaire de la Haute Côte Nord du St-Laurent: cartographie géomorphologique de la zone côtière entre Papinachois et Pointe-des-Monts, comté de Saguenay; mem. de B.A., Département de géographie, Université de Sherbrooke, 48 p., cartes au 1:50,000.

Dionne, J.C.
1970: Cartes morpho-sédimentologiques de la région de Saguenay/Lac-Saint-Jean, Québec; Environnement Canada, Directoire genéral de terres, 52 cartes au 1:50,000.

Dredge, L.A.
1971: Late Quaternary sedimentary environments, Sept-Iles, Québec; thèse de M. Sc., Département de géographie, Université de McGill, 102 p.
1976: Quaternary geomorphology of the Quebec North Shore, Godbout to Sept-Iles; thèse de Ph. D., University of Waterloo, 268 p.

Dubois, J.M.M.
1973a: Essai de classification de la zone côtière et d'identification d'unités physiographiques sur la Côte Nord du Saint-Laurent; Pointe-des-Monts à Blanc-Sablon; Ministère des Travaux publics du Canada, Étude des Rives du Saint-Laurent, 71 p., cartes au 1:1,000,000 et 1:250,000.
1973b: Essai de classification géomorphologique d'une côte en vue d'une utilisation en génie côtier; Bulletin de Recherche, n⁰10, Département de Géographie, Université de Sherbrooke, 96 p., cartes au 1:1,000,000 et 1:250,000.
1977: La déglaciation de la Côte Nord du Saint-Laurent: analyse sommaire; Géographie physique et Quaternaire, v. 31, n⁰ 3,4, p. 229 - 246.
1980: Environnements quaternaires et évolution post-glaciaire d'une zone côtière en émersion en bordure sud du Bouclier Canadien: la Moyenne Côte Nord du Saint-Laurent, Québec; thèse de Ph. D., Département de géographie et d'aménagement régional, Université d'Ottawa, 754 p.

Dumont, B.
1952: Etude agrologique du littoral de la Côte Nord; Ministère de Colonisation du Québec, rapport non publié, 115 p.

Faessler, C.
1942: La Côte Nord du Saint-Laurent de Bersimis à Matamec; Naturaliste Canadien, v. 69, p. 39 - 71.

Franconi, A., Sharma, K.N.M. et Laurin, A.F.
1975: Région des rivières Betsiamites (Bersimis) et Moisie (Grenville 1968-1969); Ministère des Richesses Naturelles du Québec, R.G.-162, 149 p., cartes au 1:250,000.

Grant, D.R.
1969a: Surficial deposits, geomorphic features and Late Quaternary history of the terminus of the northern peninsula of Newfoundland and adjacent Quebec-Labrador; Maritime Sediments, v. 5, n⁰ 3, p. 123 - 125.
1969b: Late Pleistocene re-advance of Piedmont glaciers in western Newfoundland; Maritime Sediments, v. 5, n⁰ 3, p. 126 - 128.

Grant, D.R. (cont.)
1977: Glacial style and ice limits, the Quaternary stratigraphic record, and changes of land and ocean level in the Atlantic provinces, Canada; Geographie physique et Quaternaire, v. 31, n⁰ 3, 4, p. 247 - 260.

Grenier, P.E.
1957: Région du lac Beetz, district électoral de Saguenay; Ministère des Mines du Québec, R.G.-73, 88 p., Carte 1100, 1 mi/po.

Haworth, R.T. et Sanford, B.V.
1976: Paleozoic geology of northeast gulf of St. Lawrence; Commission géologique du Canada, Étude 76-1A, p. 1 - 6.

Hind, H.Y.
1864: Observations on supposed glacial drift in the Labrador Peninsula, Eastern Canada, and on the South Branch of the Saskatchewan; Canadian Naturalist, v. 1, p. 300 - 304.

Jones, I.W.
1962: Un aperçu de la géologie de la province de Québec; Ministère des Richesses Naturelles, Québec, Rapport S-6, 13 p.

Kumarapeli, P.S. et Saull, V.A.
1966: The St. Lawrence Valley System: A North American equivalent of the East African Rift Valley System; Canadian Journal of Earth Sciences, v. 3, pg. 639 - 657.

Landry, B.
1975: La Minganie; Collège de Sherbrooke, rapp. prés. à l'Office de Planification et de Développement du Québec, 23 p.

Lasserre, J.C.
1973: Pour une définition géomorphologique et structurale de la vallée du Saint-Laurent; Revue de géographie de Montréal, v. 27, n⁰ 4, p. 381 - 390.

Laverdière, C.
1954: La région de Sept-Îles, Côte Nord du Saint-Laurent; étude morphologique; thèse de M.A., Université de Montréal, 194 p.

Lévesque, R.
1976: Cadre géographique des gisements archéologiques de la région de Blanc-Sablon; thèse de M.A., Département de géographie, Université de Sherbrooke, 213 p.

Loring, D.H. and Nota, D.J.G.
1973: Morphology and sediments of the gulf of St. Lawrence; Environnement Canada, Bulletin de l'office de recherche des pêches du Canada, n⁰ 182, 147 p.

Low, A.P.
1897: Rapport sur des explorations faites dans la péninsule du Labrador le long de la Grande-Rivière de l'Est, des rivières Koksoak, Hamilton, Manicouagan et de parties d'autres rivières; Commission géologiques du Canada, Rapport annuel, nouvelle série 1895, partie L, p. 1 - 356.

Mason, M.A.
1950: Geology in shore-control problems; dans Applied sedimentation, P.D. Trask, réd.; Wiley, New York, p. 276 - 290.

Ministère des Travaux publics du Canada
1972: Morphologie-Sédimentologie, Baie des Sept-Îles, Qué., comté de Manicouagan. Étude des Rives du St-Laurent; Cartes 1:20,000.
1973: Morpho-sédimentologie; basse Côte Nord du St-Laurent. Etude des Rives du St-Laurent; 44 p., cartes au 1:20,000.

Moign, Y.
1972: Étude dynamique d'une plage subarctique: Sept-Iles (province de Québec); thèse de doctorat, 3e cycle, Université de Bretagne Occidentale, 318 p.

Ploeg, J.
1971: Wave Climate Study, Great Lakes and Gulf of St. Lawrence; Conseil national de recherches au Canada, Mech. Eng. Rept. MH-107A, 2 vol. (CNR n⁰ 11996-97), 155 p. et 253 p.

Robitaille, B.
1954: Les îles Mingan; Publications de l'Institute d'Histoire et Géographie, Université Laval, Québec, Notes de géographie, n⁰ 6, 9 p., carte 1:506,880.

Sharma, K.N.M. et Franconi, A.
1975: Région des rivières Magpie, Saint-Jean, Romaine (Grenville 1970); Ministère des Richesses Naturelles du Québec, R.G.-163, 70 p., cartes au 1:250,000.

Stockwell, C.H., McGlynn, J.C., et al.
1970: Géologie du Bouclier canadien; dans Géologie et ressources minérales du Canada, R.J.W. Douglas, réd.; Commission géologique du Canada, Serie de la géologie économique, n⁰1.

Sunamura, T. et Horikawa, K.
1971: Predominant direction of littoral transport along Kujyukuri beach, Japan; Coastal Engineering in Japan, v. 14, p. 107 - 117.
1972: Improved method for inferring the direction of littoral drift from grain size properties of beach sands; Annual Report of the Engineering Research Institute, Faculty of Engineering, Tokyo, v. 31, p. 61 - 68.

Thom, B. et Moign, T.
1970: Beach erosion, morphology and current study at Sept-Îles; Iron Ore Company, Geotechnical Engineering Project no. B, 16 p.

Towsend, C.W.
1913: A short trip into the Labrador peninsula by way of the Natashquan river; Bulletin of the Philadelphia Geographical Society, p. 170 - 182.

Tremblay, G.
1975: Géologie du Quaternaire; région de Sept-Iles/ Port-Cartier, rapport intérimaire; Ministère des Richesses Naturelles du Québec, rapport DP-304, 43 p.

Trites, R.W.
  1971: The Gulf as a physical oceanographic system; dans 2nd Gulf of St. Lawrence Workshop, Bedford Institute of Oceanography, Darmouth, N.S., nov. 30 - déc. 3, 1970, p. 32 - 63.

Twenhofel, W.H.
  1938: Geology and paleontology of the Mingan Islands, Québec; Geological Society of America, Special Paper n⁰ 11, 132 p.

Twenhofel, W.H. et Conine, W.H.
  1921: The post glacial terraces of Anticosti Island; American Journal of Science, 5ème ser., v. 1., n⁰ 3, p. 268 - 278.

Welsted, J.
  1960: The physiography and evolution of the Natashquan Terrace; thèse M.Sc., Université McGill, 101 p.

Wynne-Edwards, H.R.
  1972: The Grenville Province; dans Variations in tectonic styles in Canada, R.A. Price and J.W. Douglas, réd., Geological Association of Canada, Special Paper n⁰ 11, p. 264 - 334.

17.

COASTAL ENVIRONMENTS ALONG THE NORTHERN SHORE
OF SOMERSET ISLAND, DISTRICT OF FRANKLIN

R.B. Taylor
Atlantic Geoscience Centre, Geological Survey of Canada, Dartmouth, Nova Scotia

Taylor, R.B., Coastal environments along the northern shore of Somerset Island, District of Franklin; in The Coastline of Canada, S.B. McCann, editor; Geological Survey of Canada, Paper 80-10, p. 239-250, 1980.

Abstract

The shores of northern Somerset Island are representative of many coasts in the east-central part of the Canadian Arctic Archipelago. Six coastal environments were distinguished along northern Somerset Island: 1) high rock cliff, 2) low rocky shore with pocket beaches, 3) gravel beach, 4) sand and gravel plain, 5) deltaic, and 6) estuarine. The first four environments were differentiated using morphologic and sedimentologic characteristics which were closely related to the underlying bedrock. The last two environments were differentiated on the basis of processes.

Wide variations in the effects of sea ice and waves on shoreline stability were indicated by observations of coastal processes, both seasonally and geographically, during 1972-1976. Only during 1974 was the shoreline significantly changed by waves. Geographically, the shores west of Cape Rennell were affected more by sea ice whereas the shores farther east were affected by higher energy waves. Beach change was greatest, hence beach stability least, between Cunningham Inlet and Garnier Bay and along the more exposed capes along northwestern Somerset Island.

Résumé

Les côtes de la partie nord de l'île de Somerset sont typiques de nombreuses côtes dans la partie centre-est de l'archipel Arctique canadien. Six milieux côtiers ont été déterminés le long de la partie nord de l'île de Somerset: 1) de hautes falaises rocheuses, 2) une côte basse et rocheuses ponctuée de plages minuscules, 3) une grève, 4) une plaine de sable et de gravier, 5) un delta et 6) un milieu estuarien. Les quatre premiers milieux ont été déterminés en faisant appel à des caractéristiques morphologiques et sédimentologiques étroitement liées au substrat rocheux. La distinction entre les deux derniers milieux repose sur l'existence de processus littoraux.

De grands écarts entre les effets de la glace de mer et les vagues sur la stabilité du littoral ont été révélés par l'observation des processus littoraux, tant saisonniers que géographiques, de 1972 à 1976. Ce n'est qu'au cours de l'année 1974 que le littoral a subi de façon marquée l'effet des vagues. Sur le plan géographique, les côtes situées à l'ouest du cap Rennell ont été davantage affectées par la glace de mer tandis que les côtes plus à l'est étaient affectées par des vagues de plus haute énergie. C'est la plage qui a le plus évolué, par conséquent c'est aussi elle qui a connu la plus faible stabilité, entre l'inlet Cunningham et la baie Garnier ainsi que le long des caps les plus exposés en bordure nord-ouest de l'île de Somerset.

INTRODUCTION

Northern Somerset Island is fringed by shores that are representative of many coasts in the east-central part of the Arctic Archipelago. The diversity of shoreline morphology was one reason for its selection as a study area. During the summers of 1974 to 1976, 335 km of shoreline was examined between M'Clure Bay and Cape Admiral M'Clintock (Figs. 17.1, 17.2). However, because of logistics, only the shoreline between Pressure Point and Garnier Bay (167 km) was studied in detail and monitored for changes over the three seasons.

In this paper the coastal environments along northern Somerset Island are described and differentiated on the basis of variations in shore morphology, beach sediments and processes. Furthermore the geographical and seasonal variation in the effects of sea ice and waves on shoreline stability are discussed.

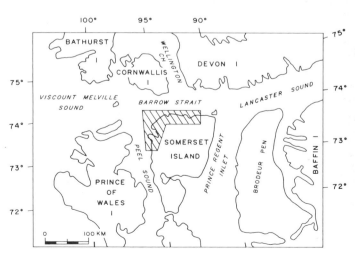

Figure 17.1. Location map of the study area.

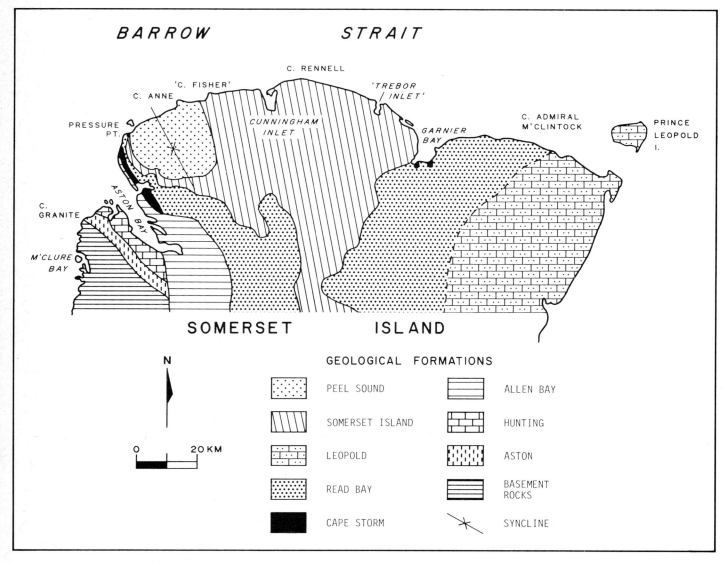

Figure 17.2. *Geological sketch map of northern Somerset Island (after Jones and Dixon, 1977 and Miall et al., 1978).*

PHYSICAL SETTING

The northern coast of Somerset Island, at 74°N latitude, is part of the high latitude - low wave energy environment of the Canadian Arctic Archipelago. There are less than 60 frost-free days each year (Canadian Hydrographic Service, 1976). The shore is protected from waves for ten months of the year by shorefast ice and/or sea ice and the subaerial beach is underlain by continuous permafrost. Only locally generated wind waves affect the study area, as wave fetch between the central Arctic Islands is short. The tides are mixed semidiurnal and have a mean range of 1.2 m at Cunningham Inlet. The shores of Somerset Island have been emerging because of postglacial crustal rebound and are characterized by well developed sequences of raised beaches. Field observations indicated the marine limit on northwestern Somerset Island is close to 120 m above sea level. At Cunningham Inlet the rate of shoreline emergence, based on ^{14}C dating of driftwood samples, averaged 0.37 cm per year during the past 5000 years. The uplift curves also indicated a decrease in shoreline emergence to the present.

GEOLOGY

Basement rocks of granite and gneiss are exposed along the western side and northwestern corner of Somerset Island. Flanking these rocks are the oldest cover rocks of Somerset Island. They are composed of well cemented quartz sandstone and dolostone of the Aston and Hunting formations (Jones and Dixon, 1977). The northern part of the island is predominantly underlain by near-horizontal Silurian limestone and dolostone. These carbonate rocks have been mapped as four formations, the Cape Storm (Kerr 1975), the Read Bay (McMillan, 1963), the Leopold (Jones and Dixon, 1975) and the Somerset Island (Miall et al., 1978) (Fig. 17.2). The youngest rocks, which are composed of distinct redbeds of sandstone, siltstone and conglomerate, are exposed in the Cape Anne syncline located between Cape Anne and Pressure Point. The types of shore morphology which have evolved and the abundance of sediment which is available for beach development are partly a reflection of differences in the underlying bedrock and its resistance to erosion.

Because of the absence of surficial glacial deposits, the beaches of Somerset Island are composed of only thin deposits of locally derived sediments overlying a bedrock surface. Thus, the slope of the beaches closely reflects the inherent slope of the underlying bedrock. In several areas the differential erosion of the horizontal beds of limestone and dolostone has resulted in the formation of marine benches.

COASTAL ENVIRONMENTS

The beaches of northern Somerset Island fringe an extensive upland that exists across most of the island. The upland rises to elevations of 150 m adjacent to the coast and 400 m in the interior. Depending on the proximity of the upland, the beaches extend from 0.1 km to 4 km inland (Fig. 17.3). The widest extension of beach occurs in two lowlands, one to the west of Garnier Bay, the other to the west of Cape Anne.

Six coastal environments were distinguished along northern Somerset Island. Five are described in this paper and the sixth, the Cunningham Inlet estuary, was described by Morison and Taylor (1978). The coastline was divided into:

High rock cliff
Low rock shores with pocket beaches
Sand and gravel plain
Gravel beach
    (a) beaches backed by a rising backshore (e.g., other raised beaches)
    (b) beach accumulation forms (e.g., barrier beaches and spits backed by a variable width of water)
Deltas
Estuaries

The first four environments were differentiated using morphological and sedimentological characteristics (Tables 17.1, 17.2) and the last two were differentiated using processes. River deltas can occur within one or more of the first four coastal environments. Each of the coastal environments is located and illustrated in Figures 17.4 and 17.5.

High rock cliffs

Only 5 km (3%) of the study area is composed of high cliffs. The cliffed shores are longest at Pressure Point and just west of 'Trebor Inlet'. (Trebor Inlet, Cape Fisher, Staples, Rennell and Cunningham beaches are unofficial place names.) These shores are similar to much of the southwestern coast of Devon Island, eastern Somerset Island and Brodeur Peninsula, Baffin Island. Cape Rennell, Somerset Island, is somewhat different from the rest of the high cliffed shores because it has a slope of only 7° to 13° and is composed of unconsolidated marine sediments over bedrock (Fig. 17.6). Shorefast ice and a semipermanent snow patch have preserved the vertical slope at the base of the cape but the upper slope has experienced severe gully erosion by spring meltwater.

Low rock shores with pocket beaches

Low rocky shores occupy the northwest corner of Somerset Island. North of M'Clure Bay the shores are underlain by granites whereas farther south the bedrock changes to gneiss and the coastal relief increases. Beach sediments are scarce because of the resistant nature of the bedrock. Narrow, discontinuous beaches and poorly developed beach features have been formed between the numerous rock outcrops. Only in the larger embayments, where additional sediment is supplied by streams, are the beaches larger. Apart from the boulders that are scattered across the pocket beaches the beach sediment is a uniform gravel size with little or no sand. The sediment is moderately well sorted and angular to subangular in shape. Most of the sediment is locally derived. Rock type and the irregular coastal morphology were the prime criteria for differentiating this environment.

Sand and gravel plain

The extensive sand and gravel plain to the west of Cape Anne corresponds to the syncline filled with younger, less resistant clastic rocks of the Peel Sound Formation. This beach environment is found along 9 km (5.4%) of the shoreline studied and it is very similar to the low-lying shores of western Bathurst Island. There are well developed beaches but no well preserved beach ridges because of dissection by rill wash and streams. This was the only coastal area along northern Somerset Island with large proportions of sand. On the raised beaches there was an average of 40 per cent sand but on the modern beach there was over 90 per cent, except for the occasional layer of gravel exposed between shifting sand bars. The raised beach sediments had a very distinct bimodal distribution, with modal classes between -4 and -5 phi and +1 and +2 phi. The gravel on the raised beach ridges was transported up and over the berm crest by higher energy waves during storms.

Figure 17.3 -

The upland surface (150 m elevation) and gravel beaches just west of Cunningham Inlet. The upper raised beaches are covered by talus or periglacial slope deposits. (GSC-165034)

Table 17.1. Shore morphology, Somerset Island, District of Franklin

1.	High rock cliff	Vertical scarps over 150 m elevation, fringed by a narrow beach less than 100 m wide and/or debris slopes; occasional shear rock face; nearshore marine bench less than a few hundred metres wide; bedrock is interbedded limestone and dolostone.
2.	Low rock shores with pocket beaches	Irregular plan and cross-sectional profile; coastal relief less than 150 m; poorly developed narrow beaches less than 500 m long; small wave-built features; nearshore of bedrock, boulders and pebbles; rock outcrops exposed at low tide; bedrock is granite.
3.	Sand and gravel plain	4 km wide lowland with slope less than 3º and relief less than 33 m; well developed beaches; beach low, berm less than 1.5 m high and foreshore slope less than 5º; wide shallow intertidal zone of 23 to 75 m (Fig. 7); bedrock is sandstone, siltstone and conglomerate.
4.	Gravel beaches	Beach zone 0.1 to 4 km wide depending on proximity of upland; bedrock mainly limestone and some dolostone.
	(a) Beaches with sloping backshore.	Steplike profile of well developed raised beaches to 90 m elevation; beach foreshore slopes average 7º ± 5º, width of intertidal 3 to 19 m (Fig. 17.7); nearshore slopes reflect slope of subaerial beach 2º to 6º; nearshore bottom composed of bedrock, boulders, cobbles and thin layer of marine silt.
	(b) Beach accumulation forms	Beaches backed by lagoons or ponds of variable dimension; barrier beaches 28 to 72 m wide, beach height to 1.1 to 2.8 m above MHTL; overwash deposits across backshore; flat nearshore bench up to 1 km wide.
5.	Deltas	Arcuate in form, braided drainage with shifting channels; margin of delta composed of cuspate spits and wave-built beach ridges; low relief backshore characterized by overwash, shore ice piles and ice push features.
6.	Estuary -- Cunningham Inlet	Semienclosed basin 7.5 km long and 5.1 at widest point; partly divided 6 - 9 m deep entrance channel, maximum depth within inlet 42 m basin dominated by Cunningham River and several smaller streams; characteristics of arctic estuary because of variable fluvial discharge resulting from limited source water, i.e., snowmelt; shores affected by locally generated waves within inlet.

The gravel originated from bedrock outcrops at the edge of the plain and from farther inland. Each spring considerable sand and gravel was dumped onto the shorefast ice and later added to the intertidal zone when the ice melted. The sand and gravel plain was differentiated on the basis of the low, flat relief and the large proportion of beach sand.

Gravel beach environment

Gravel beaches, backed by well developed sequences of raised beach ridges, are the most common shore morphology observed in the central Arctic Islands. On northern Somerset Island 141 km (84.4%) of the study area was mapped as gravel beach.

The raised beach ridges are a series of storm ridges built as the shoreline emerged. They were best developed across inherent topographic slopes of 2.5º to 5º but were also found across steeper slopes. The steeper the inherent slope the closer together were the ridges. Beach ridges at the base of the upland were often reworked by periglacial processes or covered by slope debris (Fig. 17.3).

An examination of the backshore and nearshore morphology of the present shoreline suggested that two different gravel beach environments have developed. Three quarters of the gravel beaches are immediately backed by a rising backshore of raised beach ridges. These beaches are fronted by a sloping nearshore. The other quarter of the beaches is made up of spits, tombolos and barrier beaches backed by lagoons or tundra ponds of various dimensions (Figs. 17.5, 17.7). The formation of beach accumulation forms, along certain areas of northern Somerset Island, appears to be a response to an abrupt change in coastal topography. These beaches are built across and are fronted by a wide marine bench, which is separated from the sloping raised beaches found further inland, by a scarp 8 to 9 m high (Fig. 17.8, x - x'). The scarp is associated with either a change in rock lithology or block faulting, similar to that observed by Jones and Dixon (1977) at the head of Garnier Bay. Moreover, the fact that the barrier beaches have formed along the present shoreline at a time of slower shoreline emergence suggests that the marine bench has been exposed to waves for a longer period, and that generations of beach ridges have been built at basically the same sea level. Near 'Trebor Inlet' and offshore of Cunningham Inlet, the marine bench extends 800 to 1000 m seaward at a water depth less than 2 m (Fig. 17.9). As the waves crossed the marine bench they became refracted by bottom topography and the variation in wave approach produced the discontinuous curved spits and barrier beaches.

Landward of the main barrier beach are numerous smaller ridges transverse to the shoreline. Some of the ridges consist of upheaved gravels along major frost cracks; these ridges were built up by locally generated waves within the lagoon. The larger transverse beach ridges were built before the most recent barrier beach was formed. East of Garnier Bay, the transverse beach ridges are underlain by narrow outcrops of resistant rock (Fig. 17.8). These rock promontories have acted as natural groins and trapped sediment for barrier beach development. Many of the lagoons and ponds are silting up because of the input of sediment by rivers. This fluvial debris is also a major source of sediment for beach ridge development.

The barrier beaches on either side of 'Cape Fisher' are much smaller than the beaches near Garnier Bay (Table 17.3). In the former area, waves have built one or more spits across the head of an embayment forming lagoons and ponds behind.

Table 17.2. Beach sediments, Somerset Island, District of Franklin

Coastal environment	Bedrock	Abundance of sediment	Beach unit	Texture			Moment measures			No. of samples
				Mean gravel	Mean sand	Mean silt	Mean size	Mean sorting	Mean skewness	
				(%)	(%)	(%)	(ϕ)	(ϕ)		
High rock cliff	limestone dolostone	moderate	--	slope debris, i.e., boulders, cobbles, and beach pebbles						
Low rock shores with pocket beach	granite	poor	foreshore (pocket beach)	99	1	--	-3.3	0.7	+0.4	2
Sand and gravel plain	siltstone sandstone conglomerate	good	raised beach	59	40	1	-1.9	2.8	+0.4	3
			foreshore	9	91	--	+1.1	0.7	-1.1	12
Gravel beach with sloping backshore	limestone minor amounts of dolostone and conglomerate	good	raised beach	92	7	1	-3.8	1.2	+0.8	20
			foreshore	93	7	tr	-3.3	1.1	+0.6	88
			nearshore	99	1	--	-5.0	0.9	1.8	13
Gravel beach accumulation forms		good	raised beach	95	5	tr	-3.6	0.9	0.6	8
			foreshore	92	8	tr	-3.2	1.1	0.6	32
			subsoil (foreshore)	60	22	18	-0.8	3.1	1.3	2
			nearshore	98	2	--	-4.4	0.9	2.3	2
Deltas	sandstone limestone conglomerate	good		mixed sand and gravel						
Estuary	limestone some dolostone	good	shoreline	88	7	5	-3.4	1.3	0.4	6
			offshore	predominantly mud, also bedrock and gravels alongshore						

Table 17.3. Indirect measurements of relative wave energy reworking beaches of northern Somerset Island, 1974-76

Geographical area	Barrier beach morphology				Width of beach affected (from MHTL) by waves				Upper limit (elevation) of profile change (above MHTL)		Quantitative beach changes	
	Width of beach	Weight of beach (above MHTL)		No. of beach ridges	For beach slopes ≤5°		For beach slopes >5°					
	avg max	avg	max		avg	max	avg	max	avg	max	Avg. net profile change	No. of profiles
	(m) (m)	(m)	(m)		(m)	(m)	(m)	(m)	(m)	(m)	(m³)	
Eastern beaches Cunningham Inlet to Garnier Bay	56 72	2.2	2.8	1	23.3	33.0	14.7	29.5	2.3	3.9	5.7	17
Western beaches Cunningham Inlet to Pressure Point	38 53	1.7	1.8	1 to 4	6.4	10.0	5.6	11.0	1.2	1.9	1.0	25

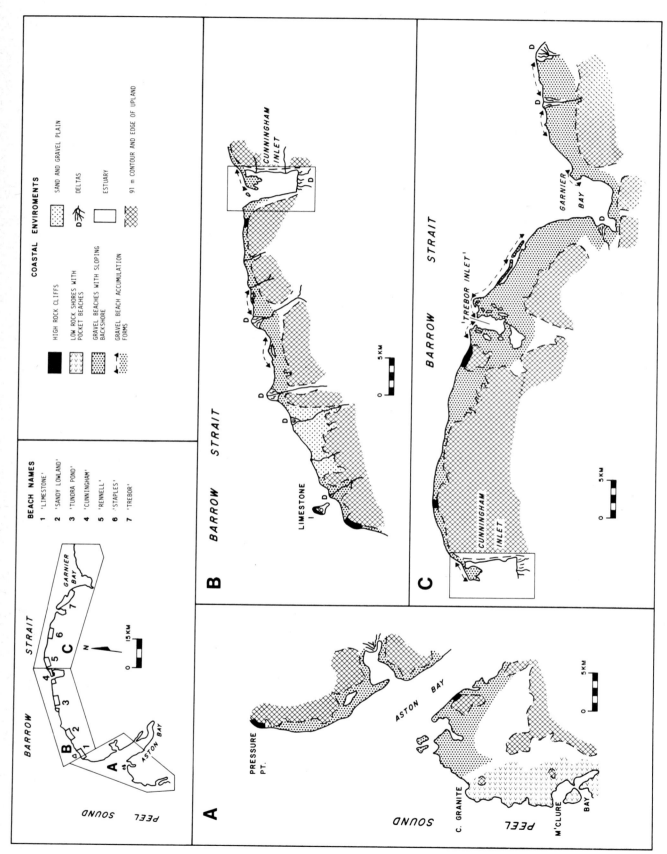

Figure 17.4. *Map of coastal environments along northern Somerset Island based on morphologic, sedimentologic and process elements.*

(a)   cliffed shore along Pressure Point; (GSC 165668)

(d)   gravel beaches and raised beach ridges at 'Staples' beach; (GSC 203216-S)

(b)   the low rocky shore with pocket beaches at Cape Granite; (GSC 203216-Q)

(e)   beach and shorefast ice lining the sand and gravel plain; (GSC 203216-R)

(c)   gravel barrier beach just east of 'Trebor Inlet'; (GSC 203216-P)

(f)   river delta at 'Cape Fisher'. (GSC 164732)

Figure 17.5.   Photographs of the coastal environments mapped in Figure 17.4.

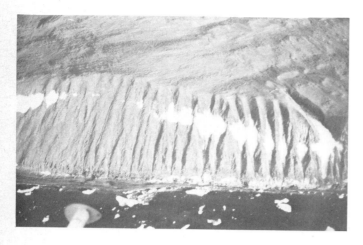

Figure 17.6. *An example of gully erosion at Cape Rennell; a 60 m high slope of unconsolidated sediments overlying bedrock which is exposed at the base. (GSC 7-20-1974)*

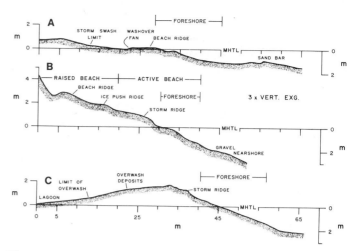

Figure 17.7. *Characteristic beach profiles of (a) sand and gravel plain, (b) gravel beach with sloping backshore and (c) gravel barrier beach. Nearshore profiles of (b) and (c) are illustrated in Figure 17.9 (1) and (4).*

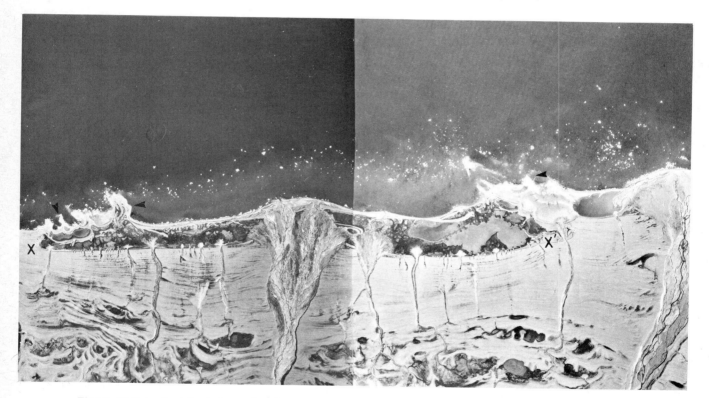

Figure 17.8. *Aerial photograph of the beach accumulation forms east of Garnier Bay and the associated abrupt change in coastal topography (along x-x'). Narrow outcrops of bedrock underlie some of the transverse beach ridges (arrows) (NAPL photo 16331-35 and 96).*

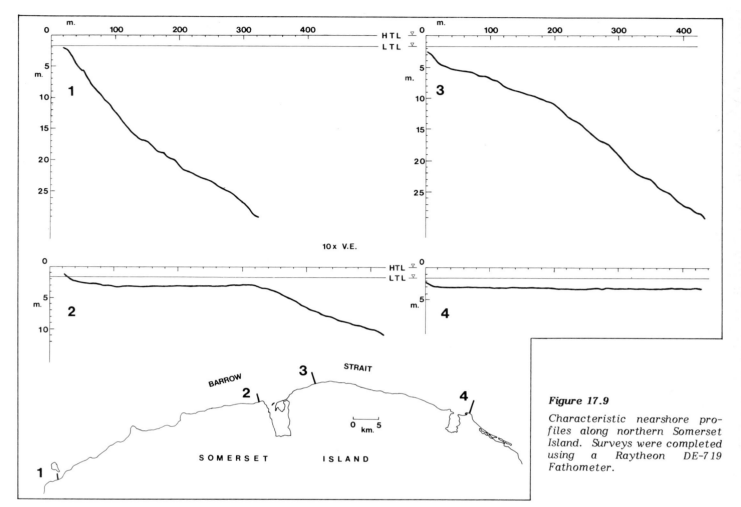

Figure 17.9

Characteristic nearshore profiles along northern Somerset Island. Surveys were completed using a Raytheon DE-719 Fathometer.

Slight variations in backshore morphology existed along the gravel beaches with a sloping backshore. Low-lying beaches with a slope of less than 3° were frequently subjected to overwash and deposition of ice and sediment. As the ice melted the backshore was left with a pitted morphology (Fig. 17.10a). Steeper sloping beaches, especially on headlands, were often affected by rafted sea ice. As a result the backshore had an irregular profile characterized by ice push ridges (Fig. 17.10b).

In 1974 sediment collected from across the foreshore of seven gravel beaches had a uniform average clast size of -3.2 to -3.3 phi, but in 1976 sediment collected from across the same beaches had a mean size of -2.6 to -3.9 phi. The change in sediment characteristics reflected a response to the most recent beach process events. The surface sediment samples contained less than 10 per cent sand but the subsoil samples at the frost table contained an average of 22 per cent sand (Table 17.2). It appears that the fines filter downward through the gravels to the frost table where they are deposited or transported downslope by subsurface rills. The coarsest sediment was observed in the nearshore.

Most of the sediment for beach development originated from the fractured bedrock exposed alongshore (Fig. 17.11) and in the nearshore. Additional sediment is dumped into the littoral zone by rivers during annual spring melt. Few trends in sediment size were detected alongshore because longshore sediment transport is restricted to short distances. Furthermore, the heterogeneous beach gravels

resulted from the proximity to source rocks (Fig. 17.11), the variable thickness of bedding in those rocks (Fig. 17.12) and the lack of substantial wave action.

Deltaic environment

There are few large river deltas along northern Somerset Island. The total length of deltaic coast, excluding the Cunningham River delta, was only 12 km or 7.2 per cent of the shoreline examined.

The rivers along northern Somerset Island have similar seasonal flow regimes to the rivers on Cornwallis Island (McCann et al., 1972). Discharge is highest during the short spring melt flood and except for occasional peaks generated by rainfall, it decreases throughout the summer. In late summer when discharge is minimal, marine processes dominate over fluvial processes and all but the largest rivers are closed off at their mouth by beach ridges.

The largest bedload and suspended sediment concentrations are deposited in the littoral zone during flood discharge. From 1972 to 1976 the rivers on Somerset Island reached flood stage between the last week in June and the second week in July. In spring, many of the rivers are blocked by snow dams and as a result often burst open and carry large amounts of material seaward. One small river, which was sampled just as it burst, had a suspended sediment concentration of 380 mg/L, which was 17 times its normal concentration during flood stage. The highest concentration of fluvial sediment entering Barrow Strait came from rivers draining the 'sand and gravel plain'.

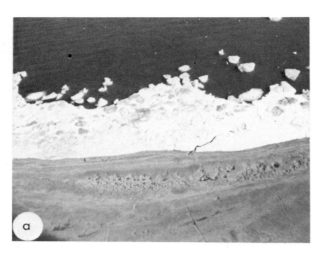

Figure 17.10. Variations in backshore morphology of gravel beaches (a) low-lying beaches with less than 3° slope are characterized by overwash and beach pitting, (GSC-170122); (b) steeper headland beaches subjected to nearly continuous ice push, (GSC 15-30 A-197).

Figure 17.11

Beach sediments are derived from underlying bedrock. In this photo chips of argillaceous Read Bay limestone have been fractured and pushed upslope by ice and waves. Further fracturing results in the beach pebbles as shown above and below bedrock. (GSC-169933)

Figure 17.12.

Rock outcrops alongshore with different thickness of beds, result in heterogeneous beach sediments. The photo shows interbedded conglomerate and sandstone rocks exposed at the shoreline at the western edge of the sand and gravel plain. (GSC-169939)

COASTAL PROCESSES AND SHORELINE STABILITY

Along northern Somerset Island, regardless of coastal type, the prime agents of shoreline change are waves and sea ice. However, additional processes are also modifying the backshore of the 'high rock cliffs' and the 'sand and gravel plain' coastal environments. Along the high cliffed shores the basal erosion of debris slopes by ice and waves is offset to varying degrees by the input of material from the upper slopes. Rockfalls, slush avalanches and gully erosion, as described by Howarth and Bones (1972) for the coastal cliffs of Devon Island, are also extending the slope foot of the Somerset Island cliffs. The 'sand and gravel plain' is dominated by fluvial and rill wash processes even though the shoreline is modified by littoral processes. Erosion of the bordering upland and the plain itself has provided material for the transgression seaward of the plain.

In the central Arctic Islands beach changes occur only during the short summer season when mobile sea ice and waves strike the coast. Based on five years of observations, the average duration of open water, when waves modified the northern Somerset coast, was 58 days. The open-water season was longest in 1974 with 72 days and shortest in 1972 and 1976 with 42 days. In contrast, Peel Sound, which lies along western Somerset Island, has an average open-water season of less than one month and in some years never lost its ice cover. Pocket beaches and the poorly developed wave-built features along northwestern Somerset Island also suggested that this is a lower energy wave environment than the more exposed northern coast.

Since waves and sea ice affect all of the coastal environments of Somerset Island, the coastline can be examined in terms of these processes and their effect on shoreline stability. Differences in the magnitude of the effects of waves and sea ice were recorded both seasonally and geographically along the coast. Between 1972 and 1976 waves produced large-scale beach changes during only one of the five years. These changes occurred during August and September of 1974 when strong onshore winds coincided with extensive open water (Taylor, 1978a). During the other four years the beaches were protected by either larger concentrations of mobile sea ice or shorefast ice. Moreover, during those four years the largest number of ice-built features (e.g., ice push ridges and shore ice piles) occurred across the coastal zone. Geographically, the shores west of Cape Rennell were affected more by sea ice than the shores farther east; conversely the shores east of Cunningham Inlet were reworked by higher energy waves than the indented shores farther west (Fig. 17.13). For instance, during summer as the sea ice moved eastward through Barrow Strait, it was blown onto Somerset Island by the prevailing northwest to west northwest winds. Consequently the shores most severely affected by sea ice were those along the west and northwest sides of capes, headlands and shoals extending into Barrow Strait. The shores most frequently subjected to sea ice pressure were located at Pressure Point, Capes Anne and 'Fisher', at the mouth of Cunningham Inlet, and adjacent to 'Rennell' beach and 'Staples' beach (Figs. 17.4, 17.13).

Sea ice was rafted farthest inland across the low relief shores of the 'sand and gravel plain' and the deltaic coastal environments, e.g., 'Cape Fisher'. Detailed observations on the characteristics and effects of the ice-built features have been dealt with in an earlier paper (Taylor, 1978b), but in general the beaches were left with a ridge and pit topography after the gouging by sea ice and the melting of ice piles.

Relative wave energy along the Somerset coast was indirectly measured using beach morphology, the width of beach zone modified by waves and the magnitude of beach change over time (Table 17.3). For example, the barrier beaches near Garnier Bay were on average 18 m wider and at

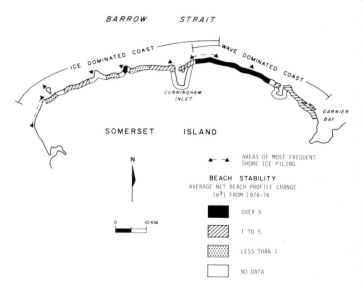

Figure 17.13. *A map of the northern Somerset coastline divided into areas of different relative wave energy and beach stability based on beach profile change. The map also shows the location of shores most frequently affected by sea ice pressures.*

least 1 m higher than the beach accumulation forms near 'Cape Fisher'. Measurements along beaches with comparable slopes showed that gravel beaches east of Cunningham Inlet were altered an average of 17 m farther inland from mean high tide level (MHTL) than the beaches at and west of Cunningham Inlet. Of the western beaches the low-lying sand and gravel plain was modified the farthest inland, i.e., 22 m.

Sequential surveys of beach profiles established along the entire study area provided a quantitative measure of the geographical variation in coastal stability. Over three seasons, 1974 - 76, the average net change at individual profiles was $5.7 \, m^3$ for profiles east of Cunningham Inlet and only $1.0 \, m^3$ for beach profiles established farther west. An exception to the small changes recorded along the western beaches was found along the northwest corner of 'Cape Fisher' where $15 \, m^3$ of sediment accretion was measured. Volumetric measurements of sediment change along whole sections of beach indicated that 'Staples' beach experienced a net accretion of $6.4 \, m^3/m$ of beach, 'Rennell' beach suffered erosion of $5.1 \, m^3/m$ of beach and 'Cunningham' beach lost a net of $0.9 \, m^3/m$ of shoreline (Taylor, 1978a).

All the evidence suggests that the beaches east of Cunningham Inlet and those along the larger capes are more dynamic and subject to greater topographic changes than the beaches west of Cunningham Inlet. The main reasons for the differences in wave energy and consequent beach stability along the coast are wave fetch, shoreline configuration and beach orientation. For much of northern Somerset Island wave fetch is limited to less than 100 km by the presence of other islands. However, north of 'Staples' beach, where the greatest shoreline changes occurred, a fetch of over 120 km is possible when both Wellington Channel and Barrow Strait are ice free. Thus, potentially larger waves can be generated north of these latter shores. West of Cunningham Inlet the shoreline is much more indented than farther east. Except for 'Cape Fisher' the beaches surveyed along northwestern Somerset Island are located in embayments. These embayments are sites of longer lasting shorefast ice and catch basins for mobile sea ice. Hence, these shores are less exposed to waves. Capes Anne and 'Fisher', on the other hand, are exposed to waves and sea ice pressures and are areas of greater beach change and instability.

The shores west of Cunningham Inlet are oriented to the north-northwest and are exposed to storms from that direction. The northwesterly storms generally blew considerable ice onto the Somerset shoreline, therefore the beaches were at least initially protected from the waves by sea ice. Storms from the east to northeasterly direction mostly affected the shores east of Cape Rennell and these storms blew less sea ice on shore, therefore the waves were able to expend their energy on the beaches. Beach overwash deposits observed on the western beaches suggested that they can be subject to higher energy waves, but there is a greater probability of open water coinciding with storms from the northeast to east than with storms from the northwest.

CONCLUSIONS

Northern Somerset Island is an example of a bedrock-dominated coast in a low wave energy - polar environment. Because of the lack of unconsolidated glacial sediments and the absence of high energy waves, the beaches consist of shallow deposits of locally derived sediment. Consequently, there is a close relationship between the resistance of the underlying bedrock to erosion and the type and availability of sediment for beach development. The types of shore morphology that have evolved are also a reflection of the differences in bedrock. Based on these relationships with the underlying bedrock, coastal environments were differentiated along northern Somerset Island. For instance, the shores underlain by resistant Precambrian rocks have a very irregular topography of rock outcrops and poorly developed pocket beaches. The small beach features are partly a function of the scarcity of sediment. The gravel beaches and the sand and gravel plain are associated with carbonate and softer clastic rocks, respectively. Both of these coastal environments have a greater abundance of sediment.

Differences in shore morphology along the shores underlain by carbonate rocks occurred because of local variations in relief and rock lithology. The high rock cliffs occurred where the upland extended to the sea. The beach accumulation forms were built in response to an abrupt change in coastal topography, from a sloping shore to a flat marine bench. Two other coastal environments were differentiated because of the fluvial processess which affect them. They were the large river deltas and the Cunningham Inlet estuary.

In addition to the morphological divisions, the Somerset shoreline can be divided into zones of relative wave energy or beach stability. The effects of sea ice and waves varied both geographically and seasonally. Geographically, higher energy waves and larger beach profile changes were recorded along the gravel beaches east of Cunningham Inlet than along the indented shores west of the Inlet.

The eastern shores were exposed to east-northeasterly storms and a longer wave fetch existed offshore. The most dynamic of the western shores were Capes 'Fisher' and Anne, which because of their exposed position were subject to severe sea ice pressure and waves. In contrast the low rocky shores of northwestern Somerset Island were the most stable and had poorly developed beaches because of the resistant bedrock and the absence of higher energy waves due to the long duration of ice cover and the short wave fetch of Peel Sound. Seasonally, it was found that the beaches of northern Somerset Island were substantially reworked by waves during only one of five summers. During the other four summers sea ice predominated, either in a protective or destructive role.

The coastal environments of northern Somerset Island are similar to many coasts of the east-central Arctic Islands. This paper provides an initial examination and understanding of those shores.

Acknowledgments

The author gratefully acknowledges the assistance of all the people involved with the project including Ray Featherstone, Doug Fisher, John Legault and Steve Morison. Logistical support was provided by the Polar Continental Shelf Project and Technical Field Support Services of the Department of Energy, Mines and Resources. Helpful comments on the paper were provided by Ted Bryant.

References

Canadian Hydrographic Service
1976: Pilot of Arctic Canada, vol. III, Supplement No. 5.; Fisheries and Marine Services, Environment Canada, p. 150.

Howarth, P.J. and Bones, J.G.
1972: Relationships between process and geometrical form on high Arctic debris slopes, south-west Devon Island, Canada; in Polar Geomorphology, Institute of British Geographers, Special Publication No. 4, p. 139 - 154.

Jones, B. and Dixon, O.A.
1975: The Leopold Formation: an upper Silurian intertidal/supratidal carbonate succession on N.E. Somerset Island, Arctic Canada; Canadian Journal of Earth Sciences, v. 12, no. 3, p. 395 - 411.
1977: Stratigraphy and sedimentology of upper Silurian rocks, northern Somerset Island, Arctic Canada; Canadian Journal of Earth Sciences, v. 14, no. 6, p. 1427 - 1452.

Kerr, J. Wm.
1975: Cape Storm Formation --- a new Silurian unit in the Canadian Arctic; Bulletin of Canadian Petroleum Geologists, v. 23, no. 1, p. 67 - 83.

McCann, S.B., Howarth, P.J. and Cogley, J.G.
1972: Fluvial processes in a periglacial environment, Queen Elizabeth Islands, N.W.T., Canada; Institute of British Geographers, Transactions, Publication no. 55, p. 69 - 82.

McMillan, N.J.
1963: North coast of Somerset Island; in Geology of the North Central part of the Arctic Archipelago, Northwest Territories, Y.O. Fortier et al., ed.; Geological Survey of Canada, Memoir 320, p. 129 - 135.

Miall, A.D., Kerr, J. Wm. and Gibling, M.R.
1978: The Somerset Island Formation: an upper Silurian to ?Lower Devonian intertidal/supratidal succession, Boothia Uplift region, Arctic Canada; Canadian Journal of Earth Sciences, v. 15, no. 2, p. 181 - 189.

Morison, S.R. and Taylor, R.B.
1978: Physical characteristics and seasonal changes in an Arctic estuarine environment; in Current Research, Part B; Geological Survey of Canada, Paper 78-1B, p. 101 - 106.

Taylor, R.B.
1978a: Beach changes, northern Somerset Island; Proceedings of Fourth International Conference on Port and Ocean Engineering under Arctic Conditions, Memorial University of Newfoundland, v. 2, p. 904 - 915.
1978b: The occurrence of grounded ice ridges and shore ice piling along the northern coast of Somerset Island, N.W.T.; Arctic, v. 31, no. 2, p. 133 - 149.

18

PHYSICAL CHARACTERISTICS OF THE
SOUTHEASTERN BAFFIN ISLAND COASTAL ZONE

G.H. Miller[1,2], W.W. Locke, III[1,2] and G.W. Locke[1]

Miller, G.H., Locke, W.W., III, and Locke, C.W., Physical characteristics of the southeastern Baffin Island coastal zone; in The Coastline of Canada, S.B. McCann, editor; Geological Survey of Canada, Paper 80-10, p. 251-265, 1980.

Abstract

The morphology and sedimentological characteristics of the littoral and inshore marine environments of the coastal zone along southeastern Baffin Island have been mapped as part of the Eastern Arctic Marine Environmental Study. The coastal zone is defined as the area between 20 m aht (the maximum limit of storm wave activity) and 20 m blt (the maximum wave base). Generalized maps of morphology and sediment characteristics are based on airphoto interpretation supplemented by low-level aircraft observations and ground-truth data. Specific sediment and morphologic data were obtained from Frobisher Bay and Hall Peninsula.

The coast of southeastern Baffin Island is generally steep and rocky due to the tectonic and recent glacial history of the area and low denudation rates. Only localized areas of sediment beaches occur, and these frequently coincide with or lie immediately below Pleistocene beaches. Sediment in the littoral zone is mostly sand-sized or coarser, including a high proportion of cobble beaches. However, areas of extensive tidal flat and regions protected from severe wave action may have finer grained sediment.

Sediment input to the littoral environment is primarily a function of the Pleistocene history of the adjacent area. Reworking of Pleistocene deposits by glaciofluvial, fluvial and marine agents resulted in localized deposits of sediment that were subsequently elevated above the sea during isostatic readjustment. These deposits are the primary sediment sources for contemporary littoral deposition, and their composition is strongly reflected in the modern littoral grain-size distribution. In areas over which glacial deposition was minimal, in situ granular disintegration of the bedrock is the prime sediment source. Reworking of these materials in the littoral environment generally results in the removal of the finer grain-size fractions leaving a residue of coarse sand and gravel. High proportions of coarse silt are added locally to the littoral zone by meltwater streams draining active glaciers in the region.

A map of the coastline density (length of coastline in 10 by 10 km grid squares) provides a convenient visual presentation of the variation in coastline configuration across the region. In general, fiord areas have lowest coastline densities, whereas shallow marine areas are most dense. There is a direct correlation between areas of high coastline density and shallow marine gradients.

A recent rise of relative sea level along eastern Baffin Island is documented by the submergence of river valleys and the burial of in situ terrestrial vegetation beneath beach sediment. The extent of sea level rise is greatest (ca. 2 m) along the outermost east coast and decreases to the west. Radiocarbon dates suggest that the onset of submergence occurred between 1500 and 2500 years B.P.

Résumé

La morphologie et la nature sédimentologique des milieux littoraux et intra-littoraux de la zone côtière située le long de la partie sud-est de l'île de Baffin ont été cartographiées dans le cadre de l'Eastern Arctic Marine Environmental Study. Les auteurs ont retenu comme zone côtière l'espace situé entre 20 m au-dessus de la laisse de haute mer (la limite maximale de l'activité des vagues de tempête) et 20 m au-dessous de la laisse de basse mer (la base minimale des vagues). Certains cartes générales de morphologie et de caractéristiques sédimentaires reposent sur l'interprétation des photographies aériennes et en complémentarité à partir d'observations d'avion à faible altitude et de données de terrain. Certains données sédimentologiques et morphologiques ont été obtenues dans la baie Frobisher et dans la péninsule Hall.

La côte de la partie sud-est de l'île de Baffin est généralement abrupte et rocheuse en raison du passé tectonique et des glaciations récentes de la région ainsi que du rythme lent de la dénudation. Seules des zones déterminées de plages à matériaux sédimentaires existent, celles-ci coincidant fréquemment avec des plages du Pléistocène quand elles ne se trouvent pas immédiatement au-dessous. Les matériaux de la zone littorale sont surtout de la taille du sable ou plus grossiers et ils comportent une forte proportion de cailloux de plage. Toutefois, certaines étendues de grands veys et des régions protégées de l'action rigoureuse des vagues possèdent parfois une granulométrie plus fine.

---

[1] Institute of Arctic and Alpine Research, University of Colorado, Boulder, Colorado

[2] Department of Geological Sciences, University of Colorado, Boulder, Colorado

L'apport en matériaux au milieu littoral dépend surtout du Pléistocène des secteurs avoisinants. Le remaniement des dépôts du Pléistocène par les agents fluvioglaciaires, fluviatiles et marins a entraîné le dépôt par endroits de matériaux qui s'étaient auparavant élevés au-dessus du niveau de la mer à l'occasion de rajustements isostatiques. Ces dépôts constituent la principale source de matériaux pour les apports littoraux contemporains et leur composition est fortement reflétée dans la granulométrie du littoral actuel. Dans les zones au-dessus desquelles les dépôts de matériaux glaciaires ont été les moins considérables, la désintégration granulaire sur place du socle rocheux représente la principale source de matériaux. Le remaniement de ces matériaux dans le milieu littoral entraîne généralement l'enlèvement des fractions granulométriques les plus fines ce qui laisse un résidu de sable grossier et de gravier. De fortes proportions de silt grossier s'ajoutent par endroits à la zone littorale par suite des écoulements d'eau de fonte provenant de glaciers actifs.

Une carte de la densité littorale (longeur de littoral dans des quadrilatères de 10 km sur 10) assure une présentation acceptable des variations de la configuration littorale à travers la région. D'une manière générale, les zones de fjords possèdent de plus faibles densités littorales, tandis que les zones marines peu profondes sont les plus denses. Il existe une corrélation directe entre les zones à forte densité littorale et les gradients marins des eaux de faible profondeur.

Une élévation récente du niveau relatif de la mer le long de la partie est de l'île de Baffin est confirmée par la submergence des vallées fluviales et l'enfouissement de la végétation terrestre sur place sous les matériaux de plages. L'élévation du niveau de la mer est la plus forte (env. 2 m) le long de la côte la plus à l'est et diminue vers l'ouest. La datation au radiocarbone permet de supposer que la submergence s'est produite entre les années 1500 et 2500 B.P.

INTRODUCTION

This study was designed to provide basic data on the physical characteristics of the coastal zone of southern Baffin Island through airphoto mapping and supplemental ground-truth data. It was undertaken as part of the Eastern Arctic Marine Environmental Survey (EAMES) Project, in response to projected fossil-fuel drilling on the continental shelf of Baffin Island. The area of study,[1] delineated from a general consideration of the surface water circulation in the Labrador Sea and Davis Strait, extends from Brevoort Island, eastern Hall Peninsula to southernmost Baffin Island (Fig. 18.1).

The objective of the study was to examine the coastal zone of southern Baffin Island (defined as the area between the 20 m aht [above high tide] and 20 m blt [below low tide] contours), and to characterize the relevant physical parameters. These include the composition and slope of the ground surface within this zone, the degree of convolution of the coastline, the morphology and sedimentological composition of the beaches and the extent of storm-wave scour.

SOUTHERN BAFFIN ISLAND

The bedrock in the study area is exclusively Precambrian crystalline rock, although Paleozoic sediments outcrop at the head of Frobisher Bay and overlie the Shield rocks farther west. The crystalline bedrock is mantled by a veneer, extensive in some places, of Pleistocene glacial, fluvial and marine sediments, and of locally significant regolith.

The general physiography of southeastern Baffin Island is controlled by the tectonic events associated with the early Tertiary rifting of the North Atlantic. Frobisher Bay and Cumberland Sound are downfaulted grabens, with Paleozoic sediments preserved in their outer reaches. Uplift of the intervening blocks was greatest along the northeastern margins. Consequently, the northeast-facing coasts are generally steeper than those that face southwest. Secondary physiographic features are the result of fluvial, glaciofluvial and glacial erosion. The evolution of the littoral environment has been controlled by both the bedrock and general physiography of the area and by Pleistocene glaciation.

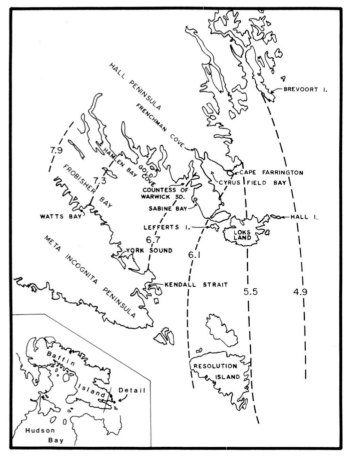

Figure 18.1. *Location map of southeastern Baffin Island including place names mentioned in the text. Contour lines are on the mean spring tidal range (m) based on data in Dohler (Fig. 17).*

---

[1] Additional data on the coastline of northern Labrador and Ungava are in Barry et al. (1977).

The resistant nature of the Precambrian Shield basement rocks and the cold, dry climate of Baffin Island preclude rapid decomposition due to chemical weathering and most erosive agents. Sediment production, thus sediment influx to the littoral zone, is limited. Because of the minimal quantities of locally derived sediment, till sheets over the interior of the island seldom attain a thickness of 1 m. In contrast, Frobisher Bay has acted as a repository for fine detritus during glacial episodes. The easily eroded, fine-grained sediments and in situ Paleozoic sediment flooring the outer parts of the bay have acted as primary sediment sources during subsequent glaciation.

During the last glaciation, Frobisher Bay was filled by a major outlet glacier draining an ice-dispersal centre over Foxe Basin or a dispersal ridge between Foxe Basin and Hudson Bay. Continental ice impinged on Hall Peninsula but did not completely cover it, and local, independent ice caps existed on eastern Hall Peninsula. Most of the glacial and emerged marine sediments of southeastern Baffin Island were deposited during the late Foxe (late Wisconsin) stade of the last glaciation. At that time, substantial volumes of unconsolidated and semiconsolidated sediment were eroded from the seafloor and redeposited along the flanks of the bay. The carbonate content of tills is high (up to 35%) and limestone accounts for as much as 20 per cent of the sediment matrix at some localities. The recent glacial history of the study area is discussed by Miller (1980) and Andrews and Miller (1979).

Glaciomarine deposits formed during the last ice maximum and subsequent retreat are found throughout the region. The highest marine features rise from 20 m aht on eastern Loks Land to about 90 m in the middle reaches of Frobisher Bay and up to about 120 m near the head of the bay. Frequent changes in relative sea level have prevented the occupation of stable, long-term beach positions. Because of the youth of the coastline and the protection of the coast by ice, beach development is minimal.

The climate of the area is rigorous, with a mean annual temperature of about -7°C and precipitation of about 25 cm annually. Of more importance to this study is the presence of sea ice, either onshore or offshore, for about thirty weeks per year. Although some ice modification of the shore is evident, it acts mainly as a protective agent limiting wave action.

The tides in the region are semidiurnal. Extreme tidal ranges have been reported from inner Frobisher Bay, where maximum tides in excess of 13 m occur every year, although the average monthly maximum over the study area is 5 to 6 m. Contours on the mean spring tidal range are shown in Figure 18.1.

MAPPING PROCEDURES

Detailed airphoto mapping

Above mean high tide

Aerial photography covering the study area is available on various scales and of several ages. Prints of approximately 800 air photographs taken in the late 1950s were obtained from the National Air Photo Library of Canada. These photographs, taken from an elevation of 30 000 feet with a six-inch lens, are at a scale of approximately 1:60 000. They were examined in stereo using a Wild ST4 mirror stereoscope with 3X oculars. Information obtained was mapped onto 1:250 000 scale topographic sheets (Department of Energy, Mines and Resources, Ottawa) using the

interpretive scheme described below. The maps are on file at the library of the Institute of Arctic and Alpine Research, Boulder, Colorado.

The interpretive scheme for Baffin Island (Appendix 1)* was designed to differentiate the material and the slope of the coastal zone. The surface above mean high tide was subdivided into five types: rock, and coarse, medium, fine and heterogeneous sediment. The slope was also subdivided into five classes: less than 5°, 5 - 10°, 10 - 20°, 20 - 45°, and greater than 45°. This scheme allows differentiation of features occupying as little as 100 linear metres of coast. However, it does not provide for a grouping of areas into physiographic 'types'. The reason for choosing a specific, rather than a general, mapping technique lies in the essential similarity of the entire southeastern Baffin Island coast. The variation in physiography within a single fiord is greater than between two points hundreds of kilometres apart, such as Brevoort Island and the coast of Frobisher Bay.

Much of the coastline is not 'simple', that is, composed of only one type of material with a constant slope. For example, a raised marine deposit may be composed entirely of fine sediment, but have a steep slope to approximately 10 m above sea level and a low-angle upper surface. In addition, coarse cobble beaches are often found at the base of such marine deposits. To such complex shoreline types, the scheme was expanded to describe each segment and a descriptor was added to represent the total distance from sea level to the +20 m contour. In addition, special features which cannot be described by this scheme, such as inlets, or that are too small to be shown on the 1:250 000 maps, such as tide pools, are mapped using symbols (see Appendix 1 for further examples).

Several problems were encountered in the application of the above technique. These can be grouped as imagery problems and interpretive problems. Difficulties in the use of the imagery arose from both the time of year and the time of day during which the photos were taken. During spring and early summer, snow and shorefast ice may obscure the coastal zone. Low-angle sun may cause shadows, whereas high-angle sun may lead to reflections. Difficulties in interpretation occurred in the assessment of slope and in materials. The airphotos grossly exaggerate the relief, thus true slope can be determined only with the aid of detailed topographic maps. However, maps available for most of Baffin Island have contour intervals of only 200 to 500 feet (60 or 150 m), and all slope estimates are approximate. Although differentiation of rock and sediment is possible, subdivision of sediment on the basis of grain size has been based mainly on the probable genesis of the deposit.

The coastline of Baffin Island shows a widely varying morphology on a scale of few kilometres. The 1:250 000 scale maps indicate this variability (Figs. 18.2 to 18.6), much of which is a function of intermixing of short lengths of common shoreline types, such as bedrock and talus. Much of the variation, particularly in the Brevoort Island area, is due also to alternating steep and very steep bedrock.

Approximately 90 per cent of the coastline is composed of bedrock, more than half of which is moderately or steeply sloping. Steep to very steep rock is typical of exposed coastal areas in high wave energy environments (Fig. 18.2) and areas recently modified by ice (Fig. 18.3). Gently sloping bedrock is most common in areas of raised marine platforms (Fig. 18.4). The remaining 10 per cent of the coastline consists of areas of sediment accumulation, nearly equally divided between coarse-, medium-, and fine-grained deposits. Most coarse sediments occur as talus slopes (Fig. 18.3), although small areas of cobble beaches and moraines do occur. Medium heterogeneous sediments occur in fluvial deposits, which are locally extensive at the mouths of major river systems (Fig. 18.5), such as Cyrus Field Bay, and at the heads of fiords (Fig. 18.3).

---

* Not supplied by author.

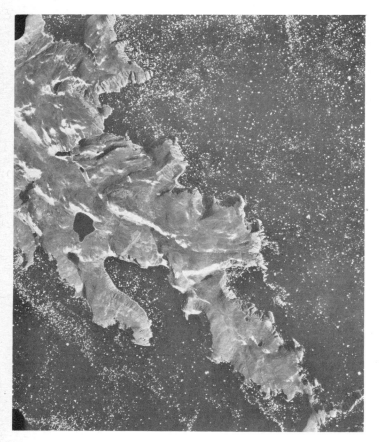

Figure 18.2.   Brevoort Island (above)

This area is typical of the coastlines facing Davis Strait. Rock is the dominant material, and it varies in slope from 45 to 90° (1); sediment accumulations are found only where the toes of talus slopes reach the sea (2); or where beaches form in protected coves (3). (NAPL Photo A16750-32)

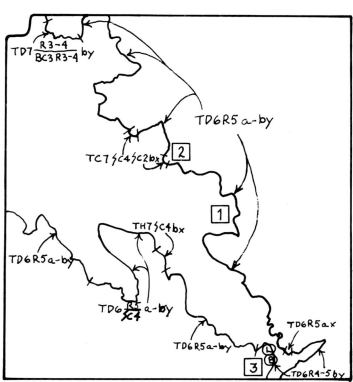

Figure 18.3.   Hamlen Bay   (facing, above)

Fiord topography is common along much of the inner coast and is characterized by extensive talus slopes (1) and moderate to steep rock surfaces (2). At the heads of the fiords, extensive deltas and fluvial distributary plains (3) are found. Note the difficulty in determining the high tide line in such areas. (NAPL Photo A16774-133)

Figure 18.4.   Lefferts Island (facing, below)

Both the south coast of Meta Incognita Peninsula and that of Hall Peninsula (shown) have relatively gentle regional slopes. Some portions of these coasts appear to be raised marine platforms with total relief of less than 60 m (1). Extensive tide flats (2) and pools (P) are common. A veneer of fine marine sediments (3) is often found in topographic lows in such areas. Note the transition to fiord topography to the north (4). (NAPL Photo A16321-2)

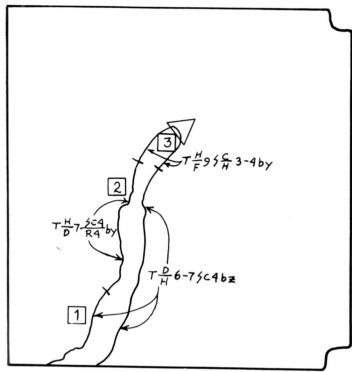

$T\frac{H}{F}9SC\frac{C}{H}3\text{-}4by$

$T\frac{H}{D}7\frac{SC4}{R4}by$

$T\frac{D}{H}6\text{-}7SC4bz$

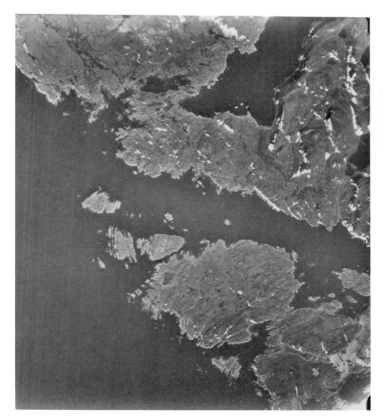

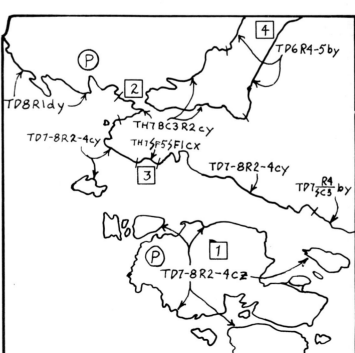

TD6R4-5by

TD8R1dy

TH7BC3R2cy

TD7-8R2-4cy

TH1SF5SF1CX

TD7-8R2-4cy

$TD7\frac{R4}{SC3}by$

TD7-8R2-4cz

Intertidal zone

A scheme similar to that described above (Appendix 1) was used to describe the intertidal zone. However, only the material (bedrock, and coarse, medium, fine and heterogeneous sediments) and width of the zone were determined. The width of the intertidal zone was classified in a five-part logarithmic scale: less than 10 m, 10 - 100 m, 100 - 1 km, 1 - 10 km, and greater than 10 km.

The airphoto mapping of the intertidal zone is much less accurate than that above mean high tide. Much of this inaccuracy stems from the narrowness of the zone and the lack of knowledge on the state of the tide.

For example, at Brevoort Island the mean tide is 4 m. If the slope of the bedrock above mean high tide is maintained through the intertidal zone, this would correspond to a width of the intertidal zone of 4 m or less (less than 0.1 mm on the airphoto). If the airphoto of such an area were taken at low tide, the intertidal zone would be evident in the form of a light-coloured, wave-scoured, vegetation-free, 'bathtub ring'. The state of the tide at the time the airphoto was taken is unknown; therefore, the observed width of the intertidal zone is always a minimum. Because of field studies in the area, we were able to approximately classify some areas in which the intertidal zone was not exposed on the airphoto.

The width of the intertidal zone is a function of the rate of sediment deposition, the bedrock slope and the tidal range. Areas with a broad intertidal zone are either major deltas such as at Frenchman Cove (Fig. 18.5), or areas of gently sloping bedrock such as at Lefferts Island (Fig. 18.4). At localities with a gentle shoreline gradient, a larger tidal range will lead to a broad intertidal zone.

Offshore slope

Information on the seafloor slope and materials to a depth of 20 m below mean low tide is scanty. The primary sources of published information on tides and bathymetry are hydrographic charts at scales of between 1:12 000 and 1:500 000, tide tables, and the Pilot of Arctic Canada (1968). Detailed depth soundings are available only for the few harbours and military installations in the area. More general bathymetry is available along shipping lanes. Inferred data are interpolated from these smaller scale maps. The remainder of the area is covered in small-scale (greater than 1:500 000) bathymetric charts, which have only sporadic soundings near the coast. Echo soundings made at the mouth of Frobisher Bay and off Hall Peninsula during the summer of 1977 are discussed later.

Because of the limited information available, the only offshore parameter mapped was the distance to the -20 m contour. This distance was mapped at a scale of 1:1 000 000. (This map has not been included here because it could not be accurately shown at a reduced scale.) Because of the wide variation in this distance, a four-part logarithmic scale was used: less than 10 m, 10 - 100 m, 100 m - 1 km, and greater than 1 km. The variation in shading on the map indicates two levels of accuracy: known, measured directly from charts or echo soundings; and inferred, where the charts were insufficiently detailed or of too small a scale.

The primary features of note are the shorelines with an extensive shallow offshore zone that occur along the south coast and in parts of Hall Peninsula, notably Cyrus Field Bay, the southeastern coast of Loks Land, Hamlen Bay and Countess of Warwick Sound. Similar zones also occur at the head of Frobisher Bay.

Coastline density map

An additional parameter of the coastal zone is the length of coast per unit area. This parameter, which will be referred to as coastline density, has been determined for southeastern Baffin Island. Because the visible length of coastline for a given area increases when examined at increasingly detailed scales, all measurements were made on the 1:250 000 series map sheets. These maps are imprinted with the Universal Transverse Mercator 10 000 m grid system, in which each grid square encloses an area of 100 km^2. The length of coastline within each square was measured and the results were contoured to emphasize maximum and minimum values. Details of the procedure are given in Appendix 2.

A specific problem arises with using the 10 000 m grid since the junction between grid zones 20V and 19V is along longitude 66°W, through the centre of the study area. Along this boundary are partial squares. To correct for their presence, the length of coastline within such 'squares' was divided by the area of the partial square and expressed as a percentage of a complete square, to normalize it to the remainder of the data.

Results of this analysis have been summarized at a scale of 1:1 000 000 and the map is included here in reduced form (Fig. 18.7). The densities can be interpreted in terms of general coastal morphology. For example, in southeastern Baffin Island, values less than 0.2 km/km^2 are typical of outer fiord coasts. Values of 0.4 - 0.6 km/km^2 represent archipelagos of high relief off some fiord mouths and rocky coasts of low relief. Densities of greater than 0.6 km/km^2 are found in archipelagos of low relief.

The technique has several major advantages. The measurements take relatively little time, can be performed by an individual with no prior knowledge of coastal geomorphology, and the 1:250 000 scale base maps may be used.

Figure 18.5. *Frenchman Cove (facing, above)*

Where major river systems reach the sea, extensive areas of raised marine and fluvial sediments occur (1), interspersed with low relief rock bosses (2). The constriction (3) restricts flow, thus defining the inlet. Note the width of the intertidal zone at this stage of the tide, which appears as a white rim around the coastline (4), and the area of reflection which could obscure such information (5). (NAPL Photo A16321-42)

Figure 18.6. *Kendall Strait (facing, below)*

Areas of extensive sedimentation without a major sediment source are uncommon. One such area has low relief (1) and is in a protected cove. Sediment occurs as a thin veneer overlying rock (2), or more extensively filling topographic lows (3). Beaches are not present. (NAPL Photo A16745-185)

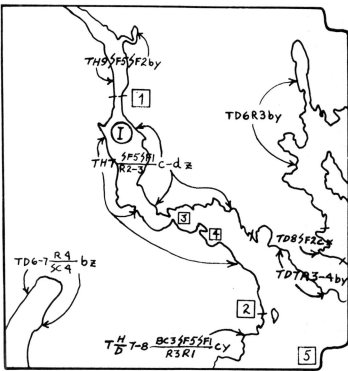

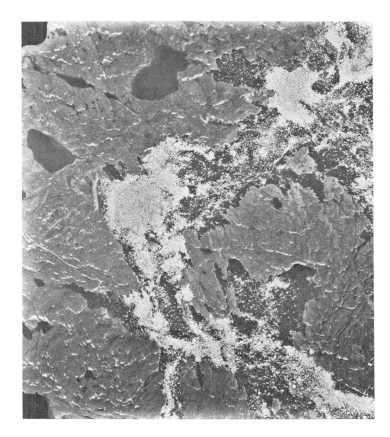

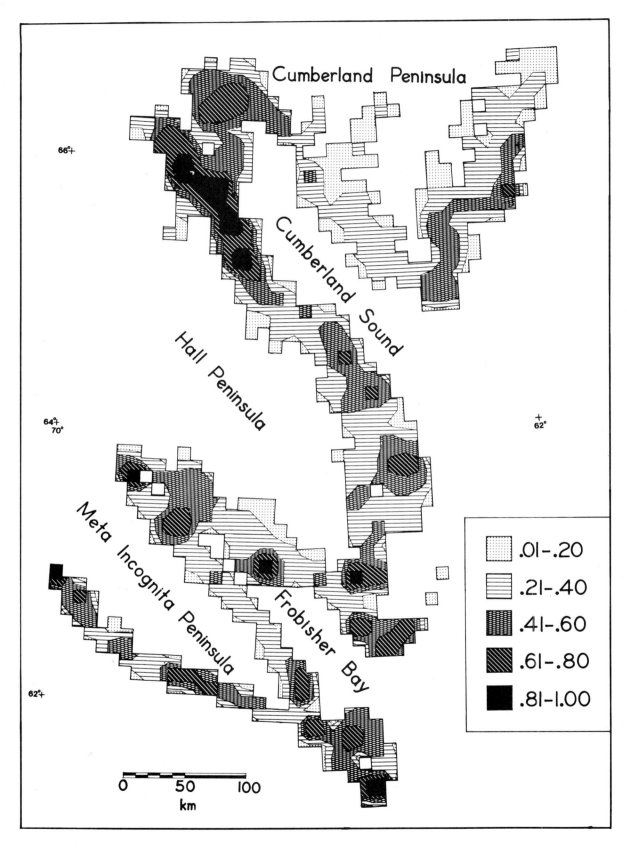

Figure 18.7. *Coastline density for southeastern Baffin Island. Average density calculated in 10 by 10 km grid sequences. Legend values are 10^2 km of coastline per 10^2 km^2 grid square.*

Results of mapping

The three mapping procedures discussed above involve different coastal zone parameters. Combining these results yields essentially four primary landform assemblages: (1) steep bedrock above mean low tide, steep offshore slope, and moderate coastline density; (2) coarse sediment with steep slopes above mean low tide, steep offshore slope, and low coastline density; (3) gently sloping bedrock above mean low tide, gentle offshore slope, and high coastline density; and (4) medium or heterogeneous to fine sediment, either steep or gently sloping above mean low tide, gently offshore slopes, and high coastline density.

The first two assemblages are characteristic of fiord and steep-walled island areas, which encompass most of the study area. Except for the inner reaches of the fiords, they are typical high-energy environments. The latter two assemblages are relatively infrequent. Assemblage 3 is found in high-energy environments, while assemblage 4 is found in low-energy environments of relatively high sediment influx. These assemblages can be used for assessment of environmental hazard.

BEACH MORPHOLOGY AND SEDIMENT CHARACTERISTICS

To obtain data on beach morphology and sediment characteristics, and to provide an independent field check on the interpretive airphoto mapping, field studies were conducted in Frobisher Bay and southeastern Hall Peninsula. The field investigations were designed to sample specific areas that would typify large stretches of the coast of southeastern Baffin Island, and to sample extreme localities to allow determination of the maximum ranges of the environmental and sedimentological variations in the littoral environment. Specific observations were made on beach morphology and sedimentology and the bathymetry of the shallow marine regions.

Additional observations included the maximum limit of storm waves and the extent of recent sea level change.

Sediment collections were analyzed for their grain size distribution (by sieve and pipette), organic matter content (loss on ignition corrected for lattice water), and carbonate content (Chittick apparatus). Determination of the grain size distribution included measurement of the fraction <2000 µm, at 1 phi increments to 8 (3.9 µm) or 11 (0.49 µm) phi. Because of the large number of coarse-grained samples, and additional sieve was used to obtain the -1 to -0.75 and -0.75 to 0 phi fractions, enabling more accurate computation of graphic measures.

Sources of littoral sediments

Littoral sediments are derived from three primary sources. In order of decreasing importance, these are: erosion and redeposition of Pleistocene glacial, glaciomarine and glaciofluvial sediments (Fig. 18.8); locally derived products of bedrock weathering; and debris from present glaciers. The modern beach sediments can be expected to reflect the sedimentological characteristics of the particle influx, as modified by sorting and abrasion during transportation and redeposition. The sedimentological characteristics of 12 samples of source sediment are summarized in Table 18.1. In situ weathering products are invariably coarse grained (GRL-3189), because of coarse grain size of the granites, gneisses and metasediments from which they are derived. Sorting is poor, and the distribution is strongly fine-skewed. In contrast, glacial rock flour (GRL-3177, 3179, Table 18.1) is composed mainly of fine sand and coarse silt, moderately to poorly sorted, with a near-symmetrical distribution. The tills and glaciomarine drifts (Table 18.1) are very similar, composed primarily of sand, poorly sorted, and moderately to strongly fine-skewed. It is likely that some till in the area would have been derived mainly from in situ weathering products, and would more closely resemble the particle size distribution of grus. Such tills are, however, restricted and are a minor source for modern beach sediment. Raised Pleistocene marine sediments show a broad range of sediment distributions, commensurate with the broad range of depositional environments represented under the umbrella of 'marine'. Common to all of these sediments, however, is strong fine-skewness. This skewness decreases as the sediment becomes finer grained.

Figure 18.8. *York Sound*

Raised Pleistocene glaciomarine deposit (right centre) serves as source of sediment for present beaches. Bay mouth bar is evidence of recent submergence.

Table 18.1. Characteristics of source sediments

Lab. No.	Elev.	>2mm	OM	Carb	pH	Graphic measures			Comment
						Mean	Sorting	Skewness	
	(m aht)	(%)	(%)	(%)		(ϕ)	(ϕ)		
				In situ weathering					
GRL-3189	3	32.2	0.3		6.2	0.35	1.09	0.41	Granular disintegration of bedrock, Loks Land
				Glacial rock flour					
GRL-3177	na	0	0		6.9	4.55	0.89	0.02	Bedload of glacial outlet stream, Watts Bay
-3179	na	0	0		5.5	4.60	1.45	0.14	Same as above
				Glacial till					
GRL-3200	180	17.8	0.73	6.2	8.0	3.63	3.85	0.45	Till, probably of marine origin
GRL-3201	230	13.8	0.56	15.9	8.3	3.42	3.50	0.42	Till (kame terrace?), Gold Cove, marine origin
				Glaciomarine sediments					
GRL-3185	2	11.4	0.64	35.5	8.1	3.97	2.70	0.34	Sabine Bay
-3186	-3	14.1	0	0.6	8.3	3.22	3.28	0.41	Same, but planed and leached by wave action.
				Pleistocene marine sediments					
GRL-3193	10	0.3	0.7	1.2	7.2	7.48	3.02	0.26	Frenchman Cove
-3198	21	8.1	0.37	21.0	8.2	5.02	3.31	0.27	Postglacial, Gold Cove
-3199	80	9.9	0.34	17.2	8.2	4.58	3.63	0.36	Late glacial, Gold Cove
-3205	55	2.4	0.26	1.5	8.3	3.40	1.90	0.47	Countess of Warwick Sound
-3206	20	25	0.29	5.6	8.3	1.85	2.48	0.39	Easternmost Loks Land

Modern beach sediment characteristics

Modern beaches occur on the southeastern Baffin Island coast in nearly all areas. The nature of the beaches, however, is different from place to place, and is a function of the influx of sediment and the energy environment. In order of decreasing frequency, beaches are most common in the following areas (see Fig. 18.1 for location of examples): (1) exposed headlands without major sediment sources (easternmost Loks Land and Cape Farrington), (2) major river mouths with high sediment input (Cyrus Field Bay), (3) protected low- to moderate-relief coasts (Gold Cove and Sabine Bay), and (4) high-relief coasts with glaciofluvial sediment input (Watts Bay). Sediment samples were collected from modern beaches within each of these environments and analyzed to determine whether or not the environment had a controlling effect on the beach sediment (Table 18.2).

Sediment samples from beaches in exposed localities vary widely in grain size distribution. Much of this can be explained by reference to the primary local sediment source. Because of the high-relief backshores and limited drainage networks, nearly all of the sediment is locally derived. Delivery to the littoral environment is accomplished by slopewash, ephemeral streams, or mass movement by rockfall or creep. The effect of the local sediment source can be seen in samples GRL-3190 and 3195,

both of which were derived from in situ weathering of bedrock. In contrast, sample GRL-3191, derived from the reworking of a Pleistocene glaciomarine unit, is markedly finer grained than most of the beach samples. GRL-3188, intermediate in size between the above samples, was identified in the field as derived from both Pleistocene sediments and in situ weathering products. Sample GRL-3194, the least sorted of the samples from exposed areas, occurred in a moderately protected, low-gradient locality, and is thus anomalous among the samples in the headland areas. Most of the samples from exposed localities are moderately sorted and nearly symmetrical, with silt and clay (<4 phi) composing less than 2 per cent of the sediment.

The drainage system in souteastern Baffin Island is immature, with most streams originating within a few kilometres of the sea. Larger rivers are located near the heads of major bays: most are structurally controlled. These major basins commonly contain extensive sedimentary deposits that supply the present rivers with an abundant sediment load. Sample GRL-3192 was collected from the mouth of such a river. It is poorly sorted and, in contrast to most of the beach and sediment samples, is very fine grained. Silt and clay account for 40 per cent of the sediment, indicative of both the sediment source (GRL-3193) and the low energy environment. Small drainages are gradational into the exposed beaches discussed above, and the sedimentary characteristics for the beaches are determined by the nature of the local sediment source.

Table 18.2. Characteristics of modern beach sediments

Lab. No.	Elev.	>2mm	OM	Carb	pH	Graphic measures			Comment
						Mean	Sorting	Skewness	
	(m bht)	(%)	(%)	(%)		(ϕ)	(ϕ)		
			Exposed headlands						
GRL-3188	6	6.8	0.02		7.3	1.63	0.97	0.05	Derived from Pleistocene sediments and weathered bedrock, Hall Island, Loks Land
-3190	0.5	25.2	0.01		6.8	-0.28	0.47	0.14	Derived from weathered bedrock (GRL-3189), Loks Land
-3191	4	8.3	0.78	1.5	8.3	3.00	1.11	-0.07	Reworked glaciomarine sediment, Loks Land
-3194	na	36.5	1.47		7.2	2.02	2.25	0.31	Rocky tidal flat, outer Cyrus Field Bay
-3195	1.5	52.2	0.05	0.2	7.3	-0.08	0.64	0.27	Weathered bedrock source, Cape Farrington
			Major river basins						
GRL-3192	1*	12.8	0.90	0.4	8.3	3.15	1.65	-0.16	Head of Cyrus Field Bay
			Protected environments						
GRL-3182	7	14.5	0.49	0.6	7.5	2.40	1.31	-0.05	Gold Cove
-3183	2	26.1	0.17	1.5	8.0	1.17	1.07	0.04	Same as above, but higher on beach
-3184	2.5	0.7	0.63	5.7	8.2	2.98	0.69	0.09	Reworked glaciomarine sediments (GRL-3185), Sabine Bay
-3196	1	5.1	2.87		7.3	2.68	2.66	0.26	Interisland channel behind Cape Farrington
-3202	5	25.2	0.52		7.0	1.13	1.09	0.13	Loks Land
			Areas of present glacial input						
GRL-3176	2	56.2	0.46	0.5	7.9	0.80	1.47	0.32	Apparently derived from weathered bedrock, Watts Bay
-3181	10	1.5	0.23	0.8	7.6	3.72	1.46	-0.07	Sampled 1 km from glacier terminus, head of Watts Bay

* m below *low* tide.

Protected low- to moderate-relief environments are common along the southwest coasts of Hall and Meta Incognita peninsulas. Raised Pleistocene marine and glaciomarine deposits are common in these areas, and the littoral sediments are not as coarse grained as those derived from in situ weathering products. Of particular interest is sample GRL-3184, which was sampled several metres from GRL-3185, the glaciomarine source material. The mean particle size of the littoral sediment is one phi class larger than that of the source, largely because of selective winnowing of the fine fraction (<4 phi; 63 μm). Sorting has improved from very poorly sorted to moderately well sorted, and the strong fine-skewness of the source sediment has been replaced by a near-symmetrical distribution. Sample GRL-3196 is an extreme case of the protected environment. The sediment is very poorly sorted and fine-skewed, and is indicative of an environment in which little winnowing of sediment has occurred.

Beaches in an area of present glaciation are subject to high influx of rock flour. Sample GRL-3181 contains the highest percentage of fine particles of all the modern beach samples, and is among the poorest sorted. Sample GRL-3176, which has an extensive local source of weathered bed-

rock (as indicated by the high percentage of very coarse sand), also shows the poor sorting and fine-skewness due to the high influx of silt and clay. It is not surprising that these samples fall within the envelope of particle size distributions determined for the Pleistocene glaciomarine sediments.

Modern beach sediments, although better sorted and with a more symmetrical particle size distribution than their source rocks, reflect the composition of the source material. The degree of similarity may be a function of both the exclusivity of the sediment source, thus the potential mixing of different sediments, and the energy of the littoral environment, thus the degree of winnowing of fines.

Beach morphology

Profiles of the littoral zone were made by level and staff at localities ranging from steep bedrock coasts to broad tidal flats (Fig. 18.9A, B, C). The profiles are, in general, logarithmic, with occasional berms slightly above the high tide level, and a general decrease in slope above that level. Exceptions occur on bedrock coasts, where the time since

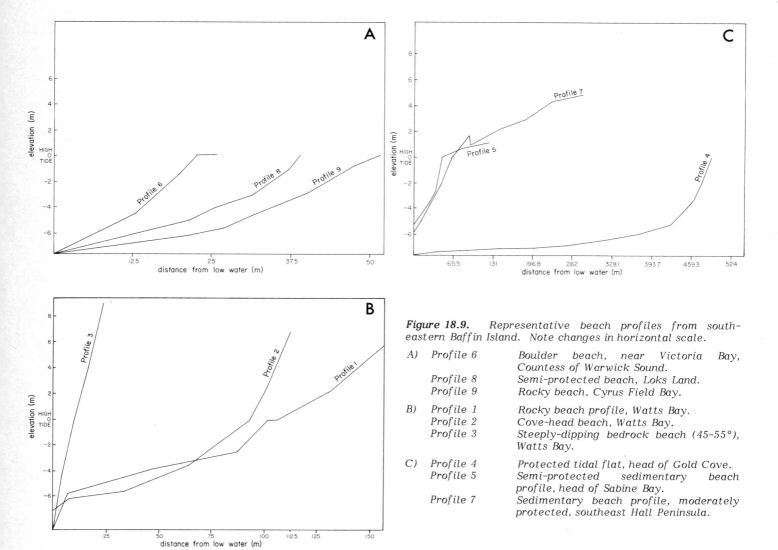

Figure 18.9. Representative beach profiles from southeastern Baffin Island. Note changes in horizontal scale.

A) *Profile 6*   Boulder beach, near Victoria Bay, Countess of Warwick Sound.
   Profile 8   Semi-protected beach, Loks Land.
   Profile 9   Rocky beach, Cyrus Field Bay.

B) *Profile 1*   Rocky beach profile, Watts Bay.
   Profile 2   Cove-head beach, Watts Bay.
   Profile 3   Steeply-dipping bedrock beach (45-55°), Watts Bay.

C) *Profile 4*   Protected tidal flat, head of Gold Cove.
   Profile 5   Semi-protected sedimentary beach profile, head of Sabine Bay.
   Profile 7   Sedimentary beach profile, moderately protected, southeast Hall Peninsula.

Figure 18.10. Sabine Bay

Note increasing grain size with increasing height in the beach profile. (Same as Profile 5, Fig. 18.9C.)

shoreline stability after isostatic uplift has not been sufficient to allow cutting of a beach profile. Sediment sampling across beach profiles reveals a gradual coarsening of the sediment towards the higher, steeper sections of beach near the high tide level (GRL-3182, 7 m bht and GRL-3183, 2 m bht; Table 18.3, and Fig. 18.10).

Bathymetric profiles, recorded on a continuous-trace echo-sounder, showed a wide variation even over short stretches of coastline. In general, soundings off high-relief coasts reveal that the land continues to drop steeply away from the shore, whereas submarine areas off low- and moderate-relief shorelines lie nearly flat. Much of Hamlen Bay, Countess of Warwick Sound, Cyrus Field Bay and the sea to the south of Loks Land are less than 20 m deep. Where deltas enter the sea at the heads of the larger bays, inlets and fiords, the foreset beds extend at the angle of repose to a depth in excess of 20 m.

Storm wave scour

The limit of recurrent storm wave activity is indicated by the upper limit of vegetation-free bedrock (Fig. 18.11), and is confirmed by the occasional presence of marine flotsam. Storm wave scour was found to be extreme along the headlands of Resolution Island, Loks Land, and the exposed reaches of southeastern Hall Peninsula. The upper limit of wave scour exceeded 30 m aht on most exposed headlands, but 4 to 5 m aht limits were more common. The orientations of reaches of greatest wave scour (northeast and southeast) suggest that major storm waves originate in both the Labrador Sea and Davis Strait. The former appears to be the dominant source area.

Recent sea level changes

Isostatic uplift of southeastern Baffin Island commenced by ca. 11 000 years BP in compensation for the reduced ice load as the Laurentide Ice Sheet receded from its glacial maximum. Eustatic sea level rose from a minimum ca. 18 000 BP to close to present day levels by 5000 BP. Initially land emerged rapidly and by 6000 BP 75 to 90 per cent had been recovered. Along the outer east coast of the area uplift probably ceased by ca. 3000 BP.

Field evidence along the entire east coast of Baffin Island points to a recent submergence of the land relative to the sea, particularly in outer Frobisher Bay and eastern Hall Peninsula. Evidence for such a phenomenon includes encroaching beaches frequently ponding minor drainages, river valleys graded below present sea level, bay mouth bars and spits (Fig. 18.8), marine sediment overlying terrestrial plant

Table 18.3. Radiocarbon dates pertaining to the Recent rise of relative sea level on eastern Baffin Island

Location	Material	Date	Comments
		(years BP)	
Clearwater Fiord, Cumberland Sound	Peat	620 ± 210 (Qu-308)	Indurated terrestrial peat, collected at high tide. Presently being wave-eroded indicating relative sea level rise
Head, Narpaing Fiord, Northern Cumberland Peninsula	Moss	750 ± 140 (GaK-3639)	In situ moss overlain by beach sands
Fiord North of Kekertelung Island, Cumberland Sound	Buried soil	830 ± 70 (Qu-305)	0.55 m aht, 0.5 m depth, developed on marine sediment, overlain by eolian sand
Broughton Island, Cumberland Peninsula	Peat	810 ± 80 (SI-2549)	Peat exposed at mean tide level, overlain by shingle beach
Canso Channel, Northern Cumberland Peninsula	Buried soil	930 ± 100 (GaK-3096)	Soil overlain by 30 cm shingle beach
Head, unnamed fiord South of Padloping Island	Buried surface vegetation	1070 ± 90 (GaK- 4309)	Vegetation mat buried by 40 cm beach sand; mat currently 0.1 m aht
Quajon Fiord, Northern Cumberland Peninsula	Organic detritus	1130 ± 80 (GSC-1845)	Fragments of vascular plants and algae 0.1 m bht, overlain by 50 cm beach sands
Sabine Bay, outer Frobisher Bay	Marsh Peat	1510 ± 240 (QC-479)	Surface of peat monolith killed by recent sea level rise, surface currently 0.5 m bht
Head, Kingnait Fiord, Southern Cumberalnd Peninsula	Peat	3320 ± 80 (SI-3457)	Basal peat date of 50 cm monolith; top of peat currently 0.5 m bht; sea level below present at onset of peat formation, since risen

Figure 18.11. *Loks Land*

Wave scour on exposed headland. Line of small ice bodies indicates mean high tide. Water level ca 5 m below high tide.

Figure 18.12. *Sabine Bay*

Partially buried, submerged peat, ca 0.5 m bht. Peat surface dated 1510 ± 240 years B.P. (QC-479).

remains (Fig. 18.12), cliffing of unconsolidated terrestrial deposits, and the erosion or burial by marine sands of Inuit tent rings and winter houses of the Thule culture. The extent of submergence is greatest along the outermost east coast and decreases to the west. It is estimated that sea level has risen relative to the land by 1 to 2 m in the last two millenia in the Loks Land area, but there is no unambiguous evidence for submergence at the head of Frobisher Bay.

Several dates have been obtained that bear on the cessation of emergence and onset of submergence (Table 18.3). The oldest date on the onset of submergence comes from outer Frobisher Bay where a salt-marsh peat in a relatively protected bay has been buried by encroaching beach sands and is currently 0.5 m bht. The uppermost part of the peat bed yielded a radiocarbon date of 1510 ± 240 years BP (QC-479). The base of a similar peat monolith collected nearly 1 m bht in Kingnait Fiord, southern Cumberland Peninsula, gave a date of 3320 ± 80 years (SI-3457), suggesting that at that time relative sea level was below present level. We suggest that submergence began between 1500 and 2500 years BP, in response to either an increased water load on the continental shelf caused by the late Pleistocene sea level rise, or the migration of a forebulge through the area.

CONCLUSIONS

Airphoto mapping and field studies of the coastline of southeastern Baffin Island confirm that most of the coast is composed of moderately sloping to steep bedrock. The only parameter used to describe the rocky coast is the coastline density, a measure of the length of coastline within a given area. Coastline density varies with the slope and geomorphic history of an area, and may have potential as an indicator of environmental hazard.

Beaches are only sporadic in favoured localites. They can be identified on airphotos, but detailed information can be obtained only in the field. The sedimentological characteristics of the beaches are in part inherited from the source materials, and in part dictated by the littoral environment. Most of the beaches, although small, are at the foot of exposed headlands. Other environments conducive to beach formation are the mouths of rivers draining areas of Pleistocene sedimentation, protected low- to moderate-relief coast, and areas with a high influx of glacial debris. The failure of the beaches to reach uniformity in sediment and morphology can be explained by the youth of the present shoreline. The outer part of Frobisher Bay was deglaciated ca. 11 000 years BP. Since that time, relative sea level has fallen 20 to 120 m over the study area. At present, the southeastern Baffin Island coast is submerging.

Acknowledgments

Field and laboratory studies were supported by a contract to R.G. Barry and G.H. Miller from the Arctic Petroleum Operators Association (APOA Project 138) entitled "The Coastal Environment of Southern Baffin Island and Northern Labrador-Ungava". This project was part of the Eastern Arctic Marine Environmental Study (EAMES). We thank Mr. G. Rempel and Mr. T. Watmore, Imperial Oil Limited, Calgary and Dr. Olaf Løken, Environment Canada for their co-ordination of the project and logistical support. Mr. H. Moulton provided field assistance; air support was provided by APEX Helicopters and Bradley Air Services Ltd. Mr. E. Sieber, Parks Canada, and Mary Pratt, INSTAAR, provided emergency radio assistance. Partial support was supplied by the National Science Foundation (U.S.A.) in grant DES-74-01857.

References

Andrews, J.T. and Miller, G.H.
  1979:   Glacial erosion and ice sheet divides, north-eastern Laurentide Ice Sheet, on the basis of the distribution of limestone erratics. Geology, v. 7, p. 592 - 596.

Barry, R.G., Krane R.G., Locke, C.W., Locke, W.W., III and Miller, G.H.
  1977:   The coastal environment of southern Baffin Island and northern Labrador-Ungava. Final Report to the Arctic Petroleum Operators Association; Calgary, Alberta APOA Project 138, University of Colorado, 166 p.

Dohler, G.
          Tides in Canadian water; Canadian Hydrographic Service, Energy, Mines and Resources, Ottawa, 166 p. (catalogue no. M54-966).

  1968:   Canadian Hydrographic Service Pilot of Arctic Canada; Marine Sciences Branch, Energy, Mines and Resources, Ottawa, 468 p.

Miller, G.H.
  1980:   Late Foxe glaciation of southern Baffin Island, N.W.T., Canada. Bulletin of the Geological Society of America, v. 91, p. 399 - 405.

19

COASTAL ENVIRONMENTS OF THE MAKKOVIK REGION, LABRADOR

Peter S. Rosen
Geological Survey of Canada, Bedford Institute of Oceanography,
Dartmouth, Nova Scotia

Rosen, Peter S., Coastal environments of the Makkovik region, Labrador; in The Coastline of Canada, S.B. McCann, editor; Geological Survey of Canada, Paper 80-10, p. 267-280, 1980.

Abstract

The Makkovik region (55°N, 59°W) has highly indented fiord-type coast that is characteristic of much of northern Labrador. Makkovik Bay, which is 31 km long, is the major embayment. The tidal range is 1.4 m, and maximum significant wave heights seaward of the area are 7.3 m, with 16 second periods. The wave activity is curtailed by ice cover about six months each year. Both modern and relict coastal forms are related to variations in wave energy. Relative estimates of wave energy are made by comparing the heights of the wave-wash zone in rocky areas.

High energy shorelines (wave-wash zone >6 m) face the Labrador Sea and consist of bedrock cliffs up to 40 m high. They are nearly devoid of sediment except for small, isolated cobble beaches at the heads of structural embayments and there is no development of boulder barricades. Low energy shorelines (wave-wash zone 0-2 m) are characterized by a more diverse shore morphology dominated by narrow sand beaches with poorly-developed back beach zones. The sources of beach sediments are glacial deposits, which flank the bays, and recent fluvial deposits. Rock outcrops are ubiquitous but typically small and intermittent. Accretional coastal landforms occur in inner Makkovik Bay, and fringe marsh forms over sand or rock in the intertidal zone in protected areas. Boulder barricades are a nearly continuous feature. Transitional energy shorelines (wave-wash zone 2-6 m) consist of pocket cobble beaches, rocky headlands, and sand beaches. Raised beaches, up to 35 m above sea level in high energy settings, are isolated cobble deposits representing preservation of a storm berm. In low energy settings, raised beaches are continuous sand ridges.

Résumé

La région de Makkovik (55°N, 59°W) possède une cóte très découpée du type à fjords qui caractérise la plus grande partie du Labrador septentrional. La baie de Makkovik, d'une longueur de 13 km, est le principal entrant de la cóte. L'amplitude de la marée est de 1,4 m et les hauteurs significatives maximales des vagues sur la façade maritime du secteur sont de 7,3 m et leur période est de 16 secondes. L'action des vagues est enrayée par le manteau glaciel pendant environ 6 mois de l'année. Les formes littorales actuelles et héritées sont toutes deux liées aux variations de l'énergie développée par les vagues. Des estimations relatives de l'énergie des vagues sont faites en comparant les différents niveaux de la zone balayée par les vagues dans les secteurs rocheux.

Des littoraux à haute énergie (zone de balayage des vagues >6 m) donnent sur la mer du Labrador et possèdent des falaises rocheuses atteignant 40 m de hauteur. Elles sont presque dépourvues de sédiments sauf pour ce qui est de petites plages caillouteuses isolées, situées au fond d'entrants structurals; il ne se forme pas non plus de barricades de blocs rocheux. Les littoraux à basse énergie (zone de balayage: 0-2 m) sont caractérisés par une morphologie plus variée et dominés par d'étroites plages sablonneuses entrecoupées de zones d'arrière-plages mal développées. Les sources de matériaux de plages sont des dépôts glaciaires situées de part et d'autre des baies ainsi que de récents dépôts fluviatiles. Les affleurements rocheux sont présents partout mais particulièrement petits et intermittents. On trouve des formes de reliefs cótiers d'engraissement à l'intérieur de la baie Makkovik et des formes marécageuses périphériques recouvrant du sable ou le substrat rocheux dans la zone intertidale de secteurs protégés. Les barricades de blocs rocheux sont des accidents presque continus. Les littoraux à énergie de transition (zone de balayage de 2 à 6 m) sont faits de petites plages caillouteuses, de promontoires rocheux et de plages sablonneuses. Des plages soulevées atteignant 35 m au-dessus du niveau de la mer dans les endroits à haute énergie sont formées par des dépôts de cailloux isolés correspondant à la préservation d'un gradin de plage. Dans les emplacements à basse énergie, les plages soulevées sont des crêtes de sable continues.

INTRODUCTION

The Makkovik Region is a highly indented fiord-type coast characteristic of much of the northern and central Labrador coastline. The purpose of this investigation was to form a model of the morpho- dynamic factors influencing subarctic shorelines.

The investigation was an experiment in devising techniques to understand the regional coastal morphodynamics in remote areas. Conventional aerial photography proved to be of little value in interpreting the narrow coastal zone without substantial ground truth information, and aerial reconnaissance was prohibitively expensive. Therefore, the coastal sediment types were mapped from a small boat in 1977. Modified zonal-type studies (Hayes et al., 1973) employing a one-man beach profiling device were made at selected sites. This assessment of the major processes served as groundwork for later dynamic studies of ice-sediment relationships. Detailed maps were prepared of coastal types (Figs. 19.15 - 19.18) for the following analysis and as a guide for future development or environmental emergencies.

SETTING

A straight-line distance of 19 km along the Labrador Sea (Cape Aillik to Pomiadluk Point) comprises the 173 km of shoreline in the study area. Makkovik Bay, which is 31 km long, is the major embayment. Six smaller embayments flank this main fiord (Fig. 19.1).

Water depths in the outer bay reach 80 m; several islands and rocky shoals in the approaches protect the bay from open ocean swell and large icebergs. In the inner bay there are several separate basins 40 to 60 m deep. Rivers drain into the head of the bay and into the head of Makkovik Harbour (Piper and Iuliucci, 1978).

The Makkovik subprovince is the southernmost part of the Nain geological province, consisting of Archean orogenic belts (Green, 1974). The coastal area is surrounded by the Aillik Series, which consists of volcanic and metamorphic rocks that have been folded into a series of north-northeasterly trending folds with synkinematic intrusions (Gandhi et al., 1969). The glacially excavated fiords that form the shoreline are aligned with the major fold belts (Fig. 19.2).

The bay and surrounding sea are generally frozen from December to early June each year. The mean ice thickness seaward of Makkovik Bay is 1.5 m (United States Oceanographic Office, 1968). Ice thicknesses of about 2 m are reported as typical for inside the bay (James Anderson, pers. com., 1977).

Long-term wind records (1963 - 1972) are available for Hopedale, 75 km to the north. Prevailing winds during the ice-free period (June to December) were from the west-southwest (offshore) direction. Mean velocities were fairly uniform (~6 m/s) from all directions except southeast. During the ice-breakup period (May to June) highest mean velocities (7 m/s) occurred from the north-northwest; winds were from the northerly quadrant (onshore) 42 per cent of this period (Fig. 19.3a, b) (Atmospheric Environment Service, 1975).

The tides in the region are semidiurnal and slightly mixed. The mean range is 1.4 m and the large tide range is 2.2 m (Canadian Hydrographic Service, 1977). The maximum significant wave heights recorded seaward of Makkovik are 7.3 m with 16 second periods (Paul Vandall, Atlantic Oceanographic Laboratory, pers. com., 1978). The wave activity is curtailed by ice cover for six months each year.

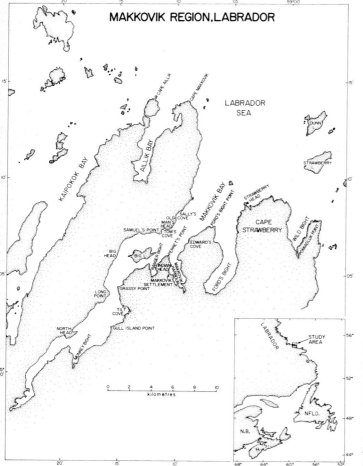

Figure 19.1. Location map of the Makkovik region, Labrador.

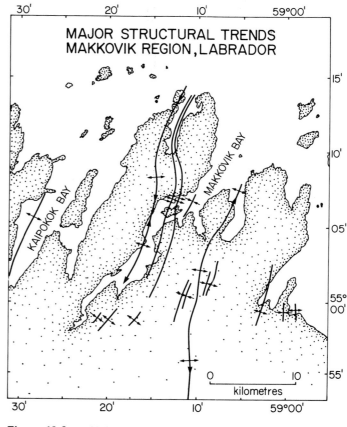

Figure 19.2. Major structural trends of the Makkovik region (after Gandhi et al., 1969). The fiords are aligned with the structural weaknesses.

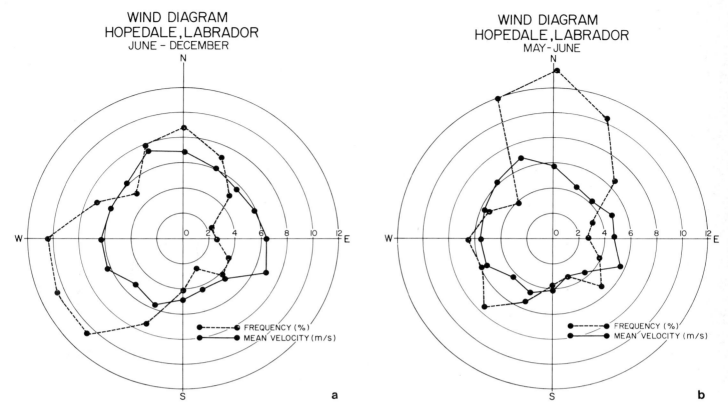

Figure 19.3. *Wind diagrams, Hopedale, Labrador (1963-1972). a) June-December, the ice-free period, b) May-June, the ice-breakup period.*

The Labrador coast is a region of glacio-isostatic recovery, resulting in a Holocene history of relative sea level fall. The coastal zone commonly contains raised shoreline sequences. Andrews (1970) calculated the average rate of Holocene sea level fall in the Nain region as 1.36 cm/year. Blake (1953) estimated that the Lake Melville area emerged at the rate of 0.4 cm/year for the last 1900 years. Wenner (1947) and Tanner (1941) suggested that the negative movement of the water line in Labrador has nearly ceased. This suggestion is based on observations of well formed rock benches that indicate sea level has been stable for a long time. In Makkovik Bay, actively eroding Pleistocene headlands appear to lend credence to this view, but this erosion is better explained by storm erosion in a sediment-starved environment. Analysis of the tide gauge records for Nain (1963-1973) shows a recent mean emergence rate of 0.53 cm/year. Although the length of this record is less than all tidal components and too short to average all storm cycles, it is indicative of the regional trend (Stacey Hicks, NOAA, pers. com., 1978) of a diminished but still active emergence.

COASTAL MORPHOLOGY

Distribution

The distribution of both modern and relict coastal forms is related to variations in wave energy. Relative estimates of wave energy were made by comparing the heights of the wave-wash zone in rocky areas (Fig. 19.4).

High-energy shorelines (wave-wash zone > 6 m) face the Labrador Sea and consist of bedrock cliffs up to 40 m high (Table 19.1). These shorelines are nearly devoid of sediment except for small, isolated cobble beaches at the heads of structural embayments. There is little or no development of boulder barricades along rocky, high-energy shorelines.

Low-energy shorelines (wave-wash zone 0-2 m) occur inside the bays, are characterized by a more diverse shore morphology, and comprise over 52 per cent of the system. Narrow sand beaches with poorly developed back beach zones are the dominant coastal form. The sources of beach sediments are glacial deposits which flank the inner bays and recent fluvial deposits. Rock outcrops are ubiquitous but typically small. Accretional coastal landforms occurring in inner Makkovik Bay, include cuspate spits, transverse bars, longshore spits and tombolos. Fringe marsh forms over sand or rock substrates in the intertidal zone in protected areas. Boulder barricades are a nearly continuous feature along low-energy shorelines.

Moderate-energy shorelines (wave-wash zone 2-6 m) are transitional and consist of pocket cobble beaches, rocky headlands and sand beaches. The sand beaches often have a well developed back beach because they are exposed to higher wave activity than low-energy shorelines.

Rock shorelines

Rock shorelines comprise 53 per cent of the area and are found at all energy levels. Rock coasts, the dominant form (82%) in high-energy areas, typically consist of barren cliffs

Table 19.1. Coastal environments, Makkovik Region, Labrador

	(km)	(%)	(% of system)
Low energy (wave-wash zone 0 - 2 m)			
Salt marsh	17.2	18.8	
Sand beach	39.1	42.8	
Rock	35.1	38.4	
Total	91.4		52.7
Moderate energy (wave-wash zone 2 - 6 m)			
Sand beach	12.6	31.6	
Cobble beach	3.8	9.5	
Rock	23.5	58.9	
Total	39.9		23.0
High energy (wave-wash zone > 6 m)			
Cobble beach	7.7	18.3	
Rock	34.4	81.7	
Total	42.1		24.3
Rock shorelines			
Fractured	48.1		27.7
Smooth	44.9		25.8
Total	93.0		53.6
Sandy shorelines	51.7		29.8
Cobble shorelines	11.5		6.6
Salt marsh shorelines	17.2		9.9

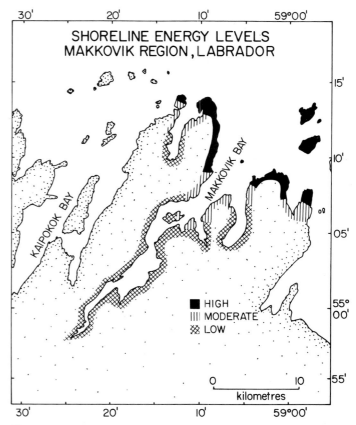

Figure 19.4. *Wave energy levels along Makkovik shoreline: high energy-wave-wash zone >6 m; moderate energy-wave-wash zone 2-6 m; low energy-wave-wash zone 0-2 m.*

with no intertidal sediment accumulations for several kilometres along the shore (Fig. 19.5). The cliffs drop below the low-water line where either a rock slope or nearshore sand prism (Piper and Iuliucci, 1978) grades into the deeper fiord basin. In low-energy areas, more abundant sediment diminishes rock outcrop to small intermittent exposures that do not extend below the midtide line.

The rocky shore was catagorized into smooth and fractured types regardless of the lithology. Fractured shore is a boulder producer because of rock type, joint patterns and orientation. Rock shores are about evenly distributed between fractured and smooth types (Table 19.1). There is little or no development of boulder barricades (q.v.) along high-energy rock shores, probably because of the absence of an active intertidal zone.

Beaches

Modern beaches

The beaches are of two distinct types, sandy and cobble. Sand beaches are the dominant coastal form in low-energy areas (42.8%) and form continuous beaches up to 5 km long. The sediment is derived from glacial and fluvial deposits commonly flanking the shoreline in the inner bay. Terrestrial vegetation extends to near the high-water line in low-energy areas, so the beach is restricted to the intertidal zone (Fig. 19.6). In moderate-energy areas, periodic larger

storm waves are influential in the development of a back beach. The region of Grassy Point - Tilt Cove - Gull Island Point is oriented away from the bay mouth, and has an abundant glacially derived sand supply. Numerous accretional coastal landforms have developed in this area including an accretional cuspate spit, transverse bars, longshore spits and tombolos tied to Pleistocene hummocks offshore (Fig. 19.7).

Sandy beaches, as most of the inner bay shorelines, are succeeded seaward by a broad sand or muddy (a relict grey marine clay) intertidal zone. Boulder barricades occur at the low-water line. Seaward of barricades, the offshore slope consistently increases and grades into fine sediment. The intertidal zone landward of the barricade has randomly scattered boulders, whereas seaward of the barricade boulders are noticeably absent.

The only sediment accumulations in high-energy environments are pocket cobble beaches that form in structural embayments (Fig. 19.8). These minor embayments can generally be ascribed to fault or joint planes, or mafic dykes. All cobble beaches are short, isolated features and the cobbles are probably locally derived. A small pocket beach on the south shore of Big Island is flanked by a mafic intrusion on the west and lighter volcanics on the east, and the beach material was dark on the west and light on the east with little mixing. Although isolated features, cobble beaches form 18 per cent of the length of high-energy areas, and are the only high-energy environment where boulder barricades form.

Figure 19.5. *A high energy rocky shore near Cape Makkovik.*

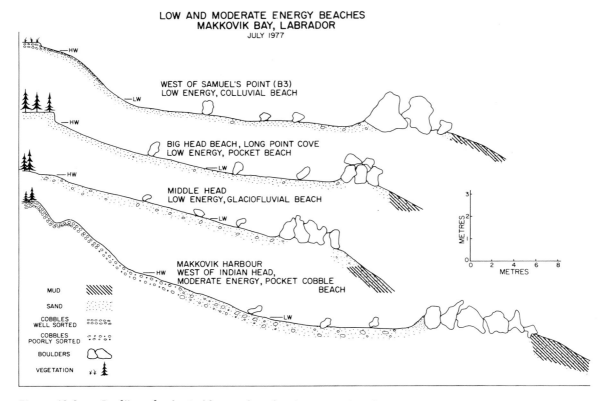

LOW AND MODERATE ENERGY BEACHES
MAKKOVIK BAY, LABRADOR
JULY 1977

WEST OF SAMUEL'S POINT (B3)
LOW ENERGY, COLLUVIAL BEACH

BIG HEAD BEACH, LONG POINT COVE
LOW ENERGY, POCKET BEACH

MIDDLE HEAD
LOW ENERGY, GLACIOFLUVIAL BEACH

MAKKOVIK HARBOUR
WEST OF INDIAN HEAD,
MODERATE ENERGY, POCKET COBBLE
BEACH

MUD
SAND
COBBLES WELL SORTED
COBBLES POORLY SORTED
BOULDERS
VEGETATION

METRES

0 2 4 6 8
METRES

Figure 19.6. *Profiles of selected low and moderate energy beaches.*

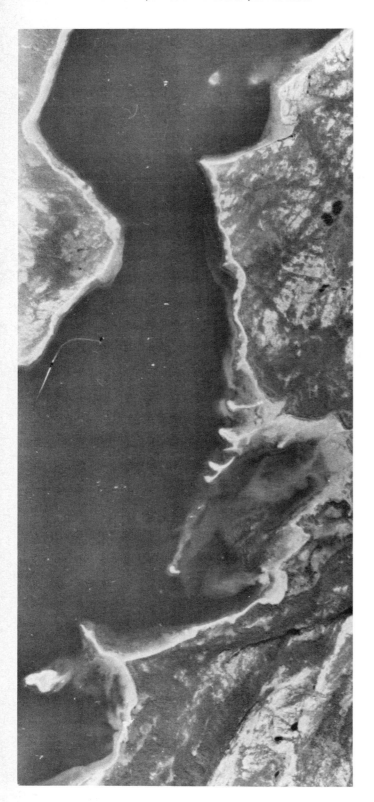

Figure 19.7. *Tilt Cove, inner Makkovik Bay. An accretional cuspare spit, transverse bars and tombolos are present.*

Raised beaches

Raised beach deposits in the Makkovik Region are evidence of regional uplift. There are two characteristic forms of raised beaches, corresponding to variations in wave energy levels. In high-energy settings, the cobble beaches in structural embayments often form vertically continuous raised sequences (Fig. 19.9). The lower intertidal zone is typically composed of unsorted sand through boulder-size material, the beach face is poorly sorted cobbles, and the storm berm is well sorted cobbles. The elevation of the highest active storm berm was up to 10 m above high water, but this position varies as a function of exposure of the beach to wave energy. The surface of the raised sequence is relict storm ridge deposits composed of well sorted cobbles. In some areas the source of cobbles was interrupted during uplift, leaving a perched raised beach above a rocky shore. Although the raised beach sequences are composed of identifiable ridges up to 35 m above sea level, correlation between sequences is not realistic, as each cobble beach is an isolated system.

Daly (1902) noted the raised beach sequences at Aillik Bay and Pomiadluk Point, and the former, north of Cape Makkovik and facing the Labrador Sea, is the most extensive cobble beach deposit in the area. Wenner (1947, p. 156) presented a profile of this raised sequence, which extends to an elevation of over 20 m.

In lower energy areas, sand beaches form long, continuous, uplifted ridge sequences. These ridges are most apparent in inner Ford's Bight (Fig. 19.10). The ridge sequences are probably relict nearshore terraces and therefore closely represent a mean sea level. They are identifiable by vegetation changes (typically ridges are dense deciduous forests). Examination of the ridges from the ground is difficult, as thick humus obscures the original sands. These raised shorelines follow the contours of the present waterline, and extend to a maximum elevation of 60 m.

Embayments

The heads of all major embayments are the lowest energy environments and have a distinct morphology. The development of fringe marsh in the upper intertidal zone is characteristic of this region. These marsh deposits are thin (generally less than 50 cm), and form over either rocky or sand substrates. Salt marsh is present on 19 per cent of all low-energy areas, and 10 per cent of the study area. Most salt marsh development is in inner Makkovik Bay. Minor embayments in high-energy areas are sites for accumulation of cobble and minor embayments in low-energy areas develop salt marsh.

A sandy deltaic apron is present in the shallow subtidal zone at the head of low-energy embayments. The size of the deposit is a function of fluvial sediment input, either presently active or relict, and there is a distinct break-in-slope at the seaward limit, corresponding to Gilbert-type topset bedding. Boulder flats are superimposed on the delta flat (Fig. 19.11).

Figure 19.8. *A raised cobble beach at Perrets Point.*

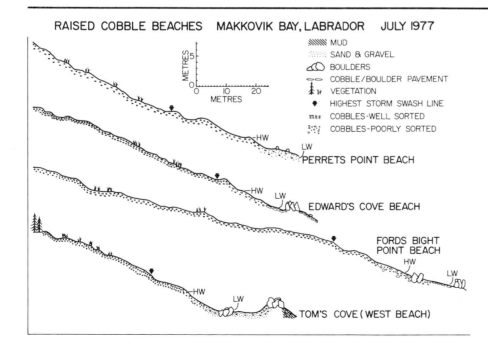

RAISED COBBLE BEACHES MAKKOVIK BAY, LABRADOR JULY 1977

MUD
SAND & GRAVEL
BOULDERS
COBBLE/BOULDER PAVEMENT
VEGETATION
HIGHEST STORM SWASH LINE
COBBLES-WELL SORTED
COBBLES-POORLY SORTED

METRES

0   10   20
METRES

PERRETS POINT BEACH

EDWARD'S COVE BEACH

FORDS BIGHT POINT BEACH

TOM'S COVE (WEST BEACH)

HW
LW

Figure 19.9.

Profiles of selected raised cobble beaches in Makkovik Bay.

Figure 19.10. *Ford's Bight. Raised low energy shorelines follow the contours of the modern shore, occurring up to a maximum elevation of 60 m.*

Figure 19.11. *An embayment. The random boulder field lies on a delta flat. Fringe marsh lines the shoreline.*

ICE FEATURES

Background

Ice controls the shore processes for six months of the year. The action of ice as a coastal sediment transport mechanism was recognized in North America by 1822 (Lee 1822, 1825; Adams 1825; Wood 1825). Daly (1902) recognized the specialized form of boulder accumulation in tidal areas, and labelled them 'boulder barricades'. Boulder barricades are rows of boulders near the low-water line that parallel the shoreline. Daly believed that wave scour was the major process forming these features, with ice serving a secondary role in moving boulders seaward from the intertidal zone. Ward (1959) suggested that the process is restricted to the ice breakup period when floes and bergs were observed to charge ashore. Tanner (1939) proposed a more suitable model for boulder barricade development. Barricades form only in areas that are regularly frozen and have considerable tidal range. He suggested that ice slabs containing boulders and other sediments are driven landward by wind, where they are piled up against the ice-foot along the shoreline. When the ice melts, a stony ridge is left behind parallel to the high-tide line. Lyell (1854) first commented on the prevalence of boulder accumulations in Labrador, and Bird (1964) noted that the finest development of boulder barricades in the Canadian Arctic is in Labrador. Løken (1962) used raised boulder barricades to map postglacial emergence of northernmost Labrador.

The Makkovik Region

Boulder barricades (Fig. 19.12) flank all shorelines except high-energy rocky areas, where there are no intertidal platforms. They are found, however, seaward of most high-energy cobble beaches. The distance of the barricades from shore increases with decreasing nearshore slope (Fig. 19.13). They occur near the LLW line, seaward of the ice hinge zone in a water depth at high tide which approximates the locally reported thickness of ice in Makkovik Bay (≈ 2 m). It is suggested that during spring breakup, ice blocks are grounded at this point, depositing and pushing boulder material brought ashore or along shore by ice rafting. As Tanner suggests, the shore-fast ice further inhibits the ice blocks from moving farther onshore.

Random ice-rafted boulder fields occur on the sandy deltaic deposits at the bay heads. They are probably related to a pileup of ice blocks during ice breakup due to the prevalent onshore winds (Fig. 19.3b). There is no development of boulder barricades at the seaward margin of these deltas in the Makkovik Region but in other areas of Labrador such as Groswater Bay, the seaward margin of boulder flats is rimmed with a barricade. Løken (1962) believed that boulder flats and barricades are related features, the formation of which is determined by the topography of the offshore zone. Since these boulders were never observed to be buried, it is assumed that each winter they are moved or lifted by ice.

Boulder barricades are an almost continuous shore feature in low-energy environments. They are common in moderate-energy areas, but become intermittent or absent in rocky high-energy areas. This appears to be due to the lack of sand to form a gradual nearshore slope. Hence ice is not grounded but randomly drops boulders along the shore during breakup. In addition, wave reflection (Gundlach et al., 1977) may prevent melt-blocks of ice from accumulating on high-energy shorelines. Boulder barricades do form seaward of pocket cobble beaches in high-energy areas. During the summer, the barricades can act as an offshore breakwater and in low-energy areas, as an intertidal sediment trap.

Figure 19.12.   *The boulder barricade at Grassy Point (low tide).*

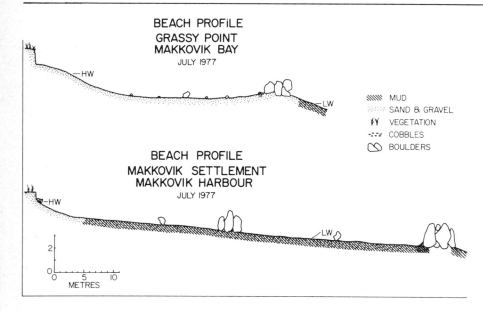

Figure 19.13.

Profiles of Grassy Point and Makkovik Settlement, demonstrating variable distance of the boulder barricade from shore. A relict barricade is present at Makkovik Settlement.

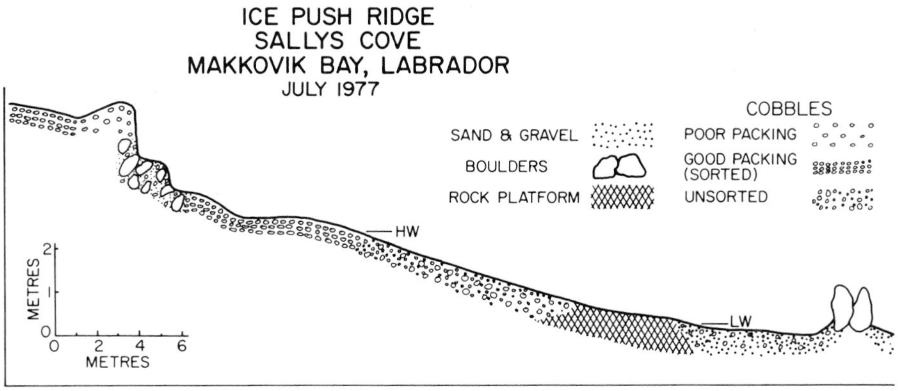

ICE PUSH RIDGE
SALLYS COVE
MAKKOVIK BAY, LABRADOR
JULY 1977

SAND & GRAVEL
BOULDERS
ROCK PLATFORM

COBBLES
POOR PACKING
GOOD PACKING
(SORTED)
UNSORTED

Figure 19.14.

Ice-push ridge and boulder barricade at Sally's Cove.

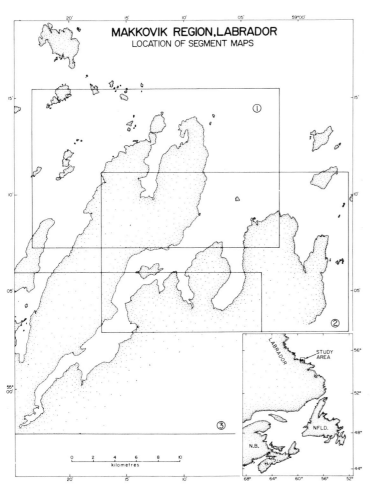

MAKKOVIK REGION, LABRADOR
LOCATION OF SEGMENT MAPS

Figure 19.15. Map showing location of segments *(Fig. 19.16-19.18) depicting shore morphology of the Makkovik region.*

Bird (1964) suggested that ice-push ridges and boulder barricades are mutually exclusive forms. Ice-push ridges were observed at only two locations, Low Point at Aillik Bay, and the seaward-facing position of Sally's Cove, Makkovik Bay. Each was oriented directly into the Labrador Sea, was on a cobble beach, and was located landward of a boulder barricade. The dearth of such a common shoreline ice feature is attributed to the boulder barricades in all sediment-rich areas. The barricades are a physical barrier to ice-push on the beachface and only in high wave energy settings can ice blocks landward of the barricades be pushed up the beach. Both ice-push sequences consisted of lunate mounds, rhythmically spaced at about 15 m intervals. The base of each ice-push ridge was composed of unsorted sand through boulder material, including quasilayered sequences from ice melt. The ridge slope was steep. The top of the features were well sorted storm ridge cobbles, pushed up by the ice. The packing of the cobbles on the top was distinctly poor (Fig. 19.14). Other minor ice features along the shoreline include ice-rafted peat blocks, boulder pavements (both landward and seaward of boulder barricades) (Fig. 19.15), and melt-deposits of sand and gravel.

CONCLUSIONS

Most of the shoreline of the Makkovik Region has a low wave energy setting. Rock cliffs occur only on the outermost shores. Salt marsh is a dominant coastal form, even though the deposits are not thick. The high-energy environment is characterized by a dearth of sediment, with minor accumulation of cobble in structural embayments. The low-energy environment is composed of continuous sandy beaches, rock and salt marsh. Low-energy embayments are characterized by fringe marsh, sandy deltaic deposits and boulder fields.

The primary landform formed by ice is the boulder barricade, which is a nearly continuous feature in sandy, low-energy areas and rare in rocky, high-energy areas. The barricade inhibits the formation of ice-push ridges in the intertidal and supratidal zones.

Two types of raised beach sequences are evident. In low-energy areas, sandy ridges are continuous for several kilometres, whereas in high wave energy areas, isolated pocket cobble beaches form.

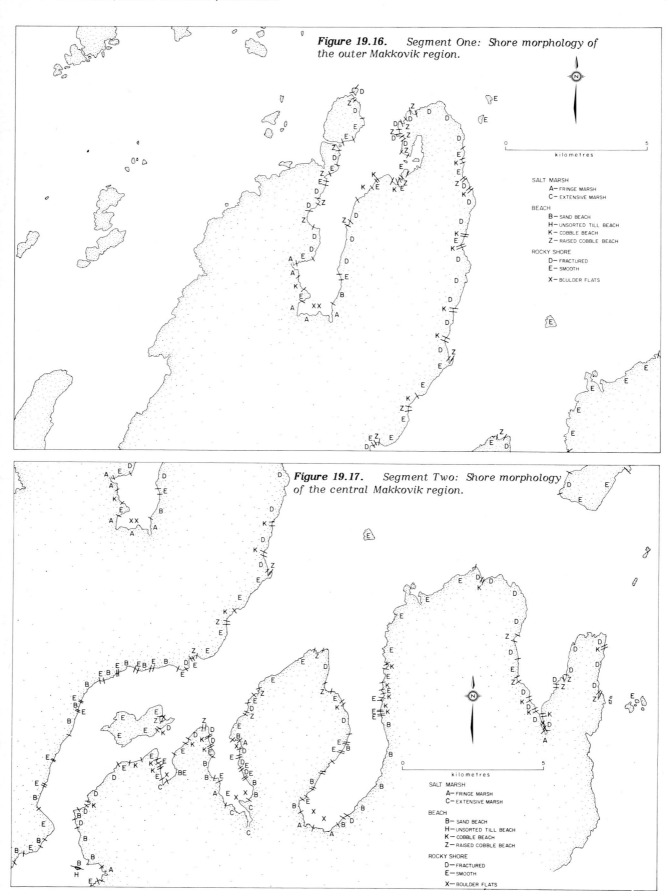

Figure 19.16. *Segment One: Shore morphology of the outer Makkovik region.*

Figure 19.17. *Segment Two: Shore morphology of the central Makkovik region.*

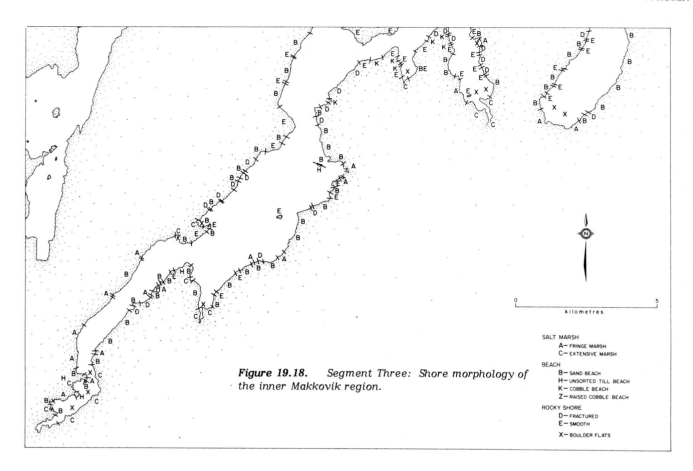

Figure 19.18. *Segment Three: Shore morphology of the inner Makkovik region.*

SALT MARSH
A— FRINGE MARSH
C— EXTENSIVE MARSH
BEACH
B— SAND BEACH
H— UNSORTED TILL BEACH
K— COBBLE BEACH
Z— RAISED COBBLE BEACH
ROCKY SHORE
D— FRACTURED
E— SMOOTH
X— BOULDER FLATS

kilometres

Acknowledgments

This study was supported by Project 770008 of the Geological Survey of Canada. I gratefully acknowledge S. Brian McCann, who provided the impetus for the initiation of this project and critically reviewed this paper. Discussions with James Anderson, Bill Anderson and Bert Winters of Makkovik proved useful in the preparation of this paper.

References

Adams, J.
    1825:   On the movement of rocks by the expansive power of freezing water; American Journal of Science, v. 9, art. XXII, p. 136 - 144.

Andrews, J.T.
    1970:   Present and postglacial rates of uplift in glaciated northern and eastern North America derived from postglacial uplift curves; Canadian Journal of Earth Sciences, v.7, p. 703 - 715.

Atmospheric Environment Service
    1975:   Canadian normals, v. 3, Wind; Environment Canada, p. 95.

Bird, J.B.
    1964:   The Physiography of Arctic Canada; John Hopkins Press, Baltimore, Maryland, p. 220.

Blake, W., Jr.
    1953:   Landforms and topography of the Lake Melville area, Labrador, Newfoundland, Geographical Bulletin, v.9, p.75 - 100.

Canadian Hydrographic Service
    1977:   Canadian tide and current tables, v. 1; Fisheries and Environment Canada, p. 79.

Daly, R.
    1902:   Geology of the northeast coast of Labrador; Harvard University Museum of Comparative Zoology, Bulletin 38, p. 203 - 270.

Gandhi, S.S., Grasty, R.L. and Grieve, R.A.F.
    1969:   The geology and geochronology of the Makkovik Bay area, Labrador; Canadian Journal of Earth Sciences, v.6, no.5, p. 1019 - 1035.

Greene, B.S.
    1974:   An outline of the geology of Labrador; Newfoundland, Department of Mines and Energy, St. John's, Information Circular No. 15, 64 p.

Gundlach, E.R., Hayes, M.O., Ruby, C.H., Ward, L.G., Blout, A.E., Fischer, I.A. and Stein, R.J.
    1977:   Some guidelines for oil spill control in coastal environments based on field studies of four oil spills; preprint submitted to ASTM Symposium on Chemical Dispersants for the Control of Oil Spills, Williamsburg, Va., 32 p.

Hayes, M.O., Owens, E.H., Hubbard, D.K. and Abele, R.W.
    1973:   The investigation of form and processes in the coastal zone; Coastal Geomorphology, Proceedings of the Third Annual Geomorphology Symposia Series, Binghamton, New York, D.R. Coates, ed.; p. 11 - 42.

Lee, C.A. (PETROS)
    1822:   On certain rocks supposed to move without an apparent cause; American Journal of Science, v.5, art. VI, p. 34 - 37.

Lee, C.A.
    1825:   Remarks on the moving rocks of Salisbury; American Journal of Science, v.9, art. III, p. 239 - 241.

Løken, O.
    1962:   The late-glacial and post glacial emergence and the deglaciation of northernmost Labrador; Geographical Bulletin, no. 17, p. 23 - 56.

Lyell, C
    1854:   Principles of geology; New York, Appleton, 834 p.

Piper, D.J.W. and Iuliucci, R.J.
    1978:   Reconnaissance of the marine geology of Makkovik Bay, Labrador; in Current Research, Part A, Geological Survey of Canada, Paper 78-1A, p. 333 - 336.

Tanner, V.
    1941:   Ruinerna på Sculpin Island (Kanayoktok) i Nain's Skärgård, Newfoundland-Labrador. Ett Förmodat nordbovists från medeltiden; Geografisk Tidskift, Bd 44, Kohenhavn.

United States Oceanographic Office
    1968:   Oceanographic Atlas of the North Atlantic Ocean, Section III, Ice; U.S. Naval Oceanographic Office Publication No. 700.

Ward, W.H.
    1959:   Ice action on shores; Journal of Glaciology, v.3, p. 437.

Wenner, C.G.
    1947:   Pollen diagrams from Labrador; Geografiska Annaler, v. 29, p. 137 - 372.

Wood, J.
    1825:   Remarks on the moving of rocks by ice; American Journal of Science, v. 9, art XXIII, p. 144 - 145.

20.

PROCESSES RESPONSIBLE FOR THE CONCENTRATION OF BOULDERS IN THE INTERTIDAL ZONE IN LEAF BASIN, UNGAVA

Bernard Lauriol and James T. Gray
Department of Geography, Université de Montréal, Montréal, Québec

Lauriol, Bernard and Gray, James T., Processes responsible for the concentration of boulders in the intertidal zone of Leaf Basin, Ungava; in The Coastline of Canada, S.B. McCann, editor; Geological Survey of Canada, Paper 80-10, p. 281-292, 1980.

Abstract

Giant boulders scattered across most of the intertidal mud flats are mainly derived from a down-gradient, seaward transfer of glacial boulders by littoral ice, and, to a lesser extent, water related processes, during postglacial emergence of the region. Boulder barricades are built up only in estuarine zones, where during spring breakup, landfast basin ice presents a barrier to the seaward movement of boulders in traction. The ice pans in the river become dammed up at these points and pressure exerted by the river current causes these ice pans to bulldoze the coarse bedload into large barricades. Similar barricades at elevations of 25 m, 40 m and 60 m indicate pauses in land emergence at circa 2000-3000 years B.P. (25 m) and 5000-6000 years B.P. (40 m and 60 m).

Résumé

Des blocs géants éparpillés à travers la plus grande partie des vasières intertidales proviennent surtout d'une pente qui a favorisé le déplacement vers la mer de blocs glaciaires par les glaces littorales et dans une moindre mesure des processus hydrauliques survenus au cours du relèvement post-glaciaire de la région. Les barricades de blocs ne sont dirigées que dans les zones estuariennes, où à l'occasion du dégel printanier, les bassins de glace fixée opposent une barrière aux mouvements vers la mer des blocs traînés. Les marres glacielles du cours d'eau forment des embâcles à ces endroits et la pression exercée par le courant du cours d'eau transforme ces marres en boutoirs qui érigent la charge grossière du lit en grosses barricades. Des barricades analogues situées à des altitudes de 25, 40 et 60 m indiquent des pauses dans l'émergence du relief il y a 2000 à 3000 B.P. (25 m) et 5000 et 6000 B.P. (40 et 60 m).

INTRODUCTION

Despite many efforts in recent years to elucidate the post-glacial emergence history of the coastal areas of northern Quebec and Labrador (Gray et al., 1980; Løken 1964; Matthews, 1967), published information on the processes and landforms of the littoral zone is scarce. Only Tanner (1939), Loken (1964) and Rosen (1979), for the fiord coast of northeastern Labrador, and Gangloff (1977), for the Diana Bay coastline at the northwestern extremity of Ungava Bay, have made observations on currently active coastal processes, and more particularly on the erosive effect of the sea ice cover.

Eventual exploitation of the mineral resources of the Labrador Trough south and west of Ungava Bay, or harnessing of the hydraulic energy potential of the large tributary rivers and tidal estuaries, will require detailed descriptions of the coastal processes and morphology. This study makes a small beginning to the task by first describing the coastal environment of Leaf Basin, a large inlet on the west coast of Ungava Bay (Fig. 20.1), and then attempting to explain two of its most striking features. These are the giant boulder fields on the intertidal mudflats and the high boulder barricades located at the mouth of Leaf River and at the head of North Arm.

COASTAL ENVIRONMENT

Leaf Basin, the tidal estuary of Leaf River, is situated in an area of north-south-trending sedimentary and volcanic rocks of the Labrador Trough, sandwiched between granite gneiss formations of Archean age, to the east and west (Fig. 20.2). The topography is closely related to the structural trend, long north-south-trending ridges 100-300 m in elevation alternating with wide flat valleys (Fig. 20.3). The lower parts of the valleys, tributary to Leaf Basin, lie below high-tide level and form long inlets and bays. The low gradients of the valley floors and the large tidal range permit the development of extensive present-day intertidal mudflats. Terrestrial zones up to the marine limit of 175 m above sea level have also been intertidal during the Holocene period, but have been subjected to progressive emergence because of glacio-isostatic recovery.

Continental ice has left its legacy on the area in the form of varying thicknesses and types of glacial, fluvio-glacial and glaciomarine deposits, subsequently subjected to disturbance by frost action and by littoral processes.

Other background elements of importance in a discussion of the origin of the intertidal boulder concentrations are the potential water- and ice-related forces operative in the intertidal zone. These include wave action, tidal currents, longshore drift, river currents and movements of sea and river ice. The effectiveness of these processes is probably time dependent, at least to some degree. Hence, the nature of land emergence during the postglacial period will be given some attention, since it has influenced the length of time the various altitudinal zones, up to the marine limit, have been subjected to the forces of the intertidal zone.

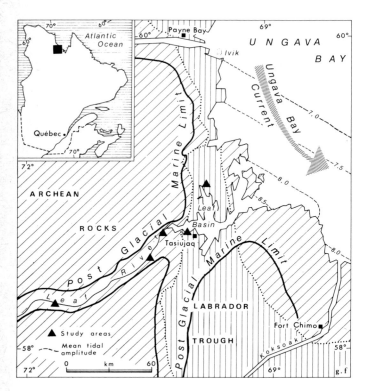

Figure 20.1. *Location of study area.*

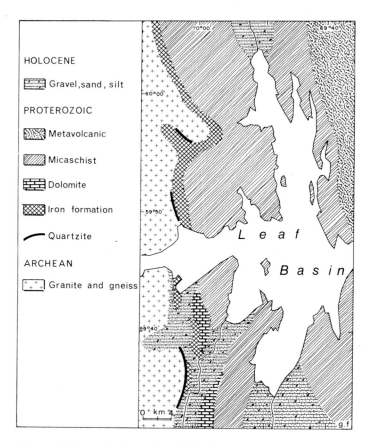

Figure 20.2. *Geology of Leaf Basin.*

Tidal information within the basin, based on a 29-day gauge record for Gauge Point (Fig. 20.3), indicates a mean and spring tidal range of 9.3 m and 14.8 m, respectively (Canadian Hydrographic Service, 1976). An extreme range of 16.6 m is shown on the Canadian Hydrographic Service chart. These figures may only approximate the true tidal ranges around the periphery of the basin. Considerable variability is expected from changes in basin geometry. As well as permitting the operation of littoral forces over a wide intertidal zone, the large tidal range leads to rapid currents and dangerous eddies in the Algerine narrows.

Wave heights and frequencies have not been measured for Leaf Basin but the limited fetch in an almost closed basin (35 km maximum in a north-south direction and 24 km maximum east-west) implies the occurrence of low waves of short wavelength, typical of medium-size lakes. They may form whitecaps and even small breakers in the surf zone in stormy conditions, but the lack of a ground swell does not permit the buildup of high-breaking waves in this zone. Longshore drift within the basin is also likely to have been rather insignificant. Both of these statements are borne out by the lack of beach ridges, spits and baymouth bars in the present littoral zone.

The annual ice regime is divided into three geomorphic phases.

The winter period lasts from December to early June and is characterized by the development and progressive thickening of an ice cover over the entire Leaf Basin and its tributary rivers, with the exception of a stretch of open water in the turbulent Algerine narrows. In the central part of the basin the ice cover is relatively smooth but in the intertidal zone the tidal oscillations lead to considerable cracking of the surface, usually in concentric zones up to 30 m across. The centres of most of these zones are characterized by cratered pustules 1 - 2 m in height and 2 - 5 m in diameter (Fig. 20.4).

The central craters are typically filled with ice blocks, well rounded from constant motion associated with the semidiurnal rise and fall of the ice pack. In some cases the ice blocks are thrust outward and contribute to the buildup of the crater rims. The ice is relatively free of debris, which indicates that the process responsible for these forms has little to do with initial surface roughness in the bottom zone.

At Baie Rouge and at Petite Rivière three miles west, several circular forms were noted without a central ice block - filled, crater zone. They measured typically 3 - 4 m in height and up to 20 m in diameter. There is a clear correlation between the distribution of these ice pustules and the distribution of large boulders, although the latter are much smaller in diameter (Figs. 20.5, 20.6). Along with the tidal cycle, the boulders may be responsible for this type of cracking and ice pustule development.

Spring lasts from mid-May to early July. Into this relatively short period is compressed almost the entire potential of sea and river ice to do effective geomorphic work. The breakup of the basin ice was observed in detail. In the early stages melting of the snow in the terrestrial zone gives meltwater runnels in the basin ice near the high-water mark, but the meltwater quickly descends to the base of the ice pack. The discharge from the large rivers also quickly disappears beneath the ice foot that fringes the basin, leaving accumulations of debris-rich ice blocks, which had been previously carried downstream.

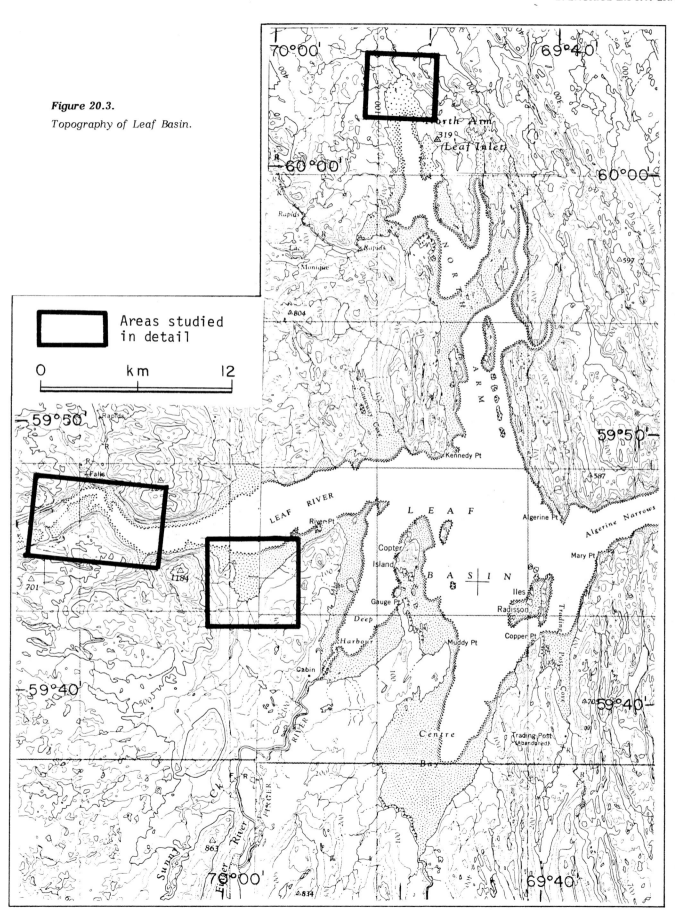

Figure 20.3.

Topography of Leaf Basin.

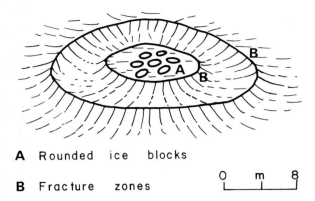

A Rounded ice blocks

B Fracture zones

0   m   8

Figure 20.4. *Diagrammatic representation of circular forms developed on the ice surface in the intertidal zone of Leaf Basin.*

As spring advances, the pressure cracks in the ice remain open, providing passages, along with the meltwater channels, for the sea water to be forced onto the surface of the ice under the pressures exerted by flood tides. Eventually the channels and cracks enlarge to the point where the ice breaks up very rapidly into a multitude of small ice pans several cubic metres in volume. Some of these ice pans melt in situ but others are carried towards the mouth of the basin where they create temporary obstructions that remain until mid-July, when Ungava Bay ice breaks up.

The ice-free summer period lasts from mid-July until late November. Although ice floes and occasional icebergs may affect the open coast of Ungava Bay during this period, this ice does not enter Leaf Basin, attested by the undisturbed soil and vegetation cover in the zone just above the high-water mark, and a smooth progression in the size of rock lichens in the same zone.

LAND EMERGENCE AND ITS POTENTIAL EFFECT

Figure 20.7, constructed from a postglacial emergence curve for Hopes Advance Bay 60 km to the north (Gray et al., 1980), shows the approximate outline of Leaf Basin at circa 7000 and 6000 years BP in relation to the present coastline. In the first postglacial millenium the western shores of Leaf Basin were exposed to the full fetch of Ungava Bay and hence to potentially important erosion initiated by wave action and by the piling up of ice floes from Ungava Bay. The potential for such processes must have diminished rapidly by 6000 years BP, as the basin by then had assumed its present almost land-locked form.

However, the rapid decline in the rate of emergence may have acted to counterbalance and even outweigh this effect. At higher elevations the intertidal zone was displaced rapidly because of rapid emergence but as the rate of land emergence slowed down, it was displaced more slowly.

Figure 20.5.

Boulder field at low tide in a small embayment on the south side of the Leaf River estuary (known was Baie de la Petite Rivière). The photograph taken at the end of June 1978 shows remnants of the ice foot still in place near the high water mark. Leaf River in the background flows from left to right.

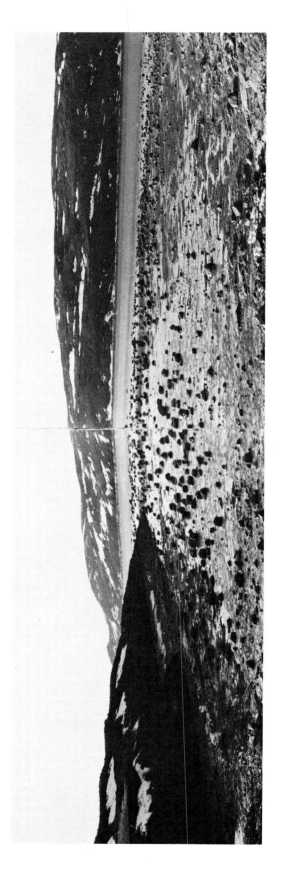

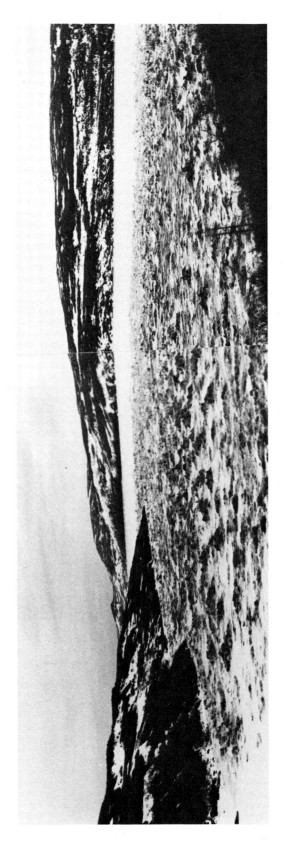

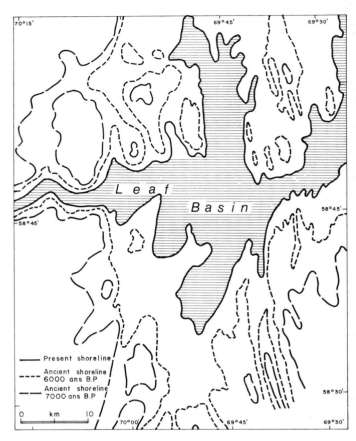

Figure 20.7. *Configuration of the Leaf Basin coastline at different intervals since deglaciation. Prepared from postglacial emergence curve for Hope's Advance Bay, 60 km to the north, but adjusted to take account of the greater total isostatic recovery of Leaf Basin.*

Figure 20.6.

Baie de la Petite Rivière from almost the same viewpoint as Figure 20.5. The photograph was taken at the end of May 1978 before spring breakup of the ice cover. It shows that the ice pustules have roughly the same pattern of distribution as the large boulders in the intertidal zone. Note also the relatively smooth ice surface in the deep water zone beyond the low tide mark.

The result is that littoral processes had progressively longer periods available for geomorphic work as their zone of operation descended towards the present sea level. Current research also indicates that land emergence was probably not continuous but interrupted by phases of sea level stability which allowed the littoral processes to play a more effective role at certain elevations.

GIANT BOULDER FIELDS AND BOULDER BARRICADES OF LEAF BASIN

Three distinct areas in the present intertidal zone were studied in detail. The Baie Rouge area is characterized by giant boulders scattered across the intertidal mudflats; the estuary of Leaf River is characterized by a large boulder barricade and delta complex; the North Arm area, by giant boulders on mudflats and by a boulder barricade and lagoon complex.

Baie Rouge area

Morphometric characteristics of the giant boulder fields, typical of Leaf Basin mudflats, were examined in detail in three sample plots each of 30 m radius (Fig. 20.8A, B, C). The morphology of the immediate coastal hinterland up to the marine limit was also studied for the role it may have played in the evolution of the boulder concentrations of the present intertidal zone.

The upper part of the slope to the west, above 174 m, is covered with a mantle of glacial till characterized by abundant perched blocks up to several metres in size. Below 174 m the moderate and steep slopes have been washed by waves as the land progressively emerged. The slopes above 100 m were exposed to the open waters of Ungava Bay during the washing process. There are no large boulder ridges and very few isolated boulders, probably because of efficient evacuation of the debris to the valley zone below, where it contributes to the accumulations of gravels and sands which overlie considerable thicknesses of silts and clays. However, the large perched boulders, which were also washed down, are strangely absent from the surface of this lowland zone and are rarely noted in stream-cut exposures. By contrast such boulders are very common in the intertidal zone (Fig. 20.9). This peculiarity in the distribution of the giant boulders provoked our initial interest and invites a careful study of the boulders themselves.

Frequency distributions of boulder lengths in the three sample plots (Fig. 20.10) reveal that the boulders are relatively isodiametrical and that the lengths are normally distributed rather than skewed to the right as is frequently found in debris accumulations. When the lengths of the boulders at each of the sites are compared using analysis of variance, no significant differences are noted. Lithologically, site B consists mainly of ferruginous boulders, whereas sites A and C are dominated by granite-gneiss boulders.

To interpret the origin of the boulders from the above data on morphometry and processes, the most probable of a proposed series of possible origins must be systematically deduced. The possible origins are illustrated diagrammatically in A, B, C and D in Figure 20.11.

In hypothesis A, there is considerable initial variability in the distribution of boulders in glacial till, but not sufficient to explain the contrast between their abundance in the intertidal zone and their sporadic occurrence in the coastal hinterland below the marine limit. A former moraine cannot be envisaged to coincide precisely with the intertidal zone. Furthermore, blocks are not found in various stages of excavation from a fine sediment matrix; the boulders lie on top of the sediments. Thus, this first hypothesis of origin can be rejected.

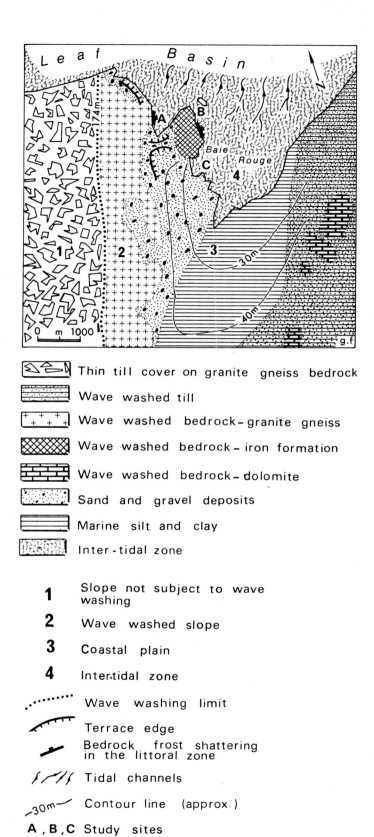

Thin till cover on granite gneiss bedrock

Wave washed till

Wave washed bedrock – granite gneiss

Wave washed bedrock – iron formation

Wave washed bedrock – dolomite

Sand and gravel deposits

Marine silt and clay

Inter-tidal zone

1 Slope not subject to wave washing

2 Wave washed slope

3 Coastal plain

4 Inter-tidal zone

Wave washing limit

Terrace edge

Bedrock frost shattering in the littoral zone

Tidal channels

30m— Contour line (approx.)

A,B,C Study sites

Figure 20.8. *Geology and morphology of the Baie Rouge study site.*

Figure 20.9.   *Boulder field at Baie Rouge. Note the wave washed bedrock subjected only slightly to frost plucking in the foreground, and the isodiametric nature of the boulders, and the manner in which they lie, fully exposed on the surface, in the middle distance.*

Hypothesis B, that of local derivation by frost-shattering of bedrock, deserves closer consideration. The frost-shattered outcrops in the iron formation close to sites A and B do provide some of the ferruginous boulders but most of the boulders are of granite gneiss composition and hence cannot have been derived from bedrock outcrops in the present littoral zone.

Hypothesis C, that of ice-rafting of debris from the mouth of Leaf River during spring breakup, perhaps aided by sudden bursting of the ice foot at the mouth of Leaf River, does not appear to be dynamically possible given the huge size of the boulders. During the spring breakup of 1977 little coarse debris was observed on the surface of the ice pans.

The remaining hypothesis, that the boulders have been progressively moved downslope to the intertidal zone during coastal emergence, seems best to fit the available facts. The boulders were initially distributed as perched blocks on a till-mantled surface between the marine limit and present sea level. Various water- and ice-related processes of the intertidal zone acted in concert with gravity to move the boulders downslope. Since isostatic readjustment with accompanying land emergence throughout the last 7000 years displaced the intertidal zone progressively downwards to its present position, the initial boulder accumulations at all levels have been subjected to the operation of the same processes that are active in the present intertidal zone. The exponential nature of the emergence curve would tend to lead to increasingly efficient evacuation of boulders downslope, since the latter spend progressively more time in the intertidal zone where they are subject to the displacement processes. This tendency is counteracted to some degree, however, by the frequently moderate or steep slopes at higher elevations, which allow washing processes to operate efficiently over a very short time interval.

If this hypothesis seems to explain reasonably well the provenance of the boulders we still do not understand in detail how the processes actually transport the boulders. During spring breakup the floating ice, fragmented into relatively small pans, may imprison the blocks and could drag a few of them seaward over short distances. Eventually over a sufficiently long time, all the blocks in the intertidal zone will be subject to transport. It is not clear, however, why such transport should take place preferentially seaward, as the accepted hypothesis of provenance implies, and as is also implied by the fact that the boulders all become completely submerged at high tide. Furrows and ridges, cited by Dionne (1978), as indicative of ice-scouring in the James Bay area, are markedly absent adjacent to the boulders. Unless these forms are obliterated quickly after their development by scour and fill processes, it is difficult to invoke the mechanism of ice push or drag.

Many of the boulders are on small pedestals of finer material created by the scouring of fine sediments from around them, suggesting that undermining processes and gravity cause a slow and almost continuous movement of the boulders in a down-gradient, seaward direction. But as the intertidal mudflats have surveyed slope angles of only 0.5° - 1.0°, it is very difficult to imagine that this is an efficient process. The blocks would have to be moved downslope at a rate exceeding the rate of postglacial emergence, which for the last 2000 years has been about 0.001 to 0.005 m/year. Not to be left stranded above the high-tide level, boulders would have to be moved at least 10 to 50 m across the low-gradient mudflats over a 100-year period, or at a rate of 0.1 to 0.5 m/year. Such rapid rates of movement are not possible through slow creep and undermining processes.

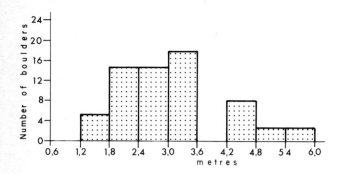

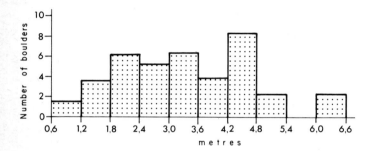

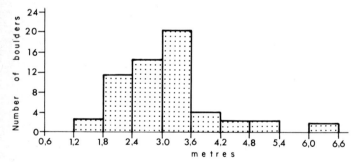

Figure 20.10. *Histogram of boulder lengths at Baie Rouge.*

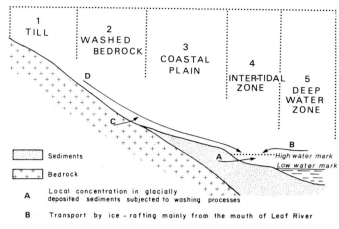

Figure 20.11. *Model of hypothetical origins of boulders of the intertidal mudflats.*

Wave action, which does not even construct storm beaches, is likely to be even less effective in moving the large boulders, and would in any case tend to transport them shorewards. Tidal currents would diverge around the blocks, operating only through undermining of the fine sediments at their base.

The conclusion is inescapable: ice pans must be the agent of transport of the giant boulders. A major reason for preferential seaward movement of the blocks may be that land-fast ice in the upper part of the intertidal zone obstructs landward movement of the fragmented pans.

Leaf River estuary

In the intertidal zone in the estuary of Leaf River is a remarkable accumulation of sand, gravel and boulders (Fig. 20.12). Triangular headlands jut out from the north and south bank into the middle of the channel. They are, respectively, 300 and 1000 m long and up to 300 m wide. The boulders on the barricades are of varying sizes and those near the base are subject to frequent bulldozing by ice pans during each spring breakup, as indicated by impact scars and

scratches on their surfaces. The blocks on the higher parts of these headlands are characterized by a mature lichen cover and shrubs of *Alnus Crispa*.

Downstream from this point are deltaic concentrations of sands and gravels, particularly close to the headlands, and also at the low-tide mark. Upstream, linear concentrations of sands and gravels occur along the river banks.

Ice may again play the key role in the origin of these forms. Leaf Basin ice cover, particularly land-fast ice close to the high-tide mark, acts as a barrier to river flow during spring breakup. At this point, where the river current is countered by the flood tide, large blocks in traction are likely to be preferentially deposited. The barrage created by the basin ice gives the river the potential to overflow its banks at this point and move debris into large ridgelike concentrations upstream from the barrier zone. This debris is smaller than that deposited in the barrier zone.

The relatively slow rate of recent emergence has facilitated the buildup of these boulder barricades to their present large dimensions. The estuarine delta deposits have also accumulated over several thousand years to almost fill the original estuary on the seaward side of the barricade.

North Arm

The intertidal zone along the eastern and western shores of the inlet (Fig. 20.13) is characterized by boulder fields similar to those at Baie Rouge, but the head of the inlet exhibits a different complex of landforms (Fig. 20.14). A small river debouches onto the intertidal zone via a delta built out onto a foreshore characterized by lagoonal depressions that retain water even at low tide. Beyond the lagoons a boulder barricade 3 - 5 m wide and 2 - 3 m high runs transversely across the head of the inlet (Fig. 20.15). Its top surface is flat and barely visible at high tide. On the seaward side of the barricade the intertidal mudflats stretch for approximately 100 m down to the low-water level. These mudflats are dotted with boulders but much fewer than on the adjacent eastern and western shores of the inlet. Landward of the barricade they are almost completely absent.

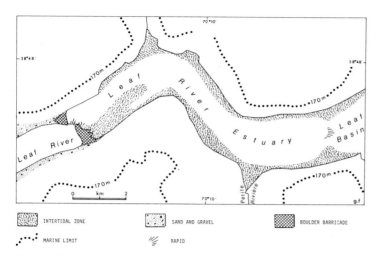

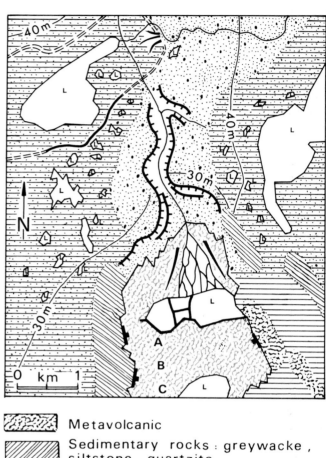

Figure 20.12. *Morphology of the Leaf River estuary.*

The intertidal boulder fields on the eastern and western shores of North Arm resemble closely those of Baie Rouge, although the individual boulders are smaller. They probably have originated in the same manner, by slow progressive downslope displacement of boulders of glacial origin to the present intertidal zone.

The boulder barricade is more difficult to explain. Barricade construction by obstruction of meltwater and ice pan discharge by land-fast basin ice at the mouth of a river, invoked previously for the barricade in the Leaf River estuary, is more difficult to envisage because of the much smaller meltwater discharge into North Arm. This appears to be the best explanation that can be advanced for the moment, however, and two factors lend some weight to it. First, the barricade at North Arm is on a much smaller scale than that at the mouth of the Leaf River. Second, the almost total absence of boulders on the landward side of the barricade indicates that displacement of boulders was probably seaward to the barrier position. As a corollary the presence of a few boulders on the seaward side of the barricade suggests the lack of an equally effective landward movement of the boulders. Dynamically the agent capable of piling up the boulders onto the barricade would be ice push and, of course, the upper limit of effectiveness, in the absence of a long fetch, would naturally correspond fairly closely with the water level at high tide. This could explain the correspondence between the summit of the barricade and the high-water mark.

THE PALEOENVIRONMENTAL SIGNIFICANCE OF BOULDER BARRICADES

If land emergence had been at a relatively continuous decelerating rate one might expect that in estuarine zones small, frequently spaced boulder barricades would be built and, with continued emergence, subsequently would be destroyed by river erosion. This is not the case. Barricade and delta complexes have been recognized at only two points along Leaf River, but they are strikingly well developed despite subsequent erosional modification (Fig. 20.16a, b). It seems reasonable to infer that they represent former intertidal zones developed during major pauses in land emergence.

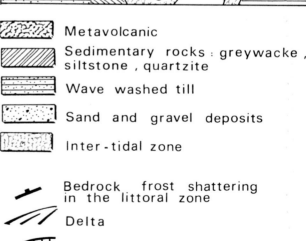

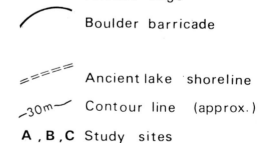

Figure 20.13. *Geology and morphology of the North Arm study site.*

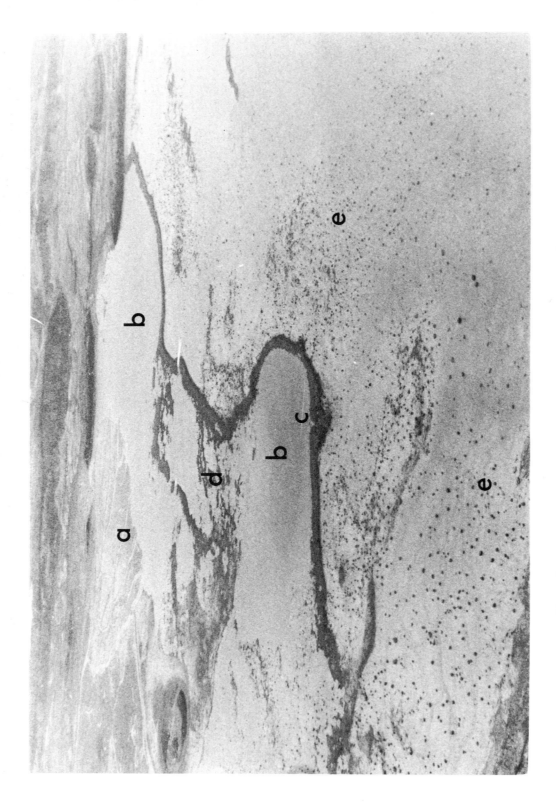

Figure 20.14. Oblique air view of a boulder barricade at the head of North Arm. One can distinguish the following elements:

a) – delta   d) – secondary boulder barricade
b) – lagoon   e) – boulder field: photograph
c) – boulder barricade   taken at low tide

Figure 20.15. *Close view of the main boulder barricade shown in Figure 20.14.*

In the hinterland of North Arm and along Finger River southwest of Leaf Basin, major boulder barricades transverse to the valleys have also been observed. Figure 20.17 shows the elevations of the boulder barricades for all three areas and indicates that, despite local variations, three important pauses can be detected at 25 m, 40 m, 60 m around Leaf Basin. The barricade complexes at these elevations appear to correlate reasonably well with the elevations of major coastal terraces also plotted in Figure 20.17.

It is difficult to place precise dates on these major pauses in land emergence, as the nearest available curve is for Hopes Advance Bay. Extrapolation from this emergence curve, however, gives a rough age range of 5000 - 6000 BP for the forms at 60 m and 40 m and 2000 - 3000 years BP for the forms at 25 m.

CONCLUSIONS

The concentration of giant boulders on the intertidal mud flats of Leaf Basin is a result of a slow but inexorable movement of boulders downslope from the upper marine limit, which kept pace with the progressive displacement of the intertidal zone downwards to its position.

On steeper gradients, water- and ice-related processes, assisted by gravity, can easily be invoked to explain such displacement. In the low-gradient situations, typical of the valley floors and of the present intertidal zone, the only processes which seem capable of moving the giant boulders sufficiently rapidly to keep pace with land emergence, are frequent imprisonment of the boulders by ice in the winter and their subsequent bulldozing seaward during spring break-up. The exact mode and rate of operation of these processes are unclear, and further observations of boulder movement over a time span of years are planned, using sequential air photography taken under low tide conditions.

The large boulder barricades and associated deltas found in the present intertidal zone at the mouth of Leaf River and at North Arm are explained by the interplay of tidal and river currents, particularly during spring breakup, when stable ice in the intertidal zone presents a barrier to the evacuation of the bed load of the river. Ice floes on the river and in the basin may play an important role in piling the debris up into large barricades transverse to the valley and, upstream from these barricades, into ridges parallel to the river banks. Estuarine delta deposits characterize the distal side of these barricades. Similar boulder barricades at elevations of 28 m and 60 m along Leaf River valley, at 25 m and 40 m in the North Arm area, and at 40 m and 60 m along Finger River valley, appear to represent former intertidal zones, developed during long pauses in land emergence, at 5300, 5600 and 6000 years BP.

Acknowledgments

The authors are indebted to Imperial Oil Limited and the Department of Indian Affairs and Northern Development for their financial support, to colleagues and students of the Geography Department of the University of Montreal for useful discussions and for field assistance, to the community of Tasiujaq who kindly lent us the use of their school as a base for our operations in the Leaf Basin area, and to S.B. McCann for suggesting improvements in the text.

References

Canadian Hydrographic Service
    1976:   Canadian tide and current tables, V. 4, Arctic and Hudson Bay; Fisheries and Marine Service.

Dionne, J.C.
    1978:   Le glaciel en Jamésie et en Hudsonie. Québec subarctique; Géographie physique et quaternaire, v. XXXII, no. 1, p. 3 - 70.

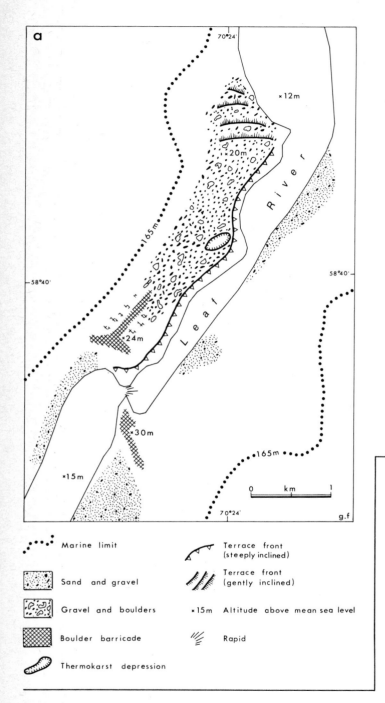

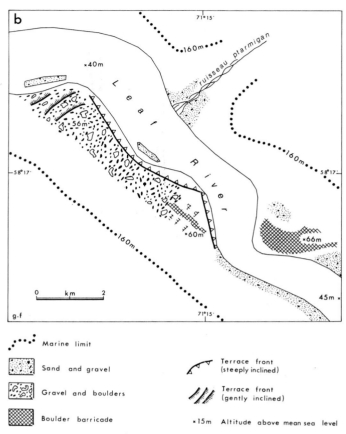

Figure 20.16. *Boulder barricade and delta complexes situated at circa (a) 25 m and (b) 60 m along the Leaf River valley.*

Altitudes metres	LEAF RIVER		NORTH ARM		FINGER RIVER	
	Boulder barricades	Coastal terraces	Boulder barricades	Coastal terraces	Boulder barricades	Coastal Terraces
10				▲		▲
20	▲	▲		▲		▲
30						▲
40			▲		▲	
50						
60	▲				▲	

Figure 20.17. *Elevations of boulder barricade and delta complexes and of coastal terraces around the margins of Leaf Basin.*

Gangloff, P.
1977: Observations sur la dynamique glacielle dans la Baie du Diana, Ungava; Annales de l'Association Canadienne-Française pour l'avancement des sciences, v. 44, no. 1, p. 93.

Gray, J.T., de Boutray, B., Hillaire Marcel, C. and Lauriol, B.
1980: Post glacial emergence of the west coast of Ungava Bay, Québec; Arctic and Alpine Research, v. 12, no. 1, p. 19 - 30.

Løken, O.
1964: The late glacial and post-glacial emergence and the deglaciation of northernmost Labrador; Geographical Bulletin, No. 17., p. 23 - 56.

Matthews, B.
1967: Late quaternary land emergence in northern Ungava; Arctic, v. 20, p. 176 - 202.

Rosen, P.
1979: Boulder barricades in central Labrador; Journal of Sedimentary Petrology, v. 49, no. 4, p. 1113 - 1123.

Tanner, V.
1939: Om de blockrika strandgordlama vid subarkiska oceankustar fore korsrstsatt och upkomst; Terra, v. 51, p. 157 - 165.

21.

GEOMORPHOLOGY OF SOUTHWESTERN JAMES BAY:
A LOW ENERGY, EMERGENT COAST

I.P. Martini[1], D.W. Cowell[2], and G.M. Wickware[2]

Martini, I.P., Cowell, D.W., and Wickware, G.M., Geomorphology of southwestern James Bay: A low energy, emergent coast; in The Coastline of Canada, S.B. McCann, editor; Geological Survey of Canada, Paper 80-10, p. 293-301, 1980.

Abstract

The southwestern coastline of Hudson and James bays in Ontario and Manitoba is the longest low gradient, emergent shoreline in the world. It maintains an uninterrupted offshore slope of about 0.5-1 m/km over a distance of approximately 1700 km. The land has been subjected to active rebound for the last 7000-8000 years, and is still rising at a rate of less than 1 m/100 years.

The Ontario coast consists of three main morphologies: coasts dominated by abundant parallel beach ridges and spits; coasts dominated by estuarine systems; and coasts with promontories and transverse ridges.

All three types of coastlines are represented in the southern part of James Bay. Longitudinal beach ridges fringe upper tidal flats on the southern and eastern sides of promontories and in areas where storm waves are not greatly attenuated by extensive sandy flats. The longitudinal ridges vary in elevation from 1.5-2 m (composite sandy and gravelly ridges), to 0.3-0.5 m (coastal single sandy bars), and in sandy flats, to 0.2 m (sinusoidal sand waves). Promontories and transverse ridges are related to bedrock highs or glacial depositional features modified by deposition of coastal sands and gravels. A marked counter-clockwise marine current in the southern part of James Bay redistributes the fluviatile materials to the southeast of estuaries, onto extensive, featureless, low lying tidal flats.

With emergence, incorporation of these features into the peatland complex is manifested through a progressive paludification of the landscape, and in older parts of the Lowland, only high ridges and promontories (higher than 1 m) with well developed coniferous forests, remain as recognizable coastal landforms.

Résumé

La côte sud-ouest des baies d'Hudson et de James en Ontario et au Manitoba représente le plus long littoral émergent à faible pente dans le monde. Ce littoral possède une pente ininterrompue jusqu'au large des côtes à raison d'environ 0,5 à 1 m/km sur une distance d'environ 1700 km. Les terres ont été soumises à un relèvement actif au cours des 7000 à 8000 dernières années et elles se soulèvent encore à un rythme légèrement inférieur à 1 m par siècle.

La côte ontarienne se compose de trois principaux types de reliefs: des côtes dominées par de nombreuses crêtes et des flèches de plage parallèles; des côtes dominées par des reliefs estuariens et des côtes à promontoires et crêtes transversales.

Les trois types de reliefs côtiers sont représentés dans la partie méridionale de la baie de James. Certaines crêtes de plage longitudinales bordent le rebord supérieur des platières sur les côtés sud et est des promontoires et dans les zones où les vagues de tempête ne sont pas atténuées par l'existence de vastes platières sablonneuses. L'altitude des crêtes longitudinales oscille entre 1,5-2 m (crêtes composées de sable et de gravier), à 0,3-0,5 m (barres sablonneuses simples), et dans les platières sablonneuses, à 0,2 m (ondulations de sables sinusoïdales). Certains promontoires et certaines crêtes transversales sont liées à la présence du socle rocheux ou de reliefs glaciaires de sédimentation remaniés par le dépôt des sables et graviers littoraux. Un courant marin assez prononcé et se déplaçant dans le sens contraire des aiguilles d'une montre dans la partie sud de la baie de James contribue à la redistribution des matériaux fluviatiles vers le sud-est des estuaires, sur de vastes veys bas et sans relief.

A mesure que l'émergence progresse, l'intégration de ces accidents dans le complexe tourbeux se manifeste par une paludification progressive du modelé et dans les vieilles parties des basses-terres, seules les hautes crêtes et les promontoires élevés (supérieur à 1 m) sur lesquelles se trouvent des forêts de conifère bien développées demeurent des formes identifiables de reliefs côtiers.

[1] Department of Land Resource Science, University of Guelph, Ontario

[2] Lands Directorate (Ontario Region), Environment Canada, Burlington, Ontario

INTRODUCTION

The coastline of Hudson Bay and James Bay bordering the Hudson Bay Lowland is an unbroken low-gradient, low-energy coast characterized by wide tidal flats and extensive salt marshes (Fig. 21.1). It is an emergent coast reflecting the flat, poorly drained plain of the Lowland, which is underlain by Paleozoic strata of the Hudson Platform (Sanford et al., 1968). The coast is emerging because of isostatic rebound at a rate of 70 to 120 cm/century (Barnett, 1966; Webber et al., 1970). The Hudson Bay Lowland was inundated by marine waters from Hudson Strait approximately 8000 years ago when the Pleistocene glaciers retreated northward. This sea is known as the Tyrrell Sea (Lee, 1960). Tyrrell Sea deposits consist of sand and gravel beach ridges, which are found throughout the Lowland, and a sparsely fossiliferous blue clay which underlies most of the Lowland except for local bedrock and Pleistocene highs (Cowell et al., 1978). A thin regressive sedimentary sequence is developing along the present coast.

Early descriptions of the coastline were those of Bell (1896) and O'Sullivan (1908). More recent studies have dealt primarily with rates of isostatic recovery (Barnett, 1966, 1970; Andrews, 1969; Hunter, 1970; Webber et al., 1970), characteristics of raised beach ridges (Moir, 1954; Simpson, 1971; Kershaw and Rouse, 1973), and salt marsh ecology (Kershaw, 1976; Glooschenko, 1978; Martini et al., 1979, 1980). This paper describes coastal processes and features in the southwestern part of James Bay, in Ontario and considers characteristics of progressive organic accumulation (paludification) as coastal features emerge from the sea (Fig. 21.1).

Climate along the coastline of Hudson and James bays is generally continental subarctic (Dfc in Köppen-Geiger system), fewer than four months having means exceeding 10°C. The average annual temperature varies from -5° along Hudson Bay to -1°C at the southern end of James Bay (Chapman and Thomas, 1968). The average annual precipitation in the southern part of James Bay is 650 mm. Wind speed at Churchill averages almost twice that at Moosonee, although at both stations the dominant wind direction is from the western quadrants. Southwesterly winds are more significant at Moosonee and northeasterly winds form a significant secondary mode throughout the ice-free season. The Hudson Bay coast lies within the zone of continuous permafrost, whereas the James Bay coast is primarily within the discontinuous zone (Brown, 1973). Shorefast ice may be present up to 9 months each year.

Tides along the James Bay coastline are of the semi-diurnal type and range from 2 to 3 m in height at the mouth of the Moose River (Environment Canada, 1977). Marine currents in James Bay are generally less than 1 knot and circulate counterclockwise.

COASTAL GEOMORPHOLOGY

The Hudson Bay Lowland coastline can be divided into three main types: coasts dominated by parallel beach ridges and spits; coasts dominated by estuarine systems; and coasts with promontories and transverse ridges.

Coasts dominated by parallel beach ridges are best displayed along the shores of Hudson Bay, where ridges recur in a semi-regular fashion up to 75 km inland. They also occur on the west side of James Bay north of Akimiski Island. A modified version of this coastal type is displayed at Cape Henrietta Maria (Fig. 21.1). This large-scale cuspate headland consists primarily of parallel shingle beach ridges with extensive longshore spits along its southeastern

side. Sand ridges south of the cape are characterized by numerous blowouts (Martini and Protz, 1980). Similar aeolian features are common on coastal ridges west of the cape.

Estuarine-dominated coasts are best represented in southern James Bay, where large rivers such as the Harricanaw, Moose, Albany and Attawapiskat are concentrated, but also occur on either side of the Winisk River estuary (Figs. 21.1, 21.2). Estuarine coasts are very flat, poorly drained and covered by a thin veneer of river-generated silt. Ice-rafted material is abundant. These coasts are characterized by wide salt and brackish marshes. Generally the brackish marshes occur on the highest parts of the tidal flats but in one instance, on the east side of Hannah Bay, salt marshes have developed up to 1 km inland of brackish marshes (marsh 'inversion', Glooschenko and Martini, 1978). Estuarine coasts occur generally in embayments which have persisted as topographically slightly lower areas throughout the Holocene. Their progressive emergence is marked by low but well defined coastal ridges and by regressive sedimentary sequences exposed in river banks (Fig. 21.2). These sequences are characterized by Tyrrell Sea clay overlain by marine and fluviatile silts and sands. These are in turn overlain by interbedded peat and silty alluvium.

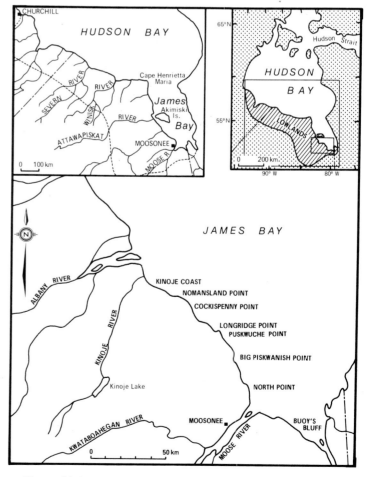

Figure 21.1. *The Hudson Bay Lowland area and the coastline of southwestern James Bay.*

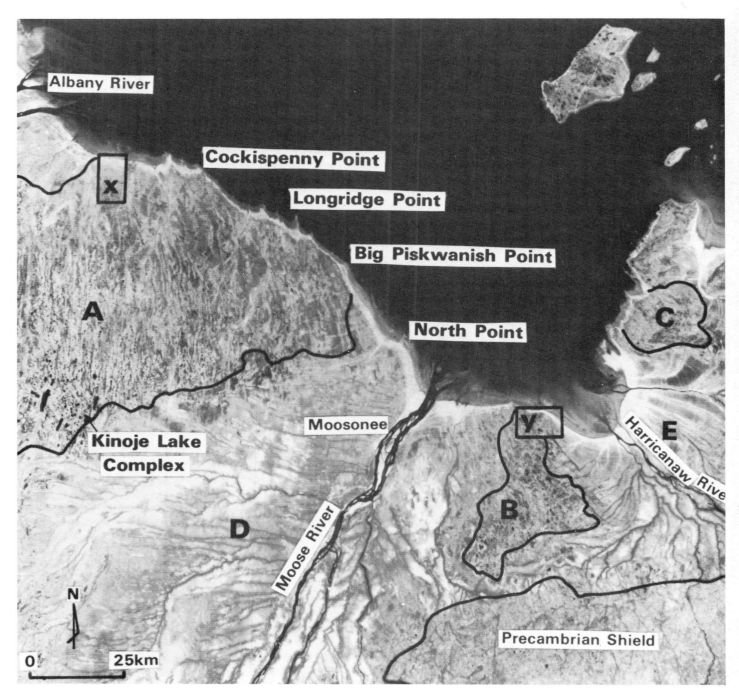

Figure 21.2. *Landsat image of southwestern James Bay (image E-1374-15496, band 6, taken Aug. 1, 1973). A, B and C are interfluvial areas underlain by extensive glacial deposits which have been modified to form beach ridge complexes. The landscape is characterized by north-south lineations which appear to terminate at the coast as narrow promontories (transverse ridges). D and E are areas dominated by closely-spaced, parallel streams and arcuate coastal ridge systems. X and Y are areas detailed in Figure 21.6 and 21.3 respectively.*

295

Coasts with promontories lie between the estuarine coasts, where there is slightly more topographic expression. Promontories are best displayed in southern James Bay although they are also seen in Hudson Bay. Figure 21.2 is a Landsat image of southern James Bay showing the areas of higher topographic expression (interfluvial) in the interior which corresponds to coasts with promontories (Fig. 21.2, areas A, B, C). This is especially noticeable north of the Moose River, where north-south trending lineations are strong and terminate at the coast as promontories (Fig. 21.2, area A). Nearest the Quebec border the lineations and associated promontories are closely spaced, delimiting narrow bays that are filled with semilunate bodies of sand ornamented by sand waves (Fig. 21.2, area C). In Quebec the promontories have been interpreted as marine-modified recessional moraines (Guimont and Laverdière, 1976a, b). The promontories and small sandy beach ridges parallel to the main coast have produced a scalloped geomorphological pattern that is retained in the emergent portion of the Lowland.

North Point and Big Piskwanish Point are major headlands which have bedrock at or near the surface (Fig. 21.2). Longridge Point is narrower but much longer, extending over 5 km onto the tidal flats. The promontories are primarily areas of erosion and seem to constitute the principal source for coastal sediments. They act as natural groynes because of their orientation with respect to prevailing waves and currents and accumulate sediment on their northwestern sides. Their southeastern sides are areas of sediment bypass. Low-gradient sandy and silty tidal flats and marshes develop on the accumulation sides with little or no coarse ice-rafted material. The sediment bypass areas have a thin, discontinuous veneer of sand, which overlies the clay substratum. These are commonly gouged and covered by ice-rafted boulders and pebbles. Sand and pebbles on these bypass areas are reworked by longshore currents and storm waves forming well developed beach ridges or spits that prograde downcurrent from the promontory.

The lineations in the interfluvial areas noted above indicate that promontories and related environments have persisted for a long time in these areas (Fig. 21.2, areas A, B, C). However, local changes are associated with emergence of the coast. These changes are best observed at Cockispenny Point and Buoy's Bluff, as illustrated by the formation and gradual filling of small half-heart shaped bays on the downcurrent side of promontories (Figs. 21.2, 21.3). The half-heart bays are rimmed by spits that initially conform with the shape of the bay. As the embayment is filled they straighten parallel to the main coast (Fig. 21.3). These changes have been especially dramatic at Buoy's Bluff because of a small island that is emerging offshore (Fig. 21.3). The island acts as an extended breakwater inhibiting beach ridge formation on the coast. A 'comet's tail' ridge is forming downdrift from the island and the main coast is undergoing rapid siltation and progradation.

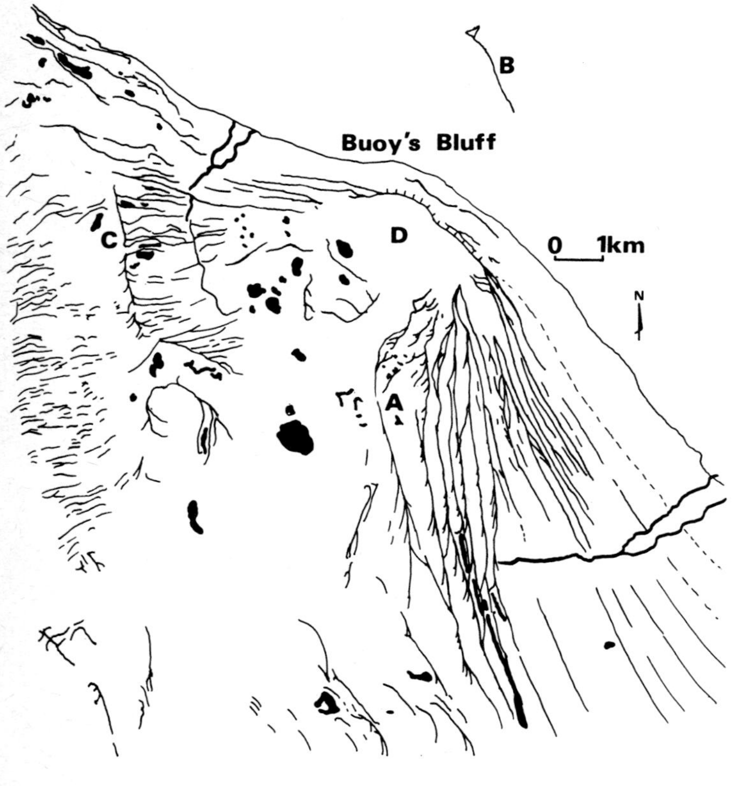

Ridges parallel to the coast

Coastal ridges are the most typical features of the coastline. They occur as sand waves, pebble and sand beach ridges and boulder ridges.

Sand waves develop on wide sandy tidal flats and are always oriented parallel to the coast (Fig. 21.4). They have a low amplitude (20 to 30 cm) and a wavelength of 10 to 40 m. Dissected by shallow, wide drainage channels, they are discontinuous and are ornamented by a variety of ripple marks most of which are modified during ebb tide. Internally, they show ripple crosslaminations dipping landward. The best forms develop in the middle to lower parts of tidal flats where waves can efficiently rework sediments for longer periods (King, 1972). On particularly flat shores, sand waves can be recognized when uplifted and incorporated into brackish marshes where they collect driftwood transported by storm waves. Because of their low amplitude they are rapidly obscured by organic accumulation.

Pebble and sand beach ridges are very common. They have a relatively steep seaward slope, a wide crest gently sloping landward and a very steep, short backslope that frequently shows lobations formed by washover sedimentation. They vary in height between 1.5 to 2 m (composite forms) and 0.3 to 0.5 m (single form). Internally they are characterized by crossbeds, usually composite, separated by erosional bounding surfaces. The ridges are composed primarily of sandy gravels, granules and sands piled up in alternating layers. These ridges are found most frequently in the upper parts of intertidal areas of higher gradient coasts, which have a relatively low rate of deposition. They are formed during storms when waves rework pebbles and sand and transport them from the flats to accumulate inland. Local sequences of high beach ridges are separated from each other by narrow, shallow swales (Fig. 21.5, W - W').

Boulder ridges parallel to the coastline are relatively rare. They form near outcrops of Paleozoic rocks or areas of glacial till. The boulders are locally reworked by ice push and fine materials are washed out. These beach ridges are either associated with boulder pavements near the coast or

Figure 21.3. *Sketch of Buoy's Bluff area. A 'half-heart' bay and associated spits and beach ridges, B emergent island with 'comet's tail' ridge, C chevron ridge complex, D bluff area cut into glacial material.*

are isolated rises in the lower parts of the tidal flats ('outer ridges', Glooschenko and Martini, 1978; Martini and Protz, 1978). They are up to 3 m in elevation and often have an open framework. They have not yet been recognized in the older parts of the Lowland. This is either due to their rarity or possibly because the outer ridges are modified as they are uplifted, forming the core of sand and gravel beach ridges.

Ridges perpendicular to the coast

Narrow promontories that extend several kilometres onto the shallow shelf are particularly common between Longridge Point and Nomansland Point (Figs. 21.1, 21.2, 21.4). They are composite forms and are here termed 'transverse ridges' (Shepard, 1952; Niedoroda and Tanner, 1970; Niedoroda, 1972a, b). They are related to bedrock highs, over which recent marine sand and fine gravels have accumulated, occasionally in seaward bifurcating ridges (Puskwuche Point, Fig. 21.4). Longridge Point, one of the longest and best developed of the transverse ridges, has bedrock exposed at its tip. It is composed of local concentrations (pods) of rounded Precambrian boulders over clay, and recent tombolo-like sandy and gravelly accumulations that join the boulder pods and outcrops to the coast. Near the main coast, the southeastern side of the narrow promontory is modified and enlarged by a spit and a longitudinal storm beach ridge, which conform to the arcuate shape of the bay.

These transverse ridges are modern analogues to numerous chevron ridges that are recognizable inland (Fig. 21.3, area C, Fig. 6, area D). The chevron ridges have developed through time by addition of numerous curved fanning-out barbs (spits and longitudinal beach ridges) on downdrift sides of narrow promontories (King, 1969, 1972). They are high features (up to 7 m) that persist inland and are common in the interfluvial area (Fig. 21.2).

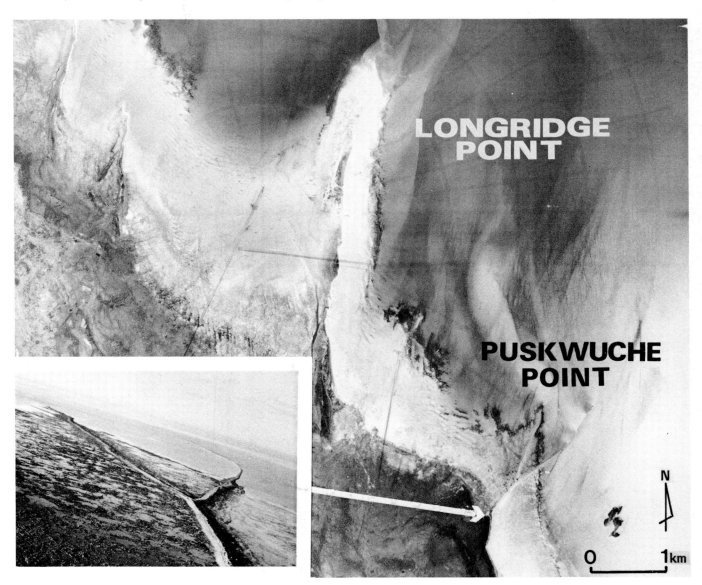

Figure 21.4. *Longridge Point – Puskwuche Point area showing well developed transverse ridges (promontories) which act as natural groynes (NAPL A2839-100). Sand waves are visible on their northwestern sides. The inset is an oblique aerial photo showing the bifurcation of Puskwuche Point.*

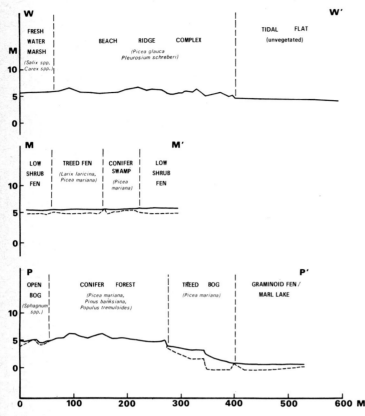

Figure 21.5. *Surveyed transects from three localities in the southern James Bay Lowland: W-W', recent coast at Big Piskwanish Point; M-M', paludified ridge 2 km inland from the Kinoje coast (Fig. 21.2 area X and Fig. 21.6 area C) — dashed line is mineral substratum surface, solid line is peatland surface; P-P', raised beach ridge complex 55 km from the coast ('Kinoje Lake Complex', Fig. 21.2).*

PALUDIFICATION OF COASTAL FEATURES

As coastal features are removed from the active marine zone through isostatic rebound, a process of organic accumulation (paludification) begins. This process results in increasing depths of peat inland from the coast, and is evidenced through a sequence of wetland types. Ultimately, and in the oldest parts of the Lowland, only the largest, best developed coastal ridges remain recognizable. The paludification process is most dynamic in the areas between the major rivers where mature peatlands form large bog and fen complexes interspersed with large beach ridges and chevron ridge complexes, recognizable because their morphology is accentuated by a forest cover (Fig. 21.2, areas A, B, C; Fig. 21.6, area D).

In the fluvial-dominated areas the substratum is composed primarily of fine sand, silt and clay and is essentially a featureless, treed fen system, except for low longitudinal ridges (Fig. 21.2, areas D and E). Coastal ridges are quickly paludified but because of their less confining nature and the better drainage of the area, they are capped by peat deposits that at an equivalent distance from the coast are thinner than peats of the interfluvial area.

Figure 21.6 is a schematic diagram of a large chevron beach complex 24 km southeast of the Albany River (in area A, Fig. 21.2). The beach complex lies 3 to 10 km from the present coast, grading into unconfined peatland toward the southwest and into a series of parallel but minor ridges toward the coast. The paludification sequence is represented by five zones marked A to E on Figure 21.6.

Zone A (Figs. 21.6, 21.7A) includes the active littoral zone with sparsely vegetated storm beaches and salt marshes, as well as young freshwater marshes immediately landward of the first ridges (wetland terminology after Jeglum et al., 1974). Peat has not yet accumulated on the ridges, which are characterized by shrub vegetation (*Salix* spp.), but reaches 5 cm in the freshwater marshes.

Zone B (Figs. 21.6, 21.7A) is characterized by freshwater marshes with open water and peat accumulations of up to 60 cm. Minor ridges, generally less than 75 cm high, separate the marshes. These are dominated by thicket swamps nearest the coast (*Salex* spp., *Alnus* spp.), and by conifer swamps with black spruce and tamarack (*Picea mariana* and *Larix laricina*) furthest inland. The ridges are capped by up to 20 cm of peat.

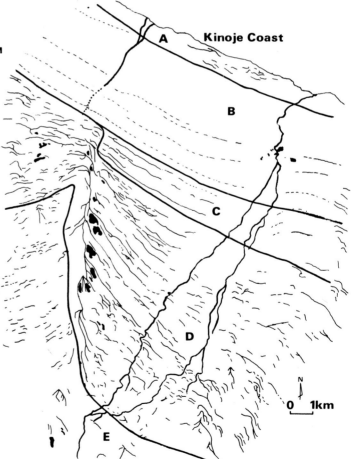

Figure 21.6. *Sketch of the Kinoje coast area (area X on Fig. 21.2) outlining the paludification sequence (see text).*

In *Zone C* (Figs. 21.6, 21.7B) the water table has reached the top of the ridges. Organic material in the swales has accumulated to the level of the ridges, thus eliminating their morphological expression and producing an essentially flat profile (Fig. 21.5, M - M'). In this zone peat depths range from 60 to 90 cm in the swales and 20 to 70 cm on the ridges (depending on their original topography). The location of the ridges is masked by dense stands of black spruce with a ground cover of sphagum. Swales are characterized by low shrub fens (*Betula glandulosa* and *Myrica gale*) with some open water.

Zone D (Figs. 21.6, 21.7C) is dominated by a chevron beach complex. The main north-south trending ridge is approximately 2.0 m in height whereas the subparallel ridges forming the barbs are from 0.75 to 1.5 m high. These latter ridges support dense black spruce forests with poorly to imperfectly drained soils and 20 to 40 cm of peat. The main ridge also supports a dense black spruce forest on a well drained podzolic soil (Martini and Protz, 1978). Peat accumulation in the swales reaches 1.4 m, effectively

masking the lower ridges. These support open graminoid fens (*Carex* spp.), moss pools and stunted black spruce on sphagnum hummocks. The larger ridges have thick (0.75 - 1 m) sphagnum accumulations with black spruce stands on their flanks. This feature appears to be characteristic of large beach ridges (in zones D and E) and some sphagnum peat layers exceed 2.5 m in thickness (Fig. 21.5, P - P').

Zone E (Figs. 21.6, 21.7D) is characterized by discontinuous ridge segments and a patterned bog and fen complex. Up to 40 cm of peat occurs on the ridge segments. An Orthic Humic Podzol (R. Protz, pers. com.) is developed under a black spruce - lichen forest cover. In the surrounding peatland complex, open bog complexes with stunted black spruce and sphagnum communities are interspersed with elongated string fen complexes. Peat depths range from 1.5 to 2.7 m, effectively isolating the surface vegetation in the bog areas from the effects of the mineral substratum. Nutrient supply to the bog communities is primarily from the atmosphere, whereas in the fen communities nutrients from the mineral soil are supplied through slow but continuous seepage.

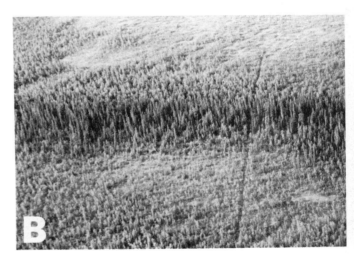

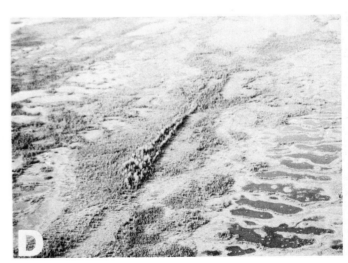

Figure 21.7. *Oblique aerial photographs showing each of the five paludification zones outlined in Figure 21.6. Figure 21.7 A corresponds to zone A (lower right), grading into zone B; 7B corresponds to zone C; 7C corresponds to zone D and 7D corresponds to zone E.*

SUMMARY AND CONCLUSIONS

The emergent, subarctic coast of Hudson and James bays is low lying but highly variable. Its evolution has been greatly influenced by the distribution of Paleozoic bedrock and glacial deposits.

The Ontario coastline can be subdivided into three major geomorphological coastal types: coasts dominated by long, parallel beach ridges; estuarine-dominated coasts; and coasts with numerous promontories and transverse ridges. Promontory-dominated coasts are the most complex.

The relatively high energy coast of Hudson Bay is characterized by a sequence of regularly spaced storm beach ridges that have developed parallel to the shore. This system has remained stable through Holocene times, as evidenced by the persistence of the ridges for approximately 75 km inland. The high-energy system is slightly modified around Cape Henrietta Maria, where extensive spits with blowouts have developed on the James Bay side.

In the southern part of James Bay the coastline is less regular and reflects the influence of local features of the Paleozoic and Pleistocene substratum. In specific cases emergence of islands such as Akimiski Island increases the protection of the coast from storm waves of the open sea. This coastline can be subdivided into coasts dominated by estuarine embayments and those dominated by promontories. The embayments are poorly drained and characterized by wide, silty, brackish marshes and by series of low, arcuate coastal ridges. Promontory-dominated coasts are best displayed in southern James Bay between the embayments. Their recurrence inland produces strong lineations, which are perhaps related to glacial fluting or drumlinoid forms modified into transverse ridges and chevron ridge complexes by marine processes.

The ridges that form perpendicular to the shore have complex origins. Some are composed of sand and fine gravel that accumulate in areas of wave refraction associated with slight rises of the bedrock. Others form as tombolo-like bars of sand and gravel that join pods of boulders, which are likely remnants of reworked glacial deposits. These transverse ridges form long, narrow promontories that extend several kilometres onto the shallow shelf and act as gigantic groynes for the northwest - southeast flowing longshore drift. Extensive sand flats are deposited in the updrift sides of the promontories, and sediment bypass zones develop on the downdrift sides. In the downdrift sides the materials that are eroded from the flats are accumulated in spits and longitudinal ridges that flare out from the promontories. As the land emerges, the association of transverse ridges and flaring-out spits and longitudinal ridges generate characteristic chevron complexes that are well preserved inland.

Coastal landscapes are modified by organic accumulation following their removal from the active marine zone by isostatic rebound. Because of paludification the landscape of the Hudson Bay Lowland evolves from one dominated by coastal landforms to one dominated by organic landforms. Only the largest features in interfluvial areas, such as promontories and storm ridges, remain recognizable in the oldest parts of the peatland complex. This complex is characterized by an extensive system of string bog and fens interspersed with mature upland conifer forests marking the major raised marine features. In the fluvial-dominated areas, coastal features are quickly paludified and become unrecognizable. These areas are characterized by extensive tracts of relatively featureless treed fens dissected by a parallel pattern of drainage.

Acknowledgments

This research was supported by Fisheries and Environment Canada (Canada Centre for Inland Waters; Canadian Forestry Service; Canadian Wildlife Service; Lands Directorate, Ontario Region; and Ocean and Aquatic Sciences). Financial support was provided by Lands Directorate, by other agencies through DSS contract 07SU KL108-7-0064, and by NSERC-Operating Grant No. A7371.

The successful study of these remote areas requires close collaboration by many agencies and individuals. We wish to extend our thanks to all of them and particularly to the field team of the Hudson Bay Lowland Project, especially Y. Desjardins who surveyed the transects represented in Figure 21.5.

References

Andrews, J.T.
  1969:   The pattern and interpretation of restrained postglacial and residual rebound in the area of Hudson Bay, N.W.T., Canada; Geological Survey of Canada, Paper 68-53, p. 49 - 62.

Barnett, D.M.
  1966:   A re-examination and re-interpretation of tide gauge data for Churchill, Manitoba; Canadian Journal of Earth Sciences, v. 3, p. 77 - 88.
  1970:   An amendment and extension of tide gauge analysis for Churchill, Manitoba; Canadian Journal of Earth Sciences, v. 7, p. 626, 627.

Bell, R.
  1896:   Proofs of the rising of the land around Hudson Bay; American Journal of Science, v. 1, p. 219 - 228.

Brown, R.J.E.
  1973:   Permafrost distribution and relation to environmental factors in the Hudson Bay Lowland; Proceedings, Symposium on the Physical Environment of the Hudson Bay Lowland, University of Guelph, p. 35 - 68.

Chapman, L.T. and Thomas, M.K.
  1968:   The climate of Northern Ontario; Meteorological Branch, Department of Transport Climatological Studies, Toronto, no. 6, 58 p.

Cowell, D.W., Jeglum, J.K. and Merriman, J.C.
  1978:   Preservation of seasonal frost in peatlands, Kinoje Lakes, Southern Hudson Bay Lowland; Proceedings, 3rd International Conference on Permafrost, Edmonton, Alberta, v. 1, p. 453 - 459.

Environment Canada
  1977:   Canadian tide and current tables; v. 4, Arctic and Hudson Bay, 71 p.

Glooschenko, W.A.
  1978:   Above ground biomass of vascular plants in a subarctic James Bay salt marsh; Canadian Field Naturalist, v. 92, p. 30 - 37.

Glooschenko, W.A. and Martini, I.P.
  1978: Hudson Bay Lowlands baseline study; Proceedings, American Society of Civil Engineers, Coastal Engineering Conference, San Francisco, v. II, p. 663 - 679.

Guimont, P. and Laverdière, C.
  1976a: Les littoral du sud-est de la Baie de James et de l'estuaire de l'Eastmain: Le milieu physique; Société de Développement de la Baie James, 133 p.
  1976b: Les types de côtés du sud-est de la Baie de James; James Bay - Environment Symposium 1976, Société de Développement de la Baie James, p. 175 - 201.

Hunter, G.T.
  1970: Postglacial uplift at Fort Albany, James Bay; Canadian Journal of Earth Sciences, v. 7, p. 547 - 548.

Jeglum, J.K., Boissonneau, A.N. and Haavisto, V.F.
  1974: Towards a wetland classification for Ontario; Canadian Forestry Service, Sault Ste Marie, Information Report O-X-215, 54 p.

Kershaw, K.A.
  1976: The vegetational zonation of the East Pen Island salt marshes, Hudson Bay; Canadian Journal of Botany, v. 54, p. 5 - 13.

Kershaw, K.A. and Rouse, W.R.
  1973: Studies on lichen dominated systems, V. A preliminary survey of a raised-beach system in northwestern Ontario; Canadian Journal of Botany, v. 51, p. 1285 - 1307.

King, C.A.M.
  1969: Some arctic coastal features around Foxe Basin and in East Baffin Island, N.W.T., Canada; Geografiska Annaler; A 51, p. 207 - 218.
  1972: Beaches and coasts; E. Arnold, London, 570 p.

Lee, H.A.
  1960: Late glacial and postglacial Hudson Bay sea episode; Science, v. 131, p. 1609 - 1611.

Martini, I.P., Morrison, R.I.G., Glooschenko, W.A. and Protz, R.
  1980: Coastal studies in James Bay, Ontario; Geoscience Canada, v. 7, p. 11 - 21.

Martini, I.P. and Protz, R.
  1978: Coastal gemorphology, sedimentology and pedology of southern James Bay, Ontario, Canada; Department of Land Resource Science, University of Guelph, Technical Memorandum 78-1, 316 p.

Martini, I.P. and Protz, R. (cont.)
  1980: Coastal geomorphology, sedimentation and pedology of northern James Bay, Ontario, Canada; Department of Land Resource Science, University of Guelph, Technical Memorandum 80-1, 117 p.

Martini, I.P., Protz, R., Grinham, D., King, W.A. and Clarke, K.E.
  1979: Studies of coastal sediments, soils, and biota. James Bay, Ontario, Canada; Department of Land Resource Science, University of Guelph, Technical Memorandum 79-1, 290 p.

Moir, D.R.
  1954: Beach ridges and vegetation in the Hudson Bay region; North Dakota Academy of Science, Annual Proceeding, v. 8, p. 45 - 48.

Niedoroda, A.W.
  1972a: Waves, currents, sediments and sand bars associated with low energy coastal environments; Transactions, Gulf Coast Associations of Geological Societies, v. 22, p. 229 - 240.
  1972b: Sand bars along low energy beaches, Part 2, Transverse bars; in Coastal Geomorphology, D.R. Coates, ed.; State University of New York, Binghamton, p. 103 - 113.

Niedoroda, A.W. and Tanner, W.F.
  1970: Preliminary study of transverse bars; Marine Geology, v. 9, p. 41 - 62.

O'Sullivan, O.
  1908: Survey of the south coast of Hudson Bay from the Severn River to Cape Henrietta Maria; Geological Survey of Canada, Summary Report, p. 93, 94.

Sanford, B.V., Norris, A.W. and Bostock, H.H.
  1968: Geology of the Hudson Bay Lowlands (Operation Winisk); Geological Survey of Canada, Paper 67-70, 118 p.

Shepard, F.P.
  1952: Revised nomenclature for depositional coastal features; Bulletin, American Association of Petroleum Geologists, v. 36, p. 1902 - 1912.

Simpson, S.J.
  1971: The York Factory area, Hudson Bay; unpubl. Ph.D. thesis, University of Manitoba.

Webber, P.J., Richardson, J.W. and Andrews, J.T.
  1970: Post-glacial uplift and substrate age at Cape Henrietta Maria, southeastern Hudson Bay, Canada; Canadian Journal of Earth Sciences, v. 7, p. 317 - 325.

22.   LE SUD-EST DE LA MER D'HUDSON: UN RELIEF DE CUESTA

Pierre Guimont et Camille Laverdière
Aménagement régional, Société de développement
de la Baie-James, Québec

Guimont, Pierre and Laverdière, Camille, Le sud-est de la mer d'Hudson: un relief de cuesta; in The
Coastline of Canada, S.B. McCann, editor; Geological Survey of Canada, Paper 80-10, p. 303-309,
1980.

Résumé

De la pointe de Louis-XIV au golfe de Guillaume-Delisle, la côte du sud-est de la mer d'Hudson
s'offre en un relief linéaire de cuesta qui fournit l'essentiel de sa définition. Les roches sédimentaires
du lieu, recouvertes de nappes basaltiques, s'inclinent radialement d'une dizaine de degrés vers les îles
de Belcher; elles font partie du long géosynclinal qui ceinturait aux trois quarts, au Protérozoïque, le
craton d'Ungava, et dont les formations rocheuses de la fosse du Labrador sont sans doute les plus
connues. Sous l'action de l'érosion sous toutes ses formes s'est développé un relief dissymétrique à
fronts tournés vers l'intérieur des terres, parfois hauts de 300 mètres, et à longs revers donnant sur la
mer. Toutefois, le littoral au sud de Poste-de-la-Baleine ne conserve que quelques segments de
roches sédimentaires, lambeaux de plus vastes surfaces, appuyés sur un socle cristallin d'âge archéen.
Depuis la déglaciation continentale, la transgression de la mer de Tyrrell et un relèvement isostatique
dans sa phase finale, le relief littoral est donc toujours représenté par une côte d'émersion.

Abstract

From Point-Louis XIV (Cap Jones) to Guillaume-Delisle Gulf (Richmond Gulf), a cuesta
morphology has given the SE Hudson Bay coastline a dominating linear relief. The sedimentary rocks,
overlapped by basaltic caps, have an angle of dip which varies in a radial configuration centred on the
Belcher Islands. They are part of the geosyncline which, in the Proterozoic era, wrapped three
quarters of the way around the Ungava Craton; the Labrador Trench formation is undoubtedly the
best known element of this geosyncline. Erosion in all its forms developed assymetrical ridges
reaching at times more than 300 metres, resulting in cuesta faces fronting inland and in long, gentle
backslopes facing the open sea. However, the littoral south of Poste-de-la-Baleine (Great Whale)
only retains a few sections of sedimentary rock, remnants of a once extensive area superimposed over
an archean crystalline shield. Since the continental deglaciation, the invasion of the Tyrrell Sea, and
the last phase of isostatic uplift, the littoral relief remains emergent in an ongoing process
of adjustment.

De la pointe de Louis-XIV au golfe de Guillaume-Delisle,
soit une distance de plus de 300 km, la côte marine à
caractère linéaire s'offre en un relief de cuesta qui fournit
l'essentiel de sa définition. Plus encore, c'est tout le grand
arc de la mer d'Hudson ou le double en longueur qui se
présente ainsi (fig. 22.1); il constitue la bordure d'un vaste
bassin qui aurait été aménagé dans le Bouclier par un impact
météoritique (Beals, 1968), et comblé de sédiments calcaires, dolomitiques et gréseux, de même que de coulées basaltiques, au début du Protérozoïque ou à l'Aphébien. Déjà
identifiées par Bell (1879) il y a cent ans et précisées par
Low (1902, 1903)---voir aussi les travaux de Parks (1949),
Kranck (1951), Woodcock (1960) et Eade (1966)---les strates
rocheuses dont le pendage varie peu sur toute la longueur de
la côte et dont l'orientation radiale se dirige au nord des îles
de Belcher, ne se redressent que de quelques degrés,
présentant des fronts de cuesta tournés vers l'intérieur des
terres. L'ensemble fait partie du long géosynclinal qui
ceinturait le craton d'Ungava et dont les formations rocheuses de la fosse du Labrador sont sans doute les plus
connues (Dimroth, 1970).

La couverture sédimentaire devait occuper une frange
beaucoup plus large du socle archéen et expliquerait, vu la
protection ainsi offerte, son allure moins perturbée. Ainsi,
Cailleux et Hamelin (1970) interprètent le tracé en dents de
scie d'une partie du réseau hydrographique par la structure
de ces roches disparues depuis longtemps: en témoignent les
tronçons inférieurs des vallées et des cours de la grande

rivière de la Baleine et du Coast qui figurent les dépressions subséquentes d'un ancien relief de cuesta, ou
l'accolement d'entonnoirs de percée. A la suite d'une longue
évolution, l'activité érosive sous toutes ses formes a ainsi
dégagé les roches cristallines et mis en valeur de longues
cuestas maintenant en position littorale ou insulaire. Ce
sont ces reliefs dissymétriques qui prennent une ampleur re-
marquable dans les régions de la Grande Île, des golfes de
Manitounouc et de Guillaume-Delisle, comme des îles de
Nastapoca plus au nord et qui atteignent en moyenne 30 m
de haut, parfois plus de 300 m (fig. 22.2).

L'écoulement glaciaire de composante allant de 255° à
285°, n'a laissé dans le territoire que peu de traces spectaculaires de son passage, sinon certains moutonnements
mais une multitude de roches dissymétriques, quelques
moulures parfois de forte taille au front des cuestas, des
micro-marques et des micro-formes très variées et bien
conservées en bordure de la mer. Sur le sens de l'écoulement glaciaire et sur les formes et marques d'érosion voir,
à part les premiers travaux de Low (1902), Portmann (1971),
Laverdière et Guimont (1975, 1977), Guimont et Laverdière
(1976) et aussi Hillaire-Marcel (1976). Quant au matériel
morainique, il demeure presque absent dans un pays aux
croupes rocheuses totalement dénudées; seules les vallées
fluviales importantes constituaient des pièges entre autres
pour leurs propres alluvions étalées et découpées en
terrasses successives.

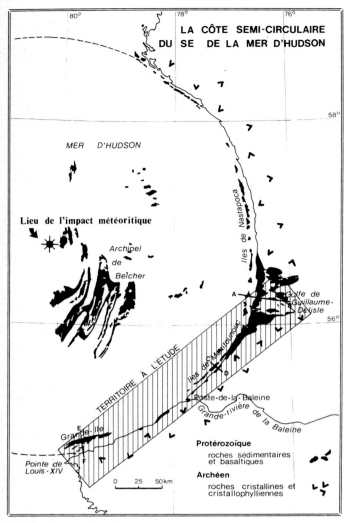

Figure 22.1. *Localisation des types de roche en place et de la zone étudiée.*

Lors de la déglaciation, les eaux de la mer de Tyrrell ont pénétré profondément à l'intérieur des terres ou jusqu'à l'altitude de 300 m; la côte actuelle, apparue sous le relèvement isostatique, demeure une côte d'émersion vu un rajustement non encore achevé, qui serait actuellement de 11 mm par an (Hillaire-Marcel et de Boutray, 1975; Archer, 1968; Hamelin et Cailleux, 1972; Hillaire-Marcel, 1976). Une côte à skjär (Dionne, 1976b), tant de l'est de la baie de James que du nord-est de la mer d'Hudson, se voit donc interrompue par ces littoraux linéaires établis au droit de fronts et de revers de cuesta.

Les dalles rocheuses des revers font face à la pleine mer ou occupent la côte est des golfes et des détroits; ils plongent doucement sous les eaux, établissant un rivage presque rectiligne, et portent plus ou moins régulièrement de multiples plages et des cordons de blocs glaciels, construits tant par les glaces actuelles que celles sous la commande des eaux tyrrelliennes. Quant aux fronts, ils forment des abrupts ou de hautes falaises tombant souvent directement dans la mer, à l'emplacement des côtes ouest des golfes et des détroits, ou dominant le socle cristallin à l'intérieur des terres. L'exploitation d'axes structuraux a permis le dégagement de vallées subséquentes qui mettent les fronts de cuesta en valeur, principalement lorsqu'elles se laissent envahir par la mer; par le recul d'entailles obséquentes et conséquentes, les raideurs s'offrent en dentelles et en festons, voire même s'abaissent à l'emplacement de trouées qui isolent ainsi des buttes-témoins et des avant-buttes, tandis que l'érosion différentielle les découpe en escaliers de géant.

On rencontre ainsi, de la Grande Île jusqu'aux premières îles de Nastapoca, plusieurs sections de côte qu'on peut distinguer selon les divers arrangements des cuestas. De la côte à pergélisol, à terrains réticulés et à toundra caractérisant la pointe de Louis-XIV ou de ses rivages bas à plages de blocs, et dalles rocheuses, se détachent de multiples îles et rochers toujours effilés, taillés en autant de basses cuestas dolomitiques qui mènent à la Grande Île, seul noyau sédimentaire et basaltique important avant les Manitounouc, et qui encombrent le détroit du même nom. Longue de plus de 50 km et parallèle à la côte, cette dernière retient l'attention par ses fronts raides mais aussi par ses très amples revers de laves noires et de dolomie; ceux-ci, comme beaucoup d'autres le long de la mer d'Hudson, portent dans leur aire intertidale les micromarques et micro-formes glaciaires les plus variées et les plus expressives du Nouveau-Québec.

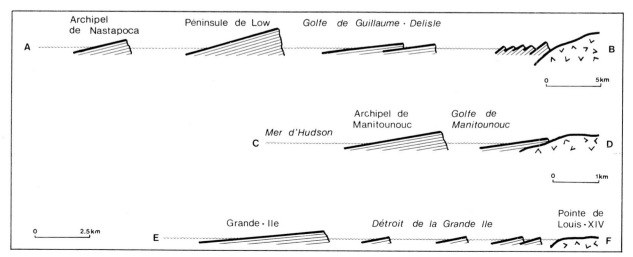

Figure 22.2. *Coupes schématiques du relief de cuesta en trois lieux de la côte du sud-est de la mer d'Hudson (exagération verticale variable).*

Figure 22.3 *A la pointe de Louis-XIV, longues cuestas dolomitiques parallèles à la côte qui articulent les îles nombreuses du détroit de la Grande Ile.*

Figure 22.5 *Des plages de blocs glaciels marquent les rivages actuels et anciens de toute la côte hudsonienne; elles soulignent ici de basses dalles cristallines au sud de Poste-de-la-Baleine.*

Figure 22.4 *La Grande Ile s'offre en falaises de fronts de cuesta, face au détroit du même nom, et en longs revers basaltiques plongeant vers la pleine mer; des plages soulevées en occupent tous les niveaux.*

Figure 22.6 *Le socle archéen dégagé depuis peu de sa couverture sédimentaire protérozöique demeure bas et peu perturbé en milieu côtier. Un littoral faiblement indenté marqué par ses plages de sable et de cailloux et une pessière riveraine le découpage de cette surface.*

Le littoral qui conduit ensuite aux abords de Poste-de-la-Baleine ne conserve que quelques segments peu larges de roches sédimentaires; ces lambeaux de plus vastes surfaces n'occupent plus que le quart de la côte et, appuyés sur un socle cristallin souvent bas et très uniforme, s'avancent en nappes surbaissées jusqu'à un ou deux kilomètres à l'intérieur des terres. La mer pénètre de nombreuses dépressions subséquentes et morcèle ainsi ce relief linéaire à fronts de cuestas serrés. Quant à la surface du Bouclier, elle s'incline d'un seul tenant vers la mer et demeure à peine marquée de petites baies à plages de sable et de blocs précédant des formes de rivage plus anciennes.

Après l'embouchure de la grande rivière de la Baleine bordée de croupes cristallines qui se redressent jusqu'à 150 m, taillée dans un large delta sablonneux qui constitue le site de l'agglomération autochtone, apparaissent les îles de

Manitounouc à quelques kilomètres au large. A l'abri de cette rangée insulaire, des dalles dolomitiques se développent de façon discontinue sur la côte est du golfe du même nom et voisinent les roches du socle archéen. Elles apparaissent dès les îles de Maver ou précèdent le littoral en longs cordons effilés aux îles Peintes, et gagnent le pays à l'est sur à peine quelques kilomètres par de vastes revers de dolomie à stromatolithes. Des cordons de blocs glaciels soulignent leur découpage et font suite à d'autres plages anciennes se succédant régulièrement à des altitudes élevées. Mais entre ces îles, ce sont surtout des terrasses d'argile soulevées par le gel et des tourbières à palses qui présentent leurs faces vives de décrépitude sur le littoral (Laverdière et Guimont, 1976). Dans le golfe de Manitounouc, une sédimentation en milieu protégé permet aussi la croissance de larges estrans à blocs glaciels.

Figure 22.7 *Terrasse d'argile soulevée par le gel et tourbière à palses s'offrant en faces vives de décrépitude et en dépressions thermokarstiques sur la côte est du golfe de Manitounouc.*

Figure 22.9 *Le long archipel de Manitounouc s'étire parallèlement à la côte hudsonienne et ses vastes revers de cuesta plongent uniformément sous la mer.*

Figure 22.8 *Des dalles dolomitiques s'appuient sur le socle archéen à l'est du golfe de Manitounouc et se présentent en fronts de cuesta tournés vers l'intérieur des terres.*

Figure 22.10 *Falaise de front de cuesta de l'île du Cap de Portland s'élevant au dessus du golfe de Manitounouc et révélant une lourde couverture basaltique en relief inversé posée sur d'épaisses strates gréseuses.*

De hautes cuestas portant noms d'île du Cap de Portland, d'île de Neilson, d'île Joyeuse et d'île du Château forment l'archipel de Manitounouc. Coiffées d'une couverture basaltique en relief inversé qui compose de larges revers uniformes, ces îles dominent parfois de 125 m le golfe, du sommet de leurs fronts de cuesta arqués et de leurs éboulis. Ces fronts taillés en dentelle dans un empilement de laves à structure en tuyaux d'orgue, reposant sur d'épaisses strates de grès, s'abaissent parfois au droit de percées conséquentes qui morcèlent ces cuestas par autant de passages ennoyés, et qui font communiquer les eaux du golfe de Manitounouc et de la mer d'Hudson.

Les profonds revers de lave noire se poursuivant cette fois sur la terre ferme en une côte des plus uniformes mais impressionnante, prolongent vers le nord les cuestas insulaires. La simplicité des longs rivages dénudés aux échancrures d'échelle décamétrique ou hectométrique révèle un patron de roc, le plus souvent nu, et de matériaux grossiers. Les fronts y sont de plus en plus élevés, et le couloir du golfe de Manitounouc trouve une continuité dans leurs vallées subséquentes. Des plages soulevées et des champs de blocs glaciels (Lagarec, 1976) se sont inscrits à tous les niveaux de ces reliefs dissymétriques au sein de minces placages; d'autres débris meubles ponctuant les surfaces structurales, de même qu'une végétation d'épinettes blanches (Payette, 1975) souligne le patron plus ou moins irrégulier de leurs dépressions. D'autres trouées transversales, résultant de la juxtaposition de percées conséquentes et obséquentes, défoncent les hauteurs littorales et sont empruntées de cours d'eau; la petite rivière de la Baleine occupe la plus importante d'entre elles entre des escarpements verticaux hauts de près de 200 m et de basses terrasses à pergélisol.

Figure 22.11 *Les îles de Manitounouc présentent des fronts de cuesta taillés en dentelle dont les strates rocheuses s'articulent en escaliers de géant. L'abaissement du relief au droit de percées obséquentes et conséquentes va jusqu'à créer des trouées ennoyées.*

Figure 22.13 *Les premières îles de Nastapoca, presque entièrement dénudées, se dressent en pleine mer et de leurs fronts de cuesta taillés en festons symétriques dominent un long détroit avant la côte.*

Figure 22.12 *La petite rivière de la Baleine qui occupe la plus importante des trouées de percée conséquente est encadrée d'abrupts latéraux hauts de près de 200 m et de talus d'éboulis imposants.*

Figure 22.14 *Le golfe de Guillaume-Delisle communique de plain-pied avec la mer au droit d'un goulet qu'enserrent des cuestas spectaculaires taillées en château fort.*

C'est finalement avec les premières îles de l'archipel de Nastapoca et la triple rangée de cuestas enserrant le détroit du même nom et le golfe de Guillaume-Delisle, que le pays sédimentaire acquiert sa plus grande extension, soit plus de 50 km. C'est aussi avec les fronts insulaires tout en festons symétriques, les cuestas du centre taillées en châteaux forts et dominant le golfe et les eaux vives à marée de son Goulet comme les collines redressées en crêts plus à l'est, que nous saisissons là un des reliefs les plus spectaculaires du Québec, si bien que l'on a proposé de faire de ce pays une réserve écologique (Payette, 1972).

Mais la côte n'est pas qu'un lieu linéaire né d'un style de contact entre terre et eau; suivant les saisons, ce sont aussi les aspects multiples et variés que prend cette bande de terre qui confine à la mer. Ainsi, le présence de la banquise en mer d'Hudson (Danielson, 1971) contre une terre ferme

enneigée (Payette et Lagarec, 1972) confère à ce contact un tout autre aspect dont il faut tenir compte: on sait l'importance du nivéo-éolien en particulier sur le pied de glace (Cailleux, 1976). En réalité, c'est tout le climat qui participe à la physionomie de la côte et qui influence entre autres l'allure de son couvert végétal, représenté dans ses formations arborées par la pessière blanche.

La seule occupation humaine de l'espace, sur les basses terrasses de la rive gauche de l'embouchure de la grande rivière de la Baleine, ne contribue-t-elle pas aussi à la création du type de côte de l'endroit, du moins ponctuellement. Et quel sera le nouveau paysage côtier du golfe de Manitounouc quand s'y amèneront, par un nouveau tracé, les eaux combinées de la petite rivière et la grande rivière de la Baleine dont on veut capter l'énergie?

Remerciements

Les recherches sur le milieu littoral au sud-est de la mer d'Hudson ont été effectuées à la demande et avec l'appui des directions de l'Environnement de la SDBJ et d'Hydro-Québec. Nous tenons à remercier M. Keith Bridger de la SDBJ (Env.) qui a revu la version anglaise du résumé.

Bibliographie

Archer, D.R.
1968:   The upper marine limit in the Little Whale River, New Quebec; Arctic, v. 21, nᵒ 3, p. 153 - 160.

Beals, C.S.
1968:   Theories of the origin of Hudson Bay; Part I, On the possibility of a catastrophic origin for the great arc of Eastern Hudson Bay; dans Science, History and Hudson Bay, Vol. II; Canada, Ministère de l'Energie, des Mines et des Ressources, p. 985 - 999.

Bell, R.
1879:   Report of an exploration on the east coast of Hudson's Bay; Commission géologique du Canada, Report of Progress 1877-78, p. 193 - 220.

Bournérias, M.
1972:   Voyage naturaliste au Nouveau-Québec; 1. La végétation au sud du 55e parallèle; 2. Poste-de-la-Baleine: les marges de l'Arctique, les marges des temps fossilifères; Paris, Sciences et Nature, nᵒ 110, p. 17 - 28.

Cailleux, A.
1972:   Principaux résultats géomorphologiques du projet Hudsonie; dans International Geography 1972, t. I; University of Toronto Press, p. 104 -105.
1976:   Formes et dépôts nivéo-éoliens sur le pied de glace, à Poste-de-la-Baleine, Québec subarctique; Revue de Géographie de Montréal, v.30, nᵒˢ 1-2, p. 213 - 219.

Cailleux, A. et Hamelin, L.-E.
1970:   Poste-de-la-Baleine (Nouveau-Québec): exemple de géomorphologie complexe; Revue de Géomorphologie dynamique, v. 19, nᵒ 3, p. 129 -150.

Danielson, E.W.
1971:   Hudson Bay ice conditions; Arctic, v. 24, nᵒ 2, p. 90 - 107.

Dimroth, E. et al.
1970:   The filling of the circum-Ungava geosyncline; dans Symposium on Basins and Geosynclines of the Canadian Shield; Commission géologique du Canada, Paper 70-40, p. 45 - 142.

Dionne, J.-C.
1976a: Les grandes cuesta de la mer d'Hudson; Canada, Énergie, Mines et Ressources, GEOS, hiver, p. 18 - 20.
1976b: Le littoral oriental de la baie de James, dans la région de Roggan, Québec; Annales de l'Association canadienne-française pour l'avancement des sciences, v. 43, nᵒ 1, p. 106.

Eade, K.E.
1966:   Fort George River and Kaniapiskau River (west half) map-areas, New Quebec; Commission géologique du Canada, Memoir 339, 83 p., carte 1155A, 1:000 000.

Guimont, P. et Laverdière, C.
1976:   Les marques, les formes et le sens de l'écoulement glaciaire de Poste-de-la-Baleine au golfe de Guillaume-Delisle, Nouveau-Québec; Annales de l'Association canadienne-française pour l'avancement des sciences, v. 43, nᵒ 1, p. 104.

Hamelin, L.-E. et Cailleux, A.
1969:   Les palses dans le bassin de la grande-rivière de la Baleine, Revue de Géographie de Montréal, v. 23, nᵒ 3, p. 329 - 337.
1972:   Succession des types de rivage pendant l'Holocène à Poste-de-la-Baleine (Nouveau-Québec); Zeitschrift für Geomorphologie, v. 16, nᵒ 1, p. 16 - 26.

Hillaire-Marcel, C.
1976:   La déglaciation et le relèvement isostatique sur la côte est de la baie d'Hudson; Cahiers de Géographie de Québec. v. 20, nᵒ 50, p. 185 - 220.

Hillaire-Marcel, C. et de Boutray, B.
1975:   Les dépôts meubles holocènes de Poste-de-la-Baleine, Nouveau-Québec; Université Laval, Québec, CEN, nᵒ 38, 47p.

Hustich, I.
1950:   Notes on the forests on the east coast of Hudson Bay and James Bay; Acta Geographica (Helsinki), v.11, nᵒ 1, p. 1 - 83.
1957:   On the phytogeography of the Subarctic Hudson Bay Lowland; Acta Geographica (Helsinki), v. 16, nᵒ 1, 48p.

Kranck, E.H.
1951:   On the geology of the east coast of Hudson Bay and James Bay; Acta Geographica (Helsinki), v.11, nᵒ 2, p. 1 - 71.

Lagarec, D.
1976:   Champs de blocs glaciels, actuels et anciens, au golfe de Richmond, Nouveau-Québec; Revue de Géographie de Montréal, v. 30, nᵒˢ 1-2, p. 211 - 225.

Laverdière, C. et Guimont, P.
1975:   Pour une typologie des micro-marques d'érosion glaciaire: exemples jamésiens et hudsoniens; Annales de l'Association canadienne-française pour l'avancement des sciences, v.42, nᵒ 1, p. 80.
1976:   Les palses de la région de Poste-de-la-Baleine, littoral sud-est de la mer d'Hudson, Nouveau-Québec; Annales de l'Association canadienne-française pour l'avancement des sciences, v.43, nᵒ 1, p. 105.
1977:   Le sens de l'écoulement glaciaire sur les littoraux jamésiens et hudsoniens, entre la Grande-Rivière et Poste-de-la-Baleine; Annales de l'Association canadienne-française pour l'avancement des sciences, v.44, nᵒ 1, p. 93.

Low, A.P.
  1902:   Report on an exploration of the east coast of
          Hudson Bay from Cape Wolstenholme to the
          south end of James Bay; Commission géologique
          du Canada, Annual Report, v. 13, pt.D, 84 p.
          maps 779-780-781, 1:500 000.
  1903:   Report on the geology and physical character of
          the Nastapoka Islands, Hudson Bay; Commission
          géologique du Canada, Annual Report, v.13, pt.
          DD, 31 p.

Parks, T.
  1949:   A report on the geology of the Nastapoka Group
          of sediments (Hudson Bay) with its contained
          lead and zinc bearing strata; unpubl. BASc.
          thesis, University of Toronto.

Payette, S.
  1972:   Le golfe de Richmond, Nouveau-Québec, réserve
          écologique n⁰ 54; De Toute Urgence (Québec), v.
          3, n⁰ 2, p. 4 - 15.
  1973:   Contribution à la pédologie de la zone hémi-
          arctique: région   de   Poste-de-la-Baleine,
          Nouveau-Québec; Naturaliste canadien, v. 100,
          n⁰ 2, p. 123 - 163.
  1975:   La limite des forêts sur la côte orientale de la
          baie d'Hudson; Naturaliste canadien, v. 102, n⁰ 3,
          p. 317 - 329.

Payette, S. et Filion, L.
  1975:   Ecologie de la limite septentrionale des forêts
          maritimes,   baie   d'Hudson,   Nouveau-Québec;
          Naturaliste canadien, v. 102, n⁰ 6, p. 783 - 802.

Payette, S. et Lagarec, D.
  1972:   Observations sur les conditions d'enneigement à
          Poste-de-la-Baleine,   Nouveau-Québec,   hiver
          1972; Cahiers de Géographie de Québec, v. 16, n⁰
          39, p. 469 - 481.

Portmann, J.-P.
  1971:   Géomorphologie   de   l'aire   myriamétrique   de
          Poste-de-la-Baleine (Nouveau-Québec); Cahiers
          de Géographie de Québec, 15e ann., n⁰ 34, p.
          53 - 76.

Wilson, C.
  1968:   Notes on the climate of Poste-de-la-Baleine,
          Quebec; Université Laval, Québec, CEN, n⁰ 24,
          92 p.

Woodcock, J.R.
  1960:   Geology   of   the   Richmond   Gulf   area,   New
          Quebec; Proceedings of the Geological Asso-
          ciation of Canada, v. 12, p. 21 - 39.

23

AN OUTLINE OF THE EASTERN JAMES BAY COASTAL ENVIRONMENTS

Jean-Claude Dionne
Environment Canada, Québec, Québec

Dionne, Jean-Claude, *An outline of the eastern James Bay coastal environments; in The Coastline of Canada, S.B. McCann, editor; Geological Survey of Canada, Paper 80-10, p. 311-338, 1980.*

Abstract

The eastern James Bay coastline extends in a general south to north direction from the mouth of Harricana and Nottaway rivers, to Point Louis XIV, for an approximate straight-line distance of 380 km. However, the extremely irregular and indented shoreline is about 1400 km long. It is fringed by more than a thousand islands, skerries and shoals of various sizes and shapes. Several hundred embayments, points, and peninsulas, composed either of crystalline rocks or unconsolidated sediments, characterize this subarctic coast. The shoreline has developed along a flat lowland area gently sloping towards James Bay. The levelled bedrock surface is a peneplane thinly mantled by Quaternary deposits. It is an emerging coastline with wide shore and nearshore zones of small slope gradient. The coast is exposed to offshore fetches up to 200 km long for about 6 months per year, and it is partly or entirely ice-covered from November to June. Although drift ice processes are very important along the shoreline, waves, currents and tides are the major processes of coastal evolution. Erosion occurs on well exposed unconsolidated deposits (islands and points) and sedimentation prevails in embayments. The eastern James Bay coastline is an excellent example of a skerry coast offering beautiful landscapes from the air.

Résumé

Le littoral oriental de la baie de James s'étend une direction générale Sud-Nord de l'embouchure des rivières Harricana et Nottaovai de part et d'autre de la péninsule de Ministikawatin, jusqu'à la pointe Louis XIV, sur une distance en ligne droite d'environ 380 km. En raison d'un tracé du littoral fort découpé et irrégulier, la longueur du trait de côte excède 1400 km. Plus d'un millier d'îles, d'écueils et de hauts-fonds de dimensions et de formes variées sont parsemés tout le long de la côte dans une bande ayant entre 10 et 25 km de largeur. Plusieurs centaines de rentrants, de pointes et de péninsules composées tantôt de roches cristallines, tantôt de matériaux meubles caractérisent cette côte subarctique découpant une plaine côtière dont la surface est faiblement inclinée vers la baie de James. La surface rocheuse aplanie est recouverte d'une mince couverture de dépôts meubles quaternaires. Il s'agit d'une côte en voie d'émersion possédant de larges zones littorales et pré-littorales. Couvert de glace de novembre à juin, le rivage est exposé durant le reste de l'année à des fetches du large atteignant jusqu'à 200 km. Bien que l'action des glaces soit très importante et soit à l'origine de divers phénomènes d'érosion et de sédimentation, les vagues, courants et marées demeurent les principaux agents de l'évolution du rivage. L'érosion prédomine dans les secteurs exposés qui sont composés de matériel meuble alors que la sédimentation s'effectue dans les rentrants et les sites abrités. Le littoral oriental de la Jamésie constitue un excellent exemple de côte à skjar ou à écueils et offre du haut des airs des paysages d'une grande beauté.

INTRODUCTION

After its discovery by the European explorers Captain Henry Hudson and Thomas James during the first half of the 18th century, the eastern James Bay coast remained largely unexplored for more than two centuries.

Early geological and geographical surveys. date back to the end of the last century and the beginning of the 20th century (Bell, 1879; Low, 1889, 1902, 1912; Kindle, 1925). Most information on geography, geology and oceanography about the area has been collected fairly recently, especially during the last two decades (Beals, 1968; Hood, 1969; Meagher et al., 1976). However, relatively little is known about the eastern James Bay coast. The author had the opportunity to survey the area during three summer field seasons (1973, 1974 and 1975) to make geomorphological observations (Dionne, 1974a, 1975a, 1976a, 1977). This report outlines the physical aspects of the eastern coastline of James Bay.

CHARACTERISTICS OF THE COASTAL AREA

Physiography

The eastern James Bay coastline extends generally south to north from the mouths of the Nottaway River (51°20' N, 78°55' W) and the Harricana River (51°09' N, 79°45' W) in the south, to Point Louis XIV (54°37' N, 79°45' W) in the north (Fig. 23.1). The straight-line distance between Broadback River and Point Louis XIV is approximately 380 km but the shoreline itself from Hannah Bay to Point Louis XIV, excluding islands, is more than 1400 km. Extremely irregular in shape, it is fringed by about a thousand islands, skerries and shoals, and many hundred of capes, peninsulas, points, bays, coves, inlets and other coastal indentations of various shapes and sizes. Shore features are spread throughout a coastal zone 5 to 25 km in width and less than 20 m in depth. In addition, numerous offshore islands are

---

Note: All photographic illustrations will be found at the end of text before the references.

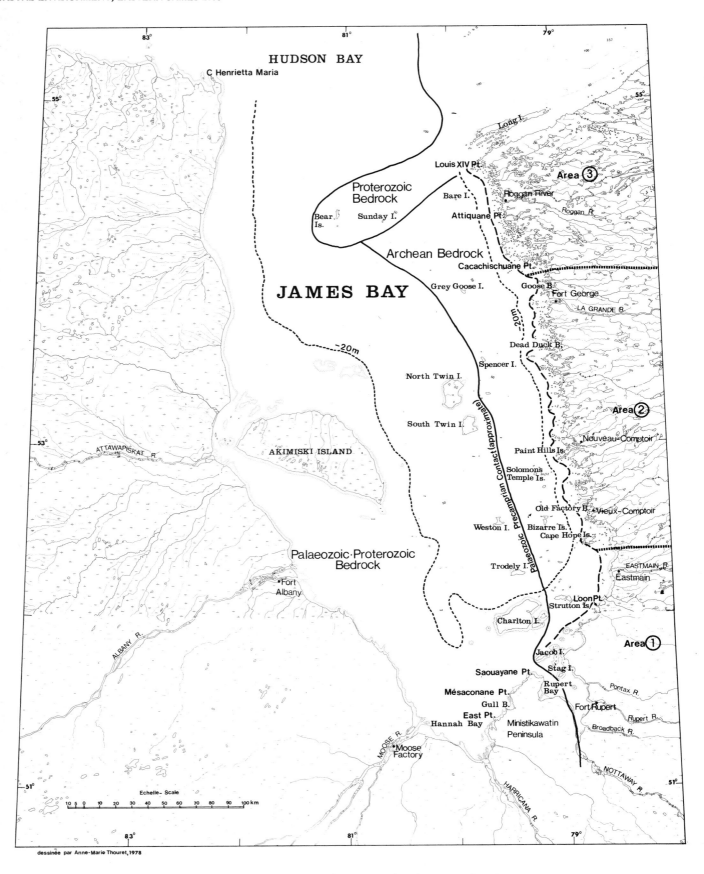

Figure 23.1.   *James Bay. Location map and main geographical names.*

spread along two main southeast-northwest alignments, one located 25 - 30 km, the other 50 - 60 km from the mainland. Charlton and North and South Twin are the largest offshore islands; Strutton, Trodely, Weston, Bizarre, Solomons Temple, Spencer and Grey Goose are medium-size islands. The eastern James Bay coastline contrasts with the western shore, which is more regular in shape, very shallow, and devoid of islands and skerries (Martini and Protz, 1978).

The coastal area is a lowland with a relief generally less than 30 m high; only a few isolated rocky hills or monadnocks stand out above the general lowland surface, the highest being Sherrick Hill (166 m) north of Rupert Bay, Cape Hope Island (90 m) between Eastmain and Vieux-Comptoir, and Paint Hills Island (60 m) in the vicinity of Nouveau-Comptoir. It is a submerged peneplane-surface cut into Archean crystalline rocks partly mantled by thin Quaternary deposits (Kranck, 1951). Two major physiographic divisions can be made. South of Eastmain River is a large, flat fluviomarine plain, and north of it is a rocky glacio-marine plain (Hardy, 1976). These major physiographic regions differ slightly from those made by Bostock (1970).

About 50 rivers discharge into James Bay, the largest being from south to north, the Harricana, Rupert, Broad-back, Eastmain and La Grande. Other, medium-size rivers are the Missisicabi, Truite, Jolicoeur, Mouton, Conn, Vieux-Comptoir, Peuplier, Sabascunica, Maquatua, Suaganstuc, Castor, Caillet, Guillaume, Piagochioui, Kapsaouis, Roggan and Phoque. In addition, there are more than twenty other small rivers draining the coastal area and discharging directly into James Bay.

The drainage system is of some importance in the shoreline development because runoff causes earlier breakup along the eastern coast, decreases water salinity in the nearshore zone, and carries sediments to the sea. Approximately 70 per cent of the freshwater input comes from the east side. La Grande and Eastmain rivers contribute about 39 per cent of the total runoff in James Bay (El-Sabh and Koutitonsky, 1974). In addition, the river estuaries of the Rupert, Eastmain and La Grande are creating a particular coastal environment.

Geology

Although the geology of the bedrock along the eastern James Bay coast is not known in much detail, early surveys (Bell, 1879; Low, 1889, 1902, 1912) and more recent surveys (Shaw, 1942; Kranck, 1951; Eade, 1966; Remick et al., 1963; Remick and Admedali, 1975; Dubé et al., 1976; and Franconi, 1978) provide valuable information on the nature, composition and age of the rocks outcropping in the coastal area.

The irregular bedrock surface of eastern James Bay coast is mainly composed of granite, gneiss and granodiorite with dikes of intrusive rocks of Archean age. Granitic gneisses are the major rock type in the northern two thirds, whereas metasedimentary gneisses are the main rock type in the southern third. Various facies have been recognized within these lithologies that partially account for differential erosion. The bedrock surface is considered to have been sculptured during a long period of erosion since Precambrian time and surficially retouched by glaciers during the Quaternary (Kranck, 1951).

The area was glaciated during the Quaternary. During the last glacial period, the Laurentide ice sheet centred in subarctic Quebec flowed radially to Hudson and James bays to the west, where it joined with the Keewatin ice sheet approximately 40 - 50 km off the present shoreline. The direction of the ice flow in the coastal area was generally

west-southwest in the northern part of the area (Point Louis XIV to Fort George), southwest in the central part (Eastmain River), and south-southwest in the south (Rupert Bay area) (Low, 1902; Craig, 1969; Guimont and Laverdière, 1976a; Hardy, 1976). Also in the southern part of James Bay area (south of Eastmain River) ice flowed from the west during the Cochrane and Rupert readvances at the end of the Wisconsin (Prest, 1970). Ice thickness during the Wisconsin maximum is estimated to be about 3000 m (Sugden, 1977).

Deglaciation of the eastern James Bay area took place about 8200 years BP. At that time, the Laurentide ice sheet split into two main ice sheets: the Hudson ice sheet in the west and the Quebec ice sheet in the east. Once separated, the Hudson ice readvanced three times over the southern part of the bay (Hardy, 1976, 1977), whilst the front of the Quebec ice sheet, located in the lowlands, remained stable for a relatively long period during which the Sakami moraine was built. During that period, a large lake developed between the two ice sheets. According to Hardy (1977), Lake Ojibway extended north to La Grande River and possibly up to the Great Whale River. Following the ice sheet retreat in Hudson Strait and Hudson Bay, a marine invasion took place about 7900 years BP (Wagner, 1967; Lee, 1968a, b). The Tyrrell Sea covered large areas of the coastal lowlands, submerging an area up to 200 km wide on the east side of James Bay. Maximum elevation reaches by the sea was 200 m in the south (Harricana River), increasing up to 300 m in the north at the latitude of Great Whale River (Hillaire-Marcel, 1976). The maximum elevation of the Tyrrell Sea was 225 m along Broadback River, 250 m along Rupert River, 275 m along Eastmain River and 290 along La Grande River.

As the ice sheet retreated from the area, isostatic recovery occurred and the Tyrrell Sea gradually withdrew to present sea level leaving shore features and marine deposits at various elevations. Residual isostatic recovery is estimated to be 120 m in the south and 150 m in the north (Andrews, 1970).

The eastern coast is thus an emerging coastline. Glaciers fashioned the Archean crystalline bedrock during the Quaternary and in places left unsorted deposits (mainly drumlins). Scattered fluvioglacial deposits (eskers, kames, deltas and outwash plains) were laid down during the retreat of the ice sheet. Most of these deposits have not been entirely buried by the marine sand-silt-clay blanket left by the Tyrrell Sea, and can be seen emerging in the coastal area.

The emerged coastal plain, especially the glaciomarine plain north of Eastmain River shows the same landform patterns as those of the present coastline. Hills and ridges are composed either of rock or unconsolidated glacial and fluvioglacial deposits on which beaches developed. The large depressions in the rock surface are usually partly filled with stratified marine silt and clay. Near the main rivers (La Grande and Eastmain) silt and clay are commonly blanketed with alluvial sand.

Based on data collected by Lee et al. (1960), Hardy (1976), Vincent (1973, 1977) and the author (Dionne, unpubl.), the general stratigraphy for the Quaternary deposits in the coastal area is as follows:

Northern area (north of Eastmain River)

(a) At the base is an irregular Archean crystalline bedrock covered by a till sheet of varying thickness deposited by the Laurentide ice sheet.
(b) Overlying the till are scattered fluvioglacial deposits of stratified sand and gravel.

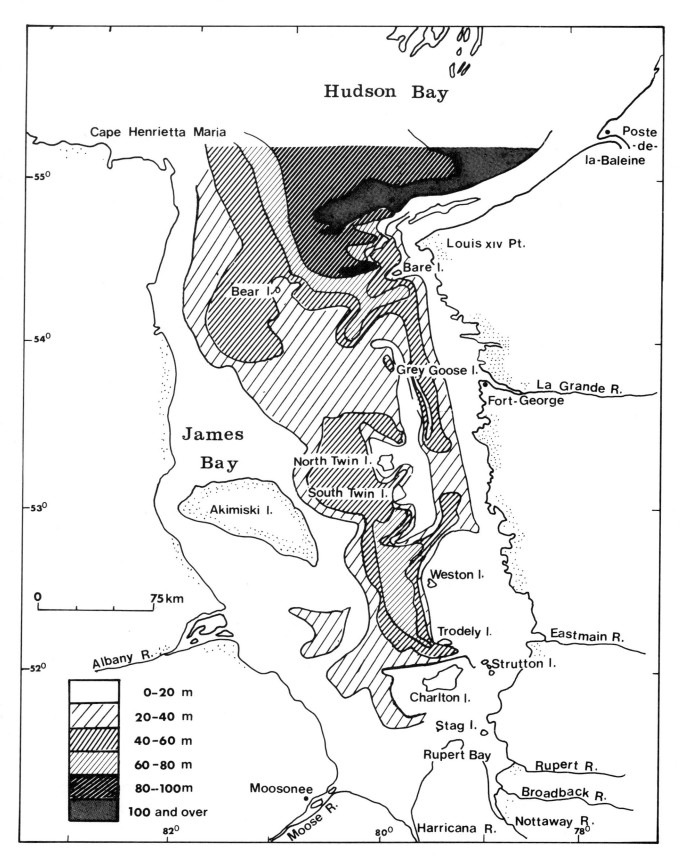

Figure 23.2.   *Bathymetry of James Bay.*

(c) Marine deep- and shallow-water deposits (stratified clay, silt and fine sand) overlie the till and the random fluvioglacial sediments.

(d) At the surface sand, gravel, cobble or boulder beaches are irregularly distributed but prevalent on and along rocky hills, drumlins and fluvioglacial deposits.

(e) Finally a few dune fields occur locally and extensive peat bogs cover poorly drained deposits.

In the major valleys (La Grande, Eastmain and Rupert) local, lacustrine sediments (stratified sand, silt and clay) lie between the basal till and the marine sediments, and alluvial sand and gravel overlie deep-water marine deposits.

Southern area (south of Eastmain)

A more complex stratigraphy exists in this area. In addition to the stratigraphic units mentioned above, locally three till units were emplaced by the Hudson ice sheet at the end of the Wisconsin. These till sheets (Cochrane I and II and Rupert) of various thickness and composition are interbedded with lacustrine sediments (Lake Ojibway) and fit into the stratigraphic column between the Laurentide till at the base and the marine deposits (Tyrrell Sea) at or near the surface. To summarize, the stratigraphic sequence from the surface to the bottom is as follows:

(a) Organic deposits (peat bogs) with a few scattered dunes developed from beaches, alluvial and reworked fluvioglacial deposits.

(b) Beaches of sand, gravel, cobbles and boulders built by the Tyrrell Sea (shore deposits).

(c) Marine shallow- and deep-water deposits (stratified fine sand, silt and clay).

(d) Lacustrine sediments (varved silt and clay).

(e) Three till sheets interbedded with lacustrine sediments.

(f) Early Lake Ojibway deposits.

(g) The Laurentide till overlying a crystalline bedrock.

Climate

The climate of the James Bay coastal area is rigorous. The mean annual air temperature is about -1°C at Fort Rupert, -2°C at Eastmain, -3°C at Fort George, and -4°C at Point Louis XIV. Winters are long and cold, the mean air temperature during the period November to April being -14°C. The lowest temperature recorded at Fort George is -48.3°C. Summers are short and relatively cold although the temperature may exceed 30°C for short periods. The mean air temperature during the summer months (June - September) is 10.1°C at Fort George and only 11.8°C during July and August. The highest temperature recorded at Fort George is 34.4°C (Villeneuve, 1967).

Mean annual precipitation is low along the eastern coast: only 679 mm at Fort George, including 2291 mm of snow.

Unfortunately, there is no meteorological station recording wind direction and velocity along the eastern James Bay coast. The two closest stations are at Moosonee, (Ontario) and Poste-de-la-Baleine (Québec). Data from these stations provide some indication of the wind conditions in the area under consideration. Mean annual wind frequency and speed do not mean much in the bay because of the long ice-covered season. Therefore wind conditions during the open season (June to November) will be summarized briefly.

At Moosonee prevailing winds during the open season are from the southwest and northwest. Other directions of frequent winds are north (June - August), south (July - November), and west (August - November). Based on mean annual frequency, 60 per cent of the winds come from the west (22% from northwest, 20% from southwest, and 13% from west). Average wind speed is highest from the northwest and southwest during the open season and ranges from 13 to 17 km per hour. The maximum observed hourly wind speed is 69 km/h and the probable maximum gust for maximum hourly speed is 96 km/h (Department of Transport, 1968).

At Poste-de-la-Baleine, the annual percentage frequency for winds from all west directions represents 42 per cent, those from all east directions, 37 per cent, those from north, 8 per cent, and those from south, 7 per cent. During the open season, prevailing winds are from the west-southwest, west and west-northwest, and from the north at the beginning of the season. Average wind speed is greater than at Moosonee. Average hourly wind speed from all west directions during the open season usually exceeds 16 km/h and reaches up to 47 km/h. The annual average speed for all west wind is 21 km/h. The maximum observed hourly speed is 96.6 km/h; the maximum observed gust speed is 127 km/h, and the maximum gust for maximum hourly speed is 133.6 km/h.

CHARACTERISTICS OF THE JAMES BAY BASIN

James Bay is a large U-shaped embayment south of Hudson Bay, and forms part of the largest inland marine water body in North America (1 300 000 km^2). The bay itself is about 450 km long and from 110 to 200 km wide for an approximate area of 32 200 km^2. This large bay is a relatively shallow continental sea, most of which is less than 40 m deep and about half less than 20 m. However, a few basins are 60 to 80 m deep. Unusual depths exceeding 100 m are only in a small basin located halfway between Point Louis XIV and Bear Island in northern James Bay (Canadian Hydrographic Service, 1971). Shallow water (less than 6 m) is common throughout a wide nearshore area along the eastern coast and the -20 m contour line is located from 5 to 15 km offshore (Fig. 23.2). In Rupert Bay, a major embayment in southern James Bay, water depths less than 3 m cover more than half of the area.

The marine geology of the bay is not well known, as indicated by data recently collected by Meagher et al. (1976). East of the Paleozoic-Precambrian contact, the bedrock is composed of Archean crystalline rocks; to the west, it is composed of Paleozoic sedimentary rocks. Bear and Sunday islands in northern James Bay belong to the Proterozoic rocks outcropping along the east coast of Hudson Bay. There is a central bathimetric high trending northwest-southeast along which occur Charlton, Trodely, Weston, Twin and Bear islands.

The topography of the bottom is not known in much detail. A generalized geomorphology map (Meagher et al., 1976) shows three main areas: ice-scoured, smoothed, and rugged. The rugged area corresponds to the Archean crystalline bedrock east of the Paleozoic-Precambrian contact. This zone, 10 to 50 km wide and occupying about 30 per cent of James Bay, is roughly parallel to the coast and has depths up to 60 m. The shelf is characterized by a rugged topography of high relief. Sediments are ponded between and draped over bedrock highs. Ponded sediments may reach up to 50 m thick and bedrock highs may protrude through the sediments and rise to sea level as small islands and shoals.

To the west is a more extensive area (about 60% of the bay) of smooth and gently undulating topography developed in the Paleozoic bedrock. The seafloor is sediment covered with low relief. Sediment thickness averages 10 m. A third area, covering about 10 per cent of James Bay, has been mapped within the smoothed topography area. It is characterized by a microrelief developed in the unconsolidated sediments that blanket the bedrock, and is interpreted as an ice-scoured bottom (Meagher et al., 1976).

The bottom of James Bay is largely blanketed by Quaternary unconsolidated deposits with an average thickness of 10 m over two thirds of the area. In the remaining third, unconsolidated sediments may be up to 50 m thick in places. Samples collected in offshore areas indicate that silt and clay are the two major components, with a fraction of sand, gravel and boulders averaging about 20 per cent and considered as ice-rafted sediments (Meagher et al., 1976). In shore and nearshore areas, mud, sand, gravel and boulders are more common. According to Meagher et al. (1976), most of the suspended sediment deposited in the bay is river-derived and not from shoreline erosion. Little of the suspended material is deposited in deltas at the river mouths and sand found at river mouths is mainly derived from erosion of emerged deltas in the coastal plain. Deltaic deposition at river mouths is somewhat ephemeral; most sediment is carried out into the more central part of the bay.

Coastal waters are estuarine. Surface salinity is higher to the north, being less than 20 per thousand and decreases progressively southward, being about 10 per thousand at the entry of Rupert Bay (Barber and Montgomery-Larnder, 1968; Barber, 1972; Pullen, 1973, 1974; Peck, 1976). Surface water temperature in the coastal area along eastern James Bay varies considerably throughout the year, cold waters prevailing everywhere. Warmest waters are found during the summer (July - August) along the shores, especially in embayments, in front of large rivers, and in Rupert Bay. Water temperatures up to 15°C are usual in the nearshore zone during a short period in summer. There is a difference of about 5°C in surface water temperatures between the south and the north.

James Bay is entirely ice covered for 3 to 4 months each year, and is partly ice covered for at least 6 months. Drift ice is frequently seen in the western part of the bay at the end of June and at the beginning of July. Along the shore freezeup is usually in November, whereas breakup is in May or June. The ice-period at shore frequently reaches up to 200 days. An icefoot 100 to 150 cm thick covers the intertidal zones for an average of 5 months. Breakup occurs first along the eastern coast, and because of the large river input, Rupert and Hannah bays are the two areas where the ice cover first disappears. Only scattered data on ice conditions are presently available, but LANDSAT photos are very useful in this regard.

The tides in eastern James Bay are semidiurnal with a moderate amplitude (Dohler, 1968; Godin, 1972, 1974). Mean and large tide ranges are 1.37 and 2.32 m at Point Louis XIV, 1.46 and 2.1 m at Fort George, 0.76 and 1.07 m at Eastmain, and 2.04 and 2.89 m at Stag Island in Rupert Bay (Canadian Hydrographic Service, 1973). The wind occasionally increases the tide height at shore as much as 2 m (Kindle, 1925; Manning, 1951). Few data are available on tidal currents but relatively strong currents are known to exist locally between islands in the nearshore zone and in narrows between offshore islands (e.g., Charlton and Strutton harbours).

CHARACTERISTICS OF THE SHORELINE

The eastern James Bay coast is a low, emerging shoreline, very irregular and highly indented. It is fringed by a myriad of islands and shoals, and can be classified as a skerry coastline. The shore and nearshore zones are shallow and gently sloping seaward. Large intertidal zones are found in the southern part (south of Nouveau-Comptoir), and in most bays north of it. Shore areas with slope gradients of 1° to 2° are widespread. The coastline is cut into either rock or unconsolidated sediments. Nearshore islands, points and peninsulas are formed mostly of crystalline rocks; however, about 30 per cent of small islands and points are made up of unconsolidated deposits, mainly glacial (drumlins) and fluvioglacial (delta-kames) deposits. There are also a few small islands covered by cobble and boulder beaches and a few flying spits.

There is no cliff or other significant escarpment along the shoreline, but a few wave-cut bluffs occur on the seaward side of some nearshore islands and on the south and southwestern sides of some large offshore islands. The areas of the highest relief are low rocky hills (monadnocks) emerging over the peneplane surface, which is mantled by relatively thin Quaternary deposits. Bays and most embayments have developed in shallow depressions in bedrock formerly filled by glacial (till) and marine sediments (stratified silts and clays).

Discontinuous sand, gravel and pebble beaches occur in the upper shore zone, especially in the vicinity of Eastmain and La Grande rivers. Cobble and boulder beaches are common along rocky shores, wave-eroded drumlins and most exposed islands in the nearshore zone, especially in the northern part of James Bay between Point Cacachischouane and Point Louis XIV.

Tidal flats are found in most large embayments and around most offshore islands. They consist of a blanket of mud or fine sand usually less than 40 cm thick, overlying stratified grey silt and clay; the surface is strewn with thousands of boulders randomly distributed from the lowest to the highest tide levels. Heavily bouldered tidal flats usually characterize wave-eroded glacial deposits. Tidal marshes up to 500 m in width fringe the upper part of large embayments. They are boulder-strewn and usually include shallow ice-made depressions. Tidal marshes are well developed in Cacachischouane, Paul, Goose, Akwatuk, Dead Duck, Moar, Black Stone, Old Factory, Hope, Conn, Boatswain and Rupert bays (Dionne, 1976c). The largest tidal marsh extends from Missisicabi to Gull Point, on the west coast of the Ministikawatin Peninsula, in southern James Bay.

From the air, the eastern coast offers outstanding scenery, but from the sea and on the ground it is a quite different picture. Kranck (1951, p. 14) noted that "compared with most parts of the World this coast is a picture of the utmost monotony." Kindle (1925, p. 230) also recognized the "intensely monotonous aspect of the coastline".

The eastern James Bay coast can be divided into three major areas: southern, central and northern.

Southern area

This area extends from Hannah and Rupert bays to Conn River (52°22'N). The shoreline consists of large open bays, and although irregular in shape, it is relatively rectilinear for long stretches. The straight-line distance between Broadback and Conn rivers is approximately 115 km but the shoreline length is about 200 km. The coastal area is a large, flat, clay plain with a few rocky hills and drumlin ridges forming points and islands. The shore slope gradient is extremely weak, and a wide, shallow water shelf extends in front of the shore zone. Only a few islands and shoals (about 15) are found in the nearshore zone. They are grouped at the entry of Rupert Bay and at the northern tip of Boatswain Bay. The shoreline around Ministikawatin Peninsula, a large flat plain less than 30 m in elevation, is approximately 170 km long and often difficult to determine precisely. Wide tidal flats, usually sandy or muddy, and occasionally bouldery (Gull to Cachechu points) characterize this coastal area. An extensive sand flat occurs in Hannah Bay, between Harricana and Missisicabi rivers; from there up to Gull Bay (a distance over 25 km), lies the largest tidal marsh along the eastern James Bay coast (Fig. 23.3). Several sand ridges and runnels occur in the intertidal zone between East and Gull points. Farther north, between Mésaconane and Cachechu points, numerous boulder ridges, nearly parallel to each other and perpendicular to the shoreline, are found throughout the tidal zone (Fig. 23.4). According to Guimont and Laverdière (1976a, b), these low ridges are wave-eroded, reworked De Geer moraines. Because similar ridges occurring elsewhere around offshore islands are variously oriented, and because these ridges do not resemble De Geer moraines observed elsewhere in the James Bay lowlands formerly submerged by the Tyrrell Sea, it is suggested that they may be another landform. A few sand and gravel spits are forming along the coast; one flying spit about 2 km long and nearly perpendicular to the shoreline occurs near Point Mésaconane. Various boulder concentrations are displayed between Redfern and Sawayane points and at Comfort and Black Bear points along the western shoreline of Rupert Bay. Although major points may indicate buried drumlins, there is no till exposed in the shore zone; most boulders are probably ice-drifted. Cabbage Willows Bay is a large shallow embayment surrounded by an immense flat clay plain with a very weak slope gradient. There is a wide muddy tidal flat fringed by a tidal marsh and a large coastal marsh occasionally inundated by spring tides and storm surge waves. A remarkable dendritic drainage pattern has developed in the clayed surface and creeks are numerous at the upper part of the tidal flat (Fig. 23.5).

On the east side of Rupert Bay, from Broadback River to Snape Point, the shore is flat and backed by a low horizontal clay plain. The smooth shoreline contains a series of large open bays. Sandy and muddy tidal flats up to 2 km wide are common; they are fringed landward by wide tidal marshes. A blanket of mud or sand, usually less than 50 cm thick, overlies stratified grey marine silts and clays. Throughout the boulder-strewn tidal flats and marshes, ice-made erosion and deposition features can be found (Laverdière and Guimont, 1975; Dionne, 1976b, 1978a).

From Sherrick Hill to Conn River, the shoreline is characterized by large open bays. There are a few scattered small islands, shoals and skerries in the nearshore zone. The low coast has developed along a flat bog-covered clay plain. Wide tidal flats occur all along this coastal stretch. In Boatswain Bay, a thin veneer of mud overlies Tyrrell Sea clay. Between Loon Point and Conn River a cover of sand up to 75 cm thick overlies stratified marine silts and clays. Extensive tidal marshes are found in Boatswain and Conn embayments and near Fiedmont Point. Tidal marshes and flats are both boulder-strewn and affected by drift-ice action. However, on the sand flat between Point Poulharies and Eastmain, which is characterized by about 20 parallel ridges and runnels (Fig. 23.6), there are only a few boulders.

Central area

The second major coastal area runs from Conn River to Paul Bay (54°N), a straight-line distance of about 180 km. Approximately 700 km long, the shoreline is very irregular and highly indented. It is characterized by an abundance of large enclosed bays of irregular shapes (Vieux-Comptoir, Black Stone, Moar, Paint Hills, Oblats, Black Whale, Dead Duck, Akwatuk, Goose and Paul bays). Hundreds of islands of various sizes, shapes and compositions are spread throughout the nearshore zone in a band about 10 km wide. Most are rocky but about 25 per cent are reworked drumlins (Figs. 23.7, 23.8). Cape Hope, Walrus and Paint Hills islands, which are composed of more resistant rocks (diabase), stand as the major relief; elevation on Cape Hope islands is 90 m.

The lowland coastal area, formed by an irregular bedrock surface thinly mantled by glacial and marine deposits, can be called a rocky glaciomarine plain.

There are many spits and beaches composed of sand, gravel, cobbles and boulders. Tidal flats are well developed in bays where they commonly exceed 1.5 km in width (Fig. 23.9). They are composed of a cover of mud or fine sand 10 to 40 cm thick overlying stratified grey marine silts and clays. The boulder-strewn surface shows various ice-made erosion and depositional features throughout the open season. In bays (Black Stone, Moar, Dead Duck, Akwatuk and Goose) wide salt marshes, boulder-strewn and usually ice-eroded, fringe bare tidal flats. Ice-made depressions in marshes are more abundant south of 54°N (Dionne, 1976c).

Small delta cones occur in the shore zone at the mouth of Vieux-Comptoir and Castor rivers (Figs. 23.9, 23.10), and a large delta plain is being built at the mouth of La Grande (Skinner, 1974). There are no cliffs or major erosional escarpments along this shore. Deposition is in embayments whereas erosion prevails around islands and points, especially in unconsolidated sediments.

Several stretches of the shoreline are rocky (Fig. 23.11). Wave erosion is rare along these stretches, but rock surfaces are often frost-shattered and partly masked by angular rock fragments pushed by ice. Some boulder ridges fringe rocky shores.

Northern area

A very complicated shoreline runs from Cacachischouane Point to Louis XIV Point (54° 37' 30" N). This very irregular and highly indented coastline fringed by a myriad of low islands resembles a labyrinth (Figs. 23.12, 23.13). The shoreline length (300 km) is more than three times the distance in straight line between the two points (80 km). When the total length of the islands spread throughout the nearshore zone is added, the shoreline length is increased about five times.

The lowland coastal area is underlain by an irregular glaciated bedrock, unevenly mantled by relatively thin Quaternary glacial, marine and coastal deposits. Low rocky hills and drumlin ridges are the major relief in this area. Although the coast is extremely indented, embayments are small and narrow (Fig. 23.14). About 500 islands of various shapes and sizes, generally less than 2 km^2 are spread throughout the nearshore zone in a band 10 to 25 km wide. Most of these islands are less than 15 m high. They are composed of Archean crystalline rocks and Quaternary unconsolidated deposits (drumlins and beaches). Tidal flats are found in most embayments previously filled by Tyrrell Sea sediments (fine sand, silt and clay). The surface is muddy or sandy and plentifully sprinkled with boulders.

Narrow marshes are restricted to the larger embayments; they are boulder-strewn and occasionally ice-eroded. Slope gradient is 1° to 3° seaward. Water depth in the nearshore zone is usually less than 6 m at low tide. Small beaches are numerous around islands, points and peninsulas. Sandy beaches are found along the main shoreline, whereas pebble, cobble and boulder beaches are common on nearshore islands exposed to western swales (Fig. 23.15). Several rocky islands are bare and exposed to rock shattering by frost.

OFFSHORE ISLANDS

Two groups of offshore islands along the eastern James Bay coast deserve a brief description because of their proximity to the main shoreline. Both groups, nearly parallel to each other, are roughly oriented northwest-southeast. The first group, including relatively low, small islands such as Strutton, Scoter, Gull, Bizarre, Pebble, Solomons Temple, Walter, Spencer, Grey Goose and Bare, occurs within the Archean bedrock area about 20 to 40 km from the mainland. The second group, including larger islands such as Charlton, Danby, Carey, Trodely, Weston, the Twins and Bear, is located over a bathymetric high in the Paleozoic bedrock area, 40 to 65 km offshore. Charlton island is about 30 km long and up to 15 km wide; North Twin Island is 25 km long and up to 18 km wide, and South Twin Island is 18 km long and up to 10 km wide. Geological descriptions for these islands (Low, 1889; Coates, 1951; Burns, 1952) are only brief.

Most offshore islands are made of thick Quaternary unconsolidated deposits overlying bedrock. Only one outcrop of (volcanic) intrusive rocks has been observed on Charlton Island. The largest islands (Charlton, Trodely, Weston and the Twins), lying west of the Paleozoic-Archean contact, are underlain by Paleozoic sedimentary formations. These islands usually are reworked fluvioglacial deltas (sand and gravel) built between the two large ice sheets of the last glacial period (the Keewatin and the Laurentide ice sheets). The deltas are aligned with a few other emerged deltas to the south in the Ministikawatin Peninsula and they apparently are the northern extension of the Harricana interlobate moraine reported by Hardy (1976, 1977). Sand and gravel beaches and occasional cobble and boulder beaches cover the surface and fringe the present shore (Figs. 23.16-23.18). Fine sand and silt deposits also occur on some of these islands (Charlton, Trodely and the Twins). Sandy, muddy or clayey tidal flats, usually boulder-strewn, are found around most of these islands. Ice-made erosion and deposition features are common on tidal flats and beaches (Low, 1889). The large proportion of Archean crystalline boulders on offshore islands (Low, 1889) possibly indicates glacial debris reworked by drift ice.

Local cliffs or wave-eroded escarpments are found along Charlton, Strutton, Trodely and the Twin islands. Small dune fields are found on Charlton, Trodely, Weston, Bizarre and the Twin islands (Dionne, 1978c). Unforested mineral palsen are abundant on the Twin islands and a few on Weston and Bizarre islands (Dionne, 1978b). Several other low islands only a few metres above sea level are emerging deltas, kames or glacial deposits being modified by wave, current and ice action.

Offshore, Solomons Temple Islands are rocky islands composed of lavas (diabase), the same rock type as the nearby Walrus and Paint Hills islands. In northern James Bay, Bare Island is a granite outcrop (Coates, 1951), whereas Bear and Sunday islands are composed of Proterozoic sedimentary rocks (Burns, 1952). Walter Island is almost wholly made up of boulders, which were tightly packed by ice on the sides and top of the island (Low, 1889).

Offshore islands are well exposed to wave action, especially to westerly and southerly winds, and can be considered as a high-energy environment. Although erosion is obvious along the islands, there are also various depositional features such as sand, gravel, and boulder beaches and ridges. Drift ice is the second most important process producing various erosion and deposition features on shores and in tidal zones (Dionne, 1978a).

A third group of islands, which occurs in the northern part of Rupert Bay, are worthy of mention. The largest three (Jacob, Tent and Stag) are made of unconsolidated deposits overlying the Archean crystalline bedrock, whereas the smaller islands (Dixon, McNabb, Moss, Gushue, Prophet, Nicholson) are rocky. Jacob and Tent islands are probably surficially reworked fluvioglacial deltas. Tent Island, an emerging delta only a few metres above sea level, is considered more recent than Jacob, Trodely and other large islands to the north. The boulder-strewn surface and tidal flats of Tent Island show active ice rafting. Stag Island, underlain by Archean crystalline bedrock, is covered by beaches. There are only two granitic gneiss outcrops on the island. On the north side, a muddy and sandy tidal flat is fringed by a marsh and covered with abundant ice-rafted boulders. A long sand and gravel beach with a few random boulders fringes the south side of the island.

PROCESSES OF COASTAL EVOLUTION

Waves, current and tides

Various processes are active today along the eastern James Bay shoreline. The most important are undoubtedly waves and currents, although they only affect the shore for 6 months a year (June to November). As westerly onshore winds prevail during the open period, incoming waves are a relatively powerful agent of coastal evolution. However, the shallow water of the nearshore and shore zones, the abundant islands, shoals and skerries, and the great irregularity of the shoreline considerably reduce the power of waves when they break on the eastern shore. Waves lose much of their energy breaking on islands and shoals, diffracting around obstacles and refracting on the bottom in the nearshore zone. Maximum wave energy, found on offshore islands and on the seaward side of the nearshore islands, is greatly reduced on the landside of nearshore islands and in embayments. Most of the offshore islands and well exposed nearshore islands are severely eroded by wave action. Beaches of well worn cobbles and boulders are common all along the western side of these islands. At first glance the eastern coast might appear to be a relatively high energy environment. However, it is important to note that wave action is restricted to a period of about 6 months a year, and that the topography and shoreline configuration greatly influence wave action along the coast. The high wave energy environment that prevails offshore is largely modified in the nearshore zone, where it is restricted locally along the coast. Thus, the coast is markedly dichotomous in regard to wave energy. The offshore islands, some nearshore islands and the well exposed coastal areas (points) can be considered relatively high wave energy environments, whereas about 70 per cent of the shoreline, especially the embayments and the sheltered zones, can be considered moderate to low wave energy environments.

In addition to the normal wave regime related to wind conditions, storm surges in James Bay (Godin, 1975) may play an important role in shore evolution. Although only a few data are available on storm surge frequency, Barber (1972) considers that the long fetches and the relatively shallow water in the bay are two factors influencing storm surges. Theoretical calculations indicate that serious storm surge inundations could occur, especially in the southern part of the bay where an amplitude up to 6 m could be expected (Barber, 1972, p. 165). During field surveys storm surges have been observed to cause occasional damage to the large marshes or bogs adjacent to the shore. For low, gently sloping areas (Hannah and Cabbage Willows bays, for example) the exact shoreline is often difficult to identify, particularly when these zones have just been inundated by a storm surge.

Little is known about coastal drift and shore currents along the eastern coast. Water circulation patterns in the bay indicate a general northward drift toward Hudson Bay (Grainger, 1960; Murty, 1972; El-Sabh and Koutitonsky, 1974). However, the pattern of currents in the shore and the nearshore zones is extremely difficult to recognize because of the highly indented coastline and the absence of adequate field observations. The influence of shore morphometry and bottom morphology results in numerous shore and nearshore currents along the eastern James Bay coast.

The major role of currents in the coastal area seems to be the transport of sediments from shore to offshore zones. For example, in Rupert Bay most of the sediment load of the four largest rivers discharging into the bay is carried seaward into the deepest basins in James Bay and possibly as far as Hudson Bay (Leslie, 1964; Pelletier, 1969; Meagher et al., 1976). The same situation prevails at the mouth of the Eastmain and La Grande rivers, where only a small amount of the sediments brought to the sea is redistributed into the nearby shore zone (Skinner, 1974). In addition, currents play an important role in ice movements, which greatly influence the pattern of erosion and sedimentation in the coastal area.

The eastern coast with a tidal range of 1 to 3 m is a mesotidal environment. The tide by itself does not play a significant role in coastal evolution except where tidal currents are strong. However, the constant water level fluctuation related to the semidiurnal tide character creates particular conditions along this low, gently sloping shore. According to Kindle (1925, p. 230), the height of the tide depends largely on the strength and direction of the wind: "A north wind may raise it nearly twice its normal height, and a south wind can reduce it in like degree. A strong wind from the sea may push the shoreline inland a half kilometer or more from the position it occupied during a period of calm weather." Relatively strong tidal currents exist between islands within the nearshore zone and seem to play an important role in bottom erosion and sedimentation.

As do waves and currents, tides greatly influence ice movement and ice action in the shore and nearshore zones.

Drift ice action

The ice that is present in James Bay for an average of 5 to 6 months a year dampens and even stops wave action. Along the shore, drift ice is a very active and significant process of erosion, transportation, sedimentation and protection (Dionne, 1978a). As recognized long ago (Low, 1889), the role played by ice is one of the major characteristics of this shore. Several erosional, depositional and sedimentological features result from ice action in the various shore environments, especially in tidal marshes and flats, the most spectacular of which are the boulder-strewn tidal flats and marshes where boulders overly a muddy, clayey or sandy substratum. Although ice action along James Bay is relatively well documented (Dionne, 1976a, b, 1978a; Guimont and Laverdière, 1976a; Laverdière et Guimont, 1975; Martini and Protz, 1978), detailed studies could help to estimate the volume of sediment displaced annually by ice and determine the exact role played by ice in the shoreline evolution.

Periglacial processes

Periglacial processes other than sea ice are active along the James Bay coast. However, they seem to have a relatively moderate geomorphological role in this subarctic region. Frost-shattering occurs on bedrock outcrops along the shore, especially in the zone just above the mean sea level. Frost-shattered rocks (granite and gneiss) have been observed at many sites, while erratic boulders of various lithologies scattered throughout tidal flats are also occasionally frost-shattered. In general, frost-shattering is not very active and is restricted locally along the coast, possibly because of the bedrock, the icefoot and the snow cover in the coastal area during most of the winter. In the intertidal zone outcrops submerged at high tide are usually not frost-shattered as indicated by glacially moulded, polished and striated surfaces often preserved intact.

Physical weathering of crystalline rocks has not been observed along the coast. If the process occurs, it seems to be of very little importance along this shore.

Frost-heaved boulders occur in few tidal marshes (Dionne, 1975b) and active patterned ground is found in the coastal area from Roggan River to Point Louis XIV. Unforested mineral palsen or mineral frost mounds with segregated ice occur in the coastal area between Roggan River and Point Louis XIV, and on the Twin Islands and two other small islands farther south (Dionne, 1978b).

Slumping and related phenomena were observed locally in the southern part of the James Bay shoreline. This occurs along coastal stretches where silt and clay have been eroded from low cliffs, along large rivers (Skinner, 1974; Guimont and Laverdière, 1976) and on some offshore islands (Trodely and the Twins).

Biological processes

As in most coastal areas in cold regions, biological action is not prominent in James Bay. Vegetation in tidal marshes and in extensive peatlands adjacent to the present shorelines plays the most significant role. Marine algae (kelp) are not widespread along the James Bay eastern shore and, have only a minor influence in the erosion and sedimentation cycles. Driftwood has often been observed at the high-tide level (Manning, 1951). Long furrows cut into sandy tidal flats by tree trunks were observed in the Eastmain area. However, these erosional features are of little importance compared to those made by ice.

Only minor animal activity in the shore zone has been observed. Tidal flats rarely show worm and mollusc activity. Bioturbation is rare and of little importance. Limestone erratics carried by drift ice from the western shore are usually severely burrowed by organisms. However, corrosion by pelecypods (i.e., *Hiatella* sp.) most probably occurred before ice rafting (Dionne, 1974b).

Chemical processes

Chemical weathering is rare or absent along the eastern James Bay coast because the absence of suitable lithologies and climatic conditions greatly inhibits chemical processes.

Wind action

Wind action is important in wave formation but its influence on coastal morphology in James Bay is not evident. There are a few dune fields on offshore islands (Charlton, Trodely, Weston, the Twins) where large quantities of sand are available. No dune complexes, however, have been observed along the present shoreline (Dionne, 1978c).

In brief, physical processes (waves, currents, tides, ice and frost) are the main agents of coastal evolution along the eastern shoreline. Biological, chemical and wind processes play a minor role along the entire coast.

CONCLUSIONS

The eastern James Bay coastline is a very complex environment. Although some morphosedimentological investigations have recently been undertaken (Skinner, 1974; Dionne, 1974a, b, 1975a, b, 1976a, b, c, 1977, 1978a, b, c; Laverdière and Guimont, 1975; Guimont and Laverdière, 1976a, b), there remains much to be done. Meagher et al. (1976, p. 328) consider that "James Bay is one of the most poorly mapped areas of Canada."

The James Bay eastern coastline can be characterized as follows:

(a) A lowland coast, structurally controlled, arising from an irregular levelled Archean crystalline bedrock, smoothed by glacial erosion and thinly mantled by Quaternary deposits.

(b) A strongly indented shoreline fringed by a myriad of islands, shoals and skerries.
(c) An emerging coastline with a gentle slope gradient and shallow coastal waters.
(d) A moderate to low wave-energy and ice- dominated environment.
(e) A shore of moderate erosion and deposition.

This coast offers beautiful landscapes from the air, which must be developed and preserved. It is recommended that large sectors, and possibly all the coastal area, be recognized as a national park or as a wildlife preserve.

References
(following photographs)

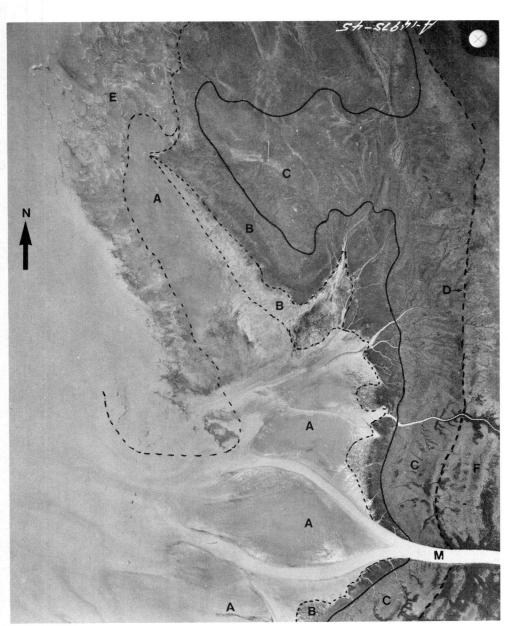

Figure 23.3.

Coastal environments N of Mississicabi River, Hannah Bay, southeastern James Bay area; an emerging flat coastal plain with a very small shore slope gradient. Although tidal range is less than 3 m, wide tidal flats and marshes characterize the coastline. Various shore zones are distinguished: A, sandy upper tidal flat; B, lower and upper tidal marshes with ice-made pans and tidal creeks; C, coastal marsh occasionally inundated and a dendritic pattern of tidal creeks; D, approximate limit reached by the present-day sea level during spring tides and storm surges; E, lower tidal flat with numerous minor ridges, possibly ice-made features; F, bog-covered coastal clay plain; M, Mississicabi River. This area is a low wave energy environment. Photo taken at approximate half tide cycle. (NAPL A14975-45; approx. scale 1:63 000)

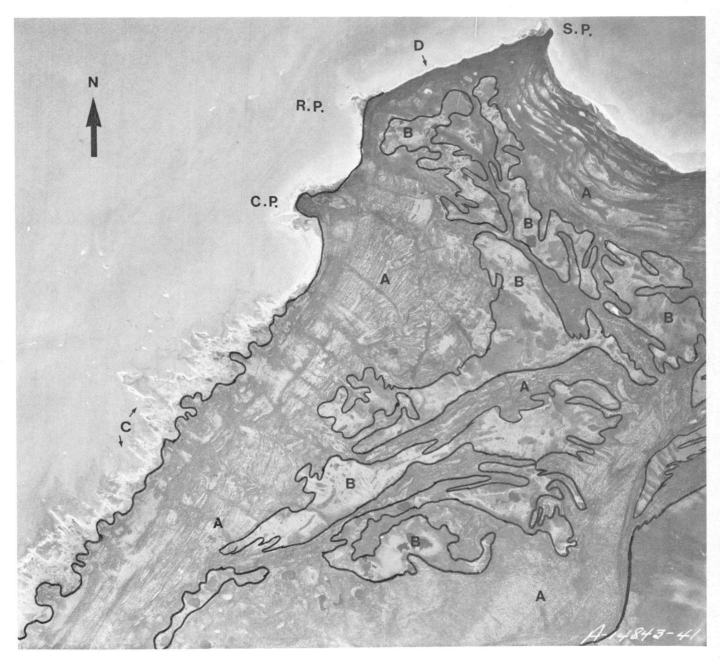

Figure 23.4. *Coastal environment northwestern Ministikawatin Peninsula, southeastern James Bay area: a prograding coastline characterized by a flight of parallel beach ridges and recurved spits (A), and a few bog-filled lagoons (B). The abundance of beaches in this area is due to an underlying fluvioglacial delta which provided large quantities of coarse sediments that were reworked by waves and currents. To the south of Cachechu Point (C.P.) are several bouldery ridges (C) oriented in a northwest-southeast direction and nearly perpendicular to the shoreline. The origin of these ridges is not satisfactorily understood. Although it has been suggested that they are wave-eroded De Geer moraines (Guimont and Laverdière, 1976), they most probably result from a complex action of various processes (waves, tides and ice). A long boulder ridge (D) runs from Redfern (R.P.) to Sawayne points (S.P.). This area is a moderate to high wave energy environment. (NAPL A14843-41)*

Figure 23.5.   *Coastal environments in Cabbage Willows Bay, an embayment in Rupert Bay, southeastern James Bay area; a very low and flat coastal area with a shore slope gradient less than 1° (50 cm per km). The following units are distinguished: a large muddy and sandy tidal flat (A) fringed by a tidal marsh (B), and an extensive bog-covered clay plain (C); D, beach ridges visible in the northwest and southeast corners; E, approximate limit of the highest tides and storm surges. The marsh is characterized by a dense dendritic tidal creek pattern, and the upper tidal flat by a pattern of small parallel creeks. This area is a low wave energy environment. Photo taken at mid-tide. (NAPL A14976-63)*

Figure 23.6. Coastal environments between Poulharies Point and Eastmain River, southeastern James Bay area; a relatively regular, well-exposed emerging shoreline developed along a low flat bog-covered clay plain. The following units are distinguished: A, a wide sandy tidal flat characterized by approximately 20 ridges and runnels; B, tidal marsh; C, raised beaches and rock outcrops; D, bog-covered clay plain; E, nearshore zone with suspended sediments being drifted northward; F, a wave-eroded emerging drumlin; R, crystalline rocky ridges; M, Mouton River; P.P., Poulharies Point. This area is a moderate wave energy environment. (NAPL A15256-12)

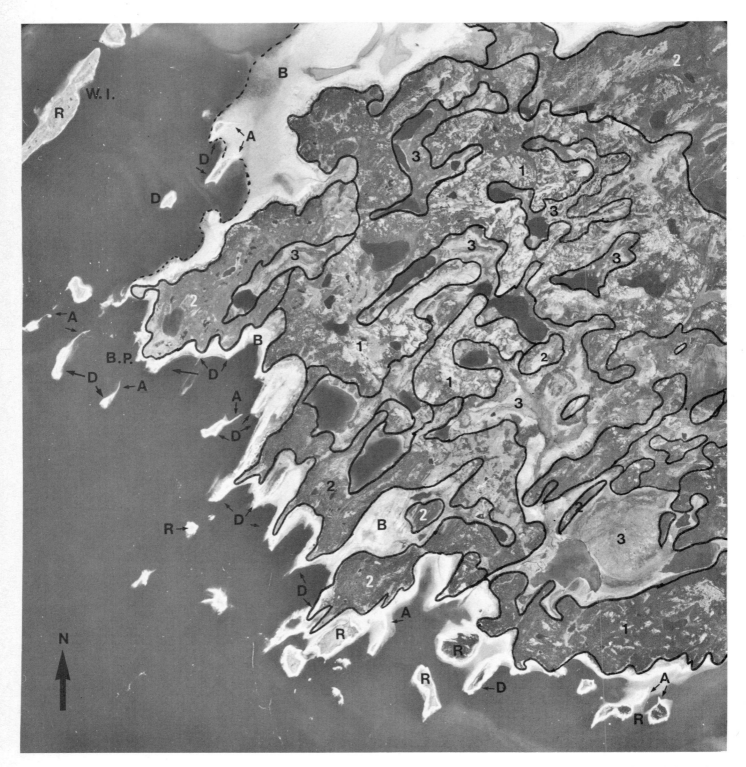

Figure 23.7. *Coastal environments between Moar and Paint Hills bays, eastern James Bay area: a highly indented shoreline developed along an emerging rocky glaciomarine plain, with numerous rock outcrops (R) and drumlin ridges. The muddy, clayey and bouldery tidal flats (B) are relatively narrow. Nearshore low islands and points are reworked emerging drumlins (D). Several geomorphic units are found throughout the coastal area: beaches and rock outcrops (1); beaches and reworked drumlins (2); and clay-filled depressions with a bog-covered surface (3). Spit tails (A) occurring on the landward side of some reworked drumlins result from wave diffraction and indicate prevailing SW swales. This area is a moderate to high wave energy environment. W.I., Walrus Island; B.P., Bourlamaque Point. (NAPL A15254-6)*

J-C. DIONNE

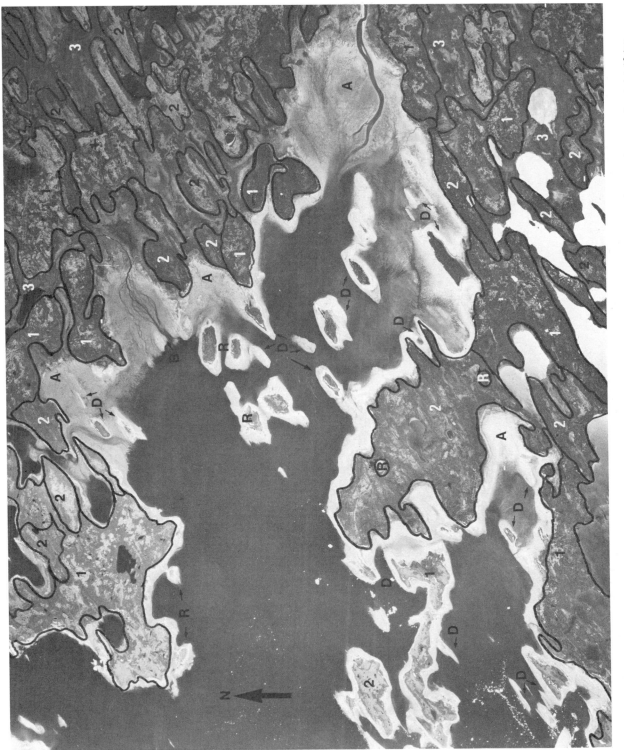

Figure 23.8. Coastal environments at Dead Duck Bay, eastern James Bay area: a large embayment approximately 12 km long with an irregular shoreline and a few low islands in the intertidal zone. This emerging coastline is bordered by wide muddy, clayey and bouldery tidal flats (A), and is composed either of crystalline bedrock outcrops (R) and drumlins (D). The bedrock is largely beach-covered (1); emerged drumlins are wave-eroded and/or caped by beaches (2); depressions (3) are clay-filled and bog-covered. Bouldery tidal flats usually surround wave-eroded drumlins. Beaches are common along rocky coastal stretches. The small Truite River flowing in the northern part of the bay has developed a braided pattern in the tidal zone (B). This area is a moderate to low wave energy environment. (NAPL A15254-174)

325

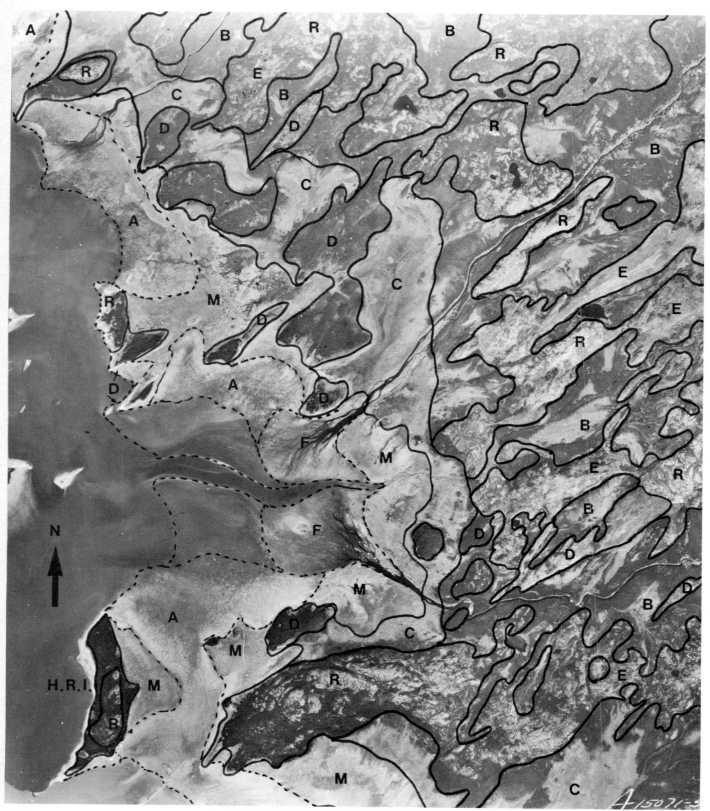

Figure 23.9. *Coastal environments between High Rock Island (H.R.I.) and Rhéaume Point, eastern James Bay area: a large shallow open bay with a few scattered islands in the tidal and nearshore zones. Wide muddy and clayey boulder-strewn tidal flats (A) and marshes (M), passing progressively inland to extensive coastal marshes (C). Shoreline developed along a low, emerging bog-covered clay plain (B) with numerous crystalline bedrock hills (R) surrounded and/or covered by beaches (E), and a few random reworked drumlins (D); small deltaic cones (F) are being built by the two small rivers discharging into James Bay. This area is mainly a low wave energy environment. (NAPL A1507 1-57)*

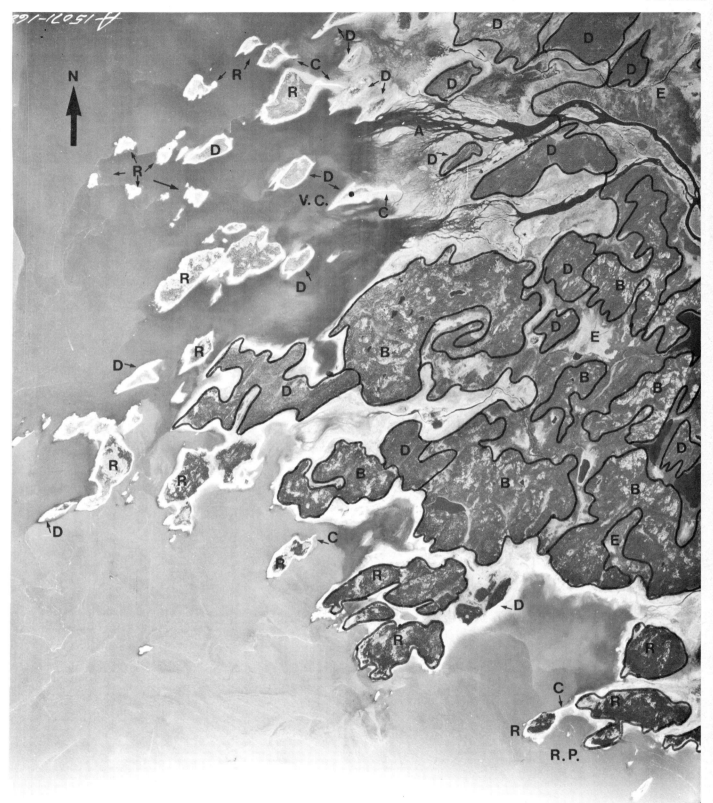

Figure 23.10. *Coastal environments between Rhéaume Point (R.P.) and Vieux-Comptoir (V.C.), eastern James Bay area: a highly irregular and low emerging shoreline fringed by numerous rocky islands (R). The coastal area is a low undulating bedrock surface with numerous rocky hills partially covered by beaches (B), and a few reworked drumlins (D), separated by bog-covered clay-filled depressions (E). A braided pattern (A) has developed at the mouth of Vieux-Comptoir River. A few tail spits (C) resulting from wave diffraction, occur on the landside of some islands. In this area islands and points are in a moderate to high wave energy environment, while embayments are low wave energy environment. (NAPL A15071-168)*

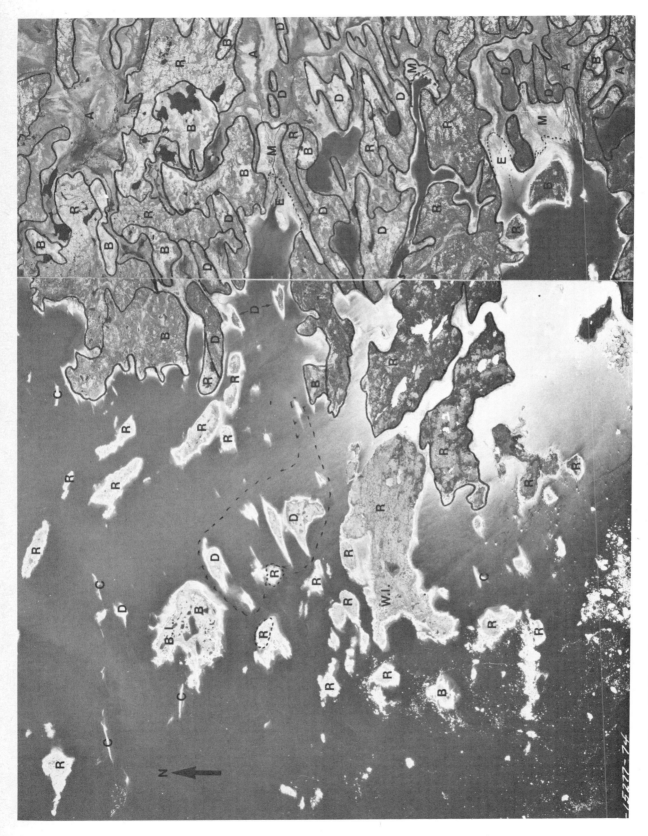

Figure 23.11. *Coastal environments in the vicinity of Walrus (W.I.) and Big islands (B.I.), south of Fort-George, eastern James Bay area: a highly irregular, indented and low rocky coastline. Most highs and islands are bedrock outcrops (R) locally covered by beaches (B), while depressions are clay-filled and bog-covered (A). There are numerous reworked or beach-covered drumlins (D); and boulder-flying spits (C) occur in the nearshore zone. Although the photo was taken nearly at high tide, tidal flats (E) are usually narrow in this area excepted at the head of the major embayments where small tidal marshes (M) also occur. This coastline is a moderate to high energy environment. (NAPL A15277-74-75)*

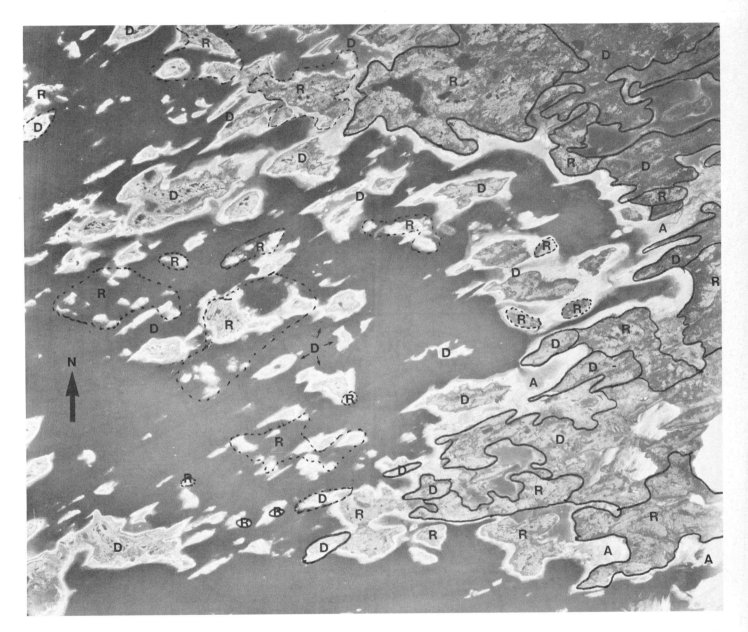

Figure 23.12. *Coastal environments south of Attiquane Point, eastern James Bay area: a greatly irregular emerging shoreline with numerous islands, shoals and skerries spread throughout the shore and nearshore zones creating a complex coastal environment, and offering an excellent example of a skjar coast. The shoreline has developed along a low rocky glaciomarine coastal plain. Islands and points are either formed by Archean crystalline bedrock (R) and reworked or beach-covered drumlins (D). Narrow muddy and sandy boulder-strewn tidal flats (A), and small tidal marshes occur at the head of major embayments. This coastal area is a low to moderate wave energy environment. (NAPL A21578-2)*

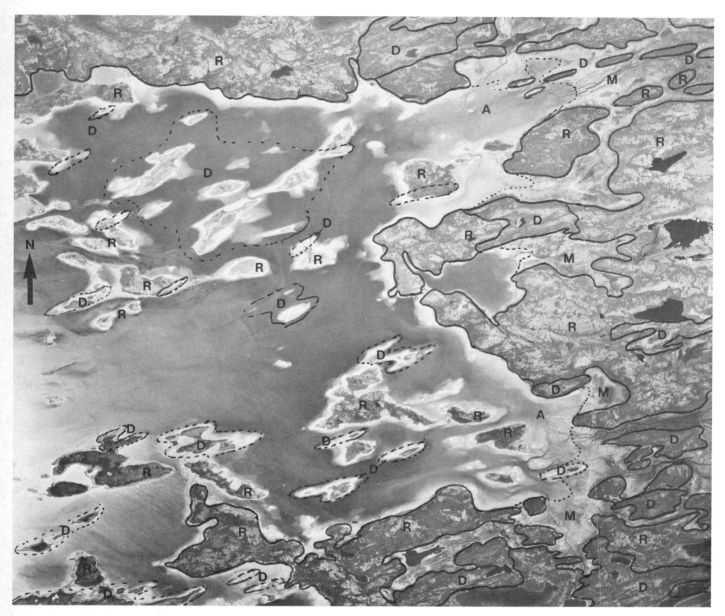

Figure 23.13. *Coastal environments north of Cacachischouane Point, northeastern James Bay area: a large irregularly shaped embayment with numerous low islands bordering a rocky coastal lowland. Islands and points are either formed of crystalline bedrock (R) and reworked or beach-covered drumlins (D). The bedrock is usually covered by thin Quaternary deposits (beaches) and depressions are filled with marine and glaciomarine fine sediments. Wide muddy and sandy boulder-strewn tidal flats (A) and narrow tidal marshes (M) occur in larger embayments. This coastline is a low to moderate wave energy environment. (NAPL A21581-116)*

Figure 23.14. *Coastal environments north of Roggan River (R.R.) northeastern James Bay area: a moderate irregular shoreline fringed by numerous islands has developed along an emerging low rocky glaciomarine plain. The bedrock (R) mantled by thick Quaternary deposits, rarely outcrops. Cobble beaches (B) intensively developed on islands and on inland highs occur on reworked drumlins and indicate a relatively high-energy environment. Depressions filled with marine and glaciomarine fine sediments are peat covered (E). Unforested mineral palsen (A) are widespread. Muddy and sandy boulder-strewn tidal flats (C) are narrow, and small tidal marshes (M) occur at the head of the largest embayments. Photo taken at about midtide. (NAPL A23480-145)*

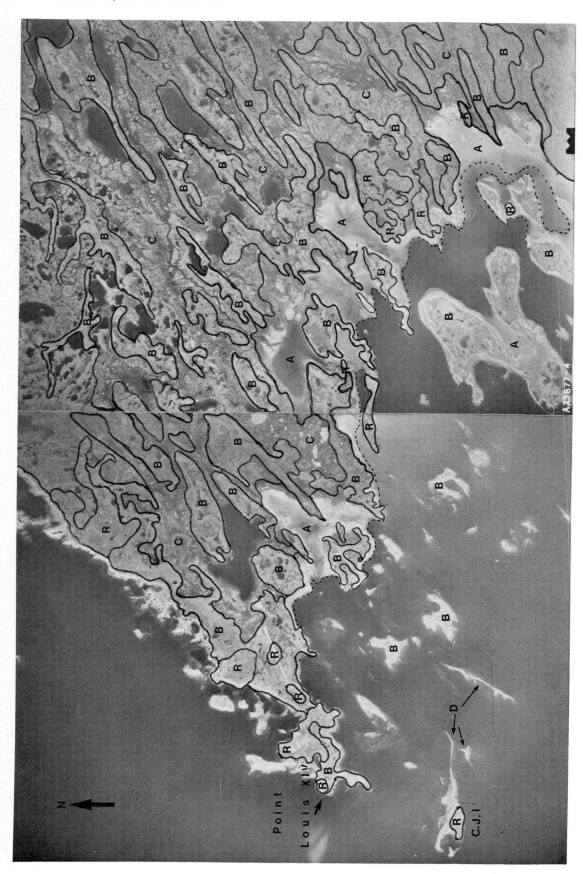

Figure 23.15. Coastal environments south of Point Louis XIV, northeastern James Bay area: a low emerging glaciomarine plain with a highly irregular shoreline fringed by a series of low islands. The following units are distinguished: A, small shallow embayments with muddy and sandy boulder-strewn tidal flats; B, beach ridges on highs and reworked drumlins; C, depressions filled with marine and glaciomarine fine sediments with several occurrences of unforested mineral palsen in depressions; D, cobble and boulder spits at Cape Jones Island (C.J.I.); R, crystalline bedrock outcrops. This area is a moderate to high wave energy environment. (NAPL A23877-2-3)

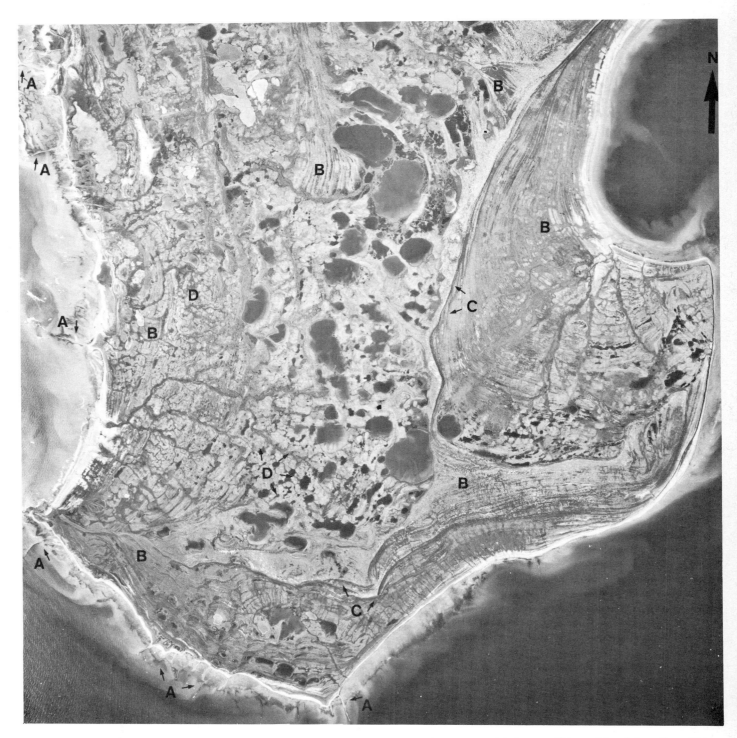

Figure 23.16. *The southern part of North Twin Island, eastern James Bay area: this large offshore island, less than 50 m above sea level, is underlain by a Paleozoic sedimentary bedrock thickly mantled by Quaternary deposits. A remarkable pattern of shore forms developed at the surface when the island emerged from the Tyrrell Sea. Flight of parallel beach ridges and recurved spits (B) and several shorelines (C) can be traced. The island central part is largely occupied by shallow rounded ponds and lakes. Fluvioglacial outwash sand and gravel were possibly emplaced between the Keewatin and Laurentide ice sheets at the end of the Wisconsin. Reworking of the fluvioglacial sediments may explain the large development of beaches. Abundant unforested mineral palsen (D) occur throughout the island indicating permafrost conditions. A few perpendicular spits (A) are found on the present day southwest and west shores. This island is located in a relatively high wave energy environment. (NAPL A16340-49)*

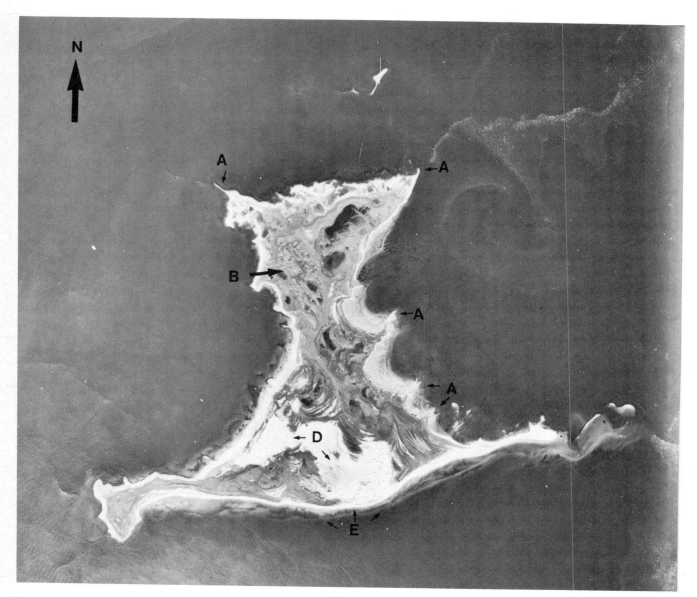

Figure 23.17. *Western Island, offshore Vieux-Comptoir, eastern James Bay area: this curiously shaped island is less than 30 m above sea level. The surface is mostly covered by sand and gravel beaches forming a flight of successive ridges. Along the shore on the south side is a wave-cut escarpment (E), and a few perpendicular spits (A). Tidal flats are narrow. In the southern part of the island are a few dune fields (D), and in the northern part are a few mineral palsen (B). This island is possibly an emerging delta built between the Keewatin and Laurentide ice sheets and therefore is a northward extension of the Harricana interlobate moraine. The island is located in a high energy environment. (NAPL A15071-180).*

Figure 23.18. *Bizarre islands, offshore Vieux-Comptoir, eastern James Bay area. These low islands, less than 30 m above sea level, appear as emerging Quaternary deposits. Their surface is largely covered by sand and gravel beaches and spits; well-rounded cobble and boulder ridges occur locally. The complex pattern of ridges and small depressions (A) on the northern side of larger islands is possibly due to ice, frost and wave action. Sandy boulder-strewn tidal flats occur on the northern side of some islands. The boulder flying spits (B) possibly indicate emerging drumlins. Since these islands are located to the west of the Paleozoic-Archean bedrock contact, the high proportion of crystalline boulders on these islands indicate a displacement to the West. A small dune field occurs on top of the largest island (D), and small palsen (C) can be observed on the two largest islands. These low emerging islands are characterized by a high energy environment. (NAPL A15071-173)*

References

Andrews, J.T.
1970: A geomorphological study of postglacial uplift, with particular reference to Arctic Canada; Institute of British Geographers, Special Publication 2, 156 p.

Barber, F.G.
1972: On the oceanography of James Bay; in James Bay; Environment Canada, Marine Sciences Branch Manuscript Report 24, p. 1 - 96.

Barber, F.G. and Montgomery-Larnder, M.
1968: The water and ice of Hudson Bay; in Science, History and Hudson Bay, C.S. Beals, ed.; Ottawa, Department of Energy, Mines and Resources, v. 1, p. 287 - 341.

Beals, C.S. (ed.)
1968: Science, History and Hudson Bay; Ottawa, Department of Energy, Mines and Resources, 2 volumes, 1057 p.

Bell, R.
1879: Report on an exploration of the east coast of Hudson Bay, 1877; Geological Survey of Canada, Report of Progress 1877-78, Pt. C, p. 1 - 37.

Bostock, H.H.
1970: Physiographic sub-divisions of Canada; in Geology and Economic Minerals of Canada, R.J.W. Douglas, ed.; Geological Survey of Canada, Economic Geology Report 1, 5th ed., p. 9 - 30, map 1254A.

Burns, C.A.
1952; Geological notes on localities in James Bay, Hudson Bay and Foxe Basin visited during an exploration cruise, 1949 (including a list of collected fossils, identified by Alice E. Wilson); Geological Survey of Canada, Paper 52-25, 16 p.

Canadian Hydrographic Service
1971: James Bay, Map 5800.
1973: Canadian tide and current tables, Vol. 4, Arctic and Hudson Bay; Marine Sciences Branch, 59 p.

Coates, D.F.
1951: Mapping the North, establishing control for aerial survey on James Bay; Canadian Geographical Journal, v. 43, p. 58 - 69.

Craig, B.G.
1969: Late-glacial and Postglacial history of the Hudson Bay region; in Earth Science Symposium on Hudson Bay, P.J. Hood; Geological Survey of Canada, Paper 63 - 53, p. 63 - 77.

Department of Transport
1968: Climatic normals, V. 5, Wind; Meteorological Branch, Toronto, 144 p.

Dionne, J.C.
1974a: Le littoral est de la baie de James dans la région de Fort-Georges; Annales de l'Association Canadienne-Française pour l'avancement des Sciences, v. 41, no. 1, p. 117.

Dionne, J.C. (cont.)
1974b: The eastward transport of erratics in James Bay area, Quebec; Revue de Géographie de Montréal, v. 28, no. 4, p. 453 - 457.
1975a: Le littoral est de la baie de James dans la région d'Eastmain; Annales de l'Association Canadienne-Française pour l'avancement des sciences, v. 42, no. 1, p. 82.
1975b: Blocs soulevés par le froid dans les schorres de la baie de James, Québec; Revue de Géographie de Montréal, v. 29, p. 161 - 166.
1976a: Le littoral oriental de la baie de James dans la région de Roggan, Québec; Annales de l'Association Canadienne-Française pour l'avancement des Sciences, v. 43, no. 1, p. 106.
1976b: Le glaciel de la région de la Grande Rivière, Québec subarctique; Revue de Géographie de Montréal, v. 30, nos. 1 - 2, p. 133 - 153.
1976c: L'action glacielle dans les schorres du littoral oriental de la baie de James; Cahiers de Géographie de Québec; v. 20, no. 50, p. 303 - 326.
1977: Paysages littoraux de la baie de James; North/Nord, v. 24, no. 5, p. 30 - 33.
1978a: Le glaciel en Jamésie et en Hudsonie, Québec subarctique; Géographie Physique et Quaternaire, v. 32, no. 1, p. 3 - 70.
1978b: Formes et phénomènes périglaciaires en Jamésie, Québec subarctique; Géographie Physique et Quaternaire, v. 32, no. 3, p. 187 - 246.
1978c: Dunes et dépôts éoliens en Jamésie et Hudsonie, Québec subarctique, Québec; Environment Canada, Lands Directorate, Information Report, 46 p.

Dohler, G.C.
1968: Tides and currents; in Science, History and Hudson Bay, C.S. Beals, ed.; Ottawa, Department of Energy, Mines and Resources, v. 2, p. 824 - 837.

Dubé, C. et al.
1976: Compilation géologique du territoire de la baie de James; Québec, Department of Natural Resources, Rapport DP-358, 6 p., 18 maps (scale: 1/250 000).

Eade, K.E.
1966: Fort George River and Kaniapiskau (West Half) map-areas, New Quebec; Geological Survey of Canada, Memoir 339, 84 p.

El-Sabh, M.I. and Koutitonsky, V.G.
1974: Physical oceanography study in James Bay; Environment Canada, Canada Centre for Inland Waters (Burlington), Report, 176 p.

Franconi, A.
1978: La bande volcanosédimentaire de la rivière Eastmain inférieure; Québec, Ministère des Richesses Naturelles, Rapport Géologique DPV-574, 177 p.

Godin, G.
1972: The tides in James Bay; in James Bay; Environment Canada, Marine Sciences Branch, Manuscript Report Services, 24, p. 97 - 142.

Godin, G. (cont.)
1974: The tides in eastern and western James Bay; Arctic, v. 27, no. 2, p. 104 - 110.
1975: Les vagues de tempête dans la baie de James; Le Naturaliste Canadien, v. 102, no. 2, p. 219 - 228.

Grainger, E.H.
1960: Some oceanographic features of southeast Hudson Bay and James Bay; Fisheries Research Board, Canada, Manuscript Report, Oceanography and Limnology Series, no. 7, 41 p.

Guimont, P. and Laverdière, C.
1976a: Les littoraux du sud-est de la baie de James et de l'estuaire de l'Eastmain. Le milieu physique; Montréal, Société du développement de la Baie James, Environnement Canada, Report, 127 p.
1976b: Les types de côtes du sud-est de la baie de James; dans Environnement Baie-James, 1976 Symposium; Montréal, Société de développement de la Baie James, Environnement Canada, p. 175 - 201.

Hardy, L.
1976: Contribution à l'étude de la portion québécoise des basses terres de la baie de James; Montréal, McGill University, Department of Geography, unpubl. Ph.D. thesis, 264 p.
1977: Le déglaciation et les épisodes lacustre et marin sur le versant québécois des basses terres de la baie de James; Géographie Physique et Quaternaire, v. 31, no. 3-4, p. 261 - 273.

Hillaire-Marcel, C.
1976: La déglaciation et le relèvement isostatique sur la côte est de la baie d'Hudson; Cahiers de Géographie de Québec, v. 20, no. 50, p. 185 - 220.

Hood, P.J.
1969: Earth Science Symposium on Hudson Bay; Geological Survey of Canada, Paper 68-53, 386 p.

Kindle, E.M.
1925: The James Bay coastal plain. Notes on a journey; Geographical Review, v. 15, no. 2, p. 226 - 236.

Kranck, E.H.
1951: On the geology of the East Coast of Hudson Bay and James Bay; Acta Geographica, v. 11, p. 1 - 71.

Laverdière, C. and Guimont, P.
1975: Le milieu bio-physique de la baie de Rupert; Montréal, Société de développement de la Baie James, Environnement Canada, Report, 159 p.

Lee, H.A.
1968a: Quaternary Geology; in Science, History and Hudson Bay, C.S. Beals, ed.; Ottawa, Department of Energy, Mines and Resources, v. 2, p. 503 - 543.
1968b: Tyrrell Sea; in The Encyclopedia of Geomorphology, R.W. Fairbridge, ed.; Reinhold, New York, p. 1179 - 1181.

Lee, H.A., Eade, K.E. and Heywood, W.W.
1960: Surficial geology, Sakami Lake (Fort George - Great Whale River area) New Quebec; Geological Survey of Canada, Map 52-1959.

Leslie, R.J.
1964: Sedimentology of Hudson Bay, District of Keewatin; Geological Survey of Canada, Paper 63-48, 31 p.

Low, A.P.
1889: Report on exploration in James Bay and country east of Hudson Bay drained by the Great Whale and Clearwater Rivers; Geological Survey of Canada, Annual Report 1887-88, v. 3, pt. J, 94 p.
1902: Report on an exploration of the east coast of Hudson Bay from Cape Wolstenholm to the south of James Bay; Geological Survey of Canada, Annual Report 1900, v. 13, pt. D, 84 p.
1912: James Bay; Ontario Bureau of Mines, v. 21, no. 2, p. 180 - 191.

Manning, T.G.
1951: Remarks on the tides and driftwood strandlines along the east coast of James Bay; Arctic, v. 4, no. 2, p. 122 - 131.

Martini, I.P. and Protz, R.
1978: Coastal geomorphology, sedimentology and pedology of southern James Bay, Ontario, Canada; Guelph University, Department of Land Resource Science, Technical Memorandum 78-1, 150 p.

Meagher, L.J., Ruffman, A. and Stewart, J.M.
1976: Marine geological data synthesis. James Bay; Geological Survey of Canada, Open File 497, 2 volumes, 561 p.

Murty, T.S.
1972: Circulation in James Bay; in James Bay; Ottawa, Environment Canada, Marine Sciences Branch, Manuscript Report Series No. 24, p. 143 - 193.

Peck, S.
1976: Nearshore Oceanography of James Bay; Montréal, 1976 Symposium Proceedings James Bay-Environment, p. 115 - 145.

Pelletier, B.R.
1969: Submarine physiography, bottom sediments and models of sediment transport in Hudson Bay; in Earth Science Symposium on Hudson Bay, P.J. Hood, ed.; Geological Survey of Canada, Paper 68-53, p. 100 - 135.

Prest, V.K.
1970: Quaternary geology of Canada; in Geology and Economic Minerals of Canada; R.J.W. Douglas, ed.; Geological Survey of Canada, Economic Geology Report 1, 5th ed., p. 676 - 764.

Pullen, T.W.
1973: James Bay data report, 1972; Environment Canada, Marine Sciences Division, Geotechnology Division, Canada Centre for Inland Waters (Burlington, Ont.), 93 p.
1974: James Bay data report, 1973; Environment Canada, Marine Sciences Directorate, Research and Development Division, Canada Centre for Inland Waters (Burlington, Ont.), 79 p.

Remick, J.H. and Admedali, S.T.
1975: Géologie de la région de Fort-Rupert, territoire de Mistassini; Québec, Ministère des Richesses Naturelles, Report DP-274, 22 maps.

Remick, J.H., Gillian, P.R. and Durden, C.J.
1963: Géologie de la baie de Rupert - rivière Missisicabi, territoires d'Abitibi et de Mistassini; Québec, Ministère des Richesses Naturelles, Preliminary Report 498, 24 p.

Shaw, G.
1942: Preliminary map, Eastmain, Quebec; Geological Survey of Canada, Paper 42-10.

Skinner, R.G.
1974: Terrain studies in the James Bay development area; Geological Survey of Canada, Open File 219, 30 p.

Sugden, D.E.
1977: Reconstruction of the morphology, dynamics and thermal characteristics of the Laurentide ice sheet at its maximum; Arctic and Alpine Research, v. 9, p. 21 - 47.

Villeneuve, G.O.
1967: Sommaire climatique du Québec; Québec Ministère des Richesses Naturelles, Service Météorologique, Rapport M-24, 168 p.

Vincent, J.S.
1973: Géologie du Quaternaire (Maps: 33E/10, 33E/11, 33E/14, 33E/15); Geological Survey of Canada, Open File 178.
1977: Le Quarternaire récent de la région du cours inférieur de la Grande Rivière, Québec; Geological Survey of Canada, Paper 76-19, 20 p.

Wagner, F.J.E.
1967: Additional radiocarbon dates, Tyrrell Sea area; Maritime Sediments, v. 3, no. 4, p. 100 - 104.

24

MORPHOLOGY AND LITTORAL PROCESSES OF THE PACIFIC COAST OF CANADA

J.J. Clague[1] and B.D. Bornhold[2]

Clague, J.J. and Bornhold, B.D., Morphology and littoral processes of the Pacific coast of Canada; in The Coastline of Canada, S.B. McCann, editor; Geological Survey of Canada, Paper 80-10, p. 339-380, 1980.

Abstract

The Pacific coast of Canada is predominantly a rocky, rugged area of islands, inlets, and fiords flanked by high mountain ranges. The morphology of the coast is controlled by structural trends of the western Canadian Cordillera, but has been modified during the Pleistocene Epoch by glacial erosion of both unconsolidated sediments and bedrock, and by deposition of till and stratified drift.

Generalized maps of the British Columbia coast showing the distribution of beaches, rock shorelines, mixed rock-sediment shorelines, and deltas are presented. The distribution, character, and dynamics of these coastal environments are discussed in the context of the geology and physiography of the Pacific margin and in terms of wave and current regimes. Previous work on littoral sediments and processes is reviewed, and a selective bibliography of readily available papers, maps, reports, and theses dealing with the morphology and sediments of the coastal zone, with related oceanography and meteorology, and with past coastal environments is included.

It is concluded that, although wave and current energy and relief differ appreciably in the various coastal environments, the dominance of resistant rocks and the low input of terrestrial detritus result in a paucity of littoral sediments in most regions. Exceptions include: (1) areas backed by cliffs of unconsolidated Pleistocene sediments or nonresistant bedrock; (2) fiords and protected embayments where deltas are forming under low wave-energy conditions; (3) exposed coastal areas where deltas are forming (e.g., the Fraser and Skeena River deltas) or where littoral currents transport sediment along the coast from river mouths to nearby depositional sites; (4) pocket beaches between resistant headlands; and (5) sheltered, very low energy sites characterized by intertidal mudflats.

The landforms and sediments associated with former postglacial shoreline positions provide evidence of the nature of earlier coastal environments. Following the late Wisconsinan glacial maximum a marine transgression to a maximum elevation of about 200 m occurred on the inner coast. During this and the following regressive phase, which resulted in large part from isostatic adjustments in the crust, voluminous stratified and nonstratified drift was deposited locally in many coastal areas. Middle and late Holocene sea levels apparently were relatively lower than at present on the inner coast, but were higher than at present on parts of the outer coast. The subsequent rise in sea level on the inner coast has been accompanied by erosion at many coastal sites. Adjustments in land-sea positions are continuing, and have been documented for the southern Georgia Depression and part of the Hecate Depression.

Résumé

La côte Pacifique du Canada est avant tout une zone littorale rocheuses et rugueuse composée d'îles, d'inlets et de fjords flanqués par de hautes chaînes de montagne. La morphologie littorale est commandée par des mouvements structuraux de la Cordillère canadienne occidentale, mais elle a été modifiée au cours du Pléistocène par l'érosion glaciaire des sédiments non consolidés et du socle rocheux ainsi que par le dépôt de till et de drift stratifiés.

Des cartes générales de la côte colombienne montrent la répartition des plages, des littoraux rocheux, des littoraux sédimento-rocheux et des deltas. La répartition de la nature et la dynamique de ces milieux côtiers font l'objet de discussion dans le contexte géologique et physiographique de la bordure du Pacifique et du point de vue des régimes de vague et de courant. Les auteurs ont procédé au dépouillement de travaux antérieurs portant sur les sédiments et processus littoraux et ils ont constitué une bibliographie choisie d'études, de cartes, de rapports et de thèses faciles d'accès qui portent sur la morphologie et les sédiments de la zone côtière; ceux-ci s'accompagnent généralement de commentaires océanographiques et météorologiques ainsi que d'observations sur les milieux côtiers antérieurs.

On peut en conclure que malgré que l'énergie due aux vagues et aux courants diffère appréciablement du relief dans les divers milieux côtiers, la dominance des roches résistantes et le faible apport des détritus terrestres résultent en une rareté des sédiments littoraux dans la plupart des régions. Les exceptions sont les suivantes: (1) les zones appuyées sur des falaises de sédiments non consolidés du Pléistocène ou un substrat de roches tendres; (2) les fjords et inlets protégés dans lesquels des deltas se forment à la faveur de vagues de basse énergie; (3) les zones côtiers exposées où des deltas sont en voie de formation (par ex. les deltas du Fraser et de la Skeena) ou encore aux endroits où des courants littoraux transportent les matériaux de la côte à partir de l'embouchure des

---

[1] Terrain Sciences Division, Geological Survey of Canada, Vancouver, British Columbia

[2] Pacific Geoscience Centre, Geological Survey of Canada, Sidney, British Columbia

cours d'eau jusqu'aux emplacements voisins propices à la sédimentation; (4) les petites plages situées entre les promontoires de roches résistantes; et (5) les emplacements abrités très pauvres en énergie et caractérisés par l'existence de vasières intertidales.

Les formes de relief et les sédiments associés à d'anciennes positions littorales post-glaciaires fournissent la preuve de la nature des anciens milieux côtiers. A la suite de l'avance glaciaire maximale du Wisconsin une transgression marine atteignant une altitude maximale d'environ 200 m s'est produite sur la côte intérieure. Au cours de cette avance et de la régression qui a suivi, par suite surtout d'ajustements isostatiques de la croûte terrestre, d'énormes quantités de drift stratifié et non stratifié se sont déposées ici et là dans de nombreuses zones côtières. Il semble que les niveaux de la mer du milieu et de la fin de l'Holocène aient été relativement plus bas que celui que l'on connaît actuellement sur la côte intérieure; mais qu'ils étaient plus hauts que celui qui existe sur certaines parties de la côte extérieure. Le soulèvement ultérieure du niveau de la mer sur la côte intérieure s'est accompagnée de l'érosion de nombreux endroits de la côte. Certains ajustements des positions respectives de la terre et de la mer se poursuivent toujours et ont déjà fait l'objet d'études en ce qui concerne la partie méridionale de la dépression Georgia ainsi qu'une partie de la dépression Hecate.

INTRODUCTION

The Pacific coast of Canada (Figs. 24.1, 24.2) is a leading-edge continental margin backed by rugged mountains up to 4000 m in elevation. It is characterized by a relatively narrow continental shelf and a complex, irregular, mainly rock coastal zone with countless inlets, fiords and islands. The coastline is itself structurally controlled but has been extensively modified by Pleistocene glaciers. The shoreline and associated littoral sediments are affected also by nongeologic factors such as nearshore currents and waves. Energy levels are highest on the exposed coasts adjacent to the open North Pacific Ocean and lowest in sheltered inshore waters of the fiords and inlets.

This paper is an overview of the Pacific coast and the littoral and nearshore processes which interact with it. Although few coastal studies, either regional or local, have been undertaken in British Columbia, we attempt to summarize and synthesize the available information and to account for some of the more spectacular coastal features. Preliminary maps of several major coastal types also are presented. We hasten to point out that, in view of the paucity of information and the level of generalization demanded in a summary of this type, our subdivision of the Pacific coastal zone is not intended to represent a final scheme; the coastal types are simply those that can be recognized with the sparse data presently available.

The organizaton of the paper is as follows: Regional studies of the British Columbia coastal zone are summarized, followed by a brief discussion of significant oceanographic and meteorological factors. Coastal morphology and littoral processes and sediments then are discussed within each of the major physiographic regions, focusing on areas where specific, local studies have been undertaken. Following a short discussion and summary of the contemporary coastal zone, changes in land-sea positions and coastal environments during late Quaternary time are summarized.

REGIONAL INVENTORIES OF COASTAL MORPHOLOGY AND SEDIMENTS

Inventories of Pacific coastal morphology and littoral sediments are limited both in scope and areal extent. Holland (1964) outlined the major physiographic subdivisions of British Columbia, summarizing them in terms of relief and surface morphology, and briefly described the coastline.

Owens (1977) in a review of the shoreline and process characteristics of Canada's coasts described the British Columbia coast in the context of other primary coastal units

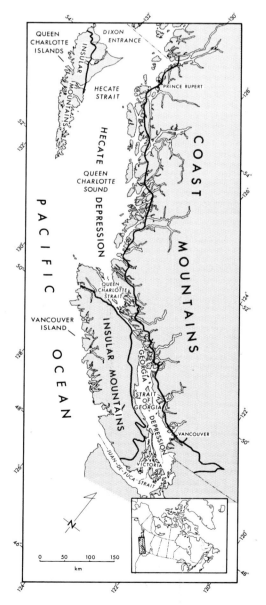

Figure 24.1. *Major physiographic subdivisions of the British Columbia coastal region.*

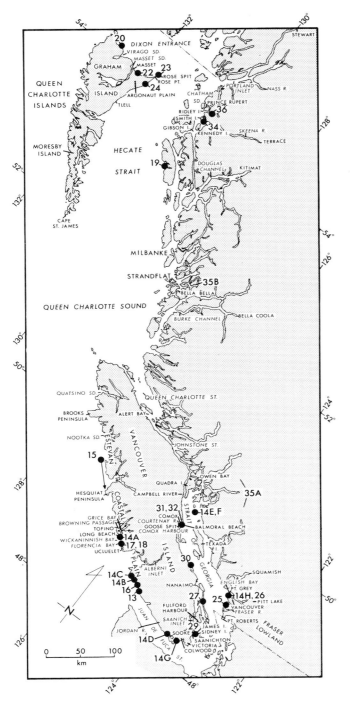

Figure 24.2. Index map with localities cited in text. Numbered, darkened circles indicate geographic locations of text illustrations.

(Arctic, Atlantic and Great Lakes). He discriminated six Pacific coastal environments---Fraser River Delta, Queen Charlotte Strait - Strait of Georgia, Juan de Fuca Strait, Outer Coast, Queen Charlotte Sound - Hecate Strait, and East Graham Island. Each of these units was defined in terms of wave exposure, fetch, tidal range, sediment availability, and the geology, backshore relief and beach character of the coastal zone.

Physical resource maps of much of the British Columbia coast have been prepared by Fisheries and Environment Canada to provide a data base for the evaluation of environmental risks of oil spillage related to tanker traffic and potential oil ports (Fig. 24.3). One set of maps prepared by R. Bell-Irving of the Habitat Protection Directorate (Canada Department of Fisheries and Environment, 1978) provides in a generalized fashion the following information for regularly spaced segments of shoreline: (1) shoreline type, "open, protected, channel, offshore reefs", (2) substrate type, "bedrock, coarse grain, fine grain, estuarine", and (3) slope of coastal zone, "flat, gradual, steep". Information is included for both the intertidal and supratidal zones and for the coast immediately inland of the supratidal zone. Except for the east coast of Vancouver Island, the information was obtained from vertical aerial photographs with little or no ground checking. A field-oriented foreshore inventory provided data for the east coast of Vancouver Island.

A second set of physical resource maps has been prepared by S. Hum of the Environmental Protection Service (Canada Department of Environment, 1976a). These maps, covering much the same areas as those by Bell-Irving, show the type of intertidal substrate (e.g., bedrock, boulders, gravel, sand, mud), locations of manmade coastal structures, and foreshore leases. They also provide limited information on slopes facing the shoreline. The data were obtained by ground-level field observation and examination of aerial photographs.

An inventory of shoreline characteristics and littoral sediments on southern Vancouver Island was made by D. Fisher for the Geological Survey of Canada (Fig. 24.3). Fisher's observations were taken from aerial photographs and transferred to 1:50 000 - scale topographic maps. The maps and accompanying report are not yet published.

Finally, the coastal environments of eastern Vancouver Island have been examined by W. Bauer for the British Columbia Ministry of Recreation and Conservation and Ministry of Environment. Bauer discriminated shoreline types ("rock, marsh, estuarine, beach") and beach stability zones ("erosional, marginal erosional, accretional"); he also determined littoral drift directions. This information, intended for use primarily by coastal resource managers, was plotted on aerial photographs and discussed in accompanying reports. The reports are unpublished and of limited availability.

METEOROLOGY AND OCEANOGRAPHY

The directions and magnitudes of the predominant winds, waves and currents which affect the coastal zone of British Columbia are summarized in this section and an attempt is made, subject to the limitations of our present knowledge, to indicate the significance of these factors to different parts of the coast.

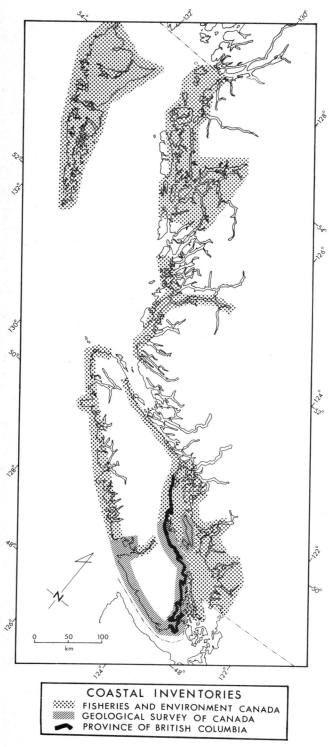

COASTAL INVENTORIES
FISHERIES AND ENVIRONMENT CANADA
GEOLOGICAL SURVEY OF CANADA
PROVINCE OF BRITISH COLUMBIA

Figure 24.3. *Regional inventories of littoral sediments and coastal morphology. The inventories for Fisheries and Environment Canada were done by R. Bell-Irving and S. Hum; the inventory for the Geological Survey of Canada, by D. Fisher; and the inventory for the British Columbia Ministry of Recreation and Conservation and Ministry of Environment, by W. Bauer. See text for details.*

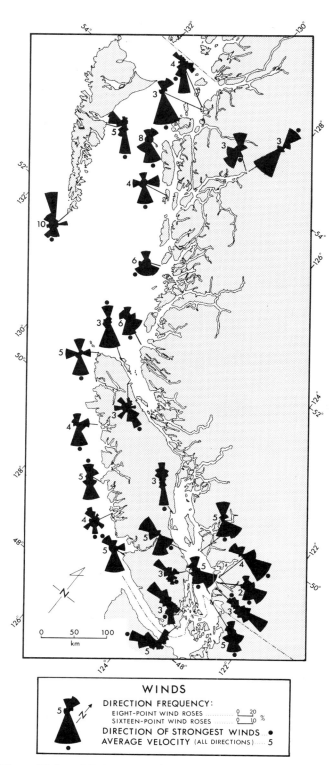

WINDS
DIRECTION FREQUENCY:
EIGHT-POINT WIND ROSES
SIXTEEN-POINT WIND ROSES
DIRECTION OF STRONGEST WINDS
AVERAGE VELOCITY (ALL DIRECTIONS) 5

Figure 24.4. *Wind roses for British Columbia coastal stations. Plotted directions are those from which the winds blow. Source of data – Canada Department of Environment (1975).*

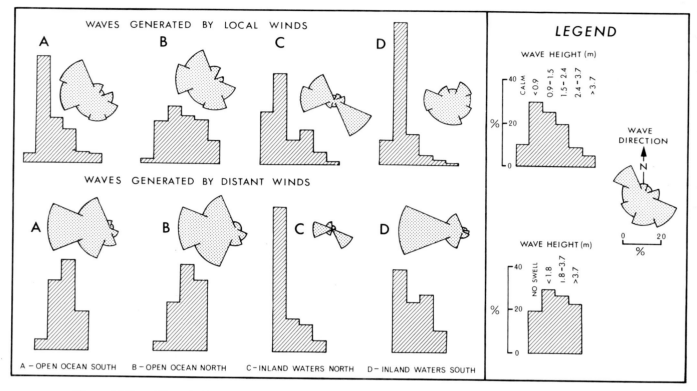

Figure 24.5. *Wave heights and directions in (A) the North Pacific Ocean off Vancouver Island, (B) the North Pacific Ocean off the Queen Charlotte Islands, (C) Hecate Strait, and (D) the Strait of Georgia. Plotted directions are those from which the waves travel. Source of data – Canadian Hydrographic Service (1976).*

Winds

Prevailing winds along the British Columbia coast are from the northwest in summer and from the southeast in winter (Fig. 24.4). Winds in coastal areas are strongest on the Queen Charlotte Islands (Canada Department of Fisheries and Environment, 1978). For example, at Cape St. James at the southern tip of the Queen Charlotte Islands winds exceed 10 m/s about 35 per cent of the time between October and April and about 15 per cent of the time between May and September (Canada Department of Fisheries and Environment, 1978, Figs. 4.3.1, 4.3.2). In most coastal areas wind velocities are greater during winter because of the regular occurrence of low-pressure systems controlled by the offshore Aleutian Low.

In addition to the prevailing northwesterlies and southeasterlies, land and sea breezes of local origin influence coastal areas. In summer under fair weather conditions, for example, modification of prevailing winds by onshore winds during the afternoon and by offshore winds during the evening and early morning causes corresponding increases and decreases in wave heights.

Wind directions also vary considerably because of local topographic effects. Although most inlets are protected from waves generated by the prevailing winds from the northwest and southeast, strong katabatic winds known as 'Squamishes' with accompanying steep, short seas are frequent in inlets when cold dense 'Arctic' air from the adjacent mountains and uplands flows seaward. Topographic effects on wind patterns are also evident at Victoria where westerlies are funnelled through Juan de Fuca Strait (Fig. 24.4).

The wind regime summarized above is a primary control on the direction and intensity of waves striking the British Columbia coast. The waves, of course, affect the distribution and character of littoral sediments.

Waves

The Aleutian Low and the North Pacific High are the major quasipermanent pressure systems producing swell and local sea waves (Canadian Hydrographic Service, 1974, 1976). During autumn and especially during winter the Aleutian Low and the associated migratory cyclones are the major causes of waves. At these times the North Pacific High is weak and displaced south. During summer, however, the North Pacific High becomes dominant off the British Columbia coast.

Most wave energy on the outer coast is in the form of long-period (up to 20 s) swell waves out of the west, southwest and northwest (Fig. 24.5). Open-ocean swell heights exceed 4 m 20 to 40 per cent of the time during winter, but only 4 to 15 per cent of the time during summer (Canadian Hydrographic Service, 1976). Likewise, open-ocean waves generated by local winds are seasonally variable, exceeding 4 m 5 to 10 per cent of the time during winter but only rarely during summer. These differences are due to the greater intensity of frontal systems over the North Pacific Ocean during winter months, which, in turn, are caused by the increased pressure gradients between marine and continental air masses. Observations with a waverider accelerometer buoy near Tofino off the west coast of Vancouver Island indicate that maximum wave heights in excess of 10 m are possible on the exposed outer coast (Canada Department of Environment, 1974).

The dominant waves, having westerly components, penetrate only those straits and inlets whose axes are parallel to the direction of wave propagation, for example Juan de Fuca Strait. There is generally a rapid decrease in swell height along the axes of the straits, so that amplification of these waves in shallow water at the open-ocean end produces higher breakers than similar processes farther inland.

In the sheltered inland waters adjacent to Vancouver Island waves are generated by local winds and are controlled, in part, by the topography of adjacent land masses. In Juan de Fuca Strait, for example, seas are primarily west-northwest and east-southeast, parallel to the axis of the strait. In all such sheltered bodies of water waves are lower than on the outer coast (Fig. 24.5). For example, measurements off the Fraser River delta, an area representative of highest energy conditions in the Strait of Georgia, indicate that waves there are always less than 4 m high, and that wave maxima in excess of 1 m occur during only 20 per cent of the measurement intervals (Canada Department of Environment, 1976b). In the Strait of Georgia and Juan de Fuca Strait waves are seasonally variable, being largest in autumn, winter and spring, and smallest in summer. Wave energy in these areas is also dependent on fetch, which varies with wind direction. In the Strait of Georgia, for example, the largest waves are generated by winds blowing southeast and northwest parallel to the long axis of the strait.

Wave energy in inland waters adjoining the Queen Charlotte Islands is intermediate between that of the open North Pacific Ocean and that of inland waters south and east of Vancouver Island. Waves in Queen Charlotte Sound are similar in direction and slightly smaller than waves in the open ocean. Swells from the west and southwest enter the sound unmodified, whereas swells from the northwest and south are attenuated by refraction and shoaling (Canadian Hydrographic Service, 1976). Likewise, swells entering Dixon Entrance from the west, southwest and northwest are rapidly attenuated as they move inland. Most waves in Dixon Entrance are the result of locally generated winds and are thus smaller than those in Queen Charlotte Sound. Finally, waves in Hecate Strait, generally smaller than those in Queen Charlotte Sound and Dixon Entrance, in part penetrate from the open ocean and in part are generated by strong cyclonic winds from the northwest and southeast. As in other areas, wave-energy levels in Queen Charlotte Sound, Dixon Entrance and Hecate Strait are seasonally variable, being greatest in autumn and winter and least in late spring and summer.

Currents

Most nearshore currents are produced by astronomical tides and by prevailing winds. The characteristics of tidal and nontidal currents along the British Columbia coast are briefly summarized below.

Tidal currents

The mean tidal range on the British Columbia coast decreases from 5 m in northern areas to about 2 m near Victoria (Figs. 24.6, 24.7, Table 24.1). A maximum range of 8.4 m has been recorded at Prince Rupert. Superimposed on this north-south trend are variations in tidal range caused by convergence, shoaling and harmonic damping due to variable water depths and to the disposition of islands, passages and embayments. The tidal range on the west coast of Vancouver Island is lower than in the Strait of Georgia and

Queen Charlotte Strait, and is lower on the west coast of the Queen Charlotte Islands than in Hecate Strait, Queen Charlotte Sound and Dixon Entrance (Fig. 24.6).

Tidal streams flood and ebb in and out of the straits, sounds and inlets. The flood entering Juan de Fuca Strait progresses east and north into the Strait of Georgia and contiguous inlets. Off the west coast of Vancouver Island the tidal flood progresses to the northwest, augmenting the prevailing northwesterly directed nontidal current in winter but reducing the southeast current in summer. The flood enters Queen Charlotte Sound and Queen Charlotte Strait, passes through the channels between Vancouver Island and the British Columbia mainland, and meets the flood which has progressed northward from Juan de Fuca Strait at the north end of the Strait of Georgia. In restricted passages, such as those at the north and south ends of the Strait of Georgia, current velocities up to 7 m/s are attained (Canadian Hydrographic Service, 1976). The flood entering Hecate Strait from Queen Charlotte Sound meets the flood from Dixon Entrance at the north end of the sound.

Ebb streams in general are in the opposite direction of the flood, although the two, in many areas, are not of equal strength. In Dixon Entrance, for example, the ebb is stronger than the flood, reflecting a net northward water flow through Hecate Strait and into Dixon Entrance (Crean, 1967; Boisvert, 1969). In addition, during much of the year, the ebb is greater on the south side, resulting in a net counterclockwise cyclonic circulation pattern (Crean, 1967). Similarly, the flooding tidal current in the Strait of Georgia is stronger and of longer duration than the ebb on the mainland side, the reverse being true on the Vancouver Island side (e.g., Waldichuk and Tabata, 1955). There is thus a net counterclockwise circulation pattern in the strait which is due to combined Coriolis and centrifugal forces, topographic effects and Fraser River discharge.

In many semienclosed water bodies the ebb and flood along the coast are highly complex, consisting of numerous 'jets', well defined tidal fronts between opposing currents, and large-scale quasipermanent back-eddies.

The numerous rivers of the British Columbia coastal region (Table 24.2) also affect the relative magnitude and duration of flood and ebb currents. In inlets and other restricted bodies of water with large freshwater inputs, the surface ebb current is stonger and runs longer than the flood, especially at freshet and when winds are directed down-channel.

Nontidal currents

The major nontidal current influencing the Pacific coast of Canada, the Subarctic Current, flows eastward across the North Pacific until it approaches the coast of North America. In the area between about 46° and 50°N and 130° and 138°W this current divides into the north-flowing Alaska Current and the south-flowing California Current. In this area of divergence surface currents are generally weak and variable in direction.

In autumn and winter surface currents off the west coasts of Vancouver Island and the Queen Charlotte Islands and in Queen Charlotte Sound and Hecate Strait are towards the north and northwest, with velocities generally 0.1 to 0.3 m/s, but occasionally 1.0 m/s or greater (Boisvert, 1969). This northerly flow is controlled primarily by the Alaska Current, which is strengthened off the Pacific coast of Canada during winter when it is enhanced by the prevailing southeasterly winds. During summer northerly directed currents persist in open waters west of the Queen Charlotte Islands. Off the west coast of Vancouver Island however, currents, although weak (<.2 m/s), are directed southward with occasional reversals. Southward flow is enhanced by northwesterly winds which are common in summer.

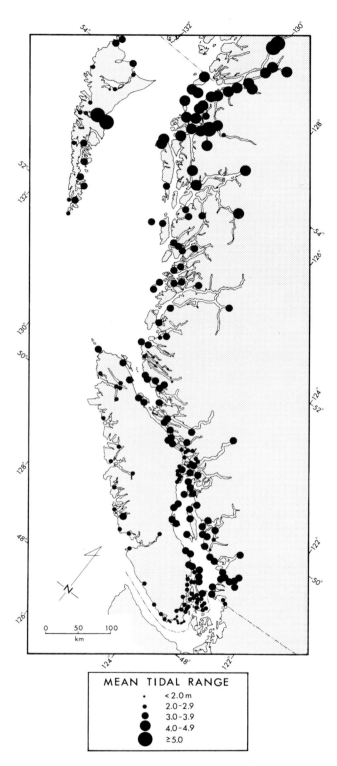

Figure 24.6. *Mean tidal range along the British Columbia coast. In general the tidal range increases towards the northwest, but is lower on the outer coast than on the inner coast. The mean tidal range generally is about 60 to 70 per cent of the large tidal range. Source of data – Canadian Hydrographic Service (1978).*

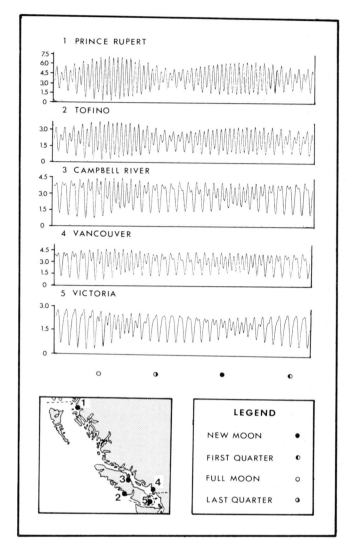

Figure 24.7. *Typical tidal curves for a one-month period (in metres). Source – Canadian Hydrographic Service (1978). See also Table 24.1.*

Ice

Sea ice plays a very minor role in the coastal processes of the region. Ice is limited to inlets where inflowing fresh river water occasionally freezes (Owens, 1977).

Synthesis

The meteorological and oceanographic factors discussed above interact in a complex fashion to control energy levels on the British Columbia coast. The character of littoral sediments and shore morphology, in turn, are affected by energy inputs by winds, waves and currents. Although energy levels vary seasonally, and although detailed studies of the energy regime at specific sites have not been conducted, the following generalizations apply (Fig. 24.8).

Energy inputs to the outer coast and to Queen Charlotte Sound are high relative to other areas. The exposed outer coast is subject to the full fury of storms generated in the North Pacific, with the result that waves striking the west coasts of Vancouver Island and the Queen Charlotte Islands are larger than waves striking other sections of the coast.

Table 24.1. Tidal data for selected ports

Location		Mean tidal range	Large tidal range	Type of tide
		(m)	(m)	
Prince Rupert	54°19'N 130°20'W	4.9	7.6	Mixed semidiurnal
Bella Bella	52°10'N 128°08'W	3.4	5.3	Mixed semidiurnal
Alert Bay	50°35'N 126°56'W	3.5	5.3	Mixed semidiurnal
Owen Bay	50°19'N 125°13'W	2.8	4.4	Mixed diurnal
Campbell River	50°01'N 125°14'W	2.9	4.6	Mixed diurnal
Vancouver	49°17'N 123°07'W	3.3	4.9	Mixed diurnal
Tofino	49°09'N 125°55'W	2.7	3.9	Mixed semidiurnal
Fulford Harbour	48°46'N 123°27'W	2.4	3.8	Mixed diurnal
Victoria	48°25'N 123°22'W	1.8	3.1	Mixed diurnal
Sooke	48°22'N 123°44'W	2.0	3.2	Mixed diurnal

Source, Canadian Hydrographic Service (1978).

Table 24.2. Water discharge characteristics of the larger gauged rivers (drainage basin areas > 260 km^2) of the British Columbia coastal area

Gauge location		Mean for period	Mean of max. month	Season of max. discharge	Drainage area	Period
		(m^3/s)	(m^3/s)		(km^2)	(a)
Mainland						
Bear R.	56°02'34"N 129°55'30"W	23	62	summer	350	7
Bella Coola R.	52°26'32"N 126°19'56"W	119	267	summer	4170	22
Dean R.	52°49'08"N 126°56'39"W	140	340	summer	7850	10
Fraser R.*	49°13'03"N 122°50'20"W	3880	9400	spring-summer	232,000	5
Homathko R.	51°00'20"N 124°56'25"W	283	697	summer	5720	17
Kemano R.	53°34'10"N 127°56'40"W	42	116	summer	<777	3
Kitimat R.	54°03'10"N 128°41'21"W	135	294	summer	1990	10
Lois R.*	49°47'42"N 124°19'03"W	21	34	winter	456	13
Nascall R.	52°29'50"N 127°17'00"W	57	118	summer	275	19
Nass R.	55°12'50"N 129°08'20"W	801	2110	summer	1920	39
Sandell R.	51°34'09"N 127°30'36"W	14	20	winter	391	10
Skeena R.	54°37'50"N 128°25'40"W	923	2860	summer	4220	42
Squamish R.*	49°47'40"N 123°12'00"W	242	501	summer	2340	24
Wannock R.	51°40'40"N 127°10'30"W	348	637	summer	3940	21
Queen Charlotte Islands						
Yakoun R.	53°36'50"N 132°12'35"W	34	63	fall	490	12
Vancouver Island						
Campbell R.*	50°02'17"N 125°17'41"W	99	132	winter	1460	22
Chemainus R.	48°52'51"N 123°41'10"W	19	39	winter	378	26
Cowichan R.*	48°46'22"N 123°42'44"W	54	118	winter	826	14
Englishman R.	49°19'00"N 124°16'58"W	13	22	winter	287	7
Gold R.*	49°42'21"N 126°06'22"W	88	148	winter	1010	18
Kokish R.	50°31'00"N 126°51'20"W	18	30	winter	311	14
Marble R.*	50°31'26"N 127°25'51"W	44	84	winter	518	11
Nanaimo R.*	49°04'07"N 123°53'13"W	41	87	winter	684	9
Nimpkish R.	50°31'22"N 127°00'51"W	129	203	winter	1760	13
Puntledge R.*	49°41'17"N 125°01'57"W	43	56	winter	583	20
Salmon R.*	50°19'14"N 125°55'14"W	66	102	winter	1200	18
San Juan R.	48°34'38"N 124°19'02"W	51	107	winter	580	15
Somass R.*	49°17'07"N 124°52'00"W	130	215	winter	1285	17

*River regulated.
Source, Water Survey of Canada (1974).

Accretive littoral landforms along this high-energy coast are rare, in large part because of the low rate at which sediment is being supplied to beaches. Some littoral transport of sediment is probably occurring, related to the net northwest movement of surface waters along the outer coast. Littoral-drift directions and rates, however, are perhaps more affected by the orientation of particular reaches of

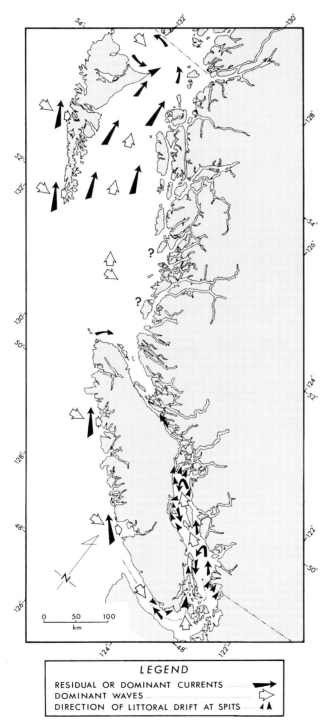

Figure 24.8. *Synthesis of oceanographic factors controlling regional littoral transport.*

LEGEND
RESIDUAL OR DOMINANT CURRENTS ....
DOMINANT WAVES ....
DIRECTION OF LITTORAL DRIFT AT SPITS

coast relative to prevailing winds and waves than by the relatively slow movement of surface waters to the northwest.

Because of its comparatively open situation and its position relative to the prevailing southeasterly winter winds, Hecate Strait is subject to high waves. In addition, there is a persistent northwest flow of surface water through Hecate Strait. As a result of these factors, along favorably oriented reaches of coast where there is an abundant supply of sediment there is strong northerly littoral transport. For example, on northeast Graham Island sediment eroded from coastal bluffs is transported northward. Littoral currents are also set up by the counterclockwise circulation of surface waters in Dixon Entrance.

The cyclonic circulation of surface waters in the Strait of Georgia may likewise influence directions of littoral transport there. Equally or more important, however, are the prevailing winds from the southeast that generate waves that move parallel to the axis of the strait. These waves apparently control, for example, the movement of coastal sediments at the southeast corner of Vancouver Island between Juan de Fuca Strait and the Strait of Georgia. Spits in this area indicate north to northwesterly transport of sediment.

In constricted passages such as those between Vancouver Island and the mainland high energy levels are attained during tidal flood and ebb, and, in contrast to other areas, wave energy is very low. Because beaches in these passages are generally narrow or absent and because sediments available for transport are sparse, littoral drift is minor.

Energy levels are lowest in the fiords and protected embayments which are common along most of the British Columbia coast. Most of the fiords are oriented so that fetch is short and waves small. However, katabatic winds flowing from mountains uplands into fiords produce relatively rough seas for short periods.

COASTAL GEOMORPHOLOGY

The coastal areas of British Columbia can be divided broadly into three physiographic regions (Holland, 1964) (Fig. 24.1): (1) the Outer Mountain area, which includes the Insular Mountains of the Queen Charlotte Islands and the Insular Mountains of Vancouver Island; (2) the Coastal Trough, which includes the Hecate Depression (encompassing the northeastern Queen Charlotte Islands, northernmost Vancouver Island and the northern mainland coast) and the Georgia Depression (comprising the areas of Vancouver Island and the lower British Columbia mainland bordering the Strait of Georgia and eastern Juan de Fuca Strait); and (3) the Coast Mountains, into which all the fiords of mainland British Columbia extend.

These regions are to a great extent structurally and lithologically controlled (Fig. 24.9) and consequently exhibit different shoreline characteristics. Vancouver Island and the southwestern Queen Charlotte Islands are composed mainly of folded and faulted volcanic and sedimentary rocks of Mesozoic age with some plutonic rocks. The northwestern Queen Charlotte Islands are a low-lying, dissected plateau of lower Tertiary (?) volcanic rocks. Weakly deformed sedimentary rocks ranging in age from Cretaceous to late Tertiary underlie the northeastern Queen Charlotte Islands, eastern Vancouver Island, and the Fraser Lowland, and also occur as a narrow fringe along parts of western Vancouver Island. The Coast Mountains are made up predominantly of plutonic rocks, but metamorphic, volcanic and sedimentary rocks of a range of ages are common.

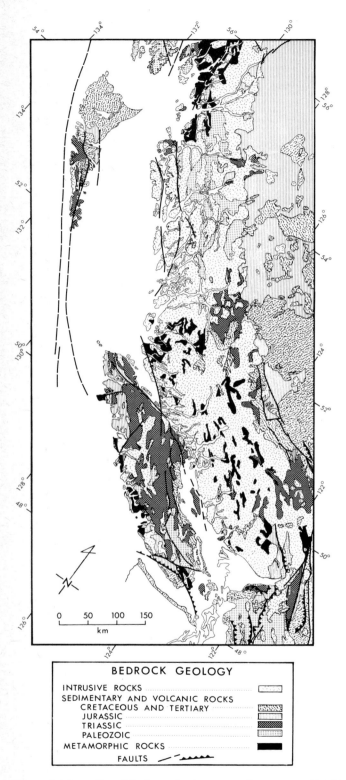

Figure 24.9. *Simplified geologic map of western British Columbia. Source – Jackson (1976).*

BEDROCK GEOLOGY

INTRUSIVE ROCKS
SEDIMENTARY AND VOLCANIC ROCKS
   CRETACEOUS AND TERTIARY
   JURASSIC
   TRIASSIC
   PALEOZOIC
METAMORPHIC ROCKS
   FAULTS

Queen Charlotte Mountains

The Queen Charlotte Mountains, the northernmost subdivision of the Insular Ranges, consist of two units---the Queen Charlotte Ranges, which form the backbone of the islands, and the Skidegate Plateau to the east and north (Fig. 24.10).

Despite their modest maximum relief of 1200 m, the Queen Charlotte Ranges are extremely rugged and plunge steeply into the sea off western Moresby Island. Sea cliffs rising nearly vertically more than 200 m are common along this segment of the coast, and consequently the littoral zone is narrow or absent in most areas. Numerous fiords indent the coastline, a few with short gravelly beaches and small deltas.

The Skidegate Plateau is an easterly sloping surface with a maximum elevation of about 800 m. It forms the coastline of most of western Graham Island. This coastline is more regular than that of Moresby Island to the south and exhibits a somewhat greater frequency of sand and gravel beaches, particularly along the eastern part of the plateau.

No studies of littoral processes or sediments have been undertaken in the Queen Charlotte Mountains physiographic region.

Vancouver Island Mountains

The Vancouver Island Mountains, with peaks up to 2200 m in elevation, occupy all of the island except for the Nanaimo and Nahwitti lowlands, which lie below 600 m (Figs. 24.11, 24.12). The west coast is indented with numerous fiords, many extending more than 50 km towards the interior of the island (e.g., Alberni Inlet, Quatsino and Nootka sounds). This physiographic unit has mainly a rugged rocky shoreline (Fig. 24.13), both on the exposed Pacific coast and along the fiords and inlets. Small deltas, marshes and gravelly beaches occur locally within the fiords.

Within this region is the Vancouver Island coastline at the west end of Juan de Fuca Strait, which is characterized by broad intertidal rock platforms developed on jointed sedimentary rocks and by an absence of beach materials or very narrow pebble-cobble and gravelly sand beaches (Fig. 24.14B).

A narrow coastal lowland, the Estevan Coastal Plain (Fig. 24.15), extends along western Vancouver Island for more than 270 km northwest from the mouth of Juan de Fuca Strait to Brooks Peninsula. In most areas it is 3 to 4 km wide, but at Hesquiat Peninsula it attains widths of up to 12 km. The coastal plain is generally lower than 50 m in elevation, the few isolated hills on the plain rarely exceeding 80 m.

Within the Estevan Coastal Plain are the only extensive beaches of western Vancouver Island (Figs. 24.14C, 24.16, 24.17). Most have developed in areas underlain by thick unconsolidated Pleistocene sediments where offshore gradients are low. At Florencia (Fig. 24.17) and Wickaninnish bays, between the towns of Ucluelet and Tofino, wide sandy beaches have developed by erosion of unconsolidated sediments through violent wave attack. In addition a dune field 40 to 50 m wide and several kilometres long at Long Beach has been produced by strong winds blowing inland from the ocean. North of Long Beach, near the town of Tofino, are broad muddy intertidal flats in the sheltered inshore waters of Browning Passage and Grice Bay.

One major study of littoral sediments and processes has been made in the Vancouver Island Mountains physiographic region. Bremner (1970) and Bremner and LeBlond (1974) described the beach at Florencia Bay, which is probably representative of high-energy beaches of the Estevan

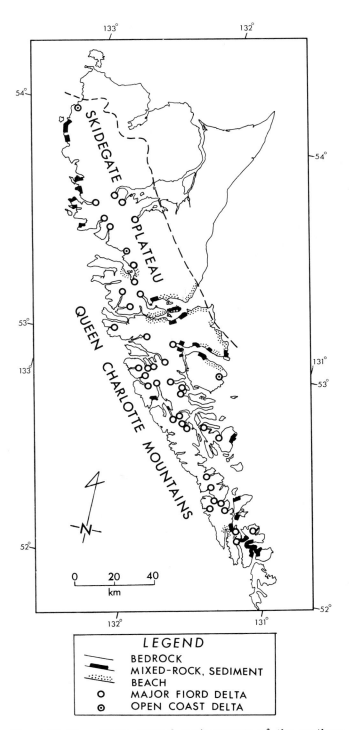

Coastal Plain. Florencia Bay is a crescent-shaped embayment with a small cuspate foreland (Sand Point) in the middle and rocky headlands at its northwest and southeast ends (Figs. 24.17, 24.18). The beach, approximately 5 km in length, is backed by a steep cliff of Pleistocene sediments. Florencia Bay itself is floored by sediments eroded from this retrograding sea cliff. A veneer of sand overlies gravel and becomes finer away from the shore. The beach in summer consists of fine sand eroded from the adjacent cliffs, and slopes seaward at less than 2.6°. During winter when wave heights at times exceed 5.75 m, the beach is less steep, and beach sediments are coarser (medium sand to gravel), except adjacent to the headlands. Much of the fine sand blanketing the summer beach is transported into Florencia Bay by violent winter waves.

Beach profiles measured by Bremner in the summer of 1968 and winter of 1969 changed in a complex fashion. Bremner (1970) attributed these changes to three controlling factors: breaker height, the position of the water table on the beach and breaker incidence angle. Breaker height controls the onshore-offshore movement of sediment. Sand is eroded from the upper foreshore and transported seaward where breakers exceed about 1 m in height, but is transported landward where breakers are smaller. Bremner observed that the intersection of the water table and the beach is the zone where profile changes are minimal. Breaker incidence angle controls the patterns of littoral currents along the beach and is thus in part responsible for the localization of accretion and erosion.

Although varying in direction somewhat with tide level, littoral drift near the middle of the beach is towards Sand Point, and at the extreme ends of the beach is away from the headlands (Fig. 24.18). Elsewhere the littoral currents vary in direction as a function of tides and wave intensity. Bremner (1970) utilized an empirical relationship similar to that devised by Caldwell (1956) and based on estimated wave energy to calculate the rate of sand transport across several profiles on the beach for one day during August 1968. The calculated littoral drift was largest near Sand Point (up to 126 m³/h) and least across profiles near the headlands (7 to 11 m³/h).

Due to the angular relationship between the prevailing wave fronts and the coast, the shoreline along the northwest half of Florencia Bay has attained an equilibrium profile approximating a logarithmic spiral (Bremner and LeBlond, 1974). Because of distortion of the incident swell by islands located in the middle of the bay, the southeast shore does not have such a log-spiral plan. However, differential erosion and deposition on the beach in that area indicate that the planimetric shape there is evolving towards a log-spiral form.

Bremner and LeBlond (1974) have further speculated on the probable evolution of the coast in the vicinity of Florencia Bay during postglacial time. During deglaciation the coast in this area may not have been embayed. However, as sea level approached its present position, erosion of unconsolidated Pleistocene sediments fronting the coast intensified, and two spiral beaches probably formed, one between the northwest headland and Florencia Island, and the other between Florencia Island and the southeast headland. When equilibrium of these spiral beaches was attained, a narrow subaerial ridge between Florencia Island and Vancouver Island may have been breached by storm waves, thereby allowing currents to pass behind the newly formed island. Erosion in this area then proceeded rapidly until Seal Rock became a resistant headland, north and south of which two new spiral beaches developed. This headland eventually was left behind as another island, and the shoreline continued to retrograde to its present configuration. Seal Rock and Florencia Island continue to exert an influence on the morphology of the beach, particularly south of Sand Point.

Figure 24.10. *Major coastal environments of the northern Insular Mountains physiographic unit. "Mixed" (rock-sediment) coastlines include rocky shorelines with patchy veneers of coarse sediment and shorelines where beach and rock reaches cannot be differentiated at the scale of the map. In general the only fiord deltas shown here and in Figures 24.11 and 24.12 are those at the heads of fiords and adjoining inlets. Smaller deltas, however, occur along the sides of many of these fiords.*

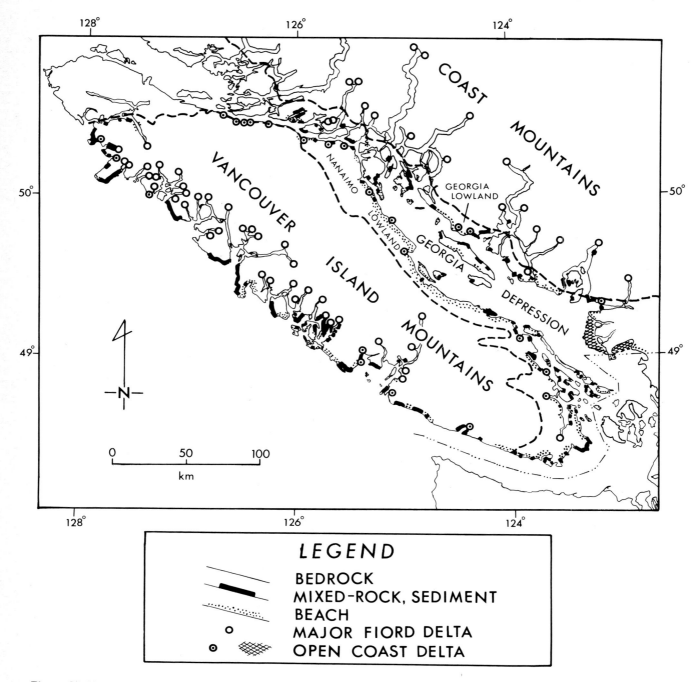

Figure 24.11. *Major coastal environments of the southern Insular and Coast mountains and the Georgia Depression.*

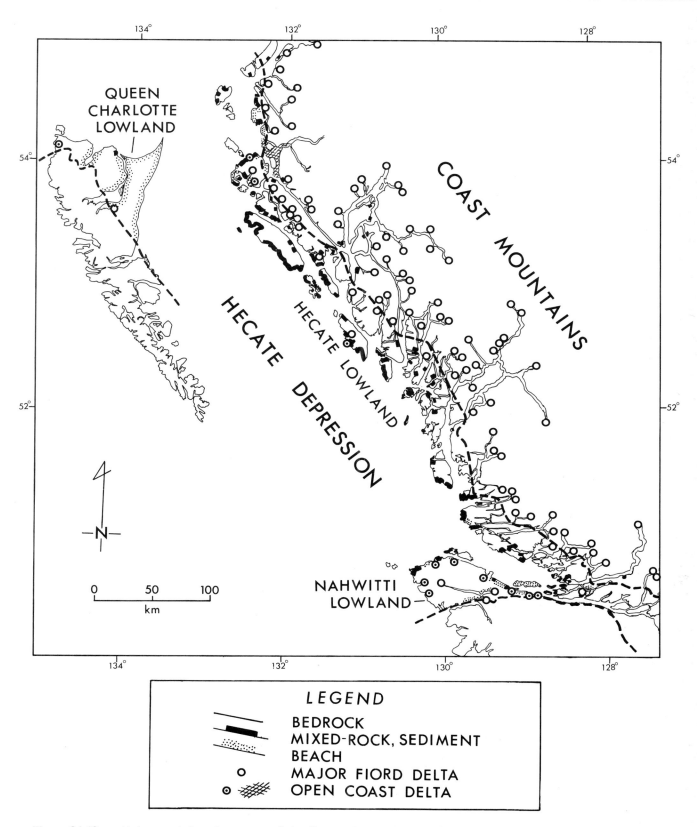

Figure 24.12.   *Major coastal environments of the Hecate Depression and northern Coast Mountains.*

Figure 24.13.   *Carmanah Point, a rocky headland on southwestern Vancouver Island. Photo BC(O)-391.*

Figure 24.14.   *(opposite)*

Representative British Columbia shorelines.

A.   *Rocky headland and broad sandy beach (background), southwestern Vancouver Island.*

B.   *Intertidal rock platform with backshore sand veneer, southwestern Vancouver Island.*

C.   *Broad sandy beach, southwestern Vancouver Island.*

D.   *Cobble-boulder beach (winter) flanked by bluff of Pleistocene sediments, southern Vancouver Island.*

E,F.   *Cobble-boulder beach veneered by sand (summer) and flanked by feeder bluffs, Strait of Georgia region.*

G,H.   *Rapidly eroding coastal bluffs, southern Vancouver Island and Point Grey, respectively.*

Figure 24.15. *Estevan Coastal Plain. View southeast from mouth of Esperanza Inlet towards Hesquiat Peninsula. Photo BC666-93.*

Figure 24.16. *Broad sandy beach of Estevan Coastal Plain, southwestern Vancouver Island. Photo BC(O)-388.*

Figure 24.17. *Photomosaic of Florencia Bay, southwestern Vancouver Island. Photos BC7237-104, 193, 194. See also Figure 24.18.*

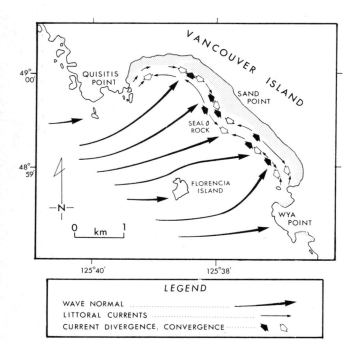

Figure 24.18. *Typical wave pattern and littoral drift directions at high and low tides, Florencia Bay. Drift directions were measured on August 2, 1968. From Bremner and LeBlond (1974, Figs. 2 and 6).*

Hecate Depression

The coastal areas of the Hecate Depression (Fig. 24.12) include the Nahwitti Lowland of northernmost Vancouver Island, the Hecate Lowland of the northern mainland, and the Queen Charlotte Lowland on the northeastern half of Graham Island.

The Nahwitti Lowland, lying north of a line between Quatsino Sound and the northwest end of Johnstone Strait, is an area of low relief below 600 m in elevation. The coastline is not highly indented with fiords and inlets typical of the west coast of Vancouver Island, but consists of shallow open embayments, commonly with rocky intertidal zones, but locally with long stretches of gravelly beach. Small deltas are numerous on this relatively open coast, and in many areas sediment is swept from river mouths along the coast in the direction of the prevailing littoral currents.

The Hecate Lowland, approximately 20 to 50 km wide, extends from Prince Rupert to Johnstone Strait and includes the islands off the northern mainland. Within the lowland is the Milbanke Strandflat, a low-lying area (in general, less than 30 m in elevation) including several islands along eastern Queen Charlotte Sound. The coastline (Fig. 24.19) is characterized by low rocky headlands and discontinuous sand, gravel and boulder beaches. The zones of beach sediments are more extensive within the strandflat than elsewhere in the Hecate Lowland.

The Queen Charlotte Lowland is a broad area of low relief, largely below 200 m in elevation. West of Masset Sound on northern Graham Island, the shoreline is developed mainly on Tertiary basaltic lavas and is irregular in shape (Fig. 24.20). However, along Virago Sound, extensive beaches have developed through erosion of unconsolidated

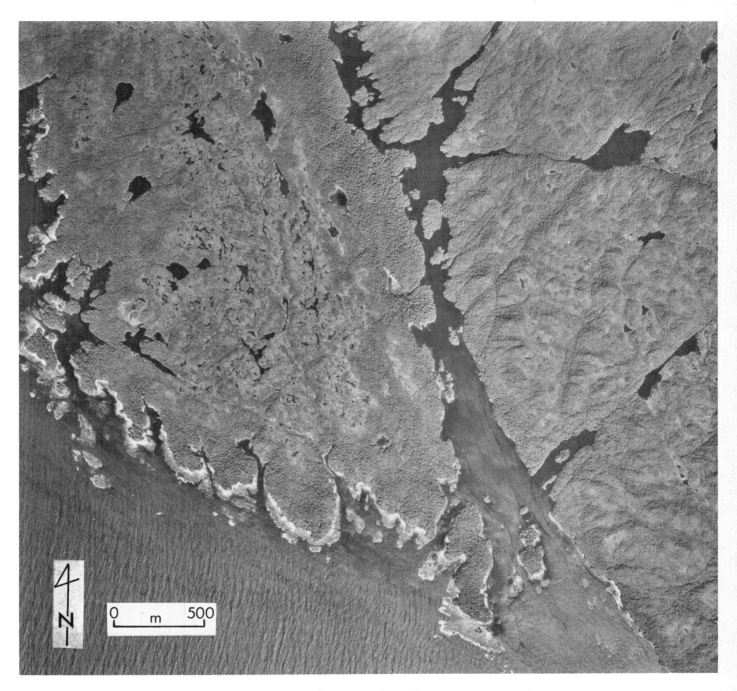

Figure 24.19. *Low relief, rocky coast of Milbanke Strandflat at east margin of Hecate Depression. Photo BC77007-006.*

sediments. That part of the Queen Charlotte Lowland east and southeast of Masset Sound, referred to as the Argonaut Plain, is underlain by thick unconsolidated sediments deposited by meltwater streams flowing northeast from a late Pleistocene ice front (Fig. 24.21). Argonaut Plain lies at or below about 175 m elevation and has only minor relief. It is along the coast bordering the Argonaut Plain that some of the most spectacular examples of evolving shoreline features in British Columbia can be found. With the exception of three small areas of bedrock, the entire distance, over 120 km, from Masset on the north coast to south of Tlell on the east coast consists of sand and gravel beaches (Figs. 24.12, 24.22).

From Masset to Rose Point at the northeast corner of Graham Island there is a continuous, wide sand beach (Fig. 24.22). The foreshore is 200 m wide with a very gentle offshore slope. The backshore consists of a series of beach ridges up to about 10 m above present sea level. Stabilized sand dunes parallel the foreshore. This northern coastal area appears, at present, to be accreting. Near Rose Point drift is towards the northeast and is contributing to the growth of a large spit (Rose Spit, Fig. 24.23). This spit has had a complex history of growth, probably beginning in early postglacial time when sea levels were relatively higher than at present.

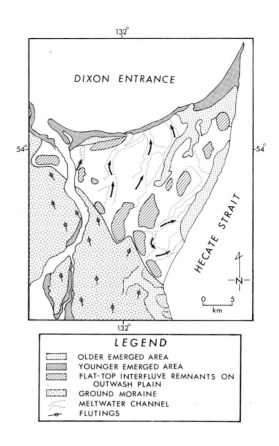

Figure 24.21. *Surficial geology of northeastern Graham Island. The extensive contemporary littoral sediments in this area are derived in part from late Pleistocene outwash (unpatterned land areas) deposited by meltwater flowing northeast from a glacier occupying the area of fluted ground moraine. Coastal areas are fringed by postglacial beach and bar systems which formed when the sea was higher relative to the land. From Sutherland Brown (1968, Fig. 2). See also Figure 24.22.*

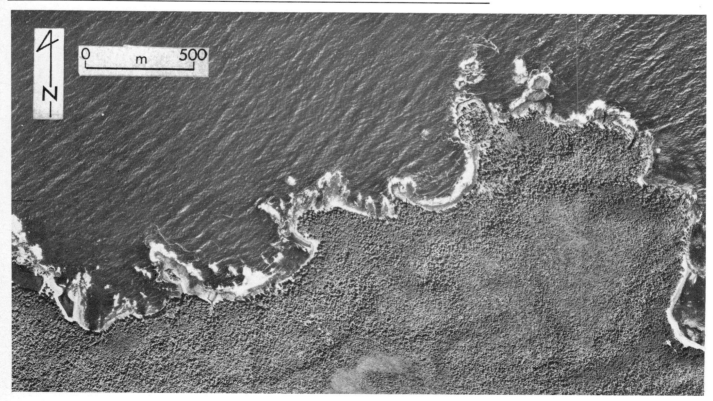

Figure 24.20.   *Irregular rocky coastline, northwestern Graham Island. Photo BC4363-159.*

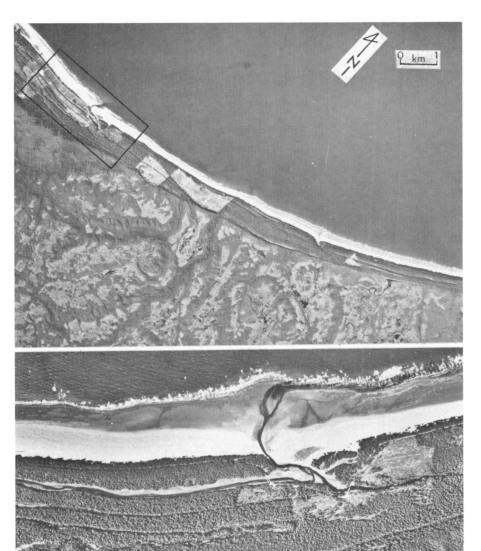

Figure 24.22

Postglacial raised beaches and dunes on north coast of Graham Island, east of Masset. These features are cut into late Pleistocene outwash (see Figure 24.21). Photos BC5630-191 (top) and BC4361-138 (bottom).

Figure 24.23. *Photomosaic of Rose Spit, eastern Graham Island. Photos BC4362-217, 218, 220.*

South of Rose Spit the foreshore area is steeper, narrower and of coarser sediment than along the north coast. Northwesterly oriented dunes are present for 100 to 200 m inland from the backshore. The east coast, in contrast to the north coast, is erosional and sediment is being actively removed from sea cliffs up to 60 m high and carried northward towards Rose Point (Fig. 24.24).

Georgia Depression

The Georgia Depression (Fig. 24.11) includes the Strait of Georgia and two marginal lowland areas, the Georgia Lowland along the mainland coast and the Nanaimo Lowland along the eastern and southern coasts of Vancouver Island. The Georgia Depression is continuous southward with the Puget Lowland in Washington State. The depression, in part structural in origin, has been extensively modified by Pleistocene glaciers, which eroded bedrock and deposited large volumes of sediment as till and stratified drift.

The Georgia Lowland is a strip of mainland 5 to 20 km wide and includes several islands in the Strait of Georgia (e.g., Texada and Quadra islands). The area is one of gently sloping upland surfaces below about 600 m elevation and underlain mainly by plutonic and Triassic sedimentary and volcanic rocks (Fig. 24.9). Major fiords cut through the lowland into the adjacent Coast Mountains to distances up to 70 km from the coast. The coastal zone is predominantly rocky, commonly with a patchy, thin sediment cover. In areas underlain by glacial sediments, there are, however, sand, gravel and boulder beaches (Figs. 24.11, 24.14E, F).

Fraser Lowland

The Fraser Lowland, included within the Georgia Lowland, extends eastward from Vancouver approximately 110 km and is bounded on the north by the Coast Mountains and on the south by the Skagit Ranges in northern Washington State. Much of this lowland is underlain by thick unconsolidated sediments, including the fluvial deposits of the Fraser River floodplain and delta, and varied glacial and nonglacial deposits of Pleistocene age.

Much of the coastal geoscience research in British Columbia has been directed towards understanding the characteristics and dynamics of the Fraser River delta system. The modern Fraser River delta, the largest deltaic complex in the province, is actively advancing into the Strait of Georgia (Fig. 24.25). The active, western front of the delta extends approximately 23 km and is fed by a network of distributary channels. Perhaps the most conspicuous features of the delta are sand and mud flats up to 6 km wide, locally crossed by distributary channels and bordered by a foreslope with an average gradient of 1.5°, but with slopes up to 23° along its inner, shallower portions (Johnston, 1921b; Mathews and Shepard, 1962; Luternauer and Murray, 1973, 1977; Scotton, 1978). Much of the western delta front is presently advancing or is in dynamic equilibrium because of the massive influx of sediment during the summer freshet (Mathews and Shepard, 1962; Luternauer and Murray, 1973). Mathews and Shepard (1962) estimated that the 7 km portion of the delta front centred on the main distributary channel is advancing horizontally about 2.3 m/a*

Figure 24.24.

Coastline of eastern Graham Island, showing strong littoral drift towards the northeast. The light-toned land area near the centre of the photo is covered by eolian sand. Photo BC4362-235.

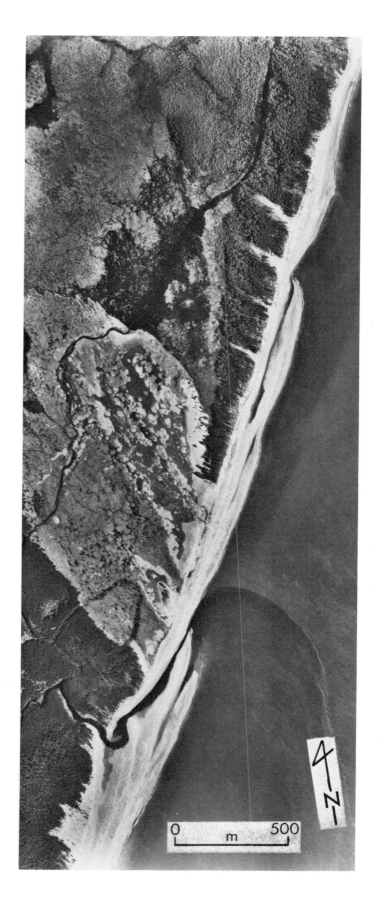

---

* a is the SI symbol for year.

Figure 24.25. *Fraser River delta. Active western delta front is separated from the inactive southern part of the delta by Point Roberts Peninsula (top). ERTS image E-1385-18365-5. The bottom photos show the most conspicuous features of the delta: the wide intertidal flats and contiguous salt marsh.*

near the low water mark, about 4.6 m/a at 38 m depth, and about 8.5 m/a at 92 m. On the other hand, Luternauer and Murray (1973) suggested that parts of the upper foreslope south of the main distributary channel have retreated horizontally as much as 12 m/a at 40 m depth between 1968 and 1972.

The inactive portion of the Fraser River delta is separated from the active delta by Point Roberts Peninsula, a ridge cored by Pleistocene sediments. This part of the delta extends approximately 13 km and includes tidal flats narrower than (approximately 4 km wide), but otherwise similar to, those of the active delta (Kellerhals and Murray, 1969). The southern foreslope, however, is less steep than the slope off the western delta front, with gradients only locally in excess of 0.3°. Principal sediment sources for the southern delta front are local rivers, eroding cliffs of Point Roberts Peninsula, and delta marshes. Some fine sediment may also be supplied in back eddies of the Fraser River.

Sediment distribution and patterns of sedimentation on the western and southern delta fronts have been summarized by Luternauer and Murray (1973, 1977) and Kellerhals and Murray (1969), respectively. On the intertidal flats there is a general gradation from sand in the lower intertidal zone to mud on the upper flats. The mud, in turn, passes into marsh. Deposits along the margins of the distributary channels are mainly fine to medium sand. Redistribution of the tidal-flat sediments by river, wave and tidal currents results in sand waves up to 1 m in height with wavelengths between 50 and 100 m. These sand waves commonly have deposits of mud in the troughs (Medley and Luternauer, 1976).

The construction of dykes, jetties and breakwaters has altered locally the natural processes on the delta. Local erosion and extension of the marsh have been induced by these structures (Medley and Luternauer, 1976; Medley, 1978; Gaspard, 1979; Hawley, 1979), although in most areas the leading edge of the marsh has remained relatively stable in position.

Seaward of the tidal flats, the upper foreslope of the active delta is primarily muddy north of the main distributary channel and sandy to the south, reflecting the dominant northward transport of Fraser River suspended sediment during freshet. Large sand waves, detected using side-scan sonar techniques, occur on portions of the foreslope (Luternauer, Swan, and Linden, 1978).

A geotechnical study of the outer tidal flats and upper foreslope of the delta (Scotton, 1978) indicated that the upper deltaic deposits have a potential for liquefaction during earthquakes. However, from laboratory analyses, Scotton concluded that the foreslope apparently is stable under static loading.

A second coastal environment in the Fraser Lowland which has been extensively studied, and yet which is completely different from the nearby Fraser River delta, is the beach-cliff system at Vancouver (Fig. 24.26). North-facing sea cliffs at Point Grey, formed largely of sand and silt, which are part of a horizontally stratified, well sorted outwash unit (Quadra Sand) exposed extensively along the coast of the Strait of Georgia, are experiencing severe erosion (Fig. 24.14H). Sediment displaced from the over-steepened sea cliffs by wind, water and gravity resides temporarily on the backshore. During periods of storm activity and high tides, the backshore apron itself is eroded, and the finer constituents of the apron (mainly sand and pebbles) are transported by littoral currents northeast and east towards Spanish Bank and possibly north into English Bay.

Recession rates of the Point Grey cliffs are locally high. By comparing surveyed maps of the cliff edge, Lum (1975) calculated an average recession rate for the part of the cliff where erosion is most severe of about 30 cm/a

between 1908 and 1974. Locally, however, average rates in excess of 60 cm/a have occurred during this interval (Fig. 24.26). More than 15 000 m³ of sediment is being eroded annually from the Point Grey cliffs (Lum, 1975) and, as a result, some buildings of the University of British Columbia located near the cliff edge are threatened.

Littoral movement of sand away from the base of the cliffs has been investigated by Eccles (1976) and Pool (1976). Both monitored beach changes at Point Grey using sequential ground-level photography and surveying. Data were correlated with wind records and predictions from wave-refraction diagrams to determine seasonal sand movement in the longshore-current direction.

The rate of sediment transport from the base of the cliffs is dramatically illustrated by the history of a sand and gravel blanket artificially emplaced to alleviate the erosion problem. The blanket was destroyed by waves, largely within one year of its construction in 1974. Sand eroded from the blanket was redeposited as a spit, which grew to a length of several hundred metres and attained a maximum volume of about 50 000 m³ (Eccles, 1976). During 1975 and 1976 the spit lengthened towards the northeast parallel to the shore and gradually evolved into a small barrier beach. The sand continued its northeast drift, and within two years of the construction of the artificial blanket the shoreline in the area had re-established its natural profile. Pool (1976) estimated that more than 30 000 ± 15 000 m³ of sand are transported annually along the beach at Point Grey by longshore currents, and speculated that some of this sand may have originated in the Fraser River rather than by erosion of the Point Grey cliffs. Tamburi and Hay (1978) likewise proposed that littoral and river currents transport Fraser River sediment northwest towards Point Grey, but that natural sediment dispersal patterns have been extensively modified by jetty and causeway construction and by dredging.

Much of the sediment eroded from the Point Grey cliffs ultimately is deposited on the broad tidal flats at Spanish Bank. However, strong littoral drift also occurs east of Spanish Bank, and there have been marked changes in shore morphology in the vicinity of Kitsilano and Jericho beaches (Fig. 24.26). Coastal structures, including groins, a wharf and a breakwater pier, have interfered with littoral transport, resulting in erosion on the east (downdrift) side and deposition on the west side of many of these structures. Dredged sediment placed on beaches in this area (average volume of fill for period from 1959 to 1968 = 5.3 x 10⁴ m³/a) also is transported east and may contribute to aggradation at shallow depths (<20 m) in the southeast corner of English Bay (Lem, 1974). However, the subtidal seafloor in this area is mainly covered by mud, which may be transported in suspension from the mouth of the Fraser River.

Finally, brief mention is made here of Pitt Lake and Pitt River, which are tributary to the Fraser River east of Vancouver. Although strictly speaking this is not a littoral system, in that the lake and river both are freshwater, tides modulate Fraser River flow and cause fluctuations in the levels of Pitt Lake and Pitt River (Ashley, 1977, 1978a, b). There is an upstream movement of sediment in the river from its confluence with the Fraser, as shown by the mineralogical similarity of Pitt and Fraser river sediments, by a decrease in grain size from the Fraser River to Pitt Lake, and by the dominance of tidal-flood bedforms in the river channel. This upstream movement of sediment has resulted in the formation of a 12 km² tidal delta at the draining end of the lake. Rhythmically layered silt and clay of the delta have been interpreted as varves, with the coarse layers deposited during winter when Fraser River discharge is low and tidally induced discharge into Pitt Lake is high, and the fine layers deposited during freshet when additional fines are added to the lake from the Pitt drainage basin (Ashley, 1977).

Nanaimo Lowland

The Nanaimo Lowland is a narrow strip of coastal plain, below 600 m in elevation and less than 30 km in width, extending along eastern Vancouver Island from Johnstone Strait on the north to Victoria on the south, and from Victoria to Jordon River on the west.

The coastline north of Nanaimo consists largely of low-gradient broad sand and gravel beaches, derived mainly through erosion of abundant unconsolidated sediments underlying the lowland. Two large deltas have developed along this part of the coast at Comox and Nanaimo. South of Nanaimo more bedrock and mixed sediment-rock intertidal zones occur, but these are interspersed with local broad beaches. In contrast to the Georgia Lowland, the east coast of Vancouver Island is not a fiord coastline; only one large fiord, Saanich Inlet, occurs in this physiographic region.

Differential erosion of nonresistant sedimentary rocks has resulted in highly indented coastlines on southern Vancouver Island and on adjacent islands at the south end of the Strait of Georgia (Fig. 24.27).

The Nanaimo Lowland exhibits some of the most interesting and dynamic littoral features on the British Columbia coast. In this area there is an abundant supply of sediments to the littoral zone from erosion of Quaternary sediments which underlie much of the lowland (Fig. 24.14D, G). In many areas these sediments are actively transported along the coast by strong littoral currents and, as a result, broad beaches, spits and bars are common (Figs. 24.28, 24.29, 24.30).

An example of such a dynamic environment is the Balmoral Beach-Goose Spit system near Comox (Figs. 24.31, 24.32; Clague, 1976b). Southeast-facing sea cliffs about 2 km long and up to 70 m high are being severely eroded by waves. As a result of wave erosion, the cliffs are unable to attain an equilibrium slope and other erosional processes, including mass movement, gullying by water flowing down the cliff faces and possibly piping, contribute to continued instability.

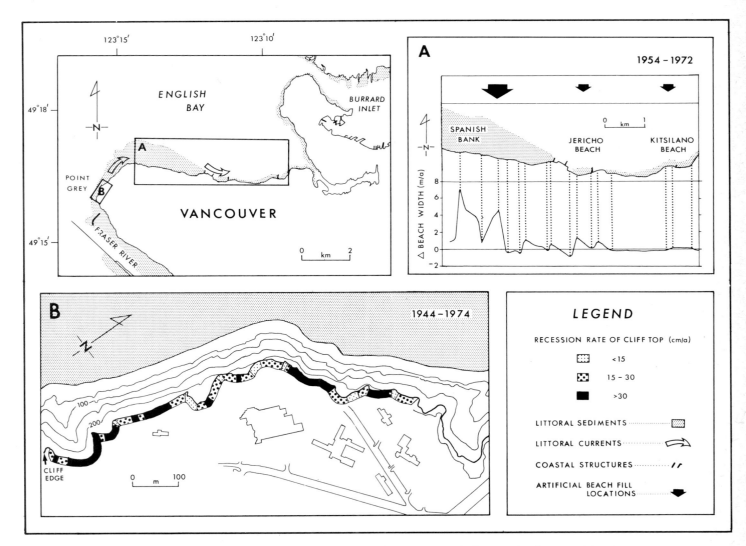

Figure 24.26. *Shoreline changes at Vancouver. Average annual changes in shore position between 1954 and 1972 are plotted in A. These changes occurred in response to the interception of easterly moving littoral sediment by man-made structures and in response to the emplacement and subsequent drift of artificial beach fill. Rates of recession of the cliff top at Point Grey from 1944 to 1974 are shown in B. From Lem (1974, Fig. 3) and Lum (1975, Fig. 4).*

Figure 24.27. *Porlier Pass, a relatively narrow, rocky passage in the southern Georgia Depression, is characterized by high tidal velocities. The pass is oriented almost perpendicular to the strike of sedimentary rocks which form the irregular shoreline. Photo A19187-16.*

As at Point Grey, sediment accumulates at the base of the cliff as a backshore apron, and is entrained by waves and transported by littoral currents. The apron is prominent in summer and fall but is generally absent in winter when storm waves cut directly into the cliff-forming Pleistocene sediments. A cobble-boulder pavement, representing the concentrated coarse fraction of sediment eroded from the sea cliffs, forms the beach during winter; this coarse sediment is largely blanketed by sand during summer. Sediment entrained at the base of the cliffs by waves is transported by littoral currents in a southwesterly direction. Goose Spit is maintained by this sediment, and its morphology is controlled in part by the combined effects of longshore currents, tidal flow in and out of Comox Harbour, and freshwater flow from the mouth of Courtenay River southeast into the Strait of Georgia (Clague, 1976b).

Although no measurements have been made of the rate of cliff recession at Balmoral Beach, rates of coastal recession have been determined for other areas of the Nanaimo Lowland, specifically for Saanich Peninsula on southeastern Vancouver Island. Foster (1976) has shown that some coastal areas on the peninsula that are underlain by unconsolidated sediments are receding at rates in excess of 30 cm/a (Fig. 24.33). Accretive landforms, mainly spits, are adjacent to many of the rapidly eroding sea cliffs in this area, as for example near Colwood and Sooke west of Victoria, and near Saanichton and on James and Sidney islands north of Victoria (Figs. 24.28, 24.29).

The deltas of the Nanaimo Lowland have not been extensively studied despite their proximity to urban and recreational areas. Notable exceptions include the Oyster River delta (Hay and Secter, 1978) and the Nanaimo River delta (Leroux, 1979) where photogrammetry has been used to document historical changes in delta and river mouth morphology and to map morpho-sedimentological domains.

Coast Mountains

The Coast Mountains lie east of the Hecate and Georgia depressions (Figs. 24.11, 24.12) and contain the heads of the fiords and inlets which dominate the British Columbia mainland coast. This region is underlain by granitic rocks of the Coast Crystalline Complex and, to a lesser extent, by sedimentary, volcanic and metamorphic rocks, mainly of Paleozoic and Mesozoic age (Fig. 24.9).

The Coast Mountains are divisible into three systems of ranges. From north to south, these are the Boundary Ranges, the Kitimat Ranges and the Pacific Ranges.

The Boundary Ranges, with elevations near the coast in excess of 2500 m, have a high proportion of glacier-covered area. Some glaciers in the Boundary Ranges terminate in the sea at the heads of fiords in southeastern Alaska.

The Kitimat Ranges, in general less than 2200 m in elevation in coastal areas, extend from the Nass River - Portland Inlet area at the north to the Bella Coola - Burke Channel area on the south. These mountains have less ice cover than the ranges to either north or south. Characteristic of the Kitimat Ranges are large lineaments, which are associated with long, straight, narrow valleys and channels. In general one set of lineaments trends northwest-southeast and the other northeast-southwest.

The Skeena River delta, second in size in British Columbia only to the Fraser, lies along the western limit of the northern Kitimat Ranges. This delta is unusual in being neither at the head of an inlet nor adjacent to a large open body of water, and in exhibiting no extensive tidal flats (Hoos, 1975). The Skeena River enters Chatham Sound and several channels adjoining Hecate Strait. In its lower reaches, the river is confined by precipitous valley walls, but is up to 3 km wide. River flow is divided by a series of passages located between islands off the river mouth. The

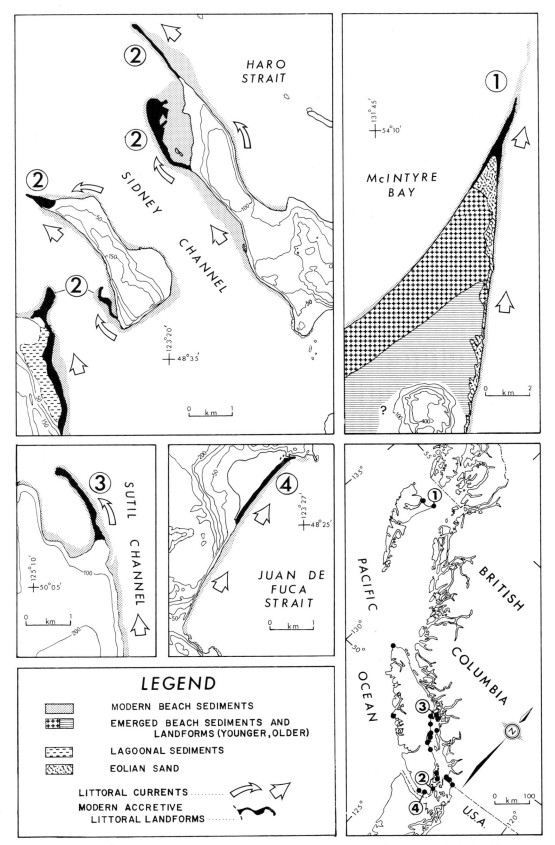

Figure 24.28. *Representative modern and ancient accretive littoral landforms of the British Columbia coast. The index map (lower right) shows the distribution of major, active spits and tombolos. Note that most of these occur in the Georgia Depression.*

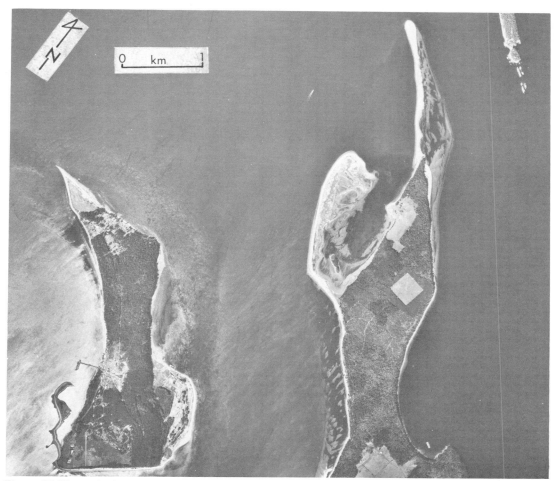

Figure 24.29. *Active spits on James and Sidney islands. Littoral drift is towards the northwest. Compare with Figure 24.28 (area 2). Photo BC5057-95.*

Figure 24.30. *Littoral bars, southeastern Vancouver Island. These bars are nourished in part by sediment transported by currents into the bay from the river mouth at the left edge of the photo. Photo BC7047-238.*

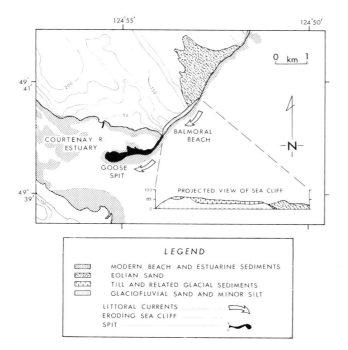

Figure 24.31. *Goose Spit-Balmoral Beach system, eastern Vancouver Island. See also Figure 24.32.*

delta front of the Skeena River extends for 30 km in approximately a north-south direction and joins the west sides of Ridley, Smith, Kennedy and Gibson islands (Luternauer, 1976b). To the west of the delta front, seafloor sediments are predominantly mud, whereas sediments on the banks and channel bottoms east and north of the slope break are mainly sand (Fig. 24.34). The margins of river channels are underlain by organic-rich mud and muddy gravel.

River flow and tidal currents have shaped sediments at the Skeena River mouth into extensive bars with megarippled surfaces. The megaripples, with wave heights and lengths as large as 0.5 m and 10 m, respectively, are produced by currents which attain velocities in excess of 1.5 m/s (Luternauer, 1976b).

Southernmost of the three major units of the Coast Mountains, the Pacific Ranges contain the highest peaks, which rise to more than 3000 m elevation. The higher areas are extensively covered by glacier ice.

The most striking feature of the British Columbia mainland coast is the system of fiords dissecting the rugged Coast Mountains (Fig. 24.35). Individual fiords range in width from 1 to 5 km and project over 100 km inland. Shorelines along fiords are predominantly steeply inclined; beaches are rare, short, and gravelly. Small and intermediate-size deltas are common (Figs. 24.11, 24.12, 24.36). Some at the fiord heads have extensive mud flats and tidal marshes upon which much of the development on this part of the coast has taken place. Stewart, Kitimat, Bella Coola, and Squamish are the larger communities located on or adjacent to fiord-head deltas.

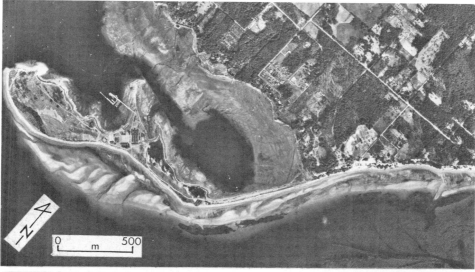

Figure 24.32.

Goose Spit — vertical (top) and ground-level (bottom) photographs. The latter is a view towards the west from the neck of the spit. Top photo BC7077-148.

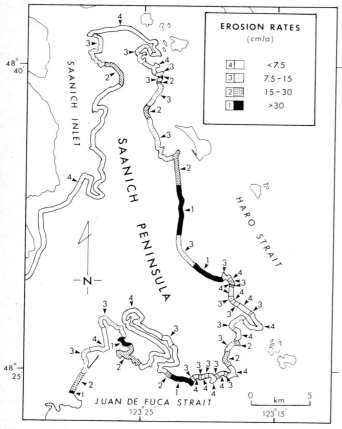

Figure 24.33. *Coastal erosion rates on Saanich Peninsula, southeast Vancouver Island. From Foster (1976, Fig. 14.4).*

The two fiord-head deltas which have been studied are those of the Squamish and Kitimat rivers (Mathews and Murray, 1966; L.M. Bell, 1975; Hoos and Vold, 1975; Bell and Kallman, 1976c). Both are rapidly prograding deltas comprising tidal flats dissected by distributary channels and terminating in foreslopes, the upper portions of which are inclined on the average about 10°. The tidal flat sediments are variable in texture, ranging from sand and gravel in active distributary channels and bars to mud in marsh areas and abandoned distributaries. Foreslope sediments are also texturally variable. For example, those on the western foreslope of the Squamish River delta are predominantly sand, whereas on most other parts of the foreslope the sediments are muddy (Mathews and Murray, 1966; L.M. Bell, 1975). Rates of advance of the Squamish Delta front have been determined by L.M. Bell (1975). Between 1930 and 1973 the western front advanced at an average rate of 6.5 m/a at a depth of 18 m, 5.7 m/a at a depth of 37 m, and 4.5 m/a at 55 m.

Sediment distribution and dispersal patterns on some fiord-head deltas, notably the Squamish and Kitimat deltas, have been extensively affected by dredging activities and by construction of river-training dykes, dock and rail facilities. For example, a former major distributary channel of the Squamish River is no longer active, as a result of construction of a training dyke. Squamish River flow is now confined to the western part of the delta and the former distributary channel is a site of mud deposition.

Major submarine slope failures have occurred on or near fiord deltas, for example, near Kitimat and Squamish. The extent and character of submarine mass-movement deposits at the head of Douglas Channel near Kitimat have been documented using echo-sounding and side-scan sonar techniques by Luternauer and Swan (1978), Swan (1978) and Swan and Luternauer (1978).

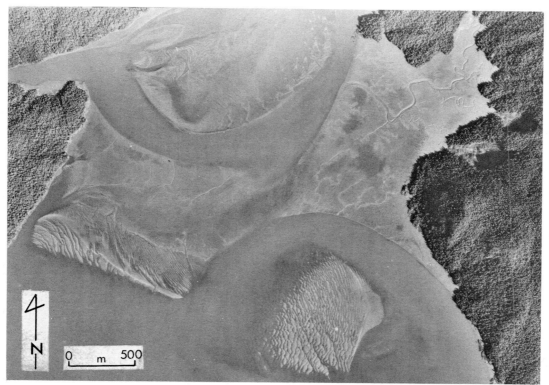

Figure 24.34. *Mudflats, megarippled bars, and channels located between rocky islands at the mouth of the Skeena River. Photo BC77100-130.*

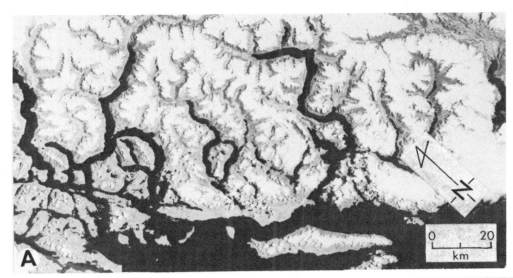

A. Southern mainland northeast of the Strait of Georgia, showing large fiords extending into the rugged Coast Mountains. Landsat image 2-0508-18245.

B. Cousins Inlet, a typical fiord of the central mainland coast. Photo A3290-90.

Figure 24.35.   Fiords of British Columbia.

Summary of coastal environments

The coastal zone of each of the major physiographic units discussed above has specific morphological characteristics, littoral sediments and energy regimes (Table 24.3). On a general level, coastlines of the three major physiographic regions differ because of fundamental differences in bedrock geology and because of the varying impact of Pleistocene glaciers. Rugged, high-relief, rocky shorelines occur throughout the mountainous regions because of the dominance of resistant rocks and the scarcity of Pleistocene unconsolidated sediments. In contrast, unconsolidated sediments and less resistant rocks underlie much of the Coastal Trough, and beaches and related features are most common there. With this in mind, we can now briefly summarize the coastal environments of each of the major physiographic regions.

The coastline of the Insular Mountains is mainly rocky and irregular. Fiords, inlets and islands characterize the coastal zone. Littoral sediments in general are rare and the intertidal zone narrow, except at fiord deltas and along part of western Vancouver Island where wide sand beaches occur adjacent to lowlands underlain by thick unconsolidated sediments. Wave energy along the exposed outer coast exceeds that of any other coastal area; however, in the fiords and sheltered embayments energy levels are relatively low.

In contrast, the coastal zone of the Hecate and Georgia depressions is characterized by a mix of rocky shorelines, beaches and deltas. Fiords are fewer, and the coast is more regular and lower in relief than in the bordering Insular and Coast mountains. Most of the shorelines of the Queen Charlotte and northern Nanaimo lowlands are sand and gravel beaches nourished through erosion of sea cliffs cored by unconsolidated sediments. Accretive landforms, mainly spits and bars, are far more common in these areas than elsewhere on the British Columbia coast. Littoral currents are strong, and wave energy is intermediate between that of the outer coast and the fiords. The Georgia and southern

Figure 24.36. *Fiord-head delta east of Prince Rupert. Photo BC77100-119.*

Table 24.3. Generalized physical characteristics and energy levels of the Pacific coastal zone

Physiographic region	Littoral environment	Shoreline morphology*	Littoral sediment source**	Wave energy[†]	Littoral current energy[†]
Insular Mountains					
Queen Charlotte Mountains	rocky, *delta*	2	2	1,2,3	3
Vancouver Island Mountains	rocky, *delta*	2	2	1,2,3	3
Estevan Coastal Plain	rocky, beach	1	1	1,2,3	2(?)
Coastal Trough					
Hecate Depression					
Queen Charlotte Lowland	beach, *rocky*	3,*1*	1	2,3	1
Hecate Lowland	rocky, *beach, delta*	1,*3*	1,2	2,3	2(?)
Nahwitti Lowland	rocky, *beach, delta*	1,*3*	1,2	2	2(?)
Georgia Depression					
Nanaimo Lowland	beach, rocky, *delta*	3,*1*	1,2	2,3	1
Georgia Lowland	beach, rocky, delta	3,*1*	1,2	2,3	1
Coast Mountains	rocky, *delta*	2	2	3	3

Note: Dominant environments and characteristics in roman type; subordinate environments and characteristics in italic type.
* 1. Irregular coastline characterized by passages, inlets and embayments; backshore relief relatively low; intertidal zone generally narrow but locally wide. 2. Fiord coastline; backshore relief high and intertidal zone narrow except at deltas. 3. Nonembayed coast; backshore relief relatively low, except for coastal bluffs; intertidal zone relatively wide.
** 1. Sea cliffs comprising unconsolidated sediments. 2. Rivers; sparse littoral sediment in rocky areas is in large part relict.
† 1. High. 2. Moderate. 3. Low.

Nanaimo lowlands have an overall lower proportion of beaches and a higher proportion of rocky shorelines than the Queen Charlotte and northern Nanaimo lowlands. However, beaches in all four areas are similar and their morphology and sediments are controlled by similar environmental factors. The other areas of the Coastal Trough, including the Nahwitti Lowland and Milbanke Strandflat, have dominantly rocky shorelines, subject to moderate and high energy levels. Sand and gravel beaches exist in a few areas where thick Pleistocene sediments occur adjacent to the coast or where the input of fluvial detritus is high.

The coastal zone of the Coast Mountains is characterized by high-relief, narrow, rocky intertidal areas and a scarcity of littoral sediments, except where deltas are forming at the heads or sides of fiords. Wave and littoral current energy levels are lower than in other physiographic regions.

PAST COASTAL ENVIRONMENTS

Past Pacific coastal environments in British Columbia have differed markedly from those of the present. At Pleistocene glacial maxima much of British Columbia, including the present coastal region, was ice-covered, with till deposited in many coastal areas and rocks and sediments eroded in others. During the waxing and waning phases of each glaciation, thick stratified drift was deposited in contact with, and at varying distances in front of, glaciers. In contrast, during nonglacial intervals drift deposits in part were reworked by rivers, waves and currents to produce diverse littoral sediments and landforms.

The paleogeography of the British Columbia coastal zone prior to the last, or late Wisconsinan, glaciation is poorly known, although there is strong evidence that at least locally it was strikingly different from that of the present. For example, early Wisconsinan and older marine and glaciomarine sediments are extensive above present sea level beneath coastal lowlands of the Georgia Depression, indicating the existence of relative high sea levels at various times prior to the Holocene. In addition much of what is now the Strait of Georgia perhaps was a floodplain, rather than a marine environment, as recently as about 20 000 to 25 000 years ago prior to the late Wisconsinan glacial maximum (Fyles, 1963; Clague, 1976a, 1977).

The evolution of the British Columbia coastal zone from the end of the last glaciation to the present has been documented in general terms by Mathews et al. (1970) and Clague (1975). Other papers, reports and theses containing information on past postglacial coastal environments are cited in the bibliography of this paper. The following is a brief summary of the postglacial development of the coast, with emphasis on changes in land-sea positions.

The present major physiographic elements of coastal British Columbia were well established by the close of the last glaciation. Large areas of the present coastal lowlands, however, were submerged during deglaciation because of isostatic depression of the crust. Stratified and non-stratified drift was deposited over much of this area as glaciers withdrew. In the Georgia and Hecate depressions and in the fiords of the Coast Mountains, for example, marine and glaciomarine muds were deposited both above and below present sea level. Recessional outwash bodies were built out into the sea and were graded to the relative high sea levels of early postglacial time.

The postglacial marine limit decreases in elevation from the inner coast towards the outer coast in the direction of decreasing late Wisconsinan ice thicknesses. For example, it is at least 200 m near Vancouver and Kitimat on the inner coast, about 75 m near Victoria, but probably less than 30 m on the Queen Charlotte Islands on the outer coast (Armstrong, 1966; Mathews et al., 1970; Clague, 1975; Alley and Thomson, 1978). Marine limits on the British Columbia coast are diachronous, related in part to the time-transgressive nature of deglaciation and in part to the complex interaction of isostatic, eustatic and diastrophic factors in different areas. Thus maximum marine submergence in the Georgia Depression occurred approximately 12 500 to 13 000 years BP, whereas in the Terrace-Kitimat area, which was deglaciated somewhat later, maximum submergence was about 10 500 to 11 000 years BP (Fulton, 1971; Clague, 1975). In contrast, sea levels may have been below those of the present in the vicinity of the Queen Charlotte Islands during the closing phase of the late Wisconsinan glaciation, perhaps because of the dominance of eustatic over isostatic effects in that area. Sea levels subsequently rose, but the postglacial marine maximum on the Queen Charlotte Islands was not attained until well after that on the inner coast (Sutherland Brown, 1968; Nasmith, 1970; Clague, 1975; Fladmark, 1975; Alley and Thomson, 1978).

Deglaciation was accompanied and succeeded by isostatic rebound. The rate of rebound exceeded that of the coeval eustatic sea level rise in most coastal areas, resulting in a relative fall in sea level. Although emergence in some regions perhaps was interrupted by short intervals when sea level, in a relative sense, was stable or rising (Mathews et al., 1970), the land-sea boundary was near its present location in most areas by about 8000 to 10 000 years BP. Exceptions are parts of the outer coast (e.g., Queen Charlotte Islands and perhaps western Vancouver Island) where the sea remained relatively higher than at present during most of postglacial time. Sea levels apparently continued to fall on the inner coast and were up to about 10 m lower than at present in the vicinity of the Strait of Georgia between about 6000 and 9000 years BP. During the past 5500 years sea levels have not fluctuated significantly on the inner coast, but have been perhaps a few metres below present sea level. In contrast, the sea was higher on at least parts of the outer coast during this interval. The differences in sea level history of these two areas is likely due to differential vertical tectonic movements resulting from the interaction of crustal plates on the Pacific continental margin.

Postglacial shifts in land-sea positions have strongly affected the evolution of the present shoreline. Drift deposits in lowland areas of the inner coastal zone were reworked by waves and currents as sea level fell relative to the land during the first few thousand years following deglaciation. Raised marine deltas, beaches and other shoreline features provide evidence of the rapid, isostatically controlled emergence of the coastal lowland during this interval. These features continued to develop at progressively lower elevations along the inner coast, at many places below present sea level after about 9000 years BP. During late postglacial time sea levels rose along the inner coast, accompanied by reworking of pre-existing littoral sediments and shoreline features and by recession of the coastline in areas underlain by unconsolidated sediments. Tide gauge records show a continuing transgression on the inner coast attributable to the worldwide shrinkage of glaciers or to tectonic subsidence (Mathews et al., 1970; De Jong and Siebenhuener, 1972). Erosion and sediment reworking accompanying this transgression play important roles in controlling coastline morphology and the disposition of littoral sediments in most beach areas of the Coastal Trough.

In contrast, modern beaches on the north coast of Graham Island apparently are prograding, perhaps because of tectonic uplift and thus a relative fall in sea level.

Sutherland Brown (1968, p. 35, 36) recognized two major complexes of raised shoreline deposits and landforms (Fig. 24.21) and attributed their formation to progressive emergence during postglacial time. The upper complex is thought to date from about 4000 to 9500 years BP, and the lower is dated archeologically as younger than 3000 years old (Fladmark, 1975, p. 158). Below the lower complex are undated wave-cut benches at present high tide.

In conclusion, the present shoreline reflects, among other things, the effects of postglacial sea level changes. The late postglacial transgresssion on the inner coast has resulted locally in recession of the coastline and in the reworking of older littoral materials. In contrast, abundant deltaic and littoral sediments were deposited on isostatically depressed, inner coast lowlands during early postglacial time. And finally, some beach areas on the outer coast, where tectonic uplift exceeds the late postglacial eustatic sea level rise, are prograding.

Changes in land-sea positions are continuing on the British Columbia coast and reflect the interplay of diastrophic and eustatic adjustments. Geodetic and tide gauge data indicate that the sea is rising relative to the land on the southern inner coast at a maximum rate of about 3 mm/a (de Jong and Siebenhuener, 1972). At least part of this rise cannot be attributed to eustacy, since differential movements in land-sea positions have been detected. For example, the rise is greater at Vancouver than at Victoria, suggesting that the former site is sinking relative to the latter (Mathews et al., 1970). Furthermore, comparison of the elevations of resurveyed benchmarks in the Fraser Lowland near Vancouver indicates downward movement of almost all stations, and an increase in the rate of displacement southward across the International Boundary (Mathews et al., 1970). Assuming an average eustatic sea level rise of 1.0 mm/a, de Jong and Siebenhuener (1972) determined absolute vertical land movements at various stations. They concluded that the Victoria area probably is being uplifted at present, whereas the Vancouver and Prince Rupert areas are subsiding at rates between 1 and 2 mm/a.

CONCLUSIONS

Contemporary coastal environments of Pacific Canada are controlled by the structure and lithology of the western Canadian Cordillera, by Pleistocene glacial erosion and deposition, and by the wave and current regimes of the eastern North Pacific Ocean. Wave and current patterns, of course, are affected by the configuration of the coastline itself, thus the above factors to some extent are interdependent.

The shorelines of the Insular Mountains and Coast Mountains are dominantly rocky and rugged, and intertidal zones commonly narrow. However, broad sand beaches are extensive between rocky headlands along the Estevan Coastal Plain of western Vancouver Island. These beaches are nourished by erosion of unconsolidated sediments and, possibly, weakly consolidated rocks fronting the coast. Much of the coastline of the Insular and Coast mountains is in steep-walled fiords and, although energy levels are relatively low in these areas, littoral sediments are scarce except where deltas are forming.

In contrast, broad beaches, spits and bars are common in parts of the Coastal Trough, particularly the Nanaimo and Queen Charlotte lowlands, where thick unconsolidated sediments supply abundant detritus to the littoral zone. This detritus is transported by strong littoral currents, the direction of transport conforming to the direction of the dominant local winds. Large deltas, such as the Fraser and Skeena, are forming in the Coastal Trough under somewhat higher energy conditions than exist in the fiords. However, where wave and current energy is sufficiently high, or where the input of fluvial sediment is too low, deltas do not form; rather, fluvial sediment is swept from river mouths along the shore in the direction of littoral transport.

Present coastal environments also have been influenced by postglacial sea level changes. Following the late Wisconsinan glacial maximum a marine transgression to a maximum elevation of about 200 m occurred on the inner coast. During this and the following regressive phase, which resulted in large part from isostatic adjustments in the crust, voluminous stratified and nonstratified drift was deposited locally in many coastal areas. This drift was the source of much of the littoral sediments deposited during subsequent postglacial time. Middle and late Holocene sea levels apparently were relatively lower than at present on the inner coast, but higher than at present on parts of the outer coast. The late postglacial rise in sea level on the inner coast has resulted in reworking of older littoral sediments and erosion of the coastline in areas underlain by unconsolidated sediments. In contrast, beaches on the north coast of Graham Island apparently are prograding, because of a probable continuing relative fall in sea level on the outer coast.

Adjustments in land-sea positions are continuing, and the sea is rising relative to the land on the inner coast. Part of this rise may be eustatic in nature, although observed differential movements in land-sea positions indicate that tectonism also is involved. Future sea level changes will affect the equilibrium of the coastal zone by enhancing or retarding wave erosion of existing shoreline features and by altering the morphology and thus the dynamics of beach and delta areas.

Acknowledgments

Drafts of this paper were critically read by J.L. Luternauer and R.E. Thomson.

Selected bibliography*

Ages, A. and Woollard, A.
1976: The tides in the Fraser Estuary; Canada Department of Environment, Institute of Ocean Sciences, Pacific Marine Science Report 76-5, 100 p.

Alley, N.F. and Thomson, B.
1978: Aspects of environmental geology, parts of Graham Island, Queen Charlotte Islands; British Columbia Ministry of Environment, Resource Analysis Branch, Bulletin 2, 65 p.

Andrews, J.T. and Retherford, R.M.
1978: A reconnaissance survey of late Quaternary sea levels, Bella Bella/Bella Coola region, central British Columbia coast; Canadian Journal of Earth Sciences, v. 15, no. 3, p. 341 - 350.

Armstrong, J.E.
1966: Glacial studies, Kitimat-Terrace area; in Report of Activities, May to October, 1965; Geological Survey of Canada, Paper 66-1, p. 50.

Armstrong, J.E. and Brown, W.L.
1954: Late Wisconsin marine drift and associated sediments of the lower Fraser Valley, British Columbia, Canada; Geological Society of America Bulletin, v. 65, no. 4, p. 349 - 363.

Armstrong, J.E., Crandell, D.R., Easterbrook, D.J. and Noble, J.B.
1965: Late Pleistocene stratigraphy and chronology in southwestern British Columbia and northwestern Washington; Geological Society of America Bulletin, v. 76, no. 3, p. 321 - 330.

Ashley, G.M.
1977: Sedimentology of a freshwater tidal system, Pitt River - Pitt Lake, British Columbia; unpubl. Ph.D. thesis, University of British Columbia, Vancouver, 404 p.
1978a: Bedforms in the Pitt River, British Columbia; in Fluvial Sedimentology, A.D. Miall, ed.; Canadian Society of Petroleum Geologists, Memoir 5, p. 89 - 104.
1978b: Interpretation of polymodal sediments; Journal of Geology, v. 86, no. 4, p. 411 - 421.

Backler, B.E.
1960: A ground-water and soil-mechanic's investigation of the erosional problem of the Pt. Grey sea cliffs; unpubl. B.A.Sc. thesis, University of British Columbia, Department of Geological Engineering, Vancouver, 101 p.

Barber, F.G.
1957a: Observation of currents north of Triangle Island, B.C.; Fisheries Research Board of Canada, Pacific Coast Stations, Progress Report 108, p. 15 - 18.
1957b: The effect of the prevailing winds on the inshore water masses of the Hecate Strait region, B.C.; Fisheries Research Board of Canada Journal, v. 14, no. 6, p. 945 - 952.
1958: Currents and water structure in Queen Charlotte Sound, British Columbia; 9th Pacific Science Congress, Proceedings, v. 16, p. 196 - 199.

Bell, L.M.
1975: Factors influencing the sedimentary environments of the Squamish River delta in southwestern British Columbia; unpubl. M.A.Sc. thesis, University of British Columbia, Vancouver, 145 p.

Bell, L.M. and Kallman, R.J.
1976a: The Cowichan-Chemainus River estuaries, status of environmental knowledge to 1975; Canada Department of Environment, Regional Board, Pacific Region, Estuary Working Group, Special Estuary Series, no. 4, 328 p.
1976b: The Nanaimo River estuary, status of environmental knowledge to 1976; Canada Department of Environment, Regional Board, Pacific Region, Estuary Working Group, Special Estuary Series, no. 5, 298 p.
1976c: The Kitimat River estuary, status of environmental knowledge to 1976; Canada Department of Environment, Regional Board, Pacific Region, Estuary Working Group, Special Estuary Series, no. 6, 296 p.

Bell, L.M. and Thompson, J.M.
1977: The Campbell River estuary, status of environmental knowledge to 1977; Canada Department of Fisheries and Environment, Regional Board, Pacific Region, Estuary Working Group, Special Estuary Series, no. 7, 346 p.

Bell, W.H.
1963: Surface current studies in the Hecate Model; Fisheries Research Board of Canada, Manuscript Report 159 (Oceanographic and Limnological Series), 27p.
1975: The Howe Sound current metering program; Canada Department of Environment, Institute of Ocean Sciences, Pacific Marine Science Report 75-7, 4 volumes, 1321 p.

Bennett, E.B.
1959: Some oceanographic features of the northeast Pacific Ocean during August 1955; Fisheries Research Board of Canada Journal, v. 16, no. 5, p. 565 - 633. Also (1958) M.A. thesis, University of British Columbia, Vancouver, 61 p.

Black, W.H.
1978: Processes affecting shore stability on Oaks Point, North Thormanby Island, B.C.; unpubl. B.A.Sc. thesis, University of British Columbia, Department of Geological Engineering, Vancouver, 81 p.

Boisvert, W.E.
1969: Major currents off the west coasts of North and South America; United States Naval Oceanographic Office, Technical Report TR-221, 37 p.

Bourne, D.R.
1974: Trace element distribution in bottom sediments of Port Moody Inlet, Port Moody, B.C.; unpubl. B.Sc. thesis, University of British Columbia, Department of Geological Sciences, Vancouver, 79 p.

Bremner, J.M.
1970: The geology of Wreck Bay, Vancouver Island; unpubl. M.Sc. thesis, University of British Columbia, Vancouver, 243 p.

Bremner, J.M. and LeBlond, P.H.
1974: On the planimetric shape of Wreck Bay, Vancouver Is.; Journal of Sedimentary Petrology, v. 44, no. 4, p. 1155 - 1165. Discussion by W.F. Tanner in (1976) Journal of Sedimentary Petrology, v. 46, no. 1, p. 258, 259; reply by P.H. LeBlond and J.M. Bremner in (1976) Journal of Sedimentary Petrology, v. 46, no. 1, p. 259 - 261.

Buckley, J.R.
1976: Currents, winds and tides of northern Howe Sound; unpubl. Ph.D. thesis, University of British Columbia, Vancouver, 228 p.

Buckley, J.R. and Pond, S.
1976: Wind and the surface circulation of a fjord; Fisheries Research Board of Canada Journal, v. 33, no. 10, p. 2265 - 2271.

Byrne, P.
1978: An evaluation of the liquefaction potential of the Fraser Delta; Canadian Geotechnical Journal, v. 15, no. 1, p. 32 - 46.

Caldwell, J.M.
1956: Wave action and sand movement near Anaheim Bay, California; United States Army Corps of Engineers, B.E.B. Technical Memorandum 68, p. 1 - 19.

* Includes published papers and maps, readily available manuscript reports, and thesis concerned only or partly with (1) contemporary British Columbia, littoral sediments, littoral processes, and coastal geomorphology, (2) past Pacific coastal environments and (3) surface and non surface currents, water circulation patterns and waves which directly or indirectly affect the British Columbia coastline.

Canada Department of Environment
1972a: Data record of current observations, Strait of Georgia, Cape Lazo to Grief Point, 1970; Marine Sciences Directorate, Pacific Region, Manuscript Report Series, v. 9, 88 p.

1972b: Data record of current observations, Strait of Georgia, Gabriola Island to Gower Point, 1969 - 1972; Marine Sciences Directorate, Pacific Region, Manuscript Report Series, v. 10, 153 p.

1972c: Data record of current observations, Strait of Georgia, Porlier Pass to Sand Heads, 1969 - 1972; Marine Sciences Directorate, Pacific Region, Manuscript Report Series, v. 11, 124 p.

1973a: Data record of current observations, Strait of Georgia, Samuel Island to Point Roberts, 1969 - 1970; Marine Sciences Directorate, Pacific Region, Manuscript Report Series, v. 12, 96 p.

1973b: Data record of current observations, Strait of Georgia, Northwest Bay to McNaughton Point, 1968 - 1969; Marine Sciences Directorate, Pacific Region, Manuscript Report Series, v. 13, 106 p.

1974: Waves recorded off Tofino, B.C., Station 103, July 5, 1970 to August 22, 1974; Fisheries and Marine Service, Marine Environmental Data Service, Ottawa, File 103, 13 p.

1975: Canadian normals, volume 3, wind (1955 - 1972); Atmospheric Environment Service, Ottawa, 144 p.

1976a: Oil and chemical spill countermeasure series; Environmental Protection Service, Pacific Region, West Vancouver. A series of maps covering portions of the British Columbia coast. Relevant maps are labelled "Physical Base, Land and Water Use" and "Physical Base, Land Status, Land and Water Use".

1976b: Waves recorded off Roberts Bank, B.C., Station 108, February 7, 1974 to April 3, 1976; Fisheries and Marine Service, Marine Environmental Data Service, Ottawa, File 108, 13 p.

Canada Department of Fisheries and Environment
1978: Potential Pacific coast oil ports: a comparative environmental risk analysis; Vancouver, 2 volumes, 119 p., supplementary appendices.

Canadian Hydrographic Service
1963: Data record of current observations, volume I, Strait of Georgia; Canada Department of Energy, Mines and Resources, Marine Sciences Branch, Victoria, 65 p.

1964: Data record of current observations, volume II, Juan de Fuca Strait; Canada Department of Energy, Mines and Resources, Marine Sciences Branch, Victoria, 116 p.

Canadian Hydrographic Service (cont.)
1966: Data record of current observations, volume III, Saanich Inlet; Canada Department of Energy, Mines and Resources, Marine Sciences Branch, Victoria, 41 p.

1967: Data record of current observations, volume IV, Ladysmith Harbour; Canada Department of Energy, Mines and Resources, Marine Sciences Branch, Victoria, 28 p.

1968a: Data record of current observations, volume V, Departure Bay; Canada Department of Energy, Mines and Resources, Marine Sciences Branch, Victoria, 24 p.

1968b: Data record of current observations, volume VI, Macaulay (McCauley) Point; Canada Department of Energy, Mines and Resources, Marine Sciences Branch, Victoria, 56 p.

1974: Sailing directions---British Columbia coast (north portion); Canada Department of Environment, Marine Sciences Directorate, Victoria, 6th ed., 416 p.

1976: Sailing directions---British Columbia coast (south portion); Canada Department of Environment, Fisheries and Marine Service, Ottawa, 10th ed., 399 p.

1978: Canadian tide and current tables; Canada Department of Fisheries and Environment, Fisheries and Marine Service, Ottawa, v.5, 96 p., and 6, 84 p.

Carne, R.C.
1974: A study of trace metal contents of Victoria Harbour, B.C. bottom sediments; unpubl. B.Sc. thesis, University of British Columbia, Department of Geological Sciences, Vancouver, 83 p.

Carswell, H.T.
1955: The ground-water and related erosion of Point Grey; unpubl. B.A. thesis, University of British Columbia, Department of Geology, Vancouver, 55 p.

Carter, N.M.
1934: The physiography and oceanography of some British Columbia fiords; 5th Pacific Science Congress, Proceedings, v. 1, p. 721 - 733.

Chang, P.Y.K.
1976: Subsurface currents in the Strait of Georgia, west of Sturgeon Bank; unpubl. M.Sc. thesis, University of British Columbia, Vancouver, 183 p.

Chang, P., Pond, S. and Tabata, S.
1976: Subsurface currents in the Strait of Georgia, west of Sturgeon Bank; Fisheries Research Board of Canada Journal, v. 33, no. 10, p. 2218 - 2241.

Clague, J.J.
1975: Late Quaternary sea level fluctuations, Pacific coast of Canada and adjacent areas; in Report of Activities, Part C; Geological Survey of Canada, Paper 75-1C, p. 17 - 21.

1976a: Quadra Sand and its relation to the late Wisconsin glaciation of southwest British Columbia; Canadian Journal of Earth Sciences, v. 13, no. 6, p. 803 - 815.

1976b: Sedimentology and geochemistry of marine sediments near Comox, British Columbia; Geological Survey of Canada, Paper 76-21, 21 p.

1977: Quadra Sand: a study of the late Pleistocene geology and geomorphic history of coastal southwest British Columbia; Geological Survey of Canada, Paper 77-17, 24 p.

Clague, J.J., Gardner, R.H., Ricker, K.E. and Donley, M.W.
1977: Bibliography of marine geoscience information, Pacific regions of Canada, 1900 - 1976; Geological Survey of Canada, Paper 77-22, 43 p.

Crean, P.B.
1967: Physical oceanography of Dixon Entrance, British Columbia; Fisheries Research Board of Canada, Bulletin 156, 66 p.

1976: Numerical model studies of the tides between Vancouver Island and the mainland coast; Fisheries Research Board of Canada Journal, v. 33, no. 10, p. 2340 - 2344.

Cretney, W.J., Wong, C.S., Green, D.R. and Bawden, C.A.
1978: Long-term fate of a heavy fuel oil in a spill-contaminated B.C. coastal bay; Fisheries Research Board of Canada Journal, v. 35, no. 5, p. 521 - 527.

Cummings, J.M.
1941: Preliminary investigation into possibilities for producing silica sand from British Columbia sand deposits; British Columbia Department of Mines and Petroleum Resources, Victoria, 54 p.

Daniel, P.E.
1978: Longshore currents in the vicinity of a breakwater; unpubl. M.Sc. thesis, University of British Columbia, Vancouver, 120 p.

de Jong, S.H. and Siebenhuener, H.F.W.
1972: Seasonal and secular variations of sea level on the Pacific coast of Canada; Canadian Surveyor, v. 26, no. 1, p. 4 - 19.

Dodimead, A.J.
1968: Oceanographic conditions in the central subarctic Pacific region, winter 1966; Fisheries Research Board of Canada, Technical Report 75, 10 p.

Dodimead, A.J., Favorite, F. and Hirano, T.
1963:   Review of the oceanography of the subarctic Pacific region (Salmon of the North Pacific Ocean, part 2); International North Pacific Fisheries Commission, Bulletin 13, 195 p.

Dodimead, A.J. and Herlinveaux, R.H.
1968:   Some oceanographic features of the waters of the central British Columbia coast; Fisheries Research Board of Canada, Technical Report 70, 26 p.

Dodimead, A.J. and Hollister, H.J.
1958:   Progress report of drift bottle releases in the northeast Pacific Ocean; Fisheries Research Board of Canada Journal, v. 15, no. 5, p. 851 - 865.
1962:   Canadian drift bottle releases and recoveries in the North Pacific Ocean; Fisheries Research Board of Canada, Manuscript Report 141 (Oceanographic and Limnological Series), 108 p.

Dodimead, A.J. and Pickard, G.L.
1967:   Annual changes in the oceanic-coastal waters of the eastern subarctic Pacific; Fisheries Board of Canada Journal, v. 24, no. 11, p. 2207 - 2227.

Doe, L.A.E.
1952:   Currents and net transport in Loudoun Channel, April 1950; Fisheries Research Board of Canada Journal, v. 9, no. 1, p. 42 - 64.
1955:   Offshore waters of the Canadian Pacific coast; Fisheries Research Board of Canada Journal, v. 12, no. 1, p. 1 - 34.

Eccles, L.K.
1976:   The study of a temporary spit formed on Towers Beach, U.B.C.; unpubl. B.Sc. thesis, University of British Columbia, Department of Geological Sciences, Vancouver, 90 p.

Farmer, D.M.
1972:   The influence of wind on the surface waters of Alberni Inlet; Canada Department of Environment, Marine Sciences Directorate, Pacific Marine Science Report 72-16, 94 p. Also (1972) Ph.D. thesis, University of British Columbia, Vancouver, 92 p.

Favorite, F., Dodimead, A.J. and Nasu, K.
1976:   Oceanography of the subarctic Pacific region, 1960 - 71; International North Pacific Fisheries Commission, Bulletin 33, 187 p.

Favorite, F., Fisk, D. and Ingraham, W.J., Jr.
1965:   First transponding oceanographic buoys in the Pacific; Fisheries Research Board of Canada Journal, v. 22, no. 3, p. 689 - 694.

Fissel, D.B.
1976:   Pressure differences as a measure of currents in Juan de Fuca Strait; Canada Department of Environment, Institute of Ocean Sciences, Pacific Marine Science Report 76-17, 63 p.

Fissel, D.B. and Huggett, W.S.
1976:   Observations of currents, bottom pressures and densities through a cross-section of Juan de Fuca Strait; Canada Department of Environment, Institute of Ocean Sciences, Pacific Marine Science Report 76-6, 68 p.

Fjarlie, R.L.I.
1950:   The oceanographic phase of the Vancouver sewage problem; Fisheries Research Board of Canada, Manuscript Report 412 (Biological Series), 23 p.

Fladmark, K.R.
1975:   A paleoecological model for Northwest Coast prehistory; National Museums of Canada, National Museum of Man, Mercury Series, Archaeological Survey of Canada, Paper 43, 319 p. Also (1974) Ph.D. thesis, University of Calgary, Calgary, 319 p.

Fleming, R.H.
1955:   Review of the oceanography of the northern Pacific; International North Pacific Fisheries Commission, Bulletin 2, 43 p.

Fofonoff, N.P. and Tabata, S.
1966:   Variability of oceanographic conditions between Ocean Station P and Swiftsure Bank off the Pacific coast of Canada; Fisheries Research Board of Canada Journal, v. 23, no. 6, p. 825 - 868.

Foster, H.D.
1972:   Geomorphology and water resource management: Portage Inlet, a case study on Vancouver Island; Canadian Geographer, v. 16, no. 2, p. 128 - 143.
1976:   Coastal erosion: a natural hazard of the Saanich Peninsula, Vancouver Island; in Victoria: Physical Environment and Development, H.D. Foster, ed.; University of Victoria, Western Geographical Series, v. 12, p. 131 - 184.

Fulton, R.J.
1971:   Radiocarbon geochronology of southern British Columbia; Geological Survey of Canada, Paper 71-37, 28 p.

Fulton, R.J. and Halstead, E.C.
1972:   Quaternary geology of the southern Canadian Cordillera; 24th International Geological Congress, Guidebook, Field Excursion A02, 49 p.

Fyles, J.G.
1963:   Surficial geology of Horne Lake and Parksville map-areas, Vancouver Island, British Columbia; Geological Survey of Canada, Memoir 318, 142 p. Also (1956) Ph.D. thesis, Ohio State University, Columbus, 283 p.

Garrison, R.E. and Luternauer, J.L.
1969:   Textures of calcitic cements formed during early diagenesis, Fraser Delta, British Columbia; in Carbonate Cements; Bermuda Biological Station for Research, Special Publication 3, p. 106 - 109. Also in (1971) Carbonate Cements, O.P. Bricker, ed.; Johns Hopkins University, Studies in Geology, no. 19, p. 151 - 154.

Garrison, R.E., Luternauer, J.L., Grill, E.V., Macdonald, R.D. and Murray, J.W.
1969:   Early diagenetic cementation of recent sands, Fraser River delta, British Columbia; Sedimentology, v. 12, no. 1/2, p. 27 - 46.

Gaspard, J.F.
1979:   Beach erosion, immediately south of the Tsawwassen causeway, Vancouver, British Columbia; unpubl. B.A.Sc. thesis, University of British Columbia, Department of Geological Engineering, Vancouver, 116 p.

Giovando, L.F.
1973:   The effluent outfall proposed for the Five Finger Island area, Nanaimo, B.C.: oceanographic and related considerations; Canada Department of Environment, Marine Sciences Directorate, Pacific Marine Science Report 73-12, 130 p.

Giovando, L.F. and Tabata, S.
1970:   Measurements of surface flow in the Strait of Georgia by means of free-floating current followers; Fisheries Research Board of Canada, Technical Report 163, 69 p.

Goodman, J. and Thompson, T.G.
1940:   Characteristics of the waters in sections from Dutch Harbour, Alaska, to the Strait of Juan de Fuca and from the Strait of Juan de Fuca to Hawaii; University of Washington, Publications in Oceanography, v. 3, no. 3, p. 81 - 103, and app., p. 1 - 48.

Green, D.R., Bawden, C., Cretney, W.J. and Wong, C.S.
1974:   The Alert Bay oil spill: a one-year study of the recovery of a contaminated bay; Canada Department of Environment, Marine Sciences Directorate, Pacific Marine Science Report 74-9, 42 p.

Grieve, D.A.
1977: Behaviour of some trace metals in sediments of the Fraser River delta-front, southwestern British Columbia; unpubl. M.Sc. thesis, University of British Columbia, Vancouver, 133 p.

Grieve, D.A. and Fletcher, W.K.
1975: Trace metals in Fraser Delta sediments; in Report of Activities, Part B; Geological Survey of Canada, Paper 75-1B, p. 161-163.
1976: Heavy metals in deltaic sediments of the Fraser River, British Columbia; Canadian Journal of Earth Sciences, v. 13, no. 12, p. 1683-1693.
1977: Interactions between zinc and suspended sediments in the Fraser River estuary, British Columbia; Estuarine and Coastal Marine Science, v. 5, no. 3, p. 415-419.

Hall, K.J. and Fletcher, W.K.
1974: Trace metal pollution from a metropolitan area: sources and accumulation in the lower Fraser River and estuary; International Conference on Transport of Persistent Chemicals in Aquatic Ecosystems (National Research Council of Canada), Proceedings, sect. 1, p. 83-87.

Harris, R.G. and Rattray, M., Jr.
1954: The surface winds over Puget Sound and the Strait of Juan de Fuca and their oceanographic effects; University of Washington, Department of Oceanography, Technical Report 37, 101 p.

Hawley, P.M.
1979: Erosional stability of a dredged borrow pit on southern Roberts Bank, Fraser River delta, British Columbia; unpubl. B.A.Sc. thesis, University of British Columbia, Department of Geological Engineering, Vancouver, 65 p.

Hay, D. and Secter, J.P.
1978: A developmental case history, Oyster River, B.C.; in Coastal Zone '78; Symposium on Technical, Environmental, Socioeconomic and Regulatory Aspects of Coastal Zone Management (American Society of Civil Engineers), v. 2, p. 1419-1431.

Herlinveaux, R.H.
1954a: Surface tidal currents in Juan de Fuca Strait; Fisheries Research Board of Canada Journal, v. 11, no. 1, p. 14-31.
1954b: Tidal currents in Juan de Fuca Strait; Fisheries Research Board of Canada Journal, v. 11, no. 6, p. 799-815.
1962: Oceanography of Saanich Inlet in Vancouver Island, British Columbia; Fisheries Research Board of Canada Journal, v. 19, no. 1, p. 1-37.

Herlinveaux, R.H. (cont.)
1972: Oceanographic features of Saanich Inlet 9 May - 2 July, 1968; Fisheries Research Board of Canada, Technical Report 300, 53 p.

Herlinveaux, R.H., Bishop, S.O., Fulton, J.D., Pease, A.K., Stephens, K. and Parsons, T.R.
1966: A study of the physical, chemical and biological oceanographic conditions at Nanoose Bay, Vancouver Island; Fisheries Research Board of Canada, Manuscript Report 208 (Oceanographic and Limnological Series), 82 p.

Herlinveaux, R.H. and Tully, J.P.
1961: Some oceanographic features of Juan de Fuca Strait; Fisheries Research Board of Canada Journal, v. 18, no. 6, p. 1027-1071.

Holland, S.S.
1964: Landforms of British Columbia, a physiographic outline; British Columbia Department of Mines and Petroleum Resources, Bulletin 48, 138 p.

Holland, S.S. and Nasmith, H.W.
1958: Investigation of beach sands; British Columbia Department of Mines and Petroleum Resources, Victoria, Miscellaneous Report, 8 p.

Hoos, L.M.
1975: The Skeena River estuary, status of environmental knowledge to 1975; Canada Department of Environment, Regional Board, Pacific Region, Estuary Working Group, Special Estuary Series, no. 3, 418 p.

Hoos, L.M. and Packman, G.A.
1974: The Fraser River estuary, status of environmental knowledge to 1974; Canada Department of Environment, Regional Board, Pacific Region, Estuary Working Group, Special Estuary Series, no. 1, 518 p.

Hoos, L.M. and Vold, C.L.
1975: The Squamish River estuary, status of environmental knowledge to 1974; Canada Department of Environment, Regional Board, Pacific Region, Estuary Working Group, Special Estuary Series, no. 2, 361 p.

Huggett, W.S., Bath, J.F. and Douglas, A.
1976a: Data record of current observations, volume XIV, Johnstone Strait, 1973; Canada Department of Environment, Institute of Ocean Sciences, Victoria, 155 p.
1976b: Data record of current observations, volume XV, Juan de Fuca Strait, 1973; Canada Department of Environment, Institute of Ocean Sciences, Victoria, 169 p.

Hum, S.
1977: The development and use of resource sensitivity maps for oil spill countermeasures; in 1977 Oil Spill Conference; American Petroleum Institute, Publication 4284, p. 105-110.

Ingraham, W.J., Jr.
1967: The geostrophic circulation and distribution of water properties off the coasts of Vancouver Island and Washington, spring and fall 1963; United States Fish and Wildlife Service, Fishery Bulletin, v. 66, no. 2, p. 223-250.

Ingraham, W.J., Jr. and Hastings, J.R.
1967: Seasonal surface currents off the coasts of Vancouver Island and Washington as shown by drift bottle experiments, 1964-65; United States Department of Commerce, National Oceanic and Atmospheric Administration, Technical Report NMFS SSRF-699, 9 p.

Jackson, E.V.
1976: Generalized geological map of the Canadian Cordillera; British Columbia Department of Mines and Petroleum Resources, Victoria.

Johns, R.E.
1968: A study of the density structure and water flow in the upper 10 m of a selected region in Bute Inlet, British Columbia; unpubl. M.Sc. thesis, University of British Columbia, Vancouver, 74 p.

Johnston, W.A.
1921a: Pleistocene oscillations of sea-level in the Vancouver region, British Columbia; Royal Society of Canada, Transactions, Series 3, v. 15, sect. 4, p. 9-19.
1921b: Sedimentation of the Fraser River delta; Geological Survey of Canada, Memoir 125, 46 p.
1921c: The occurrence of calcareous sandstone in the recent delta of Fraser River, British Columbia, Canada; American Journal of Science, Series 5, v. 1, no. 5, p. 447-449.
1921d: The age of the recent delta of Fraser River, British Columbia, Canada; American Journal of Science, Series 5, v. 1, no. 5, p. 450-453.
1922: The character of the stratification of the sediments in the recent delta of Fraser River, British Columbia, Canada; Journal of Geology, v. 30, no. 2, p. 115-129.

Jones, R.K.
1977: Surficial materials of the south-western Fraser Lowland; Canada Department of Fisheries and Environment, Lands Directorate, Vancouver, map with descriptive notes.

Keenan, C.J., Kinnear, A.C., Sanders, F.H., Tully, J.P., Waldichuk, M., Wigen, S.O. and Young, R.B.
1966: Current observations in Cordova Bay and predictions on sewage dispersal; Fisheries Research Board of Canada, Manuscript Report 197 (Oceanographic and Limnological Series), 53 p.

Kellerhals, P. and Murray, J.W.
1969: Tidal flats at Boundary Bay, Fraser River delta, British Columbia; Bulletin of Canadian Petroleum Geology, v. 17, no. 1, p. 67 - 91. Also in Holocene Tidal Sedimentation, G. de V. Klein, ed.; Dowden, Hutchinson & Ross, Inc., Stroudsburg, Pennsylvania, p. 118 - 142 (1976).

Kern, C.B.
1968: The black sands of Wreck Bay (Florencia Bay); unpubl. B.A.Sc. thesis, University of British Columbia, Department of Geological Engineering, Vancouver, 39 p.

LaCroix, G.W. and Tully, J.P.
1954: The anomaly of mean sea level in Seymour Narrows, B.C.; Fisheries Research Board of Canada Journal, v. 11, no. 6, p. 853 - 883.

Laing, A.C.
1975: An environmental study of the Chemainus River delta, Vancouver Island, British Columbia; unpubl. B.Sc. thesis, University of British Columbia; Department of Geological Sciences, Vancouver, 104 p.

Landry, L.P.
1976: Radar tracking of drift drogues in Pendrell Sound and Port Mellon, June and September 1974; Canada Department of Environment, Institute of Ocean Sciences, Pacific Marine Science Report 76-8, 52 p.

Lang, A.H. and Muller, J.E.
1975: The geology of Long Beach segment, Pacific Rim National Park, and its approaches; Geological Survey of Canada, Miscellaneous Report 24, 56 p.

Leckie, P.G.
1936: The mineralogy of the sands in the vicinity of Vancouver; unpubl. M.A. thesis, University of British Columbia, Vancouver, 19 p.

Lem, G.N.
1974: Shore changes and sand movement at the south shore of English Bay, Vancouver, Canada; unpubl. B.A.Sc. thesis, University of British Columbia, Department of Geological Engineering, Vancouver, 53 p.

Leroux, J.
1979: Evaluation of the morphosedimentologic character of a section of the Nanaimo River delta tidal flats using photogrammetric techniques; unpubl. B.Sc. thesis, University of British Columbia, Department of Geological Sciences, Vancouver, 55 p.

Lum, K.
1975: Erosion of the Point Grey cliffs, University of British Columbia; unpubl. B.A.Sc. thesis, University of British Columbia, Department of Geological Engineering, Vancouver, 40 p.

Luternauer, J.L.
1975a: Fraser Delta sedimentation, Vancouver, British Columbia; in Report of Activities, Part A; Geological Survey of Canada, Paper 75-1A, p. 467, 468.
1975b: Fraser Delta sedimentation, Vancouver, British Columbia; in Report of Activities, Part B; Geological Survey of Canada, Paper 75-1B, p. 171, 172.
1976a: Fraser Delta sedimentation, Vancouver, British Columbia; in Report of Activities, Part A; Geological Survey of Canada, Paper 76-1A, p. 213 - 219.
1976b: Skeena Delta sedimentation, British Columbia; in Report of Activities, Part A; Geological Survey of Canada, Paper 76-1A, p. 239 - 242.
1976c: Fraser Delta sedimentation, Vancouver, British Columbia; in Report of Activities, Part B; Geological Survey of Canada, Paper 76-1B, p. 169 - 171.
1977: Fraser Delta sedimentation, Vancouver, British Columbia; in Report of Activities, Part A; Geological Survey of Canada, Paper 77-1A, p. 65 - 72.

Luternauer, J.L., Linden, R.H. and Thomson, R.E.
1978: Applications of side-scan sonar to geoenvironmental research in the coastal waters of British Columbia; in Current Research, Part B; Geological Survey of Canada, Paper 78-1B, p. 181 - 186.

Luternauer, J.L. and Murray, J.W.
1973: Sedimentation on the western delta-front of the Fraser River, British Columbia; Canadian Journal of Earth Sciences, v. 10, no. 11, p. 1642 - 1663.
1977: Fraser Delta field trip; Geological Association of Canada, Mineralogical Association of Canada, Society of Economic Geologists, Canadian Geophysical Union, 1977 Annual Meeting, Field Trip Guidebook, Trip 12, 24 p.

Luternauer, J.L. and Swan, D.
1978: Kitimat submarine slump deposit(s): a preliminary report; in Current Research, Part A; Geological Survey of Canada, Paper 78-1A, p. 327 - 332.

Luternauer, J.L., Swan, D. and Linden, R.H.
1978: Sand waves on the southeastern slope of Roberts Bank, Fraser River delta, British Columbia; in Current Research, Part A; Geological Survey of Canada, Paper 78-1A, p. 351 - 356.

Mackay, B.S.
1954: Tidal current observations in Hecate Strait; Fisheries Research Board of Canada Journal, v. 11, no. 1, p. 48 - 56.

Marles, E.W.
1973: Bibliography of oceanographic information for the inside waters of the southern British Columbia coast. Volume I, physical oceanography; Canada Department of Environment, Marine Sciences Directorate, Pacific Marine Science Report 73-1, 82 p.

Marles, E.W., Lusk, B.M. and Rapatz, W.J.
1973: Summary of hydrographic and oceanographic information on some British Columbia estuaries; Canada Department of Environment, Marine Sciences Directorate, Pacific Marine Science Report 73-7, 56 p.

Marmer, H.A.
1926: Coastal currents along the Pacific coast of the United States; United States Coast and Geodetic Survey, Special Publication 121, 80 p.

Mathews, W.H.
1972: Geology of Vancouver area of British Columbia; 24th International Geological Congress, Guidebook, Field Excursion A05-C05, 47 p.

Mathews, W.H., Fyles, J.G. and Nasmith, H.W.
1970: Postglacial crustal movements in southwestern British Columbia and adjacent Washington State; Canadian Journal of Earth Sciences, v. 7, no. 2, pt. 2, p. 690 - 702.

Mathews, W.H. and Murray, J.W.
1966: Recent sediments and their environment of deposition, Strait of Georgia and Fraser River delta (a manual for field conferences); Tenneco Oil and Minerals, Ltd., Calgary, 87 p.

Mathews, W.H. and Shepard, F.P.
1962: Sedimentation of Fraser River delta, British Columbia; American Association of Petroleum Geologists Bulletin, v. 46, no. 8, p. 1416-1438. Discussion by K. Terzaghi in (1962) American Association of Petroleum Geologists Bulletin v. 46, no. 8, p. 1438-1443.

Mayers, I.R.
1968: An analysis of the form and origin of the Fraser River delta's subaqueous slump deposits; unpubl. B.Sc. thesis, University of British Columbia, Department of Geophysics, Vancouver, 49 p.

McLean, D.G.
1975: Marine erosion at Towers Beach, U.B.C.; unpubl. B.A.Sc. thesis, University of British Columbia, Department of Geological Engineering, Vancouver, 127 p.

Medley, E.
1978: Dendritic drainage channels and tidalflat erosion, west of Steveston, Fraser River delta, British Columbia; unpubl. B.A.Sc. thesis, University of British Columbia, Department of Geological Engineering, Vancouver, 70 p.

Medley, E. and Luternauer, J.L.
1976: Use of aerial photographs to map sediment distribution and to identify historical changes on a tidal flat; in Report of Activities, Part C; Geological Survey of Canada, Paper 76-1C, p. 293-304.

Morris, S., Leaney, A.J., Bell, L.M. and Thompson, J.M.
1979: The Courtenay River estuary, status of environmental knowledge to 1978; Canada Department of Fisheries and Environment, Regional Board, Pacific Region, Estuary Working Group, Special Estuary Series, no. 8, 355 p.

Mysak, L.A.
1977: On the stability of the California undercurrent off Vancouver Island; Journal of Physical Oceanography, v. 7, no. 6, p. 904-917.

Nasmith, H.
1970: Pleistocene geology of the Queen Charlotte Islands and southern British Columbia; in Early Man and Environments in Northwest North America, R.A. Smith, and J.W. Smith, eds.; University of Calgary, Archaeological Association, 2nd Annual Paleo-Environmental Workshop, Proceedings, p. 5-8.

Northcote, K.E.
1961: Distribution of sulphur, iron, copper and zinc in modern marine sediments of Mud Bay, Crescent Beach, B.C.; unpubl. M.Sc. thesis, University of British Columbia, Vancouver, 44 p.

Owens, E.H.
1977: Coastal environments of Canada: the impact and cleanup of oil spills; Canada Department of Fisheries and Environment, Environmental Protection Service, Economic and Technical Review Report EPS-3-EC-77-13, 413 p.

Parker, B.
1977: Tidal hydrodynamics in the Strait of Juan de Fuca-Strait of Georgia; United States Department of Commerce, National Oceanic and Atmospheric Administration, Technical Report NOS-69, 56 p.

Peacock, M.A.
1935: Fiord-land of British Columbia; Geological Society of America Bulletin, v. 46, no. 4, p. 633-695.

Pickard, G.L.
1953: Oceanography of British Columbia mainland inlets. II. Currents; Fisheries Research Board of Canada, Pacific Coast Stations, Progress Report 97, p. 12, 13.
1956a: Physical features of British Columbia inlets; in Ocean Floors around Canada; Royal Society of Canada, Transactions, Series 3, v. 50, p. 47-58.
1956b: Surface and bottom currents in the Strait of Georgia; Fisheries Research Board of Canada Journal, v. 13, no. 4, p. 581-590.
1961: Oceanographic features of inlets in the British Columbia mainland coast; Fisheries Research Board of Canada Journal, v. 18, no. 6, p. 907-999.
1963: Oceanographic characteristics of inlets of Vancouver Island, British Columbia; Fisheries Research Board of Canada Journal, v. 20, no. 5, p. 1109-1144.

Pickard, G.L. and Rodgers, K.
1959: Current measurements in Knight Inlet, British Columbia; Fisheries Research Board of Canada Journal, v. 16, no. 5, p. 635-678.

Pool, M.I.
1976: Sand sources, volumes and movement patterns on Wreck Beach, Vancouver, British Columbia; unpubl. M.A.Sc. thesis, University of British Columbia, Vancouver, 107 p.

Retherford, R.M.
1972: Late Quaternary geologic environments and their relation to archaeological studies in the Bella Bella-Bella Coola region of the British Columbia coast; unpubl. M.Sc. thesis, University of Colorado, Boulder, 128 p.

Ricker, K.E.
1974a: Effects of the Burrard Inlet oil spill on various geologic intertidal environments; in Report of Activities, Part B; Geological Survey of Canada, Paper 74-1B, p. 205-207.

Ricker, K.E. (cont.)
1974b: Inventory of marine surficial geology, sedimentology, geomorphology, Quaternary paleontology and palaeoecology, geochemistry and related studies of the Pacific shelf of Canada. Part I ---coastal areas of British Columbia, Washington and Alaska; Geological Survey of Canada, Open File 197, 46 p.
1975: Inventory of marine surficial geology, sedimentology, geomorphology, Quaternary paleontology and palaeoecology, geochemistry and related studies of the Pacific regions of Canada. Part I---coastal zone of British Columbia, and adjacent waters off Washington and southeast Alaska. Part II---continental rise and abyssal regions of the N.E. Pacific Ocean; Geological Survey of Canada, Open File 276, 143 p.

Schlagintweit, M.B.
1979: Erosion of a dredge spoil at the mouth of the North Arm of the Fraser River; unpubl. B.A.Sc. thesis, University of British Columbia, Department of Geological Engineering, Vancouver, 54 p.

Schumacher, J.D., Pearson, C.A, Charnell, R.L. and Laird, N.P.
1978: Regional response to forcing in southern Strait of Georgia; Estuarine and Coastal Marine Science, v. 7, no. 1, p. 79-91.

Scotton, S.
1978: The outer banks of the Fraser River delta, engineering properties and stability considerations; unpubl. M.A.Sc. thesis, University of British Columbia, Vancouver, 127 p.

Shand, J.A.
1953: Internal waves in Georgia Strait; American Geophysical Union, Transactions, v. 34, no. 6, p. 849-856.

Shepard, F.P. and Milliman, J.D.
1978: Sea-floor currents on the foreset slope of the Fraser River delta, British Columbia (Canada); Marine Geology, v. 28, no. 3/4, p. 245-251.

Sibert, J. and Reimer, P.
1976: Textural analysis of the surficial sediments of the Nanaimo River delta; Fisheries Research Board of Canada, Manuscript Report 1405, 21 p.

Sternberg, R.W.
1968: Friction factors in tidal channels with differing bed roughness; Marine Geology, v. 6, no. 3, p. 243-260.
1971: Measurements of incipient motion of sediment particles in the marine environment; Marine Geology, v. 10, no. 2, p. 113-119.

Sutherland Brown, A.
1968: Geology of the Queen Charlotte Islands, British Columbia; British Columbia Department of Mines and Petroleum Resources, Bulletin 54, 247 p.

Sverdrup, H.U.
1940: The currents of the Pacific Ocean and their bearing on the climates of the coast; Science, v. 91, no. 2360, p. 273 - 282.

Swan, D.
1978: Acoustic imaging of the seabed in northern Kitimat Arm, B.C.; unpubl. B.Sc. thesis, University of British Columbia, Department of Geophysics and Astronomy, Vancouver, 72 p.

Swan, D. and Luternauer, J.L.
1978: Mosaic of side scan sonar records, northern Kitimat Arm, B.C.; Geological Survey of Canada, Open File 579, map with descriptive notes.

Swinbanks, D.D.
1979: Environmental factors controlling floral zonation and the distribution of burrowing and tube-dwelling organisms on Fraser Delta tidal flats, British Columbia; unpubl. Ph.D. thesis, University of British Columbia, Vancouver, 274 p.

Swonnell, D.W.
1970: The origin of rill patterns on a beach; unpubl. B.A.Sc. thesis, University of British Columbia, Department of Geological Engineering, Vancouver, 118 p.

Tabata, S.
1954: The physical oceanography of Bute Inlet; unpubl. M.A. thesis, University of British Columbia, Vancouver, 101 p.
1972: The movement of Fraser River-influenced surface water in the Strait of Georgia as deduced from a series of aerial photographs; Canada Department of Environment, Marine Sciences Branch, Pacific Marine Science Report 72-6, 69 p.
1975: The general circulation of the Pacific Ocean and a brief account of the oceanographic structure of the North Pacific Ocean. Part I---circulation and volume transports; Atmosphere, v. 13, no. 4 p. 133 - 168.

Tabata, S., Giovando, L.F. and Devlin, D.
1971: Current velocities in the vicinity of the Greater Vancouver Sewerage and Drainage District's Iona Island outfall--1968; Fisheries Research Board of Canada, Technical Report 263, 110 p.

Tabata, S., Giovando, L.F., Stickland, J.A. and Wong, J.
1970a: Current velocity measurements in the Strait of Georgia---1967; Fisheries Research Board of Canada, Technical Report 169, 245 p.

Tabata, S., Giovando, L.F., Stickland, J.A. and Wong, J. (cont.)
1970b: Current velocity measurements in the Strait of Georgia---1968; Fisheries Research Board of Canada, Technical Report 178, 112 p.
1970c: Current velocity measurements in the Strait of Georgia---1969; Fisheries Research Board of Canada, Technical Report 191, 72 p.

Tabata, S. and Pickard, G.L.
1957: The physical oceanography of Bute Inlet, British Columbia; Fisheries Research Board of Canada Journal, v. 14, no. 4, p. 487 - 520.

Tabata, S. and Stickland, J.A.
1972a: Summary of oceanographic records obtained from moored instruments in the Strait of Georgia---1969-1970: current velocity and seawater temperature from Station H-06; Canada Department of Environment, Marine Sciences Branch, Pacific Marine Science Report 72-7, 132 p.
1972b: Summary of oceanographic records obtained from moored instruments in the Strait of Georgia---1969-1970: current velocity and seawater temperature from Station H-16; Canada Department of Environment, Marine Sciences Branch, Pacific Marine Science Report 72-8, 144 p.
1972c: Summary of oceanographic records obtained from moored instruments in the Strait of Georgia---1969-1970: current velocity and seawater temperature from Station H-26; Canada Department of Environment, Marine Sciences Branch, Pacific Marine Science Report 72-9, 141 p.
1972d: Summary of oceanograhic records obtained from moored instruments in the Strait of Georgia---1968-1970: current velocity from Stations F-11, M-10 and I-31; Canada Department of Environment, Marine Sciences Branch, Pacific Marine Science Report 72-10, 22 p.

Tabata, S., Stickland, J.A. and de Lange Boom, B.R.
1971: The program of current velocity and water temperature observations from moored instruments in the Strait of Georgia---1968-1970 and examples of records obtained; Fisheries Research Board of Canada, Technical Report 253, 222 p.

Tamburi, A. and Hay, D.
1978: An introduction to river mechanics and the lower Fraser River; Canada Department of Public Works, Pacific Region, Marine Civil Engineering Section, Vancouver, 72 p.

Terzaghi, K.
1956: Varieties of submarine slope failures; 8th Texas Conference on Soil Mechanics and Foundation Engineering, Proceedings, iv, 41 p.

Thomas, D.J.
1975: The distribution of zinc and copper in Georgia Strait, British Columbia: effects of the Fraser River and sediment-exchange reactions; unpubl. M.Sc. thesis, University of British Columbia, Vancouver, 110 p.

Thomas, D.J. and Grill, E.V.
1977: The effect of exchange reactions between Fraser River sediment and seawater on dissolved Cu and Zn concentrations in the Strait of Georgia; Estuarine and Coastal Marine Science, v. 5, no. 3, p. 421 - 427.

Thompson, W.F. and Van Cleve, R.
1936: Life history of the Pacific halibut; International Fisheries Commission, Report 9, 184 p.

Thomson, R.E.
1974a: Longshore current generation by internal waves in the Strait of Georgia; Canadian Journal of Earth Sciences, v. 12, no. 3, p. 472 - 488.
1974b: The tides (The physical oceanography of the B.C. coast---part 1); Pacific Yachting, Power and Sail, v. 9, no. 2, p. 14 - 18, p. 72, 73.
1974c: Tidal currents (The physical oceanography of the B.C. coast ---part 2); Pacific Yachting, Power and Sail, v. 9, no. 3, p. 32 - 37, p. 66 - 68.
1975a: Waves (The physical oceanography of the B.C. coast---part 3); Pacific Yachting, Power and Sail, v. 9, no. 4, p. 34 - 37, p. 62, 63.
1975b: The Strait of Georgia (The physical oceanography of the B.C. coast---part .4); Pacific Yachting, Power and Sail, v. 9, no. 5, p. 42 - 45, p. 140 - 145.
1975c: Currents in the Strait of Georgia (The physical oceanography of the B.C. coast---part 5); Pacific Yachting, Power and Sail, v. 9, no. 6, p. 58 - 61, p. 78 - 80.
1975d: Surface currents in the Strait of Georgia (The physical oceanography of the B.C. coast---part 6); Pacific Yachting, Power and Sail, v. 10, no. 1, p. 62 - 67, p. 96, 97.
1975e: Currents in Juan de Fuca Strait (The physical oceanography of the B.C. coast---part 7); Pacific Yachting, Power and Sail, v. 10, no. 2, p. 84 - 91.
1975f: Inlets, sills, tide lines and temperatures (The physical oceanography of the B.C. coast---part 8); Pacific Yachting, Power and Sail, v. 10, no. 5, p. 30, 31, p. 67 - 71.

Thomson, R.E. (cont.)

1975q: Upwelling---bringing cold water to the surface (The physical oceanography of the B.C. coast---part 9); Pacific Yachting, Power and Sail, v. 11, no. 1, p. 46 - 54.

1976a: Tidal currents and estuarine-type circulation in Johnstone Strait, British Columbia; Fisheries Research Board of Canada Journal, v. 33, no. 10, p. 2242 - 2264.

1976b: Tidal waves (tsunamis) (The physical oceanography of the B.C. coast---part 10); Pacific Yachting, Power and Sail, v. 11, no. 4, p. 34 - 36, p. 69 - 72.

1976c: Winds, waves and whitecaps (The physical oceanography of the B.C. coast---part 11); Pacific Yachting, Power and Sail, v. 11, no. 6, p. 46 - 54.

1976d: Tidal currents and the '76 Swiftsure (The physical oceanography of the B.C. coast---part 12); Pacific Yachting, Power and Sail, v. 12, no. 5, p. 44 - 47, p. 80, 81.

1977a: Currents in Johnstone Strait, British Columbia: supplemental data on the Vancouver Island side; Fisheries Research Board of Canada Journal, v. 34, no. 5, p. 697 - 703.

1977b: Waves in shallow water (The physical oceanography of the B.C. coast---part 13); Pacific Yachting, Power and Sail, v. 13, no. 4, p. 44 - 49, p. 73 - 75.

1977c: Johnstone Strait and Discovery Passage (The physical oceanography of the B.C. coast---part 14); Pacific Yachting, Power and Sail, v. 14, no. 2, p. 46 - 48, p. 54 - 61.

Tiffin, D.L., Murray, J.W., Mayers, I.R. and Garrison, R.E.

1971: Structure and origin of foreslope hills, Fraser Delta, British Columbia; Bulletin of Canadian Petroleum Geology, v. 19, no. 3, p. 589 - 600.

Trites, R.W.

1955: A study of the oceanographic structure in British Columbia inlets and some of the determining factors; Fisheries Research Board of Canada, Manuscript Report 611 (Biological Series), 180 p. Also (1955) M.Sc. thesis, University of British Columbia, Vancouver, 125 p.

1956: The oceanography of Chatham Sound, British Columbia; Fisheries Research Board of Canada Journal, v. 13, no. 3, p. 385 - 434.

Tully, J.P.

1937a: Gradient currents; Biological Board of Canada, Pacific Biological Station, Pacific Fisheries Experimental Station, Progress Report 32, p. 13, 14.

1937b: Oceanography of Nootka Sound; Biological Board of Canada Journal, v. 3, no. 1, p. 43 - 69.

Tully, J.P. (cont.)

1938: Some relations between meteorology and coast gradient-currents off the Pacific coast of North America; American Geophysical Union, Transactions, 19th Annual Meeting, pt. 1, p. 176 - 183.

1942: Surface non-tidal currents in the approaches to Juan de Fuca Strait; Fisheries Research Board of Canada Journal, v. 5, no. 4, p. 398 - 409.

1949: Oceanography and prediction of pulp mill pollution in Alberni Inlet; Fisheries Research Board of Canada, Bulletin 83, 169 p.

Tully, J.P. and Dodimead, A.J.

1957: Properties of the water in the Strait of Georgia, British Columbia, and influencing factors; Fisheries Research Board of Canada Journal, v. 14, no. 3, p. 241 - 319.

Tully, J.P. and Doe, L.A.E.

1953: Surface waters off the Canadian Pacific coast; Fisheries Research Board of Canada, Manuscript Report 550 (Biological Series), 14 p.

Tully, J.P. and Waldichuk, M.

1953: The oceanographic phase of the Nanaimo sewage problem; Fisheries Research Board of Canada, Manuscript Report 547 (Biological Series), 77 p.

Uda, M.

1963: Oceanography of the subarctic Pacific Ocean; Fisheries Research Board of Canada Journal, v. 20, no. 1, p. 119 - 179.

United States Naval Oceanographic Office

1967: Atlas of surface currents, northeastern Pacific Ocean; Hydrographic Office Publication 570, 12 charts.

Waldichuk, M.

1957: Physical oceanography of the Strait of Georgia, British Columbia; Fisheries Research Board of Canada Journal, v. 14, no. 3, p. 321 - 486.

1958a: Drift bottle observations in the Strait of Georgia; Fisheries Research Board of Canada Journal, v. 15, no. 5, p. 1065 - 1102.

1958b: Summer oceanography in Osborn Bay, B.C.; Fisheries Research Board of Canada, Pacific Coast Stations, Progress Report 110, p. 6 - 12.

1963: Drift bottle observations in the Strait of Georgia and its contiguous waters, and off the west coast of Vancouver Island; Fisheries Research Board of Canada, Manuscript Report 147 (Oceanographic and Limnological Series), 104 p.

Waldichuk, M. (cont.)

1964: Dispersion of kraft-mill effluent from a submarine diffuser in Stuart Channel, British Columbia; Fisheries Research Board of Canada Journal, v. 21, no. 5, p. 1289 - 1316.

1965: Water exchange in Port Moody, British Columbia, and its effect on waste disposal; Fisheries Research Board of Canada Journal, v. 22, no. 3, p. 801 - 822.

1967: Currents from aerial photography in coastal pollution studies; 3rd International Conference on Water Pollution Research, Proceedings, v. 3, p. 263 - 284.

Waldichuk, M. and Tabata, S.

1955: Oceanography of the Strait of Georgia. V. Surface currents; Fisheries Research Board of Canada, Pacific Coast Stations, Progress Report 104, p. 30 - 33.

Waslenchuk, D.G.

1973: The analysis and correlation of sediments from the Fraser River, the Point Grey cliffs and beaches, and Spanish Banks, at Vancouver, B.C.; unpubl. B.Sc. thesis, University of British Columbia, Department of Geological Sciences, Vancouver, 82 p.

Water Survey of Canada

1974: Historical streamflow summary, British Columbia to 1973; Canada Department of Environment, Inland Waters Directorate, Water Resources Branch, Ottawa, 694 p.

White, W.H. and Northcote, K.E.

1962: Distribution of metals in a modern marine environment; Economic Geology, v. 57, no. 3, p. 405 - 409.

Whiticar, M.J.

1974: Trace elements in recent bottom sediments of False Creek, Vancouver, British Columbia; unpubl. B.Sc. thesis, University of British Columbia, Department of Geological Sciences, Vancouver, 109 p.

Wiese, W.

1971: Geological setting and surficial sediments of Fatty Basin, a shallow inlet on the west coast of Vancouver Island, British Columbia; unpubl. M.Sc. thesis, University of British Columbia, Vancouver, 104 p.

25.

GENESIS OF MORPHOLOGIC FEATURES ON THE WESTERN DELTA FRONT OF THE FRASER RIVER, BRITISH COLUMBIA – STATUS OF KNOWLEDGE

John L. Luternauer
Cordilleran Geology Division, Vancouver, British Columbia

Luternauer, John L., Genesis of morphologic features on the western delta front of the Fraser River, British Columbia – status of knowledge; in The Coastline of Canada, S.B. McCann, editor; Geological Survey of Canada, Paper 80-10, p. 381-396, 1980.

Abstract

Major morphologic features on the western front of the Fraser River delta include: sand swells, mud pools and dendritic drainage networks on the tidal flats; gullies (sea valleys) and sandwaves on the slope.

Low (<0.5 m), long wavelength (50-100 m) sand swells have developed extensively (a) on the northernmost flats within a V-shaped area bounded by jetties which is open to the sea and (b) adjacent to the jetty on the north side of the Main Channel. Among the northernmost swells, those on the central lowermost flats are parallel to the break in slope and appear to have formed in response to wave action alone. Swells adjacent to and paralleling the jetties formed in response to the combined effect of refracted waves and along-jetty currents. The swells adjacent to the Main Channel are parallel to the break in slope and have been sculpted by wave action. No sand swells parallel this jetty probably because channel water escaping across the structure has restricted the accumulation of sand against it.

Mud pools are forming on those parts of the upper tidal flats (a) into which fine sediment is directed, (b) where wave and current energy is low, and (c) where local depressions or shoreline configuration form traps.

Relatively fine-textured dendritic drainage networks develop primarily on the less permeable mud pools adjacent to the upper tidal flat marshes, or where eelgrass growth is dense on sandy surfaces adjacent to dredged basins or the delta slope. Network extension within one of the mud pools suggests erosion in this environment is promoted by sheetwash from the topographically higher marsh and bioturbation.

Major gullies (sea valleys) incise the delta slope off present and former channel mouths. These features may develop because of mass wasting and/or turbidity currents and may be maintained by the sliding of accumulated gully bottom sediments and the flushing action of tidal currents.

The northern section of the slope on which muds are being deposited, appears to be devoid of major bedforms, but on some parts of the sandy southern slope fields of asymmetric waves (2-3 m height; ∼30 m length) extend to depths in excess of 100 m. These waves are generated primarily by flood tidal currents.

Résumé

Les principaux accidents morphologiques du front occidental du delta du Fraser sont les suivants: des monticules de sable, des vasières et un réseau de drainage dendritique sur les veys; des couloirs (vallées sous-marines) et des ondulations de sable sur le versant.

Les bourrelets sableux bas (<0,5 m) à ondes longues (50-100 m) se sont formés sur de vastes étendues (a) sur les platières les plus au nord dans un secteur en forme de V et délimitées par des jetées ouvertes sur la mer et (b) à côté de la jetée sur la rive nord du chenal principal. Parmi les bourrelets les plus au nord, ceux qui sont situés au centre des platières inférieures sont parallèles à la rupture de pente et semblent s'être formés seuls par suite de l'action des vagues. Certains bourrelets adjacents aux jetées et parallèles à ces mêmes jetées se sont formés par réaction à l'effet combiné des vagues réfléchies et des courants longeant la jetée. Les bourrelets adjacents au chenal principal sont parallèles à la rupture de la pente et ont été sculptés par l'action des vagues. Aucun monticule de sable ne se forme parallèlement à cette jetée, probablement parce que l'eau du chenal s'échappant par des ouvertures de la structure interrompt la dérive longeant la jetée.

Des vasières se forment sur le schorre (a) dans lequel de fins matériaux se déposent (b) aux endroits où l'énergie des vagues et des courants est faible et (c) où des dépressions éparses ou la configuration littorale forme des pièges.

Des réseaux de drainage dendritiques à travers des matériaux à texture relativement fine se forment surtout sur les vasières les moins imperméables situées à côté des marais de schorre, ou aux endroits où la croissance des zostères est dense, c'est-à-dire sur les surfaces sableuses qui avoisinent les bassins dragués ou le versant du delta. L'étendue du réseau à l'intérieur d'une des vasières permet de présumer que l'érosion dans ce milieu est favorisée par le ruissellement en nappe provenant du marais topographiquement supérieur et de la bioturbation.

Les principaux couloirs (vallées sous-marines) entaillent le versant du delta au-delà des embouchures actuelles et anciennes du chenal. Ces particularités peuvent se former à la faveur des mouvements de masse ou des courants de turbidité et elles sont entretenues par le glissement des sédiments accumulés en contre-bas des ravines ainsi que par l'action d'entraînement des courants de marée.

La partie nord du versant sur lequel des boues se déposent, semble être dépourvue de lits principaux, mais sur certaines parties du versant sableux situé au sud, des champs d'ondulations asymétriques (2 à 3 m de hauteur; ∿30 m de longueur) atteignent des profondeurs dépassant 100 m. Ces ondulations sont surtout produites par des courants de flot.

INTRODUCTION

This report presents a general description of the major morphological features on the Fraser Delta western tidal flats and slope, and discusses the processes contributing to their formation. Sources of more detailed related information and studies currently in progress also are identified.

General geographic and geological setting

The Fraser River delta extends from New Westminster south into Boundary Bay and west into the Strait of Georgia (Fig. 25.1). It is bounded to the north by Burrard Peninsula (on which lies Vancouver), to the east by the Surrey uplands and to the southwest by Point Roberts Peninsula, a former island (Fig. 25.1). The surficial geology of these areas, with the exception of Point Roberts Peninsula south of the International Border, has been described by Johnston (1923) and Armstrong (1956, 1957). Burrard Peninsula consists of two pre-Pleistocene bedrock ridges trending east-west, overlain mainly by glacial and raised littoral deposits. These same types of Pleistocene material also constitute much of Point Roberts Peninsula. Surrey uplands evolved from glaciomarine gravelly clay deposits.

The first summary reports on the geological development of the delta were prepared by W.A. Johnston over 50 years ago (Johnston, 1921a, b, 1922, 1923). Since then, studies by Armstrong (1956, 1957), Mathews and Shepard (1962) and Mathews et al. (1970) have added to knowledge of the evolution of the delta. The foregoing reports indicate that the present Fraser River delta began to fan out from the gap in the uplands at New Westminster (Fig. 25.1) about 8000 years ago. By then the last of the Pleistocene ice had disappeared from the Fraser Canyon and local postglacial rebound was virtually complete. The delta has since prograded approximately 30 km into the Strait of Georgia and has built up deposits 90 - 200 m thick over Pleistocene sediments. Minor eustatic fluctuations, tectonically induced warping of coastal areas, extreme river floods, and intense storms from the Strait of Georgia have caused variations in the regular patterns of sedimentation, but the thickness of uppermost sediment units suggest that sedimentary environments have remained relatively stable.

General morphological character

The western delta front, unlike the southern front at Boundary Bay is fed by a network of distributary channels (Figs. 25.1, 25.2). The most conspicuous feature is a broad tidal flat, with a gradient of approximately 0.05° (.0005), which is part of a platform approximately 6 km wide extending from the dykes at the edge of the cultivated Recent alluvium to the break in slope at approximately 9 m below lowest normal tide level (Luternauer and Murray, 1973). The part of the delta foreslope which is not dissected by gullies (Fig. 25.2) has an average gradient of approximately 1.5° (Mathews and Shepard, 1962) but may be inclined as steeply as 23° along its upper reaches (Swan Wooster Engineering Co. Ltd., 1967; Scotton, 1977).

MAJOR INFLUENCES ON THE PRESENT MORPHOLOGICAL CHARACTER OF THE DELTA FRONT

Fluvial

The present Fraser River drains an approximately 233 000 km^2 area of geologically diverse terrain (Mathews and Shepard, 1962). Although sediment supply can range widely, approximately 20×10^6 tons of sand and mud are annually carried to the delta distributary system (W.L. Krueder, Inland Waters Directorate, Environment Canada, pers. com.). These sediments reflect their varied sources and contain volcanic rock fragments, quartzite, chert, quartz, feldspar, amphiboles, epidote, pyroxene, chlorites, micas, magnetite and montmorillonoid minerals (Mackintosh and Gardner, 1966; Griffin et al., 1968; Garrison et al., 1969; Grieve, 1977). About 80 per cent of the annual runoff courses through the river during the freshet months of May through July as snowpacks melt (Hoos and Packman, 1974). Within the distributary system 80 - 85 per cent of water flow is confined to the Main Channel with the remainder divided fairly evenly between the North and Middle Arms and Canoe Pass (Fig. 25.1) (Tywoniuk, 1972). The distribution of sediment flow has not been investigated in any detail but it is known that the proportion of sand to mud in transport is greatest in the Main Channel (A. Tamburi, pers. com.).

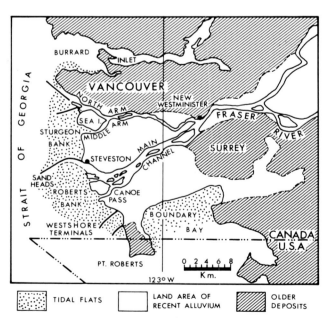

Figure 25.1. *General location and geology of the Fraser River Delta. The western delta front extends from the North Arm distributary to Point Roberts Peninsula.*

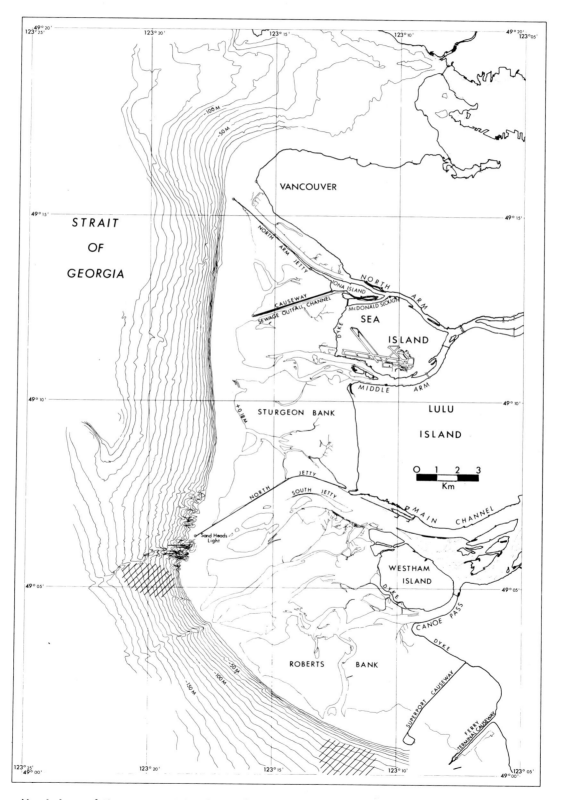

Figure 25.2. *Morphology of the western delta front of the Fraser River. Cross-hatched areas of the slope define zones with highest bedforms (generally 2-3 m). The features off the Main Channel extend into part of the slope usually blanketed with muddy sediments and cannot be considered "sand" waves.*

Figure 25.3

Mosaic of colour imagery obtained over the western delta front on August 7, 1972 (during waning stage of river freshet) displaying surface of tidal flats and plumes of sediment-charged river water intruding the Strait of Georgia. (NAPL RSA 30518-58, 60)

Oceanographic

During the freshet the sediment-charged plume from the Main Channel extends far into the Strait of Georgia (Fig. 25.3). The Coriolis effect acts in concert with tidal drag to deflect the plume towards the Sturgeon Bank slope on a flooding tide, but even on an ebbing tide more fine sediment tends to be directed to the north both because the southeasterly ebb tidal drag on the plume can be balanced by the Coriolis effect (Thomson, 1977) and because the surface water within a few kilometres of the edge of Sturgeon Bank appears to flow persistently to the north, regardless of tidal phase, during the summer (Giovando and Tabata, 1970; Tabata et al., 1971; Tabata, 1972). This northerly drift, which is evident when the Strait is well stratified, may develop as internal gravity waves break obliquely against the Sturgeon Bank slope (Thomson, 1975a).

Once sediment is deposited on the delta front it is redistributed on the tidal flats by wind-generated waves, longshore and tidal currents (mean tidal range is 2.6 m; extremes can exceed 5.4 m (Thomson, 1977)), and river wash. Sediments on the delta slope are reworked primarily by tidal currents. Strongest winds cross the tidal flats from the south, southeast and northwest (Atmospheric Environmental Service, Canada). Northwest winds have the longest fetch (~100 km) and, consequently, generate the highest waves (Thomson, 1977). Average wave height over the slope is about 0.6 m and maximum significant wave height is about 1.5 m, even during winter storms (Hoos and Packman, 1974). On the basis of these values Thomson (1977) has calculated that the most probable maximum waves arriving at the edge of the tidal flats would be 2.9 m. Some of the "most devastating waves" can be expected to develop when deep-water waves reaching the flats are amplified by both the shoaling of the bottom and by the effect of wind opposing an ebbing tide reinforced by a high Fraser River discharge (Hoos and Packman, 1974).

Over the delta slope tidal currents tend to parallel bathymetric contours and flood currents are somewhat stronger and of longer duration than ebb currents (Pickard, 1956; Thomson, 1975b; Luternauer et al., 1978) (Fig. 25.4). It has been established that near the bottom tidal currents are strong enough to transport sand-sized material (Luternauer et al., 1978).

Man-imposed

Approximately 4×10^6 tons of sediment (consisting mainly of sand) is dredged annually from the Main Channel and North Arm (Pretious, 1972). As this material is dumped on channel margins and over the delta slope off the mouths of these channels, it is removed from estuarine circulation.

In addition to altering the sediment budget, dredging the Main Channel may also influence sediment circulation by contributing to the intrusion of the 'salt wedge' from the Strait of Georgia. Mathews and Shepard (1962) speculated that this tongue of salt water could inhibit the down-channel movement of sand on a northward-flooding tide while permitting the silt and clay suspended load to be carried over the Sturgeon Bank slope. Conversely, it was suspected that as the tide ebbs and the wedge retreats downstream, both mud and sand escape from the river and flow south over the Roberts Bank slope. This southerly dispersal of sand has, in fact, been supported by a tagged sand experiment performed within and at the margins of the Main Channel (British Columbia Research, 1975).

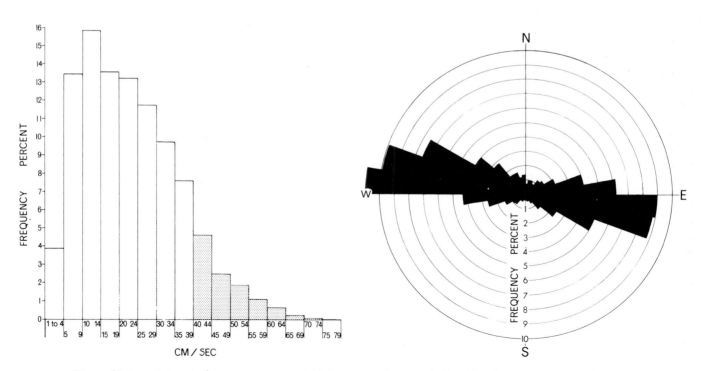

Figure 25.4. *Velocity frequency-per cent histogram and current direction frequency-per cent rose compiled from data acquired during 94 day period by current meter moored at 77 m depth at centre of sand wave zone on southern Roberts Bank (Fig. 25.2). Stippled bars on histogram indicate velocities probably capable of generating general sediment motion on the slope.*

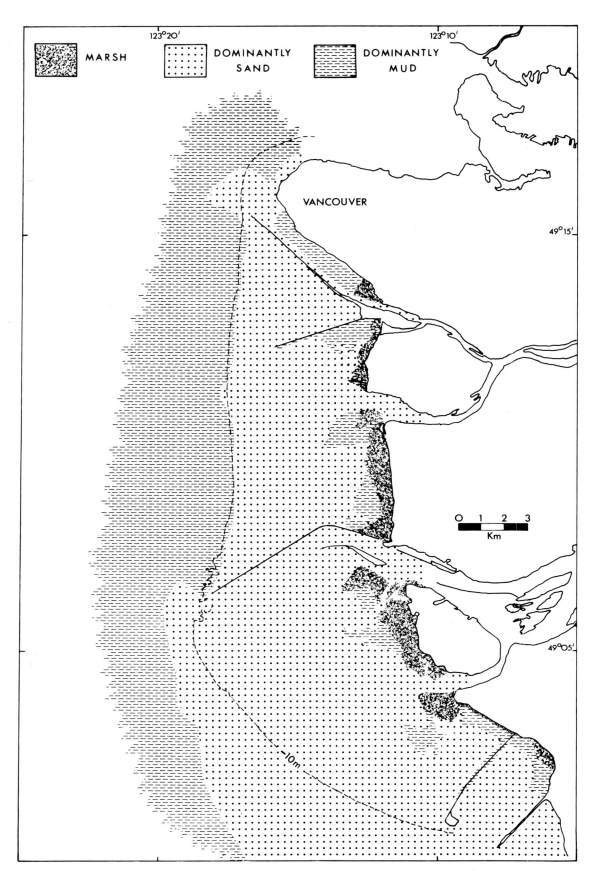

Figure 25.5 *General sediment distribution and marsh zones. The muddy area in the North Arm distributary is largely a booming ground.*

As sediment is discharged from the river distributaries onto the tidal flats its free circulation is impeded by the jetties and causeways which have been erected across the flats (Fig. 25.2). These structures also shelter segments of the tidal flats from river wash and contribute to the development of along-jetty currents (Thomson, 1977; Daniel and LeBlond, 1977).

Mass wasting and gravity flows

Various forms of mass wasting and gravity flows may also contribute, albeit at varying frequencies, to the redistribution of sediment deposits on the delta slope. Mathews and Shepard (1962), Tiffin (1969) and Tiffin et al. (1971) have suggested that the large hummocks (foreslope hills) evident at the base of the slope off the Main Channel were formed by a massive slide which occurred approximately 200 years ago. Scotton (1977) has stated that "earthquake stability analysis indicates that [Sturgeon and Roberts Bank] sediments could be liquified by an earthquake of a magnitude and duration which is within the range of possible seismic activity of the area", but he adds "there is no proven evidence of previous liquefaction on the banks..." and "the surveys which have thus far been carried out on the subaqueous slopes have found no evidence of mass wasting other than the previously discussed [hummocks]."

It would appear that the bulk of down-slope sediment movement is concentrated in the slope gullies which extend off the major distributaries and may involve a combination of sliding (Mathews and Shepard, 1962) and turbidity currents (Scotton, 1977).

Earlier deposits

Seismic and sampling surveys strongly suggest that the present sediment distribution off Roberts Bank also reflects the presence of earlier foreset deposits or residual Pleistocene sediment (Mathews and Shepard, 1962; Tiffin, 1969; Pharo and Barnes, 1976; Luternauer, 1976a).

PRESENT SEDIMENT DISTRIBUTION

The sediment distribution resulting from all the above processes and influences is displayed in summary form in Figure 25.5, which is adapted from Luternauer (1976a) and Medley and Luternauer (1976).

DESCRIPTION AND GENESIS OF MORPHOLOGICAL FEATURES

Sand swells

The large-scale, elongate, parallel bedforms crossing the tidal flat surface are here described as swells because the features have a subdued asymmetry and impart a gently undulating character to the intertidal surface (Fig. 25.6). In places they occur over broad areas similar in extent to the multiple parallel sandbar zones described by Nilsson (1973). The individual swells may extend several hundred metres, have wavelengths ranging from 50 - 100 m, and heights that generally do not exceed 0.5 m (Medley and Luternauer, 1976).

The following conditions are considered to contribute (although all may not be essential) to the formation of multiple parallel sandbars in the marine environment (Zenkovitch, 1967; Nilsson, 1973; Parker, 1975; Komar, 1976):

(1) broad, low gradient coastal platform consisting of almost 100 per cent sand-sized sediment,
(2) repeatedly breaking and reconstructing waves or standing waves, or both,
(3) variable wave heights, and
(4) high tidal range.

These conditions are either known to exist or are suspected to exist at the Fraser Delta front. The extent to which they may interact to determine the character of the sand swells is only now being studied.

Sand swells have not developed extensively on Roberts Bank but are evident across broad expanses of Sturgeon Bank (Fig. 25.7). The swells found along the outer flats tend to parallel the break in the slope. Those which have developed adjacent to jetties and causeways are oriented anywhere from near normal to near parallel to these structures. One field of swells lies neither on the lower flats nor adjacent to manmade structures, but extends shoreward from the central flats on southern Sturgeon Bank and meets the vegetated marsh (Fig. 25.8). Most individual features within this field are parallel to the north-south oriented marsh front although several of them have a more northwesterly strike.

The sand swells on the outer flats probably form as water waves, driven by northwesterly or westerly winds, migrate across the tidal flats during different stages of the tide. The orientation of the swells adjacent to the North Arm jetty and sewage causeway (Fig. 25.7A) and the gradually lengthening spit at the end of the causeway suggest that wave-induced along-jetty currents coupled with refracted waves have been instrumental in the development of these sand bodies. Sand composing these bedforms may be supplied from the North Arm, by littoral drift from the south or by erosion of the central part of the V-shaped area.

Figure 25.6. *Sand swells on upper tidal flats west of Steveston and north of the Main Channel.*

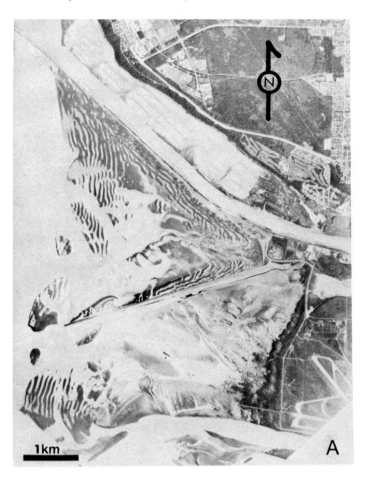

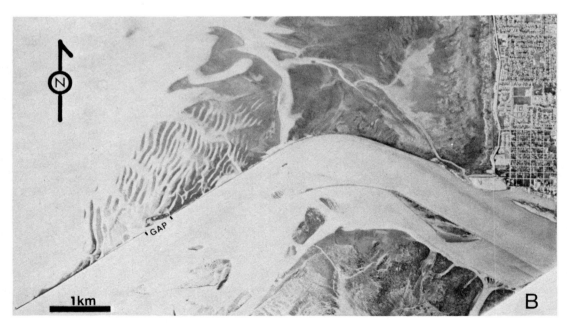

Figure 25.7. *Fields of sand swells (multiple parallel sand bars) on (A) northern and (B) southern Sturgeon Bank on June 20, 1978. Note: (1) spit/sand swell which has formed (and is extending eastward) on the north side of the end of the sewage causeway; (2) rudimentary channel forming at midsection of upper tidal flats between causeway and North Arm jetty; (3) curved swells near junction of jetty and causeway. All these features suggest the presence of along-jetty currents which drain seaward across the midsection of the V-shaped area. In Figure 25.7B the location of the largest gap in the jetty is indicated. (NAPL A37597-152, 160)*

Water driven along the jetty and causeway meets at the junction of the two structures then drains off along the midsection of the V-shaped area, where a shallow channel is gradually forming in the locally more silty sediments (Medley and Luternauer, 1976). A similar circulation pattern has been documented for the area bounded by the Tsawwassen ferry causeway and Point Roberts Peninsula (Daniel and Le Blond, 1977) (Figs. 25.1, 25.2) where, however, dense eelgrass growth has suppressed the development of sands swells.

The sand swells lying immediately to the north of the Steveston North Jetty (Fig. 25.7B) tend to parallel the break in slope. Few, if any, sand forms parallel the jetty. This field of swells would appear to be shaped primarily by the direct influence of wind-driven waves migrating across the flats. The development of sand bodies paralleling the jetty is probably inhibited by water flow north across this jetty which has tended to limit the accumulation of sand against the structure.

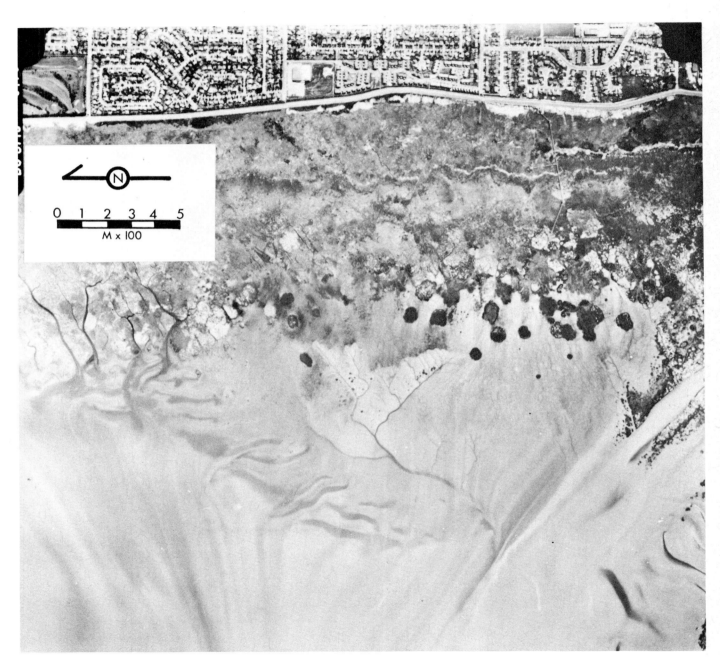

Figure 25.8. *Vertical view of mud pool – dendritic drainage network – sand swell complex on upper tidal flats west of Steveston on July 14, 1976. Sand swell field at bottom right is the same as that pictured in Figure 25.6. Note path of ebb tidal flows draining the tidal flats. (Government of British Columbia air photo B.C. 5719: 170)*

The field of sand swells on southern Sturgeon Bank, which extends from the flats into the marsh (Fig. 25.8) and north along the marsh front, appears to have been sculpted mainly by waves approaching normal to the shoreline and possibly by a northward-flowing longshore current. The field is a moderately stable feature (Figs. 25.8, 25.9), which may have developed in part from dredged sands dumped early in the century north of the partially completed jetty and dispersed by tidal creeks and long shore currents. The northwest-southeast trending features evident within the field may have been superimposed on the generally north-south oriented swells by escaping ebb-tidal water (Fig. 25.8).

Sand swell fields have not developed on Roberts Bank to any significant extent (except south of the U.S. border), probably because it is sheltered from the larger waves approaching from the northwest and southeast and because finer suspended matter and river wash, from the largely unconfined south side of the part of the Main Channel crossing the flats, will suppress the development of the features (Parker, 1975) or eradicate them if they are generated.

Mud pools

Mud is accumulating in the bulrush-sedge-cattail marsh on the upper tidal flats and at sites fringing this marsh (Fig. 25.5) which may be periodically vegetated with algae and eelgrass. The limits of all but one of the mud pools varies seasonally and annually. The one exception lies just north of the Steveston North Jetty and is bounded by the two fields of sand swells described earlier (Figs. 25.6, 25.8). Cores obtained within this pool indicate that the predominantly muddy sediments are at least 63 cm thick (Medley, 1978).

Previous studies (see Klein, 1964) of such fine-sediment intertidal deposits indicate that they form along the upper flats because this area is submerged for relatively short periods and consequently is not as frequently scoured and reworked by waves and currents. The specific sites on the upper flats where the mud pools develop probably are further governed by the location of shallow depressions, shoreline configuration and the dispersal routes of suspended sediments derived from distributaries and resuspended from the outer flats.

Dendritic drainage networks

Arborescent drainage systems are most evident where mud is accumulating on the tidal flats. However, they do develop on eelgrass-covered sandy surfaces on southernmost Roberts Bank adjacent to dredged basins and near the break in slope.

Medley (1978) has prepared a study of one of the most extensive dendritic drainage networks developing on the Fraser Delta foreshore. This feature lies to the west of Steveston (Fig. 25.1) within the mud pool enclosed by sand swell fields discussed earlier (Figs. 25.6, 25.8, 25.9). It is estimated that the feature began to evolve early in this century and has extended towards the shore at rates as high as 1 m/month (Fig. 25.9). Network extension is promoted by bioturbation and sheetwash from the topographically higher marsh. The severity with which the creek system has degraded the mud flat surface in places (Fig. 25.10) gave rise to concerns that it might eventually erode what is considered an ecologically important marsh (Hoos and Packman, 1974). However, the pattern of vascular plant colonization adjacent to smaller creeks which have already reached the marsh (Fig. 25.11) suggests the extensive dendritic drainage network may actually promote marsh colonization. As the network creeks become intergrated with the existing marsh drainage system the 'moat', which now lies between the marsh and the heads of the network creeks (Fig. 25.12), will be drained and no longer inhibit rhyzome propagation, which appears to proceed more vigorously where the substrate is not perpetually saturated (A. Moody, pers. com.). Tidal creeks also generate new areas favourable to marsh grass colonization by funnelling in suspended sediments which build up interfluvial sites.

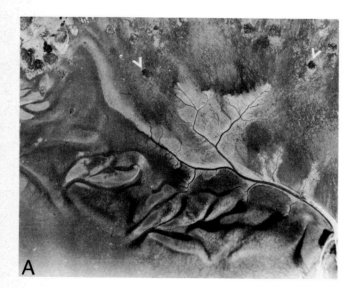
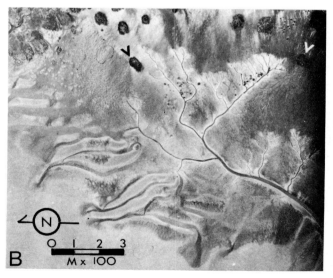

Figure 25.9. *Two views of the sand swell field and dendritic drainage network developing within muddy sediments trapped between marsh and swell field. Photo A was obtained on April 1954; Photo B on July 1974. General character of swell field has remained unchanged but erosive front of creek system has advanced shoreward. Arrow heads identify identical marsh outliers in both photos. (A) – NAPL A13977-18; (B) Integrated Resources Photography Inc. air photo 142:82.*

Figure 25.10

View of erosive front (nick point) at head of one of creeks within dendritic drainage network which has developed in mud pool on upper tidal flat west of Steveston (Fig. 25.8).

Figure 25.11

View of upper tidal flats west of Steveston immediately north of Main Channel. Note in foreground that marsh colonization adjacent to creeks is related to the extent to which tidal creeks have become integrated with pre-existing marsh drainage (Medley, 1978).

Figure 25.12

Oblique view of section of dendritic creek network in mud pool on upper tidal flat west of Steveston. Note featureless part of flats between marsh front and creeks. This part of flats is awash with water draining from marsh. By concentrating this flow and directing it to the lower flats local creeks make intertidal surface adjacent to channels more suitable for vascular plant colonization (note scattered clumps of vegetation on dry tidal flat surface in foreground). (Medley, 1978).

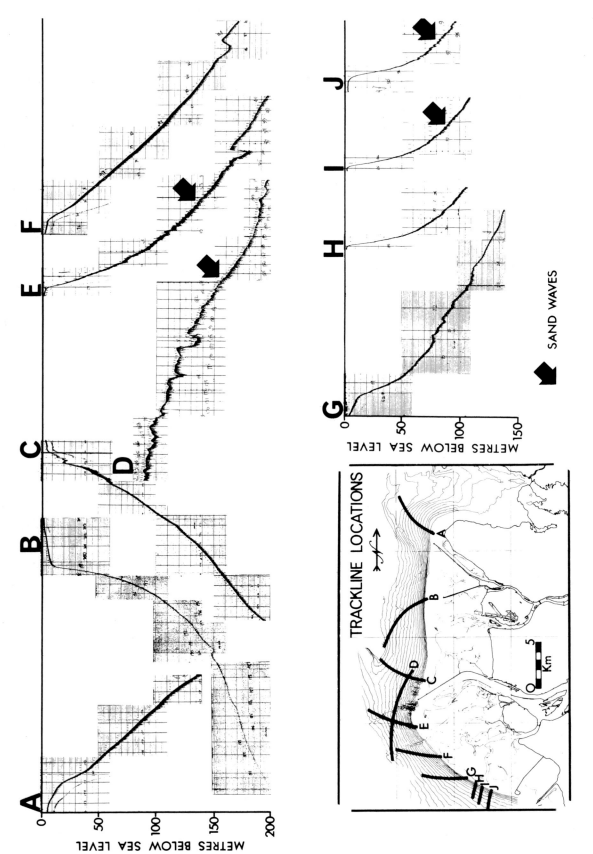

Figure 25.13. *Selected echo-sounding records from a 1974 Canadian Hydrographic Services survey of the Fraser River Delta slope. Variable vertical exaggeration.*

Slope gullies (sea valleys)

Well defined gullies (or sea valleys, as F.P. Shepard, pers. com. has referred to them) crease the delta slope to approximately 200 m off the Main Channel and off the common mouth of three tidal/distributary channels approximately 4 km south of Sand Heads Light (Figs. 25.2, 25.13). Smaller gullies are evident at such places as the lower slope off the Middle Arm and at the head of the slope immediately north of Sand Heads Light. The best defined features lie at the head of the Main Channel gully. These are approximately 500 m wide and 20 - 40 m deep.

Several processes are considered to contribute to the formation of such features: turbidity currents, activity of benthic animals, tensional or graben faulting, lateral erosion leading to undercutting and slumping, and upbuilding in the form of levees (Coleman et al., 1974; Andrews and Hurley, 1978).

General studies of the geomorphic and geotechnical character of the Fraser River Delta slope suggest that the two major gullies were formed as a result of mass wasting or turbidity currents and may be maintained by the sliding of accumulated gully-bottom sediments and the flushing action of tidal currents (Mathews and Shepard, 1962; Terzaghi, 1962; Scotton, 1977; Shepard and Milliman, 1978). Although a section of the Main Channel gully (Fig. 25.13; trackline D) has a more or less flat bottom and steep sides, it is premature to suggest that this feature may have originated as a tensional fault, as has been proposed for similarly shaped gullies on the Mississippi Delta (Coleman et al., 1974).

The short gully, the head of which lies 150 m off the mouth of the Middle Arm (Figs. 25.2, 25.13), is just below one of the steepest parts of the delta slope. If turbidity currents triggered by failed deposits at the head of the slope generated this feature then the upper part of the valley now lies buried under fine sediments subsequently discharged from the Middle Arm and Main Channel. However, the short valley may have simply resulted from a localized mudflow in the water-charged very fine slope deposits.

The short valleys at the head of the slope immediately north of Sand Heads (Fig. 25.2) may be, in part, remnants of earlier valleys formed when the Main Channel of the Fraser River disgorged its sediments on this part of the slope from 1886 to 1900 (Public Works Canada, 1949). Since the Steveston North Jetty was completed in 1932 (Public Works Canada, 1949) enough coarse sediment may still reach the area immediately north of Sand Heads to cascade down and scour the upper slope. However, deposition farther down the slope may be proceeding fast enough to compensate for such erosion and gradually bury the lower reaches of valleys formed earlier.

Sand waves

Sand waves, which have been observed to depths of more than 100 m (Figs. 25.2, 25.13 - 25.15), are best developed and are found in greatest profusion on the Roberts Bank slope off the mouth of the Main Channel and off the Superport (Fig. 25.2) (Luternauer, 1976b). The southern zone has been most extensively studied because Public Works Canada's proposed training of the Main Channel may alter the sediment budget of this part of the slope and because of its proximity to existing port facilities and proposed new developments.

As the area is approached from the west, subdued, straight-crested wave-forms oriented approximately north-south first come into view (Fig. 25.14). These grade into higher waves with more sinuous crests. Towards the centre of the zone the features are disjointed and lobate, with heights of approximately 3 m and wavelengths of 30 m or more (Luternauer et al., 1978) (Fig. 25.15).

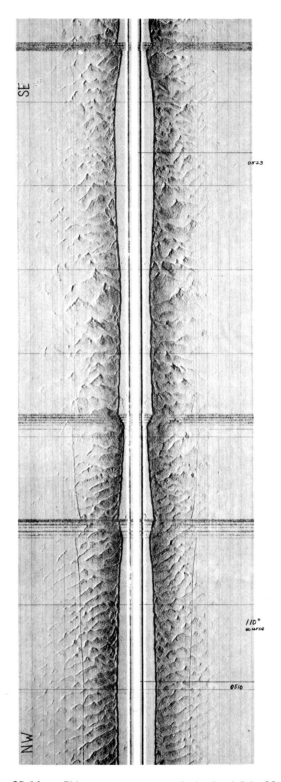

Figure 25.14. *Side-scan sonar record obtained July 22, 1976 from edge to centre of sand wave zone on southern Roberts Bank slope (Fig. 25.2). Record spans area approximately 2 km long and 300 m wide at a 70-80 m depth.*

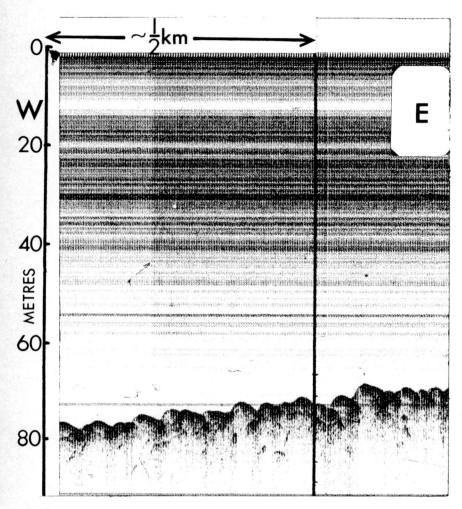

Figure 25.15.

Section of sounding record obtained coincidentally with side-scan sonar record displayed in Figure 25.14. Steep (lee) slopes of waves continue to face west in spite of fact ebbing tide had been running to the east over 5 hours. The tidal range during this tidal cycle was only average for this area and it is possible that the larger bedforms are being generated or reformed only during peak current flows.

Local currents 3 m above the bottom were monitored for 94 days and it was estimated that current velocities were high enough to permit general sediment motion for at least 10 per cent of this period (Sternberg, 1971; Luternauer et al., 1978) (Fig. 25.4). Whenever the writer has sounded this area the lee side of at least the larger waves has always faced west. This observation coupled with measurements that indicate that flood currents are slightly stronger and of longer duration than associated ebb currents, suggests that there is a net westerly transport of sand through this site. This would lead to erosion of the slope, as there is no significant fluvial source of sand to the east (Luternauer et al., 1978). A PISCES submersible dive has revealed ledges and what appear the be lag deposits (mud chips) within the sand wave zone (Luternauer, 1976a).

Detailed revisory surveys of the Roberts Bank slope planned for the summer of 1979 should reveal whether this part of the slope with sand wave fields is, in fact, receding or whether sand waves are just better developed where there is only a veneer of loose sand on earlier, better consolidated sediments.

SUMMARY

The major morphological features on the western delta front of the Fraser River are sand swells, mud pools and dendritic networks on the tidal flats and gullies (sea valleys) and sand waves on the delta slope. Sand swells have formed primarily in response to wind-generated waves or the combined effect of waves and longshore currents. Where wave and current energy may be adequate to generate swells river wash and silt deposition may inhibit their development. Mud pools have formed on those parts of the upper tidal flats (a) into which fine sediment is directed, (b) where wave and current energy is low, and (c) where local depressions or shoreline configuration form traps. Relatively fine textured dendritic drainage most commonly develops within less permeable muddy zones. An extensively studied example (Medley, 1978) indicates that the erosion front (nick point) can migrate as fast as 1 m/month. Continuous sheetwash from the topographically higher marsh and bioturbation promote this erosion. Mechanisms contributing to local gully (sea valley) formation have not been studied in detail, but it is suspected that mass wasting or turbidity currents, sliding of accumulated gully-bottom sediments and the flushing action of tidal currents may all play a part. The largest sandwaves on the southernmost slope of the western delta front appear to be generated by flood-tidal currents.

Acknowledgments

The author wishes to thank B.D. Bornhold and J. Harper for reading and making several improvements to the text and L. Sarracino for performing grain size analyses.

References

Andrews, J.E. and Hurley, R.J.
1978: Sedimentary processes in the formation of a submarine canyon; Marine Geology, v. 26, M47 - M50.

Armstrong, J.E.
1956: Surficial geology of Vancouver area, British Columbia; Geological Survey of Canada, Paper 55-40, 16 p.
1957: Surficial geology of New Westminster map-area, British Columbia; Geological Survey of Canada, Paper 57-5, 25 p.

British Columbia Research
1975: Silt tagging and sediment tracer study---Project 2329; prepared for Public Works Canada.

Coleman, J.M., Suhayda, J.N., Whelan, T. and Wright, L.D.
1974: Mass movement of Mississippi River delta sediments; Transactions, Gulf Coast Geological Societies, v. 24. p. 49 - 68.

Daniel, P. and LeBlond, P.H.
1977: Longshore currents near the Tsawwassen jetty; in Program with Abstracts, 1977, Geological Association of Canada, Annual Meeting, Vancouver, B.C., v. 2, p. 15.

Garrison, R.E., Luternauer, J.L., Grill, E.V., Macdonald, R.D. and Murray, J.W.
1969: Early diagenetic cementation of recent sands, Fraser River Delta, British Columbia; Sedimentology, v. 12, no. 1/2, p. 27 - 46.

Giovando, L.F. and Tabata, S.
1970: Measurements of surface flow in the Strait of Georgia by means of free-floating current followers; Fisheries Research Board of Canada, Technical Report 163, 69 p.

Grieve, D.A.
1977: Behaviour of some trace metals in sediments of the Fraser River delta-front, southwestern British Columbia; unpubl. M.Sc. thesis, University of British Columbia, Vancouver.

Griffin, J.J., Windom, H. and Goldberg, E.D.
1968: The distribution of clay minerals in the world ocean; Deep-Sea Research, v. 15, no. 4, p. 433 - 459.

Hoos, L.M. and Packman, G.A.
1974: The Fraser River Estuary---status of environmental knowledge to 1974; Report of the Estuary Working Group, Environment Canada, Regional Board, Pacific Region, Special Estuary Series, no. 1, 518 p.

Johnston, W.A.
1921a: Sedimentation of the Fraser River Delta; Geological Survey of Canada, Memoir 125, 46 p.
1921b: The age of the recent delta of Fraser River, British Columbia, Canada; American Journal of Science, Series 5, v. 1, no. 5, p. 450 - 453.
1922: The character of the stratification of the sediments in the recent delta of Fraser River, British Columbia, Canada; Journal of Geology, v. 30, no. 2, p. 115 - 129.
1923: Geology of the Fraser River delta map-area; Geological Survey of Canada, Memoir 135, 87 p.

Klein, G. de V.
1964: Sedimentary facies in Bay of Fundy intertidal zone, Nova Scotia, Canada; in Deltas and Shallow Marine Deposits, Proceedings 6th International Sedimentology Congress, The Netherlands and Belgium---1963, L.M.J.V. van Straaten, ed.; Developments in Sedimentology, v. 1, Elsevier, New York, p. 193 - 199.

Komar, P.
1976: Beach Processes and Sedimentation; Prentice-Hall, Englewood Cliffs, N.J., 429 p.

Luternauer, J.L.
1976a: Fraser Delta sedimentation, Vancouver, British Columbia; in Report of Activities, Part A; Geological Survey of Canada, Paper 76-1A, p. 213 - 219.
1976b: Fraser Delta sedimentation, Vancouver, British Columbia; in Report of Activities, Part B; Geological Survey of Canada, Paper 76-1B, p. 169 - 171.

Luternauer, J.L. and Murray, J.W.
1973: Sedimentation on the western delta-front of the Fraser River, British Columbia; Canadian Journal of Earth Sciences, v. 10, no. 11, p. 1642 - 1663.

Luternauer, J.L., Swan, D. and Linden, R.H.
1978: Sand waves on the southeastern slope of Roberts Bank, Fraser River Delta, British Columbia; in Current Research, Part A, Geological Survey of Canada, Paper 78-1A, p. 351 - 356.

Mackintosh, E.E. and Gardner, E.H.
1966: A mineralogical and chemical study of lower Fraser River alluvial sediments; Canadian Journal of Soil Science, v. 46, no. 1, p. 37 - 46.

Mathews, W.H., Fyles, J.G. and Nasmith, H.W.
1970: Postglacial crustal movements in southwestern British Columbia and adjacent Washington State; Canadian Journal of Earth Sciences, v. 7, no. 2, pt. 2, p. 690 - 702.

Mathews, W.H. and Shepard, F.P.
1962: Sedimentation of Fraser River Delta, British Columbia; American Association of Petroleum Geologists Bulletin, v. 46, no. 8, p. 1416 - 1438.

Medley, E.
1978: Dendritic drainage channels and tidal flat erosion, west of Steveston, Fraser River Delta, British Columbia; unpubl. B.A.Sc. thesis, University of British Columbia, Department of Geological Sciences, Vancouver, 70 p.

Medley, E. and Luternauer, J.L.
1976: Use of aerial photographs to map sediment distribution and to identify historical changes on a tidal flat; in Report of Activities, Part C; Geological Survey of Canada, Paper 76-1C, p. 293 - 304.

Nilsson, H.D.
1973: Sand bars along low energy beaches (Part 1) ---multiple parallel sand bars of southeastern Cape Cod Bay; in Coastal Geomorphology, D.R. Coates, ed.; Publications in Geomorphology, State University of New York, Binghamton, p. 99 - 102.

Parker, W.R.
1975: Sediment mobility and erosion on a multi-barred foreshore (southwest Lancashire, U.K.); in Nearshore Sediment Dynamics and Sedimentation, J.Hails and A.Carr, eds.; Wiley, Toronto, p. 151 - 179.

Pharo, C.H. and Barnes, W.C.
1976: Distribution of surficial sediments of the central and southern Strait of Georgia, British Columbia; Canadian Journal of Earth Sciences, v. 13, p. 684 - 696.

Pickard, G.L.
1956: Surface and bottom currents in the Strait of Georgia; Journal, Fisheries Research Board of Canada, v. 13, p. 581 - 590.

Pretious, E.S.
1972: Downstream sedimentation effects of dams on the Fraser River, British Columbia; Department of Civil Engineering, University of British Columbia, Water Resources Series 6, 91 p.

Public Works Canada
1949: History of improvements 1871 to date---Fraser River System, Province of British Columbia; Dominion Public Works Department (revised to 1957).

Scotton, S.
1977: The outer banks of the Fraser River Delta; engineering properties and stability considerations; unpubl. M.A.Sc. thesis, University of British Columbia, Vancouver.

Shepard, F.P. and Milliman, J.D.
1978: Sea-floor currents on the foreset slope of the Fraser River Delta, British Columbia (Canada); Marine Geology, v. 28, p. 245 - 251.

Sternberg, R.W.
1971: Measurements of incipient motion of sediment particles in the marine environment; Marine Geology, v. 10, p. 113 - 119.

Swan Wooster Engineering Co. Ltd.
1967: Planning study for outer port development at Vancouver, B.C. (in three parts); prepared for National Harbours Boards, Vancouver.

Tabata, S.
1972: The movement of Fraser River - influenced surface water in the Strait of Georgia as deduced from a series of aerial photographs; Pacific Marine Science Report 72-6, 69 p., Marine Sciences Branch, Pacific Region, Institute of Ocean Sciences, Patricia Bay.

Tabata, S., Giovando, L.F. and Devlin, D.
1971: Current velocities in the vicinity of the greater Vancouver sewerage and drainage districts Iona Island outfall---1968; Fisheries Research Board of Canada Technical Report 263, 110 p.

Terzaghi, K.
1962: Discussion of "Sedimentation of Fraser River Delta, British Columbia" by Mathews and Shepard (1962); American Association of Petroleum, Geological Bulletin, v. 46, no. 8, p. 1438 - 1443.

Thomson, R.E.
1975a: Longshore current generation by internal waves in the Strait of Georgia; Canadian Journal of Earth Sciences, v. 12, p. 472 - 488.
1975b: The physical oceanography of the British Columbia coast. Part VI. The Strait of Georgia; Pacific Yachting, v. 9, p. 42 - 45, 140 - 145.
1977: The oceanographic setting of the Fraser River delta front; unpubl. manuscript, Institute of Ocean Sciences, Patricia Bay.

Tiffin, D.L.
1969: Continuous seismic reflection profiling in the Strait of Georgia, British Columbia; unpubl. Ph.D. thesis, University of British Columbia, Vancouver.

Tiffin, D.L., Murray, J.W., Mayers, I.R. and Garrison, R.E.
1971: Structure and origin of foreslope hills, Fraser Delta, British Columbia; Bulletin of Canadian Petroleum Geology, v. 19, p. 589 - 600.

Tywoniuk, N.
1972: Sediment budget of the lower Fraser River (estuary); Water Survey of Canada, Paper presented at 13th International Conference on Coastal Engineering, Vancouver, 6 p.

Zenkovitch, V.P.
1967: Processes of Coastal Development; Oliver and Boyd, Edinburgh, 738 p.

26

STRATEGY FOR HYDRAULIC, GEOLOGIC AND
GEOTECHNICAL ASSESSMENT OF GREAT LAKES SHORELINE BLUFFS

R.M. Quigley[1] and A.J. Zeman[2]

Quigley, R.M. and Zeman, A.J., Strategy for hydraulic, geologic and geotechnical assessment of Great Lakes shoreline bluffs; in The Coastline of Canada, S.B. McCann, editor; Geological Survey of Canada, Paper 80-10, p. 397-406, 1980.

Abstract

Along the Great Lakes, extensive shoreline inventory and mapping activities carried out for long term planning and environmental impact purposes, have led to an increasing need for concise geotechnical classification schemes suitable for strip mapping.

This paper reviews the hydraulic and geotechnical controls that most affect the instability and erosion rates of the Pleistocene bluffs along the Canadian Great Lakes shoreline. Data from Lake Erie are used to illustrate the relationship between wave power impacting on the shoreline and long term erosion rates. Short term deviations from the long term correlations are caused by such factors as large storms and wind set-ups, lake level variations, changes in bottom topography, and changes in slope morphology and geology. These "events", which are significant over the short term, must not be confused with long term trends.

Specific recommendations concerning the types of strip maps required and mapping strategy are presented. These are based on two study areas in the central and western sections of the north shore of Lake Erie.

Résumé

Le long des Grands lacs, un vaste inventaire littoral et des travaux considérables de cartographie ont été effectués aux fins de planification à long terme et d'études des répercussions écologiques; ces travaux ont mis en lumière le besoin de plus en plus pressant d'établissement de schémas de classification géotechnique concis convenant à la cartographie en bandes.

La présente étude passe en revue les contrôles hydrauliques et géotechniques qui affectent le plus l'instabilité et la vitesse d'érosion des escarpements du Pléistocène le long du littoral canadien des Grands lacs. Certaines données provenant du lac Erié servent à illustrer le rapport entre la puissance des vagues déferlant sur le littoral et la vitesse d'érosion à long terme. Certaines déviations à court terme appartenant aux corrélations à long terme sont provoquées par des facteurs comme les tempêtes violentes et les montées de niveau dues aux vents, les variations du niveau du lac, l'évolution dans la topographie du fond et l'évolution morphologique et géologique des versants. Tous ces facteurs, qui ont leur importance sur une courte période, ne doivent pas être confondus avec les tendances à long terme.

Les auteurs présentent certaines recommandations spécifiques concernant les types de cartes en bandes requises et les méthodes cartographiques envisagées. Celles-ci ont été préparées en fonction de deux zones d'études appartenant aux secteurs centre et ouest du littoral nord du lac Erié.

INTRODUCTION

As a growing population presses against the shoreline of the southern Great Lakes, land values are augmenting and the costs of shoreline erosion and protection are increasing dramatically. These financial pressures combined with natural shoreline hazards have led to intensive strip mapping along the shorelines and to attempts to classify the hazards for purposes of publication.

This paper suggests approaches to strip mapping that will relate the results of short-term mapping projects to their perceived long-term usage. Our comments pertain specifically to shoreline bluffs where geotechnical factors (slope instability and soil erodibility) feature significantly in erosion-retreat processes. Of particular significance are the long cyclic variations in Great Lakes water levels, which have a profound effect on bluff morphology and retreat mechanisms. These cycles in shoreline geomorphology may be completely overlooked by short-term mapping projects (1 - 5 years duration).

Bluff erosion results from the complex interaction of nearshore hydraulic conditions and the erodibility and instability of bluff materials. During a mapping project it is essential to consider both the spatial and temporal variability of the natural processes causing erosion at a study site. Of most significance spatially are abrupt changes in geology, stratigraphy and groundwater as they affect both the erodibility and the bluff instability mechanisms over a short stretch of shoreline.

From the temporal point of view, long-term lake level variations of up to 1 m are vitally important at some sites such as Port Bruce, described here. At other locations annual variations or even daily or hourly variations during major storms are more significant, especially if the toe of the bluffs consists of easily erodible granular materials. Also important are the time-dependent aspects of soil softening that lead to intermittent landsliding at intervals of from 1 to 30 years, depending on local geotechnical conditions.

---

[1] Faculty of Engineering Science, University of Western Ontario, London, Canada

[2] Hydraulics Research Division, National Water Research Institute, Burlington, Ontario

Although the comments in this paper pertain specifically to the soil bluffs of the north shore of Lake Erie, the principles are fundamental to all soil or soft rock bluffs which exhibit long-term softening and time-dependent instability.

STUDY LOCATIONS AND EROSION RATES

The two bluff sites selected for comparative study are near Colchester at the west end of Lake Erie and near Port Bruce in central Lake Erie (Fig. 26.1). Although the wave climate is dominated by southwest winds at both sites, the total average wave power is nearly five times greater at Port Bruce than at Colchester. Furthermore, the water level at Colchester is drawn down during strong southwest winds whereas it rises about 0.5 m at Port Bruce (Gelinas and Quigley, 1973). Gelinas (1974) has related the 150-year erosion rates along the central part of the north shore of Lake Erie to calculated wave power (Fig. 26.2). Bluff edge erosion rates vary from about 0.5 to 2.5 m/a* from west to east in response to increasing breaking wave power of 0.5 to about 2.0 kW/m. The erosion rates between Port Stanley and Port Bruce are extraordinarily high because of high-velocity landslides in wet silty soils, as discussed by Quigley et al., (1977). At Colchester, the bluffs are eroding at rates of 0.5 to 2 m/a but in response to breaking wave power of only 0.3 to 0.4 kW/m, as discussed later. Strip maps showing both the bluff edge retreat rates and the impacting wave power that maintains the retreat are fundamental to a shoreline mapping project.

A summary plot of the volumetric retreat rates for the entire north shore of Lake Erie is shown in Figure 26.3. The enormous volumes being eroded from the central part of the Lake Erie shoreline (up to $13 \times 10^5 \, m^3/a$ for 1955-1973) result from the 2.5 m/a retreat of bluffs that are up to 42 m high. In the Colchester area, volumetric erosion is minor in comparison (only $1 \times 10^5 \, m^3/a$ maximum for 1972-1977) largely because the bluffs are much lower. Strip maps showing volumetric erosion rates are obviously vital to sediment loading and related chemical loading problems.

PORT BRUCE CLAY BLUFFS

Retreat rates and mechanisms vary considerably along the central Lake Erie north shore bluffs (Quigley et al., 1977). At the Port Bruce study site slope instability modes range widely in response to the cyclic water levels of Lake Erie, as discussed in some detail by Quigley and Di Nardo (1980). The most significant aspect of this site is that it illustrates a deep-seated instability cycle of up to 30 years that probably occurs only during extended periods of low lake level. A mapping project normally would completely overlook such a long cycle.

A detailed plan of the Port Bruce site is shown in Figure 26.4. In 1964, the bluff edge was characterized by small slides about 10 to 20 m long, which extended about 3 m back from the bluff edge and broke out of the slope about 15 m down the 40 m high bluffs. From 1964 to 1971 the bluffs

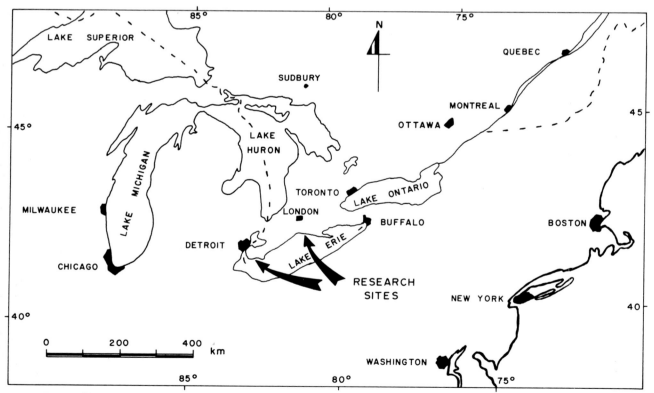

Figure 26.1. *Location of research sites on the north shore of Lake Erie. Colchester and Port Bruce sites are indicated by the left and right arrows respectively.*

---

* a is the SI symbol for year.

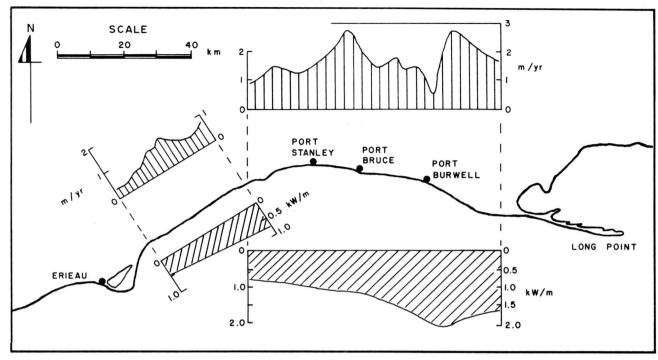

Figure 26.2. *Central Lake Erie north shore showing 150-year erosion rates and calculated wave power (adapted from Gelinas and Quigley, 1973).*

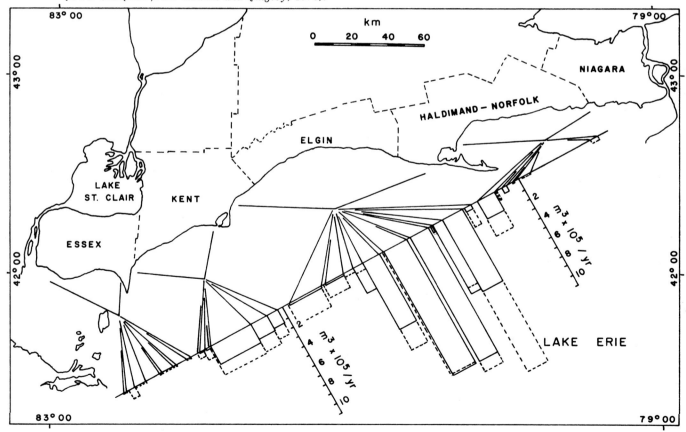

Figure 26.3. *Lake Erie north shore showing volumetric erosion rates; long term (1955-1973) in solid lines; short term (1972-1977) in dashed lines (from Shore Property Studies, Ocean and Aquatic Sciences, Fisheries and Environment Canada, 1977).*

steepened dramatically at the toe as lake levels rose by 1 m, yet the stepped appearance produced by the bluff edge slides remained the most visible feature along the bluffs (top of Figure 26.5). From 1971 to 1977 the bluff edge slides and the stepped appearance disappeared, probably because water levels rose in the surface sands and seepage and surficial sloughing increased at the face of the bluffs. Obviously mapping over a long period would have been necessary to establish the above bluff edge features.

In 1964, a single, huge, very slowly moving slide developed, as shown on the plan in Figure 26.4. The slide was at least 200 m long and extended back about 40 m from the bluff edge. The displacement on the scarp of the slide, only a few centimetres in 1964, had increased to about 5 m by 1977.

By 1978 the entire slide had disappeared and no further large-scale instability was apparent. As discussed at length by Quigley and Di Nardo (1980), it is believed that this large slide represents long-term instability that develops only during extended periods of low water level and reduced erosion. Such slides are therefore highly dependent on time and on lake levels and require very extended study or mapping periods to be detected.

The slope evolution is illustrated by the composite profile shown in Figure 26.5 for the period from 1964 to 1977. The rise in water level steepens the lower slopes by increasing wave attack and toe erosion whereas the upper slopes remain essentially unaffected since they are controlled by bluff edge processes. Again, a given mapping project would have to extend over the correct sequence of years to establish the cyclic changes in geomorphology.

Using the ideas developed above, long-term predictions were developed for the Port Bruce site (Figure 26.6). A long water level cycle of 30 years is assumed and the variation in average bluff slope angles and volumetric erosion rates are predicted based on the past 12 years of observational data shown by the solid curves. It is obvious that one must assess field mapping observations on the basis of the predictions, especially the presence or absence of large long-term landslides. Predictions are, for example, that another slide would not develp until it is triggered by the rise in lake level in 1993. Such a slide probably would not develop if a short water level cycle occurs, since the hard clayey soil would not have softened enough for a failure to develop (Quigley and Di Nardo, 1980).

COLCHESTER SILT-SAND BLUFFS

A variety of strip maps have been prepared describing the hydraulic and geotechnical conditions along 28 km of the western Lake Erie north shore in the Colchester-Pidgeon Bay area (Fig. 26.1).

This stretch of shoreline was selected in 1976 for a comprehensive shoreland management study by federal and provincial agencies since it contains a range of shoreline flooding and erosion problems typical of the Great Lakes region. For study of coastal management alternatives, it is also significant that this particular shoreline contains diverse protective structures, and that shoreline properties fall into several land use and land ownership categories.

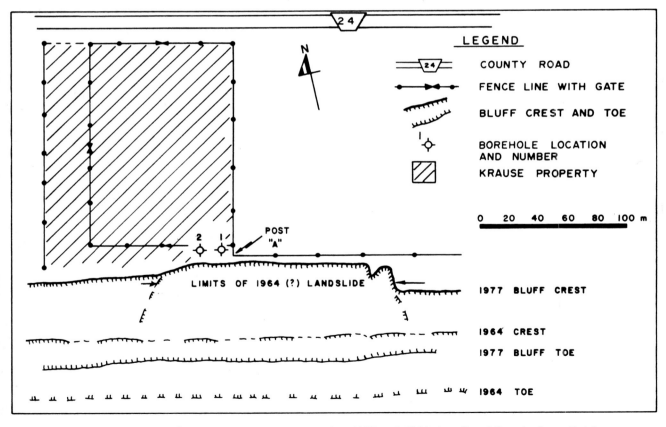

Figure 26.4. *Plan of Port Bruce landslide showing 1977 and 1964 shoreline (directly from Quigley and Di Nardo, 1980).*

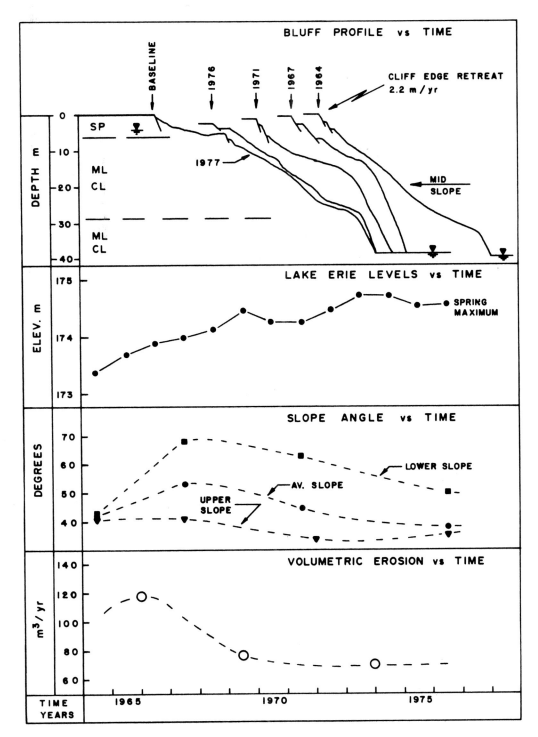

Figure 26.5. *Bluff slope evolution, 1964 to 1977. Horiz. scale = vert. scale in upper diagram. (Directly from Quigley and Di Nardo, 1980).*

The geotechnical strip maps described here were compiled using existing data from previous studies, new topographic maps at a scale of 1:2000, and new geotechnical information obtained in 1977 in connection with the shoreland management study mentioned above (Dillon, M.M., Ltd., 1976).

The general topographic conditions of the shoreline are illustrated in Figure 26.7, which contains a plan and profiles showing bluff height and slope angle. For purposes of this paper, only those sections of shoreline having bluffs higher than 10 m will be discussed. It is also important to note that these bluffs are essentially undeveloped and free from shoreline protection, so that erosion rates may be compared with those of the unprotected bluffs of the Port Bruce area.

Erosion rates for the Colchester shoreline are plotted along with the calculated wave power in Figure 26.8. The wave power values were obtained as follows. First, the wave climate was hindcasted from a ten-year synthesized wind climate for Lake Erie (Richards and Phillips, 1970). With this information as an input, values of the root mean square wave height and the wave velocity were calculated using a computer program developed by Skafel (1975) for the prediction of littoral drift transport. The wave power at the breaking point was then calculated for different wind directions following the procedure given in the U.S. Army Corps of Engineers Shore Protection Manual (1973).

The highest wave power values were derived for prevailing southwest winds, as expected, in the range of about 0.12 to 0.17 kW/m of shoreline. The total wave power varies from about 0.28 to 0.42 kW/m (Fig. 26.8).

A poor correlation was found between wave power and long-term erosion of the entire length of shoreline for a variety of reasons, including variable stratigraphy and erodibility of soils, highly variable bluff heights and extensive manmade modification to the shoreline, especially since 1947. For the bluffs higher than 10 m, the erosion rate for the period 1931 to 1947 was from 0.5 to 2 m/a (Fig. 26.8). The correlation between wave power and 1931-1947 recession rates follows a steeper line than the one established by Gelinas (1974) for the central Lake Erie north shore, but it is not statistically significant (r < 0.6) for the amount of correlation points available.

The weak correlation between wave power and erosion rates is in part attributable to heterogeneous soil stratigraphy (Fig. 26.9) and hence differential erodibility of the Colchester and Pidgeon Bay bluffs. For engineering purposes, it appears advantageous to simplify complex geological information available from a borehole exploration program by the use of the Unified Soil Classification, as shown in Figure 26.9, instead of using traditional geological descriptions. Another explanation of the poor correlation could be the variable orientation of the shoreline relative to the dominant southwesterly wave direction.

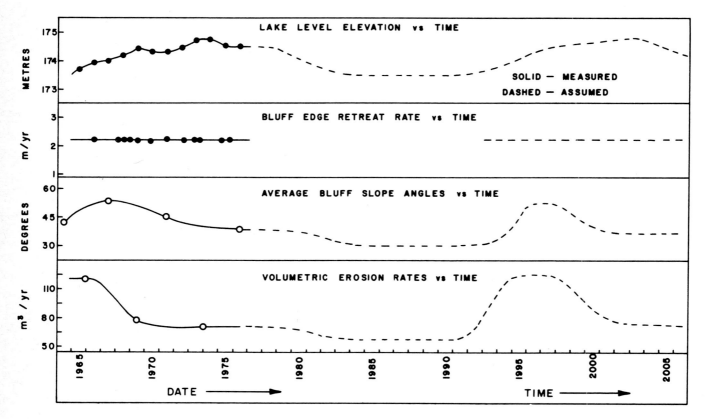

Figure 26.6. *Cyclic lake level, slope angle and volumetric erosion rate variations with time (directly from Quigley and Di Nardo, 1980).*

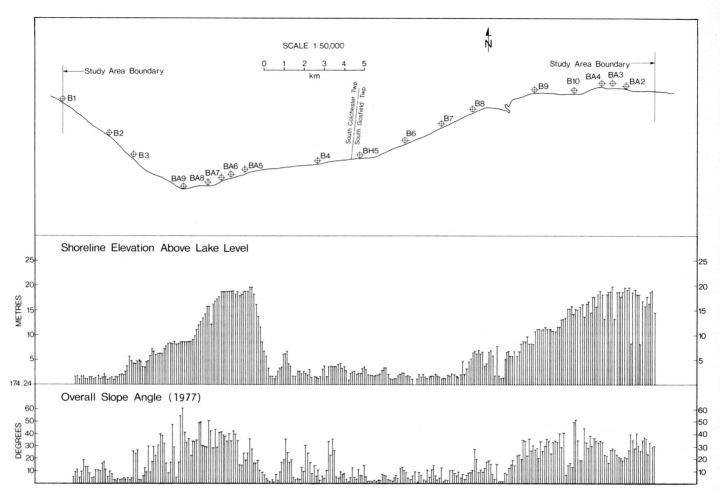

Figure 26.7. *General topography of Colchester-Pidgeon Bay shoreline.*

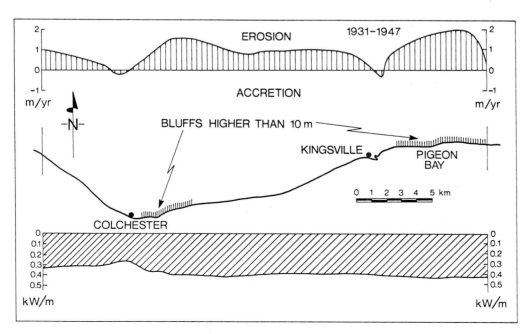

Figure 26.8

Colchester-Pidgeon Bay shoreline showing 16-year erosion rates and calculated wave power (bluff sections noted).

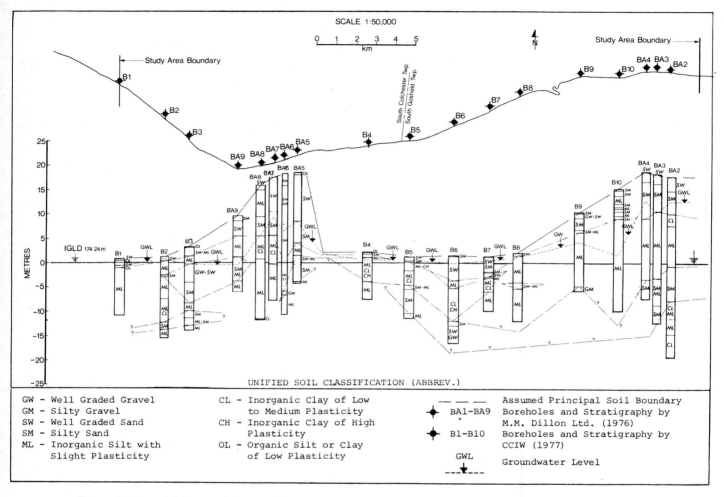

Figure 26.9. *Colchester-Pidgeon Bay shoreline showing stratigraphy based on Unified Soil Classification System.*

DISCUSSION AND CONCLUSIONS

The long-term, bluff edge erosion rates were correlated with average wave power by Gelinas (1974) and Gelinas and Quigley (1973) for the central Lake Erie north shore, as shown on Figure 26.10. The plot, despite the scatter, shows clearly, as would be expected, that the erosion rate increases with increasing breaking wave energy.

Limitations to such an average or long-term correlation are identified by numbers on the plot:

1. Small waves generally break against small toe beaches without impacting against the bluffs and should have a minimum effect on erosion, suggesting that the correlation curve should bend down.

2. Very large waves may also break well offshore of the bluffs so the correlation may bend down at high energy levels.

3. Wind setups such as are common on Lake Erie will enable wave impact directly against the bluff toe causing increased erosion and an upward shift to the correlation.

4. Lower lake levels are known to markedly decrease shoreline erosion problems, indicating a downward shift to the correlation.

5. High lake levels markedly increase erosion, at least over the short term, suggesting an upward shift to the correlation.

6. Many other factors affect the correlation at specific sites. These include: (i) cyclic changes in bottom topography and the resultant breaking point of waves, (ii) the study interval discussed as a temporal factor in this paper, (iii) variable erodibility of soils at the bluff toe, (iv) stratigraphy and groundwater conditions as they influence time-dependent loss of strength, and (v) the overall soil mechanics of the site in relation to short- and long-term bluff stability.

The erosion data for western Lake Erie, also plotted in Figure 26.10, show a much steeper correlation (or none at all), indicating completely different controls on retreat rates. The bluffs in the Colchester-Pidgeon Bay area consist of much siltier soils at the toe and it is believed that erodibility is a much more significant factor than for the clayey soils of the north shore of Central Lake Erie.

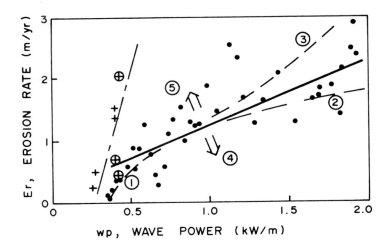

EXPLANATION

- POINTS FOR CENTRAL LAKE ERIE FROM GELINAS, 1973 & 1974
⊕ PIDGEON BAY BLUFFS
+ COLCHESTER SOUTH BLUFFS
① SMALL WAVES
② LARGE WAVES
③ WIND SET-UPS
④ LOWER LAKE LEVEL
⑤ HIGHER LAKE LEVEL
⑥ OTHER FACTORS:
    CYCLIC BOTTOM TOPOGRAPHY
    STUDY TIME INTERVAL
    VARIABLE ERODIBILITY
    STRATIGRAPHY & HYDROLOGY
    SOIL MECHANICS OF BLUFF FAILURE

Figure 26.10. *Erosion rate vs wave power correlation for bluffs of central and western Lake Erie north shore.*

The question of soil or rock erodibility as a function of impacting wave power is still largely a matter of conjecture rarely referenced in the literature. The recent work of Sunamura (1977) represents an interesting start to a very complex problem of rock and soil erodibility.

On the basis of the previous discussions of specific sites and general correlations, the following recommendations are made with respect to shoreline mapping strategy:

1. Strip maps of breaking wave power (impacting wave power if possible) are a vital part of any comprehensive shoreline study, since it is wave attack which maintains erosion regardless of all other factors.
2. Strip maps of long-term (average) cliff edge retreat rates are necessary for long-term planning. Short-term retreat rates are highly variable and dependent on cyclic lake levels and many other factors.

3. Strip maps of volumetric erosion are necessary to resolve lake loading problems.
4. Strip maps of bluff height give a very rapid impression of coastal characteristics.
5. Strip maps of bluff slope angle, however, are relevant only to the time when measured, as illustrated by the Port Bruce case study.
6. Strip maps illustrating the contained stratigraphy are likely to be very complex, as shown by Figure 26.9 of this paper, even when coded by systems such as the Unified Soil Classification System. Nevertheless, such information is necessary to assess variations in soil erodibility and those soil conditions controlling slope failure modes.
7. 'Geotechnical' strip maps should also be developed; however, this is a very complex problem, as illustrated by the multimode stability situation at the Port Bruce site as a function of lake level and time. At present, designation as surficial or deep-seated instability would seem to be adequate for regional mapping purposes.
8. Finally, detailed site specific studies should be maintained over many years to assess the real processes and their variability, as has been done for Port Bruce. These studies would serve as control sites for interpretation of the reliability of regional strip maps.

Acknowledgments

The research carried out at Port Bruce was financed by research funds to R.M. Quigley from the National Research Council of Canada. The research carried out at Colchester was financed by the Canada Shore Damage Task Force and the Hydraulics Research Division of the National Water Research Institute, Canadian Centre for Inland Waters. A.J. Zeman is indebted to J.S. Falloon for assistance and to M.G. Skafel for advice in connection with wave power calculations.

References

Dillon, M.M., Ltd.
    1976: Essex County shoreline; Soils report on bluff areas---Colchester - Pidgeon Bay, Appendix C, May, 96 p.

Gelinas, P.J.
    1974: Contribution to erosion studies, Lake Erie north shore; unpubl. Ph.D. thesis, University of Western Ontario, London, Ontario, 116 p.

Gelinas, P.J. and Quigley, R.M.
    1973: The influence of geology on erosion rates along the north shore of Lake Erie; Proceedings, 16th Conference on Great Lakes Research, p. 421 - 430.

Quigley, R.M. and Di Nardo, L.R.
    1980: Cyclic instability modes of eroding clay bluffs, Lake Erie north shore bluffs at Port Bruce, Ontario, Canada; Zeitschrift für Geomorphologie, Supp.-Bd 34, p. 39 - 47.

Quigley, R.M., Gelinas, P.J., Bou, W.T. and Packer, R.W.
    1977: Cyclic erosion-instability relationships; Lake Erie North Shore Bluffs; Canadian Geotechnical Journal, v. 14, p. 310 - 323.

ASSESSMENT OF GREAT LAKES SHORELINE BLUFFS

Richards, T.L. and Phillips, D.W.
1970: Synthesized winds and wave heights for the Great Lakes; Department of Transport, Meteorological Branch, Climatological Studies No. 17.

Skafel, M.G.
1975: Computation of wave refraction and longshore sediment transport rates; Canadian Centre for Inland Waters, unpubl. report.

Sunamura, T.
1977: A relationship between wave-induced cliff erosion and erosion forces of waves; Journal of Geology, v. 85, no. 5, p. 613 - 618.

U.S. Army Corps of Engineers
1973: Shore protection manual; United States Coastal Engineering Research Centre, Fort Belvoir, Virginia.

27.

THE MORPHOLOGY AND PROCESSES OF THE
LAKE SUPERIOR NORTH SHORE

Brian A.M. Phillips
Department of Geography, Lakehead University, Thunder Bay, Ontario

Phillips, Brian A.M., The morphology and processes of the Lake Superior north shore; in The Coastline of Canada, S.B. McCann, editor; Geological Survey of Canada, Paper 80-10, p. 407-415, 1980.

Abstract

The paper reviews the origin of the basic morphology of the Lake Superior north shore and discusses the morphology and processes of the rock, coarse material and finer material shoreline segments. Attention is drawn to the inherited nature of some rock platforms and the modern origin of others. Raised boulder beaches and unusual elements of the morphology of the immediate offshore zone are considered. The importance of the extreme storm event is emphasized, and the significance of the effects of ice and snow on the present beaches is addressed.

Résumé

La présente étude fait le point au sujet de l'origine de la morphologie fondamentale du littoral nord du lac Supérieur et permet d'approfondir la morphologie et les processus concernant les matériaux rocheux et grossiers ainsi que les matériaux plus fins appartenant à certains segments de la rive. L'attention est attirée sur la nature héritée de certaines plates-formes rocheuses et les origines plus récentes de certaines autres. Il est aussi question de plages soulevées et recouvertes de blocs ainsi que de phénomènes morphologiques inhabituels dans la zone immédiatement au large du littoral. L'importance de l'apparition de tempêtes très violentes est soulignée de même que la signification des effets de la glace et de la neige sur les plages actuelles.

INTRODUCTION

The Ontario coast of Lake Superior is composed of Precambrian rock formations, locally overlain by Pleistocene and younger surficial sediments. For much of its length, the lakeshore topography is characterized by sharply rising coastal hillslopes, an indented shoreline plan, and deep water immediately offshore. There is no tide, the offshore water is always cold, and underwater visibility is usually excellent.

Unlike the marine coasts of Canada, which share the common phenomenon of eustatic changes of sea level, the Superior basin experienced a unique association of oscillating lake levels and differential isostatic movements. Though, as with most marine coasts, the Superior coast existed prior to the Wisconsin glaciation, the morphology of the present coast owes much to the varied events of deglaciation, and the shoreline bears many indications of this inheritance.

MORPHOLOGY AND DEGLACIAL HISTORY

Wisconsin deglaciation first exposed the southwestern end of the Superior basin where a proglacial lake, Lake Duluth (11 500 years BP, initial level 315 m) was formed. As the ice front receded northeastwards, successively larger, but lower, lakes formed, Lake Minong (9500 years BP, initial level 128 m) being the first to assume a shape similar to that of the present lake (Farrand, 1969). By 8000 years BP, the lowest stage, Lake Houghton (initial level 114 m), was established. Coupled with deglaciation, isostatic recovery was initiated and completed first in the southwest, the amount and duration of uplift increasing to the northeast. As a consequence, the lake levels that left an indication of their shorelines form a closely spaced series of features on the Minnesota coast, but diverge to the northeast where they form distinct, widely spaced raised shorelines on the

Ontario northern shore. A complication arises because following Lake Houghton the water level rose slowly to culminate in the Nipissing Lake stage about 5500 years BP (initial level 185 m). On the Minnesota coast this event was transgressive, the Nipissing waters occupying and reworking older shorelines, and submerging the Minong shoreline southwest of Grand Marais. On the Ontario north shore, however, the rate of uplift exceeded that of the transgression and the Nipissing shoreline is now found at a lower elevation than the Houghton Lake shoreline. The Ontario coast is thus one upon which continuous relative water level decline has taken place. The Minong shoreline is now found on the 300 m contour, and present water level (183.6 m) rests at its lowest relative position since deglaciation.

The position of recessional ice margins has also contributed to present coastal morphology. The coast between Thunder Bay and Nipigon is swathed in fluvioglacial sediments, through which rock outcrops protrude. The lowlands and shallow waters of Thunder Bay, Black Bay and Nipigon Bay result from proglacial drainage during two phases of ice readvance. About 10 000 years BP, ice advanced to the Hartmann/Dog Lake moraine (Saarnisto, 1974), forming lakes which drained into the Kaministiquia valley, then an arm of the Beaver Bay Lake stage (Fig. 27.1). Shortly afterwards, waters impounded between the deteriorating ice and the moraine broke through the Dog Lake moraine and built a large delta in the quiet waters near Kakabeka. Subsequent erosion of these deposits by the Kaministiquia River has supplied the receding lakeshore with large quantities of silt and sand. Consequently, the Minong and Nipissing shorelines formed against surficial materials and the present shoreline is composed of gently cliffed, friable sediments between scattered rock headlands and islands, fronted by shallow waters with offshore bar development.

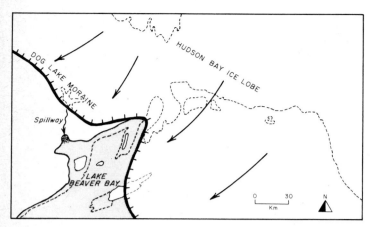

Figure 27.1.   The Ontario north shore 10 100 years B.P.

When a later ice advance formed the Nipigon moraine (Fig. 27.2), proglacial drainage poured along several channels into Black Bay. Shortly after, a large water body in the Lake Nipigon basin, impounded between the moraine and deteriorating ice, drained southwards into Nipigon Bay. As a result the rock outcrops of the Black Bay peninsula and St. Ignace Island are surrounded by fluvioglacial sediments, which bear the marks of the successive shorelines that followed Lake Minong. The bays now form shallow shelves bordered by sand beaches and spits, with occasional rock outcropping on the shore.

The Nipigon moraine does not continue to the east because of the chain of hills that lies along the Nipigon-Marathon coast. It has been assumed that the ice margin lay along this shore in contact with Lake Minong (Zoltai, 1965; Saarnisto, 1974) but a re-examination of the Minong shoreline suggests otherwise. In several places the coast is cut by river valleys, which drain the interior lowlands and pass through the coastal hills. In the Little Pic valley (Fig. 27.2) a cross-valley end moraine is fronted by a large deltaic feature on the 300 m contour and it appears that the ice lay on the landward side of the coastal hills, with tongues of ice pushing through to the margin of Lake Minong in places. The water bodies that formed behind these hills as ice deteriorated laid down large areas of varved and massive clays, and choked the valleys with coarser sediments. Subsequent drainage from the interior supplied the successively lower lake levels with an abundance of material. As a consequence, along the rock coastline there are in places large depositional features which form ridge and dune or deltaic surfaces that can be traced inland to elevations approaching the Minong shoreline. At Terrace Bay, a stepped series of deltaic features formed by the Aguasabon River can be traced from the townsite at over 300 m, down to the present river-mouth beach. Thus, in contrast to the relatively static rock coast, there are limited areas where the shore is supplied with fluvial sediments and with materials easily eroded from the edges of the existing depositional features. In these areas present transport processes are very active.

Much of the rest of the Ontario coast of Lake Superior is composed of smoothed rock surfaces, largely washed clear of any previous till cover by the declining lake levels. A striking feature of these areas is the occurrence of cobble surfaces, generally referred to as raised beaches (Fig. 27.3).

There are isolated areas of accumulated cobbles at all elevations between lake level and 300 m. A typical site consists of a mass of subangular cobbles with diameters ranging from 8 to 48 cm and commonly occupying a hollow in the bedrock topography. The surface of many of the cobble surfaces is fashioned into a ridge and swale topography commonly considered to be the product of wave action. Irregular, subparallel ridge forms, 3 to 30 m in wavelength and 0.3 to 3 m in amplitude, form lakeward sloping surfaces of between 1° and 10°, sometimes broken by localized steplike discontinuities. Most surfaces are composed primarily of local bedrock debris with only a few erratics. The basal portion of the boulder fields exposed along the present shore is generally composed of large erratic blocks and rounded boulders resting either on bedrock or, in some locations, on massive or varved clay deposits (Dell, 1972).

The central question in the interpretation of these cobble surfaces is whether they represent the accumulated products of wave action, and therefore testify to the prevailing depositional environments of earlier lakeshores, or whether they represent the wave-modified surfaces of pre-existing masses of cobble materials accumulated by processes other than wave action. This question has not been satisfactorily resolved. Farrand (1969) assumed that each ridge is a storm beach ridge but detailed mapping reveals little correlation in morphology or elevation between adjacent sites, and the suggestion that at least some of the ridges may have been formed contemporaneously in an offshore environment (Tovell and Deane, 1966) remains an interesting one. The lack of rounding and sorting does not correlate with the implied level of wave vigour required to wash loose materials from the exposed rock surfaces, collect them together in topographic hollows and fashion them into beach ridges. On the other hand, alternative origins involve the problem of time, since this coast saw a continuous decline in lake level from the 300 m contour as soon as it was free of the ice. Because the margins of these cobble surfaces form the present shoreline in many places, it is pertinent to seek an answer, and this enquiry involves the study of the present beach and offshore zones.

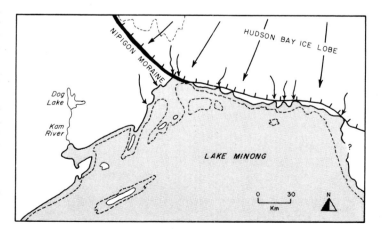

Figure 27.2.   The Ontario north shore 9000 years B.P.

Figure 27.3. *Raised cobbled beach with eroded present margin.*

THE PRESENT ROCK SHORELINE

Following the Nipissing transgression (5500 years BP, initial level 185 m) water level in the Superior basin fell to the Lake Algoma phase (3200 years BP, initial level 181 m) and has slowly risen again to its present level of 183.6 m. This rise has been transgressive on most of the Superior coast and isostatic recovery is complete. It follows that lake level has been at, or near, its present relative elevation for less than 3000 years. Lacking major climatic shifts of wind and wave directions, though recognizing variations in the frequency and intensity of weather phenomena, we may assume that no great changes in coastal energy environments have taken place in the last 3000 years.

The rock coastline of the Ontario north shore is characteristically lacking in distinct coastal features such as cliffs and platforms. It is largely composed of glacially scoured rock surfaces and irregular piles of blocky debris, which are typical of many glaciated emergent coasts. In many places glacial striae are unworn by swash and broken edges have remained angular. This apparent lack of active rock wear by present wave action is contradicted by the well developed rock platforms in places. These occur across rock types no less resistant to erosion than is regionally typical and are basically similar to the intertidal platforms of the marine coasts of Canada, though generally rougher in their topography.

Backed by cliffs and supporting a modern cobble beach, the platforms extend offshore at an inclination of 2° to 4°, abruptly dropping into deeper water along a crenulate outer margin in 5 to 6 m of water (Fig. 27.4). Those parts of the platforms near the beach line show signs of recent abrasive wear but most of the surfaces are covered by a layer of large rounded cobbles and blocky debris, including some over 3 m in diameter, and, on the outer margin especially, there is evidence of glacial fluting and smoothing. Though modern wave action clearly freshens and modifies the platforms where loose material is available for abrasion, the features are much older than the present phase of shoreline modification. They are considered to represent the remains of a rock shoreline of Sangamon (?) age (Phillips, 1977). Though convincing evidence has not yet been found on the Ontario shore, the continuation of the platform beneath raised beach materials and a local till on the Minnesota shore, support this vew. The morphology of the underwater platform and its buried portion show ice modification, but a characteristic wavecut notch and abrasion surface occur below the till (Fig. 27.5).

Figure 27.4.   Offshore platform – air view of typical coastal segment.

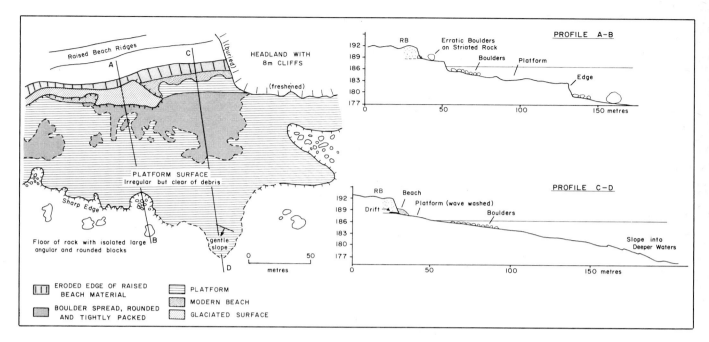

Figure 27.5. *Part of the offshore rock platform — Deronda area.*

This proposal means that the platforms are sections of an ancient rock shoreline, little of which has survived the erosion of Wisconsin and perhaps earlier glaciations. Thus the basic morphology of the present coastline appears to be inherited from a previous long-standing water level.

Some care must be taken not to overstate the concept of 'inheritance'. There are locally developed, narrow, almost horizontal wavecut benches and abrasion ramps at present lake level, especially on certain volcanic rocks, and rock removal is locally very effective under present-day storm wave processes. The recent slight rise in lake level has contributed to this modern phase of rock erosion. Nonetheless, much of the character of the present rock shoreline is due to the exhumation and modification of previously existing rock topography.

COARSE MATERIAL SHORELINES

There is an abundance of boulders and cobbles along the present shore as large volumes of deeply weathered bedrock and thin overlying till were washed by falling water levels into local topographic hollows, many of which now lie at present lake level. Cobble beaches are thus a fairly common feature, and in almost all instances they are backed by abandoned cobble 'beach ridges'. Again, historical considerations are involved, for the present beach is often composed of materials already resting in place or only transported short distances. Relatively little combing down of the eroded margin of older deposits produces a steep beach profile and offshore shelf of well rounded cobbles, which give the impression of highly effective present wave activity. There is noticeable rounding of initially angular debris which enters the beach zone, but, as much of the material is already well rounded, this present beach characteristic is largely an inherited one (Fig. 27.3).

Because of the size and mass of the majority of cobbles, only wave events of high energy have much effect on the beach profile. The geomorphic significance of the occasional storm event is highlighted by studies of the lower

series of raised cobble surfaces, which show marked discontinuities in profile and plan. Lower sets of ridges truncate earlier ones, and clifflike erosional faces cross the pattern of ridges and swales. These abrupt changes in morphology are linked with the Algoma and subsequent minor lake stages, but their marked lack of correlation of elevation, even within small areas, suggests that they do not represent regional water level changes. The situation is summarized by a site on Cobinosh Island, Rossport, where two adjacent boulder fields face east and west, respectively (Fig. 27.6.) On the eastern one a major discontinuity takes the form of a convex ridge of boulders that transgresses unevenly across earlier straighter sets of ridges in the embayment to an elevation of 190 m. In the western bay a clifflike slope truncates earlier ridges across the bay at a slope foot elevation of 187 m. Significantly, the elevation difference between these two features (3 m) is almost the same as that between present storm levels in the two bays. This and other evidence suggest that the discontinuities are due to short-term high energy events and not lengthy water level phases. At this site and many others the abrupt morphological changes that are preserved appear to be the product of rare extreme storm conditions. The present cobble beaches show similar effects of the infrequent high energy event in their morphology.

Simple tests involving the surveying of marked boulders show that movement of large material is impeded by the packing of adjacent boulders and takes place only in severe storm conditions. Storm waves breaking on the steep beach face have most of their energy directed upwards, and percolation being high, little backwash occurs. Following a storm, the junction of the wave-worked profile and that of the raised beach surface is sharpened, and foam and wind-carried flotsam is found resting on the lichen-covered surface, many metres inland from the edge. The smaller marked cobbles appear to be thrown upwards and fall back on the beach face. Larger boulders rotate or shift slightly. In effect, the profile does not change much and longshore movement of material is very limited. The profile appears

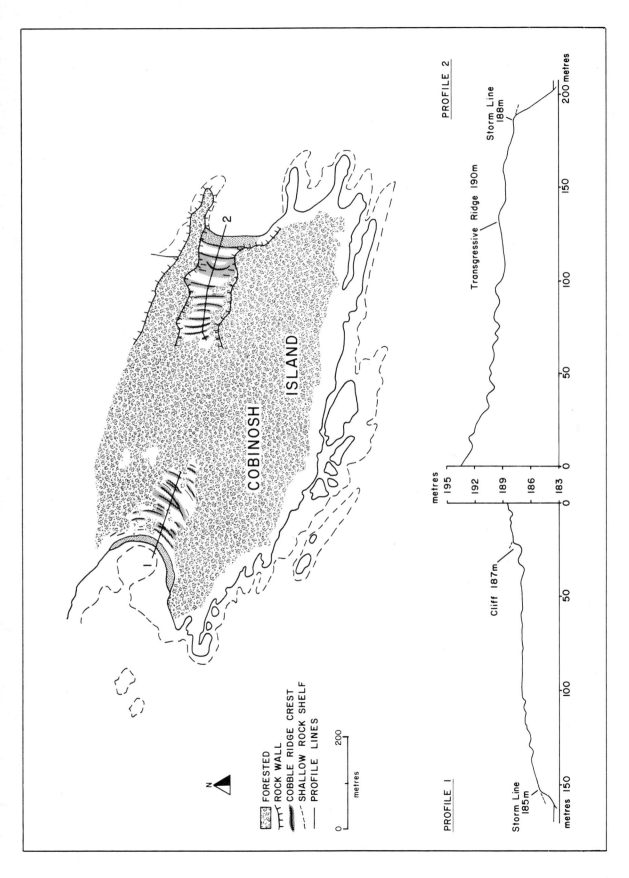

Figure 27.6.   *Cobinosh Island – plan and profiles.*

to be a stable one, as is its continuation offshore. In most cases the offshore shelf of boulders falls abruptly into deeper water at an angular junction in about 3 - 4 m depth. Examination of this steep face shows that an occasional boulder has rolled down onto the clay or sand floor below, but in general the feature is closely interlocked and appears stable. It is suggested that slight water level rise after the Algoma Lake stage resulted in general erosion of all formerly deposited materials by storm wave events and that once initiated, the present beach profiles have been maintained and freshened only by storm waves. Some corroboration is provided by local commercial fishermen who remember three storms of the last 50 years which damaged coastal fishing and mining installations and left log booms stranded high above the beach. These extreme events wholly eradicated or formed nearshore shoals and one may infer that much of the erosion of the older beach material results from these infrequent high energy events and is sustained by the more frequent annual storm events.

FINE MATERIAL SHORELINES

A more dynamic situation exists at those infrequent points on the coastline where sands and silts occur in the shore zone because of the erosion of older accumulations of fine sediments. A study of slope and sorting characteristics of four sand and silt beaches of the north shore demonstrates that the sediments are moderately to well sorted, unimodal and leptokurtic, reflecting the effect of modern wave conditions on a single source of material, the already sorted raised beach materials.

Although rivers have contributed large quantities of silt and sand to the previous shorelines and continue to supply sediment, the slight water level rise in recent times has terminated long-term aggradation and initiated erosion of the margin of previously accumulated materials. At Neys Provincial Park a silt/sand beach 30 m wide extends for 2.5 km east from the mouth of the Little Pic River (Phillips, 1974). Behind the beach lies a 3 km^2 area of sand ridges and dunes built out from the rock shoreline since Nipissing times. Characteristic of shallow offshore areas of the north shore, a set of two to four offshore bars front the beach zone. These shift position but are always present in some form. At times of high discharge the Little Pic River forms a plume of silt-laden waters across Ashburton Bay, over 6 km^2 in area. This sediment contributes largely to the lake floor, not the beach, and it is only in such situations that any more than a few centimetres of recent sediment covers the glacial clay floor.

A study of beach erosion, determined by levelled profiles in 1974 and 1978, reveals that as much as 3 m of raised beach material have been removed during this period, with trees over 90 years old being undercut. The beach appears to have widened and shallowed in gradient (Fig. 27.7), with much of the eroded material deposited offshore and trapped by the Caldwell Peninsula to the east. One or two high-magnitude storm events alone are probably responsible for this erosion.

The few silt/sand beaches of the Ontario north shore are under increasing recreational pressure, and several are now contained within provincial parks. Because these beaches are highly mobile and are in most cases dependent upon sediment supply from fluvial or wave erosion of existing fine sediments, they are susceptible to erosion and present problems in shoreline management.

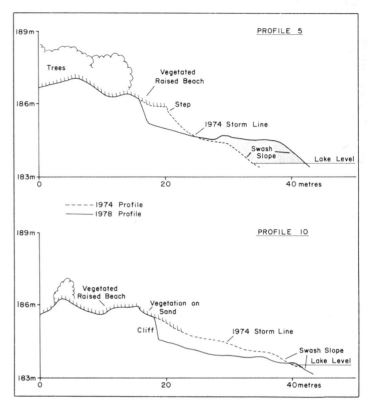

Figure 27.7. Neys Provincial Park beach erosion study – sample profiles.

THE EFFECTS OF ICE AND SNOW ON SHORELINES

In common with arctic coasts of Canada (Taylor and McCann, 1976), the Superior coastline is locked in ice for part of the year. During this period normal beach processes cease, and snow and ice play a small but significant role in shaping beach morphology, particularly in finer materials (Davis, et al., 1976). The final fall storm event before freezeup determines the character of the beach profile that is frozen and retained until wave action can again modify it. The upper parts of sand and shingle beach profiles usually freeze by December, and a frozen surface layer 4 - 12 cm is formed in irregular patches, which eventually coalesce. Wave action continues to modify the lower parts of the profile until the lake freezes. Should a high energy wave event occur in this period, the impermeable, snow-covered beach face may be cliffed along its lower margin and have new material thrown onto its surface. This material is frozen into the snow layer above the initial beach surface. After freezeup, groundwater still flows below the frozen beach surface, usually issuing along a spring line near water level. This results in the buildup of a layer of ice 2 to 6 cm thick on the treads and minor swales of the lower profile, and does much to protect the profile from later wave activity. Throughout the winter snow and ice build up on the beach face and together with the frozen layer compact the underlying materials. During March, as

Figure 27.8. Microfeatures resulting from melt of snow and ice on a sand and shingle beach.

early afternoon thaw periods become more frequent, thermodenudation is active. The southerly-facing frozen steps of the lower profile begin to collapse, and running water undermines the frozen layer, which thaws along its exposed margin. In addition, the snow and ice cover becomes riddled with small channels, and the wave-thrown materials included in the midprofile are transported and deposited in hollows and holes within the ice. As spring thaw progresses these sediments are lowered to form microfeatures superimposed on the initial beach surface. Though varied in size and shape, these features commonly take the form of mounds of well sorted coarse or fine materials on a surrounding surface of quite different grain size (Fig. 27.8). In the lower part of the profile these features seldom survive ice breakup and the first wave action.

Ice breakup often does not affect the beach profile. In some years ice is pushed on shore during this period but the beach-fast ice and protective ice pans of the lower profile tend to allow overriding without destructive effect. Only exceptional push into the midprofile results in ice push features in the sand and gravel surface. The raised cobble and sand ridges do not show more than occasional evidence of ice push activity either. The first major wave event of April inherits the December profile, superimposed with a variety of melt features, and establishes a new wave-formed profile.

SUMMARY

The Superior north shore is unlike much of the marine and southern Great Lakes shorelines of Canada. Endowed with a basic character by the events of deglaciation, the present coastal zone is varied in its topography and sediment materials and is subjected to major though infrequent storm wave events. Rock wear is only locally more than minor, but exhumation of the rock topography and erosion and re-sorting of earlier deposited materials is actively proceeding. The nature of the raised cobble beaches, the 'interglacial' rock platform, and the immediate offshore morphology remain to be thoroughly explained. The role of ice and snow requires better assessment.

References

Davis, A., Golsmith, V. and Golsmith, Y.
1976: Ice effects on beach sedimentation: examples from Massachusetts and Lake Michigan; Révue de géographie de Montréal, v. 30, p. 201 - 206.

Dell, C.I.
1972: The origin and characteristics of Lake Superior sediments; Proceedings, 15th Conference on Great Lakes Research, p. 361 - 370.

Farrand, W.R.
1969: The Quaternary history of Lake Superior; Proceedings, 12th Conference on Great Lakes Research, p. 181 - 197.

Phillips, B.A.M.
1974: A palaeogeographic summary; Chapter 2 in unpublished Earth Science Inventory, Neys Provincial Park, Ontario Ministry of Natural Resources, compiled by W. Billings.
1977: Shoreline inheritance in coastal histories; Science, v. 195, p. 11 - 16.

Saarnisto, M.
1974: The deglaciation history of the Lake Superior region and its climatic implications; Quaternary Research, v. 4, p. 316 - 339.

Taylor, R.B. and McCann, S.B.
1976: The effect of sea and nearshore ice on coastal processes in Canadian Arctic Archipelago; Révue de géographie de Montréal, v. 30, p. 123 - 132.

Tovell, W.M. and Deane, R.E.
1966: Ancestral Lake Superior shorelines, Montreal River harbour area, Ontario; Geological Association of Canada, Proceedings, v. 17, p. 53 - 63.

Zoltai, S.C.
1965: Thunder Bay surficial geology; Ontario Department of Lands and Forests, Map S265.

28

MORPHOLOGY AND SEDIMENTOLOGY OF MULTIPLE PARALLEL BAR SYSTEMS, SOUTHERN GEORGIAN BAY, ONTARIO

Robin G.D. Davidson-Arnott and Glenn F. Pember
Department of Geography, University of Guelph, Guelph, Ontario

Davidson-Arnott, Robin G.D. and Pember, Glenn F., Morphology and sedimentology of multiple parallel bar systems, southern Georgian Bay, Ontario; in The Coastline of Canada, S.B. McCann, editor; Geological Survey of Canada, Paper 80-10, p. 417-428, 1980.

Abstract

The morphological and sedimentological characteristics of multiple parallel bars at Wasaga Beach and Christian Island in southern Georgian Bay are described. Although maximum fetch lengths are very different for the two beaches (Wasaga Beach 170 km; Christian Island 10 km) the morphology of the two bar systems is similar. Up to eight bars are present, aligned roughly parallel to the shoreline. Individual bars, which are typically symmetric or asymmetric landward, can be traced for distances exceeding 1.5 km, though the bars closest to shore are shorter and more irregular in shape. Bar height averages 20-30 cm and spacing between bars is 20-30 m. The major control on the occurrence of the multiple parallel bars appears to be the very gentle offshore slope (0.005 to 0.01) which, in conjunction with the limited fetch length, results in a high breaker index (spilling breakers).

Sedimentary structures preserved in the bar sediments were studied in resin peels made from box cores. At Wasaga Beach the lakeward slope is characterized primarily by low-angle planar bedding, whereas, on the bar, units with indistinct structures appear to reflect the presence of plane bed and of very low amplitude ripples formed under slightly lower bed velocities. Trough sediments are characteristically darker than bar-crest sediments and include both ripples and plane bed. At Christian Island the sedimentary structures reflect much lower wave conditions. Plane bed units are generally absent and the bars are characterized by ripple trough cross-stratification and occasionally by tabular units. Trough sediments are generally massive suggesting deposition of fines from suspension.

Résumé

Les auteurs décrivent ici la nature morphologique et sédimentologique de nombreux cordous parallèles situés à Wasaga Beach et dans l'île Christian (sud de la baie Georgienne). Malgré que les longueurs maximales de fetch soient très différentes pour les deux plages (Wasaga Beach 170 km; île Christian 10 km) la morphologie des deux groupes de cordons est analogue. On trouve jusqu'à 8 cordons, plus ou moins alignés parallèlement au littoral. Des cordons individuels, qui sont assez typiquement symétriques ou asymétriques face à la côte, peuvent être suivis sur des distances dépassant 5 km, bien que les cordons les plus rapprochés de la rive soient plus courts et de formes plus irrégulières. La hauteur des cordons se situe en moyenne entre 20 et 30 cm et l'espacement entre les cordons est de 20 à 30 m. Le principal mode de formation des cordons parallèles multiples semblent être la pente très douce du large (0,005 à 0,01) laquelle, conjointement avec la longeur limitée du fetch, donne lieu à un indice élevé de déferlement (brisant d'étalement).

Certaines structures sédimentaires préservées dans les sédiments de cordon ont été étudiées dans des pelures de résine préparées à partir de carottes de soutirage. A Wasaga Beach, la pente en direction du lac se caractérise surtout par l'angle faible de son litage planaire, tandis que sur le cordon, des unités possédant des structures non distinctes semblent refléter la présence de lits plats et de rides de très faible amplitude formés par suite de la vélocité légèrement inférieur du lit. Les sédiments de dépression sont particulièrement plus foncés que les sédiments de la crête du cordon et ils comprennent à la fois des rides et un lit plat. Dans l'île Christian, les structures sédimentaires reflètent des conditions de vagues beaucoup moins marquées. Certaines unités du lit plat sont généralement absentes et les cordons sont caractérisés par une interstratification des creux de rides et parfois par des unités tabulaires. Les sédiments de dépression sont généralement massifs ce qui permet de présumer du dépôt des particules fines provenant du transport en suspension.

INTRODUCTION

The nearshore zone of most sandy coasts is frequently characterized by wave-formed bars. These bars are generated by sediment transport under wave action and wave-generated nearshore currents and, in general, they are absent only in areas exposed to long-period swell or where the nearshore slope is so steep that waves break at the shore-line. It is evident that different bar types form in response to different controlling processes, or at least to differing combinations of processes, and thus the morphology, sedimentology and stability of the bars are a reflection of these differing processes. On the basis of qualitative morphological and process differences, Greenwood and Davidson-Arnott (1979) classified wave-formed bars into six groups, though they recognized that transitional types occur. The work presented here focuses on one type of bar which has received somewhat limited attention, namely multiple parallel bars (Group 3 of Greenwood and Davidson-Arnott, 1979; see also Zenkovitch, 1967; Nilsson, 1973, 1978;

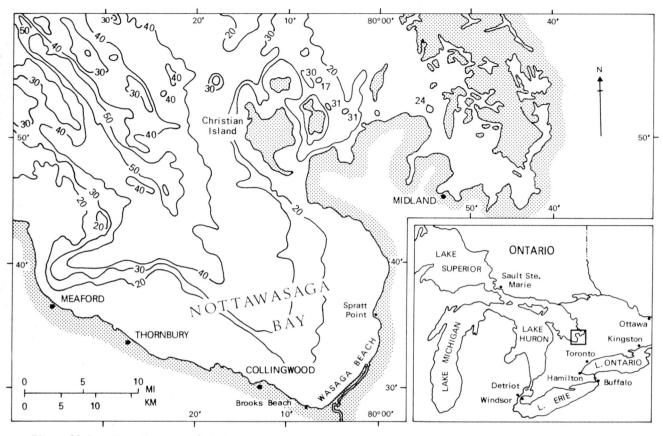

Figure 28.1. *Location map of study areas.*

Lau and Travis, 1973; Exon, 1975). This group of bars is associated with very gentle offshore slopes and areas with a restricted fetch length. The number of bars ranges from 4 to more than 30, oriented parallel to the shoreline, and commonly extending unbroken for several kilometres. They are generally less than 0.5 m in height and nearly symmetrical in form. Wave length tends to increase offshore, but only very slowly. To date there is no satisfactory explanation for their formation nor, with the exception of Nilsson (1978), has there been much attempt to measure actual wave and current processes associated with the bars.

The paper describes the morphology and sedimentology of multiple parallel bars found at two locations in southern Georgian Bay, Ontario. The work is part of a more extensive study of beaches in this area carried out in 1977 as a prelude to choosing a site for detailed process-response measurements. The two systems are similar in general form but there are considerable differences in the wave climate to which each is exposed and in the internal sedimentary characteristics of the bars. These differences form the basis for a discussion of the controls on the formation and maintenance of the bars.

STUDY AREA

The two bar systems occur at Wasaga Beach and at Christian Island, southern Georgian Bay (Fig. 28.1). The bedrock of the area consists of Paleozoic carbonates and shales, overlain by varying thicknesses of glacial, glaciofluvial and glaciolacustrine sediments. The Simcoe lowlands, of which Wasaga Beach is a part, are characterized by clay and sand

plains, and small morainic ridges (Chapman and Putnam, 1966). In contrast, Christian Island is part of the Simcoe uplands and is characterized by numerous bedrock cliffs in limestone and has only a thin veneer of sediments.

Wasaga Beach is located at the head of Nottawasaga Bay, which forms the southernmost extension of Georgian Bay. Considerable sediment accumulation has taken place at the head of the bay since the retreat of the Wisconsinan ice sheet and several raised beaches and an extensive barrier complex related to Algonquin and Nipissing lake levels are present (Martini, 1974, 1975). Wasaga Beach itself consists of a modern spit approximately 15 km in length, which has grown eastward, diverting the course of the Nottawasaga River (Fig. 28.1 and presently forms the longest sandy beach in Georgian Bay. The multiple parallel bars are in the nearshore area along most of the length of the spit. The study site is about halfway along the spit opposite the Wasaga Beach Provincial Park office (Fig. 28.3).

The nearshore slope is gentle (0.005 to 10 m depth; Fig. 28.2). Most of the nearshore area consists of fine sand but lag deposits of gravel and boulders resulting from the winnowing of till occur towards the east and west of the bay (Ball, 1978). The bay is exposed towards the northwest to the full length of Georgian Bay, with an effective fetch of approximately 170 km. No good measured wave data are available for Nottawasaga Bay but a wave hindcasting study (Davidson-Arnott and Pollard, 1980) indicates that deep-water storm waves characteristically have significant wave heights ranging from 0.75 m to 1.75 m, with periods of 4 to 7 seconds. Breaker height values at Wasaga Beach, however, are somewhat lower because of frictional attenuation as

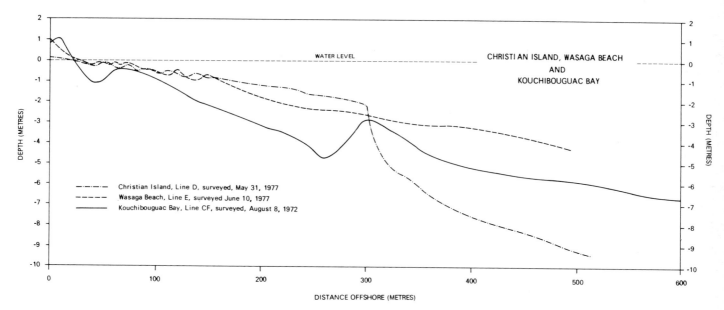

Figure 28.2. *Typical nearshore profiles at Wasaga Beach and Christian Island (this study) and Kouchibouguac Bay, New Brunswick (from Greenwood and Davidson-Arnott, 1975).*

waves shoal over the very gentle nearshore slope. These form spilling breakers, breaking being initiated on the lakeward side of the outer bar. Breaking is generally confined to the wave crest and the waves decrease in height gradually as they cross succeeding bars towards the beach face.

Most of the beaches on Christian Island are narrow and are composed primarily of cobbles or mixed cobbles and sand, but in the large bay at the south end of the island (Fig. 28.1) considerable sand accumulation has taken place on a shallow, bedrock-controlled ledge. In contrast to the extensive gentle slope at Wasaga Beach, water depths increase abruptly over a steep slope from 2.0 to 2.5 m down to 6.0 m (Fig. 28.2). A multiple parallel bar system is characteristic of the nearshore zone over much of the gently curving bay for a distance of 6 km. The bay itself is much more sheltered than Wasaga Beach and the longest fetch is about 10 km towards the southwest. It is possible for waves generated within the main body of Georgian Bay to refract around the islands to the east and reach Christian Island through the narrow passage between the island and the mainland. However, this would be accompanied by considerable dispersion of energy and waves reaching the study area would be considerably reduced in height. The study site at Christian Island is just west of the ferry dock in the bay (Fig. 28.4).

Field work carried out between May 15 and July 15, 1977 consisted primarily of surveying, echo sounding and box coring. At each site nine lines, spaced at 30 m intervals, were surveyed at least twice to determine the morphological characteristics of the bars and their spatial and temporal variability. A Raytheon DE719 echo sounder was used to extend the profiles up to 600 m offshore. Sedimentary structures within the bars were studied in resin peels obtained from box cores taken with a Klovan-type box corer (Davidson-Arnott and Greenwood, 1974). The cores were obtained by wading in shallow water and by SCUBA in deeper water, during low wave conditions. Sedimentary units within each core were sampled for grain size analysis after removal of the peel.

BAR MORPHOLOGY

Aerial photographs, both vertical and oblique, show up to nine bars in both localities. The outer bars are very regular, are roughly parallel to the shoreline and to each other, and extend for hundreds of metres alongshore. The spacing of the outer bars is fairly regular, though there is a slight lakeward increase in spacing at Wasaga Beach. Bars occasionally join (or bifurcate) at a Y-shaped junction similar to these observed in transverse oscillatory ripples.

Surveyed profiles show fewer bars, probably because several are of very low amplitude, and the regularity of the bars is less apparent than from the air (Table 28.1; Figs. 28.5, 28.6). Bar height is less than 50 cm and, although the outer bars are usually higher than the inner ones, there is no regular offshore progression. Likewise, the bar spacing shows no regular offshore increase and may be quite variable along individual profiles. The outer bars at Wasaga Beach tend to be slightly higher and the spacing slightly greater than at Christian Island but these differences are only minor. In both cases the slope on which the bars are developed is very gentle and water depths over the bar crest increase very slowly, with the outer crest generally at depths of less than 1.0 m.

Bar shape is quite variable from nearly symmetrical to asymmetrical landward (Figs. 28.5, 28.6). The bars at Wasaga Beach, particularly the outer ones, have a greater tendency to landward asymmetry (steeper landward slope) than do those at Christian Island, and, in this respect, they bear a greater resemblance to nearshore bars such as those described by Saylor and Hands (1970), Davis and Fox (1972), and Greenwood and Davidson-Arnott (1975).

The inner bars show no tendency to migrate onshore and weld onto the berm by the process described by Davis and Fox (1972), Davis et al. (1972) and Sonu (1973). They do not appear to be destroyed by storms, though changes in their location and size do take place during periods of high wave activity. The profiles at Wasaga Beach (Fig. 28.5) show the growth of an outer bar as a result of a period of high wave activity (breaker heights 0.75 to 1.0 m) between June 2 and 5, 1977. Observations just at freezeup in late November

Figure 28.3

Oblique aerial photograph of study area at Wasaga Beach, June 1977.

Figure 28.4

Oblique aerial photograph of study area at Christian Island, June 1977.

showed the bars still present at Wasaga Beach after the fall storm period. The bars appear to be affected very little by ice during the winter. Despite the presence of ice from early December 1977 to early May 1978, with several lines of ice volcanoes marking successive stages in the growth of the shorefast ice, the bars were present immediately after ice breakup. Surveys carried out less than a week after the shorefast ice disappeared showed essentially the same bar configuration. During the period of ice breakup there were no storms and the shorefast ice eventually floated free under the influence of offshore winds.

BAR SEDIMENTOLOGY

The nearshore bars in both areas are developed in fine- to medium-grained well sorted quartz sands (Table 28.2). The sediments from Wasaga Beach are somewhat finer and slightly better sorted than those at Christian Island. Dark, heavy minerals are very noticeable in both areas though they account for less than 5 per cent of the total distribution. They are useful, however, in highlighting the sedimentary structures in resin peels because the fine grain size reduces the relief produced in the peels. In general sediments in the bar troughs are darker than on the crests because of the accumulation of organic matter there.

Table 28.1. Summary of bar morphology statistics

	Date of observations	$\overline{X}$	Range	Number of observations
Christian Island, 9 lines				
Number of bars	May 30	4.1	4 – 5	
	June 16	4.6	4 – 6	
Bar height (cm)	May 30	20.5	8 – 30	36
	June 16	19.7	7 – 40	43
Bar spacing (m)	May 30	25.5	17 – 45	28
	June 16	22.1	17 – 36	34
Wasaga Beach, 9 lines				
Number of bars	May 19	3.2	2 – 4	
	June 10	4.2	3 – 5	
Bar height (cm)	May 19	24.9	9 – 45	29
	June 10	29.1	9 – 45	38
Bar spacing (m)	May 19	28.7	16 – 40	20
	June 10	29.3	12 – 55	29

The number of observations for bar height and spacing reflect the number of bars present along each profile.

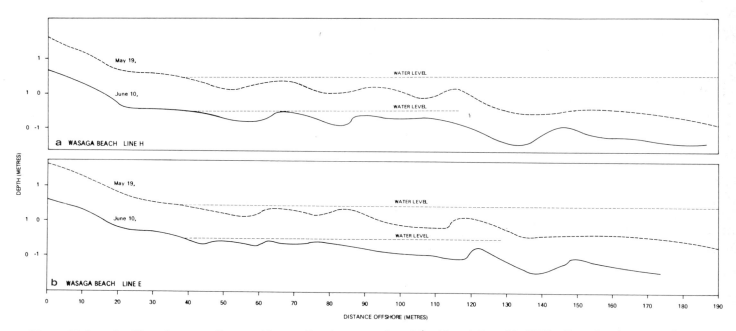

Figure 28.5. *Profiles along two lines at Wasaga Beach surveyed on May 19 and June 10, 1977. Note development of a new outer bar between the two survey dates. Heights are relative to mean water level for Georgian Bay.*

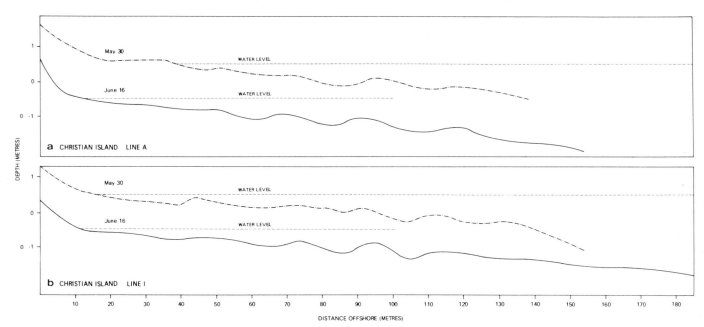

Figure 28.6. *Profiles along two lines at Christian Island surveyed on May 30 and June 16, 1977.*

During periods of low wave activity, ripples are present on the bar crest but are less distinct in the trough. No detailed study of the sequence of bedforms across the bars during high wave activity has yet been made and the number of cores collected is still insufficient to permit the establishment of a definitive facies model. The cores, however, provide a useful insight into the sedimentary processes that may be significant in the formation and maintenance of the bars and some preliminary observations are presented. Because of the differences found between the cores from Wasaga Beach and Christian Island, the two beaches are described separately.

Wasaga Beach

Cores were taken along two lines, E and H, across the outermost bar and the next bar landward. In addition to the two surveys carried out on May 19 and June 10, these two lines were surveyed each time cores were taken. As a result of light or offshore winds, wave action during this period was negligible except for the period June 2 - 7 when strong onshore winds generated waves with breaker heights of 0.75 to 1.0 m. The outer bar (Fig. 28.7) almost certainly grew during this period of high wave activity. Cores taken across this bar penetrate through the full thickness of bar accretion and into the underlying structures and thus allow the internal structure of the bar to be determined. The full sequence of six cores taken across this outer bar along line H is shown in Figure 28.8 and their location is shown in Figure 28.7.

Sedimentary structures in the prestorm lower unit are predominantly small-scale cross-stratification produced by asymmetrical wave ripples, and subhorizontal planar bedding resulting from sheet flow under high bed velocities (Fig. 28.8A, C, D, 28.9A). These structures are typical of those found in the zone of shoaling waves and have been reported for many areas (e.g., Inman, 1957; Clifton et al., 1971; Reineck and Singh, 1973; Davidson-Arnott and Greenwood, 1976). The ripples are formed under relatively low bed velocities and as velocities increase, either as a result of higher waves or shallower water, the ripples are washed out to form a plane bed. The zone of lunate megaripples found by Clifton et al. (1971) and Davidson-Arnott and Greenwood (1976) appears to be absent here as there is little evidence

of dune crossbedding. This may be due partly to the lower degree of current asymmetry associated with very short period waves, but more probably reflects the fine grain size of the sediments at Wasaga Beach, which should lead to direct transition from asymmetrical ripples to plane bed without any intermediate dune phase (Clifton, 1976).

The distinct sorting of light and dark minerals and the fact that individual laminae can be traced clearly across the width of the core are typical of plane bed units. The formation of the type of lamination is still poorly understood, though Clifton (1969) has documented it on the swash slope and recently Bridges (1978) has proposed a model for the formation of horizontal laminae under unidirectional flow based on sediment transport during the 'bursting' cycle. The continuity of individual laminae and distinct sorting suggests that macroturbulence associated with wave breaking is absent.

The sedimentary structures in the upper part of cores shown in Figures 28.8B to F and 28.9B are distinctly different from the lower unit. Individual laminae are not as easily distinguished and it is often difficult to identify the exact kind of sedimentary structure. Traces of ripple trough cross-stratification are present, and in many cases these appear to be formed by landward migrating ripples. Occasionally, these foresets are considerably larger than the the usual ripple cross-stratification (Fig. 28.8C). In other cases (Fig. 28.8D, 28.9B) quasi-horizontal lamination appears to have been produced by the rapid migration of ripples with little preservation of forest laminae. Observations on the bars while waves 1.0 - 1.5 m in height were breaking showed the presence of very low ripples on the outer bar crest. The ripples were about 0.5 cm high and about 5.0 cm in wave length. Unlike the distinct straight-crested ripples found during low wave activity, these ripples were irregular in shape with discontinuous crests. Ripple heights increased somewhat in the troughs and towards the beach. It is likely that the ripples on the outer bar represent a stage just prior to the formation of a planar bed. The low amplitude and irregular crestal shape would account for the indistinct,

Table 28.2. Summary of sediment size statistics from samples taken from box cores

	Wasaga Beach	Christian Island
Number of samples	11	7
Size (φ)	3.24 (3.16 - 3.30)	2.82 (2.68 - 3.02)
Standard deviation (φ)	0.28 (0.26 - 0.32)	0.49 (0.23 - 0.63)
Skewness	-0.5 (-1.05 - 0.08)	-0.11 (-0.46 - 0.25)

Samples were sieved at quarter phi intervals and the statistics derived from moment measures.

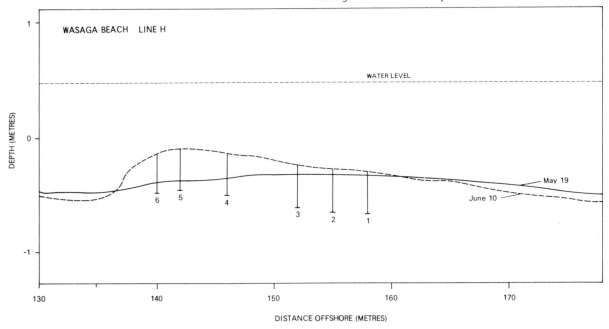

Figure 28.7. *Profile across the outer bar along Line H, Wasaga Beach, showing the development of the bar and the location of the box cores taken on June 12. The vertical bars indicate the actual depth of penetration of the box cores.*

0   10   20   30 mm

←Shoreline

Figure 28.8

Photographs of resin peels made from the box cores shown in Figure 28.7. A-F correspond to 1-6.

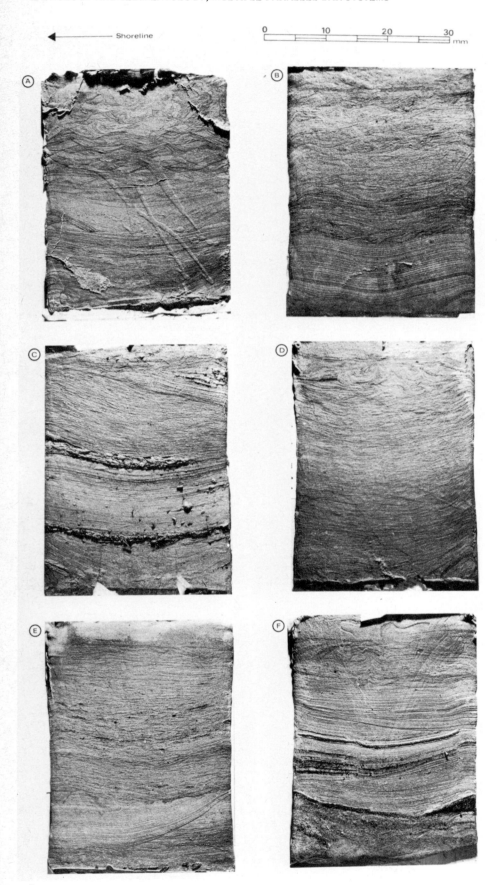

A- lakeward slope outer bar;
B- bar crest outer bar;
C- trough, outer bar;
D- crest, second bar;
E- landward slope, second bar
F- trough second bar;

Photographs of resin peels made from box cores taken at Wasaga Beach.

Figure 28.9

complex structures preserved. In short, the characteristics of the upper unit probably reflect wave breaking across the bar, with complex, rapidly changing flow conditions and bedforms alternating between irregular ripples and plane bed. Since the waves break primarily as spilling breakers, the bottom half of the wave remains largely intact, thus maintaining an asymmetrical landward oscillatory flow decreasing in intensity as the wave height decreases. Most of the structures preserved within the bar show landward migration and suggest that the bar itself formed by landward transport of sediment from offshore.

The landward slope and crest of the second bar are characterized by structures resulting from the rapid migration of ripples. Quasi-planar bedding appears to be produced when sedimentation rates are low (Fig. 28.9E, upper half of 28.9D). In some cases, however, more of the ripple is preserved, producing tabular units of ripple cross-bedding (lower portion of Fig. 28.9D). Because the wave had already broken once, the effect of turbulence produced by wave breaking on sediment transport near the bed is likely to be less than on the outer bar.

In the trough landward of the bar, the deeper water appears to prevent turbulence associated with wave breaking from reaching the bed and the sedimentary structures are much better defined than on the bar. Many of the trough sediments consist of subhorizontal planar units with individual sets separated by erosion surfaces, which appear to reflect local scour and deposition associated with slight shifts in the location of the bar and trough. Since bed velocities in the trough should be lower than on the crest the planar bedding is difficult to explain. The trough sediments are also characterized by the accumulation of organic debris, shell fragments and flakes of mica during periods of low wave activity. These may be buried by new sediments to form distinct bands (Fig. 28.9C, F) whose curvature reflects that of the trough.

Christian Island

Six peels from cores taken at Christian Island are shown in Figure 28.10. Cores taken lakeward of the outer bar in the zone of shoaling waves (Fig. 28.10A, B) are characterized by ripple trough crossbedding typical of asymmetrical wave ripples and are similar to the structures found at Wasaga Beach. In both peels the lower portion of the cores is characterized by units which appear to have been subjected to considerable pressure leading to distortion of the structures. These are separated from the overlying units of ripple cross-stratification by a distinct erosion surface. The most likely cause of this distortion of the lower unit is the growth of ice during the winter and the erosion surface probably represents the limit of subsequent reworking of sediments by wave action after the ice had melted.

Unlike the sediments at Wasaga Beach, units of planar bedding are not common in cores from the outer bar or zone of shoaling waves. The only evidence for planar beds is in the lower units of Figure 28.10A and B. Because of the much lower waves affecting the beach at Christian Island and the somewhat coarser sediments found here, it is likely that bed velocities are seldom high enough to generate a plane bed.

The lakeward slope, crest and landward slope of the outer bar are characterized by ripple trough cross-stratification similar to that in the zone of shoaling waves just described (Fig. 28.10C - F) and by tabular units of ripple cross-stratification resulting from the rapid migration of straight-crested ripples (Fig. 28.10C, D). These latter units obviously result in considerable accretion. In the central portion of Figure 28.10C there appears to be a well defined

transition from the tabular units to trough cross-stratification typical of symmetrical wave ripples, which probably reflects a gradual reduction in the rate of ripple migration. It is not clear whether this transition is one from high to low wave activity or vice versa, although the former seems the more likely. However, a few field observations suggest that the tabular units may be produced by migration of ripples under relatively low wave activity in very shallow water. In any event, the presence of the tabular units of ripple crossbedding is interesting because they are usually associated with unidirectional, rather than oscillatory, flow.

Several cores taken at Christian Island showed evidence of the presence of ice, including the two previously referred to (Fig. 28.10A, B). The large pebble at the bottom of Figure 28.10F is probably a result of ice rafting during breakup.

DISCUSSION AND CONCLUSIONS

Comparison between Wasaga Beach and Christian Island

The morphological characteristics of the two systems appear to be very similar (Figs. 28.3 - 28.6). In general the outer bars are continuous over long distances whereas the inner bars tend to be more discontinuous and, at Christian Island, some low transverse forms occur near the beach. There is some minor variation along individual profiles in bar spacing, height and asymmetry (Table 28.1), but in both areas the general profile form remains the same throughout the year and from year to year.

The major differences between the two systems are revealed in their internal sedimentary characteristics and can be attributed primarily to differences in wave energy resulting from the short fetch length for Christian Island. At Wasaga Beach numerous units of planar bedding occur on, and lakeward of, the outer bar, reflecting relatively high bed velocities. In contrast, the bar and zone of shoaling waves at Christian Island are characterized almost entirely by units of ripple cross-stratification. The trough sediments at Wasaga Beach reflect deposition in the presence of fairly strong currents, but the largely structureless trough sediments at Christian Island appear to result from fine material settling out of suspension in relatively still water in the lee of the bars. The sedimentary structures found at Christian Island are similar to those described by Exon (1975) from an area in the Baltic Sea with roughly the same fetch exposure and sediment size. Thus, the internal sedimentary structures of the bar systems confirm that Wasaga Beach is a much higher energy environment than is Christian Island. Flow conditions controlling sediment transport at Wasaga Beach are considerably greater in magnitude but it still remains to be determined whether the actual patterns of flow are also different.

Bar equilibrium

The form of the nearshore area on a sandy coast is generally considered to be one that is in dynamic equilibrium with incident wave and current conditions, though in many areas, including Christian Island and Wasaga Beach, where the range of wave conditions is limited, the average profile may change very little in its general form from one season to the next. Although a detailed explanation of the controls on the bar systems described here can be achieved only through actual field measurements of wave and current processes associated with the bars, comparison of the morphological and sedimentological characteristics of the two systems with each other and with the nearshore profile in other areas can give some insight into the nature of these controls.

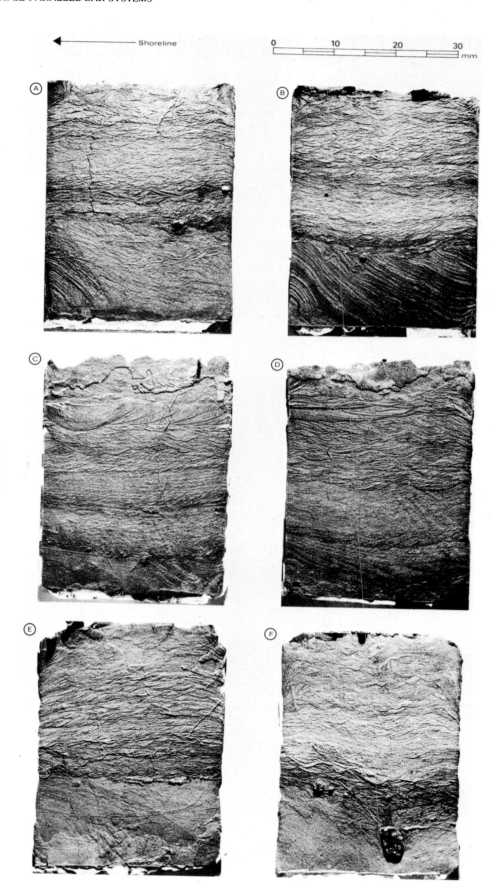

Figure 28.10

Photographs of resin peels made from box cores taken at Christian Island: (A,B) lakeward of outer bar; (C,D) lakeward slope, outer bar; (E,F) bar crest, outer bar.

Although there are minor differences, the morphological characteristics of the bars at Wasaga Beach and Christian Island are essentially similar, and thus the controls on the profile should be similar. The fact that Wasaga Beach is exposed to much larger storm waves initially suggests that this is not the case and that the controlling processes are quite different. It is likely, however, that a key parameter, breaker type, is similar. Because of the short fetch length at Christian Island, only steep, short-period waves forming spilling breakers can be generated. The deepwater waves of Wasaga Beach have a much longer wave period, but the very gentle offshore slope results in a breaker index (Galvin, 1972) which is also well within the range of spilling breakers. One result of this is that energy dissipation through breaking and the consequent reduction in wave height occur slowly. This gives rise to multiple break points and consequently to multiple bars. Because the reduction in wave height at each breaker location is comparatively small, the bars tend to be quite low in height and regular in spacing. The fact that energy is dissipated uniformly over the full width of the barred zone may also account for the absence of any morphological indication of rip-cell circulation.

A comparison of the nearshore profile at Wasaga Beach with that for Kouchibouguac Bay, New Brunswick (Davidson-Arnott and Greenwood, 1974, 1976; Greenwood and Davidson-Arnott, 1975, 1979) tends to support the importance of breaker type on bar form. The wave climate of the two areas appears to be very similar. Both experience long periods of calm produced by offshore winds and significant wave action results from strong onshore winds during the passage of depressions. The effective fetch lengths for wave generation during these periods are roughly the same and wave heights predicted for Wasaga Beach are similar to those measured in Kouchibouguac Bay. It is obvious from Figure 28.2, however, that the equilibrium profiles are very different. The nearshore slope at Kouchibouguac Bay is much steeper than that at Wasaga Beach (0.03 compared with 0.005) and, for the same values of breaker height and wave period, this results in a breaker index which is close to the transition from spilling to plunging breakers, whereas that for Wasaga Beach is well within the spilling breaker category. Loss of height at each breaker line is, therefore, likely to be much greater than at Wasaga Beach, resulting in fewer, but larger bars.

In conclusion, consideration of the nearshore profile and the wave climate in three areas suggests that the characteristics of wave breaking, particularly the transition from spilling to plunging breakers, is an important control on the nearshore equilibrium. However, although breaker type is controlled initially by the incident wave climate, other factors such as the nearshore slope can have considerable effects on this, and thus on the resulting equilibrium profile. The multiple parallel bars described here, therefore, should not be regarded in isolation, but rather as part of a complex continuum of possible nearshore morphologies. Further work on these relationships will necessitate direct measurement of wave and current processes and resulting sediment transport in the nearshore zone.

Acknowledgments

We wish to thank J. Ball, R. Szudy and P. Hale for their assistance in the field. The Ontario Ministry of Natural Resources gave us permission to work in the Wasaga Beach Provincial Park and the Christian Island Band Council gave permission to work within the Christian Island Indian Reserve. We are grateful for the help provided by the Parks Superintendent and other personnel at the Wasaga Beach Provincial Park during the 1977 field season. Various members of the support staff in the University of Guelph Geography Department helped in the field study and in the preparation of the manuscript, including B. Reynolds, M. Finoro, M. Adamson, P. Banister, J. Clegg and B. Nixon. The study was supported by a National Research Council of Canada operating grant and a University of Guelph Research Advisory Board grant to the senior author.

References

Ball, J.R.
    1978:   The geomorphology and sedimentary characteristics of the lake shelf off Wasaga Beach, Ontario; unpubl. M.Sc. thesis, University of Guelph, 116 p.

Bridges, J.S.
    1978:   Origin of horizontal lamination under turbulent boundary layers; Sedimentary Geology, v. 20, p. 1 - 16.

Chapman, L.J. and Putnam, D.F.
    1966:   The Physiography of Southern Ontario; University of Toronto Press, Toronto, Ontario, 386 p.

Clifton, H.E.
    1969:   Beach lamination---Nature and origin; Marine Geology, v. 7, p. 553 - 559.
    1976:   Wave-formed sedimentary structures: A conceptual model; in Beach and Nearshore Sedimentation; R.A. Davis, Jr. and R.L. Ethington, eds.; Society of Economic Paleontologists and Mineralogists, Special Publication 24, p. 126 - 148.

Clifton, H.E., Hunter, R.E. and Phillips, R.L.
    1971:   Depositional structures and processes in the non-barred high energy nearshore; Journal of Sedimentary Petrology, v. 41, p. 651 - 670.

Davidson-Arnott, R.G.D. and Greenwood, B.
    1974:   Bedforms and structures associated with bar topography in the shallow-water wave environment, Kouchibouguac Bay, New Brunswick, Canada; Journal of Sedimentary Petrology, v. 44, p. 698 - 704.
    1976:   Facies relationships on a barred coast, Kouchibouguac Bay, New Brunswick, Canada; R.A. Davis, Jr. and R.L. Ethington, eds.; Beach and Nearshore Sedimentation, Society of Economic Paleontologists and Mineralogists, Special Publication 24, p. 149 - 168.

Davidson-Arnott, R.G.D. and Pollard, W.H.
    1980:   Wave climate and potential longshore sediment transport patterns, Nottawasaga Bay, Ontario; Journal of Great Lakes Research, v. 6, p. 54-67.

Davis, R.A., Jr. and Fox, W.J.
    1972:   Coastal processes and nearshore sand bars; Journal of Sedimentary Petrology, v. 42, p. 401 - 412.

Davis, R.A., Jr., Fox, W.T., Hayes, M.O. and Boothroyd, J.C.
    1972:   Comparison of ridges and runnel systems in tidal and non-tidal environments; Journal of Sedimentary Petrology, v. 42, p. 413 - 421.

Exon, N.F.
1975:   An extensive offshore sand bar field in the western Baltic Sea; Marine Geology, v. 18, p. 197 - 212.

Galvin, C.J., Jr.
1972:   Wave breaking in shallow water; Waves on Beaches and Resulting Sediment Transport, R.E. Meyer, ed.; Academic Press, p. 413 - 455.

Greenwood, B. and Davidson-Arnott, R.G.D.
1975:   Marine bars and nearshore sedimentary processes, Kouchibouguac Bay, New Brunswick, Canada; in Nearshore Sediment Dynamics and Sedimentation, J.R. Hails and A. Carr, eds.; Wiley, New York, p. 123 - 150.
1979:   Marine bar sedimentation and equilibrium; Canadian Journal of Earth Sciences, v. 16, No.2.

Inman, D.L.
1957:   Wave generated ripples in nearshore sands; U.S. Army Corps of Engineers, Beach Erosion Board Technical Memorandum 100, 42 p.

Lau, J. and Travis, B.
1973:   Slowly varying Stokes waves and submarine longshore bars; Journal of Geophysical Research, v. 78, p. 4489 - 4497.

Martini, I.P.
1974:   Wasaga Beach: a Quaternary classic landscape, its geological history and biological carrying capacity of the sand dunes; in Quaternary Environments, Geographical Monograph 5, York University Series, University of Toronto Press, Toronto, Ontario, p. 61.
1975:   Sedimentology of a lacustrine barrier system at Wasaga Beach, Ontario, Canada; Sedimentary Geology, v. 14, p. 169 - 190.

Nilsson, H.D.
1973:   Multiple parallel sand bars of southeastern Cape Cod Bay; in Coastal Geomorphology, D.R. Cootes, ed.; State University of New York, Binghamton, p. 99 - 102.
1978:   Multiple longshore sandbars: Occurrence and origin along a low-energy shoreline in Cape Cod Bay, Massachusetts; Abstracts with Program, Geological Society of America, 13th Annual Meeting, Boston, p. 78.

Reineck, H.E. and Singh, I.B.
1973:   Depositional Sedimentary Environments; Springer-Verlag, New York, 439 p.

Saylor, J.H. and Hands, E.B.
1970:   Properties of longshore bars in the Great Lakes; American Society of Civil Engineers, Proceedings of 12th Conference on Coastal Engineering, p. 839 - 853.

Sonu, C.J.
1973:   Three-dimensional beach changes; Journal of Geology, v. 81, p. 42 - 64.

Zenkovitch, V.P.
1967:   Processes of Coastal Development; Oliver and Boyd, Edinburgh, 738 p.

ADDENDUM

Glenn Pember was killed in a car accident in July 1979. The work presented here forms part of his M.Sc. thesis, which he was in the process of completing at the time of his death. I would like to express my sincere condolences to his family.

Robin Davidson-Arnott

29.

POSTGLACIAL EVOLUTION AND MODERN PROCESSES
AT POINT PELEE, LAKE ERIE

J.P. Coakley
National Water Research Institute, Canada Centre for Inland Waters
Burlington, Ontario

Coakley, J.P., Postglacial evolution and modern processes at Point Pelee, Lake Erie; in the Coastline of Canada, S.B. McCann, editor; Geological Survey of Canada, Paper 80-10, p. 429-437, 1980.

Abstract

Geomorphological indicators of Holocene shoreline transgression are observed on Great Lakes coasts as well as those in marine regions of North America. One example is Point Pelee, a 80 km² cuspate foreland situated in the western portion of Lake Erie. Reconstructions of the history of Point Pelee show that, since its formation about 3500 years ago as a much larger coastal landform, the Point has retreated steadily westward and become aligned more north-south as lake levels rose. The hypothesized mode of retreat is similar to that of modern barrier island/lagoon systems found along the southeastern coast of the United States. Average rates on this long-term evolution have been estimated at 1.7 m/a for the eastern side, 0.3 m/a for the west side, and 4 m/a for the tip.

Rates of evolution over the past 55 years show an apparent reduction from those mentioned above, except for unprotected, low-lying parts of the east side, where accelerated shoreline retreat is apparent. Modern processes linked with this trend include increasing frequency of overwash occurrence during storm surges, a deficiency in littoral drift supplies, and cultural interference with the shoreline.

Résumé

Les auteurs ont observé des indicateurs géomorphologiques de la transgression holocéne du littoral qu'ont connue les rives des Grands lacs de même que celles des régions marines d'Amérique du Nord. Comme exemple de ce phénomène, on fait état de la pointe Pelée, un saillant triangulaire de 80 km² situé dans la partie ouest du lac Érié. La reconstitution du passé de la pointe Pelée montre que puisque sa formation date d'il y a environ 3 500 ans, époque à laquelle il s'agissait d'une forme littorale beaucoup plus considérable, la pointe a régressé régulièrement vers l'ouest et a pris une orientation nord-sud à mesure que le niveau du lac s'est élevé. Le mode de régression présumé est analogue à celui des îles-barrières ou réseau de lagunes contemporaines que l'on trouve le long de la côte sud-est des États-Unis. La vitesse moyenne de cette évolution sur une longue période a été estimée à 1,7 m par année pour son côté est et de 0,3 m par année pour le côté ouest ainsi que 4 m par année pour la pointe extrême.

La vitesse d'évolution au cours des 55 dernières années connaît un certain ralentissement par rapport à celle dont on vient de parler, sauf en ce qui concerne les parties basses et non protégées situées du côté est, où la régression littorale accélérée est évidente. Certains processus actuels relatifs à cette tendance comprennent la fréquence croissante du surbalayage par les vagues pendant les soulèvements de tempête, une lacune dans les apports de drift littoral et une interférence due à l'action de l'homme sur le littoral.

INTRODUCTION

One of the most striking coastal landforms along the shorelines of the Canadian Great Lakes is the large cuspate foreland of Point Pelee (Fig. 29.1). This remarkably symmetrical foreland, projecting north-south from the western Lake Erie Shoreline, comprises approximately 80 km² of dune ridges, sand plains, wetlands and barrier beaches, and constitutes a valuable recreational and wildlife ecological resource. The southern part is occupied by Point Pelee National Park.

In recent years much attention has been drawn to the apparently accelerated and alarming rates of recession observed at Point Pelee, especially along its eastern shoreline (Fig. 29.2). The question naturally arises as to whether this recession signifies the modern reversal of a previously existing accretionary trend (and as such is linked with cultural activities along the shoreline), or whether it is part of the normal trend toward recession noted along most of the Lake Erie shoreline. The investigation of this question was the main objective of the studies carried out by the Canada Centre for Inland Waters at Point Pelee in 1974 (Coakley, 1977).

The purpose of this paper is to compare modern trends in Point Pelee shoreline evolution, that is, trends dating back to the early 1900s, to the long-term trends deduced from the reconstruction of Point Pelee evolution presented previously (Coakley, 1976, 1977). The modern process regime at Point Pelee will also be discussed in terms of its role in these modern trends.

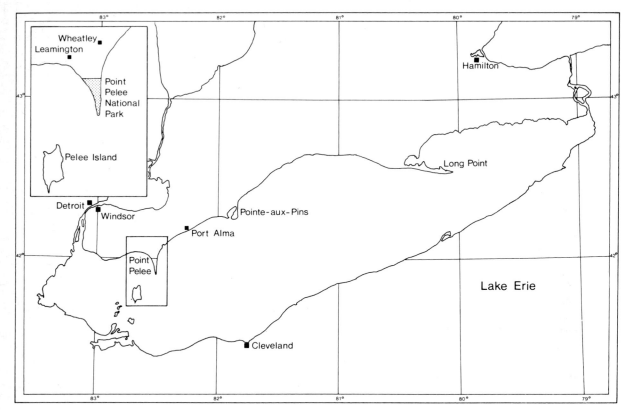

Figure 29.1.   *Location map of Point Pelee.*

POSTGLACIAL EVOLUTION OF POINT PELEE

Since a model of the formation and evolution of Point Pelee up to the present has been already presented by Coakley (1976), it will not be repeated in detail. Briefly stated, it contends that Point Pelee originated as a much larger coastal feature extending much farther to the east and south approximately 3500 years ago when Lake Erie levels were 3 to 4 m lower than at present. Since that time the Point has retreated to its present position in response mainly to rising levels in the basin, and also to changing wave energy conditions. This steady landward regression of the eastern shoreline is readily comparable with the shoreward retreat during Holocene times of barrier island/lagoon coasts in the eastern United States, for example. Furthermore, the analogy is strengthened by the morphological similarities apparent between the large shoal area, extending approximately 10 km to the south Point Pelee, and the cape shoal retreat massifs which characterize the cuspate forelands (capes) of the South Carolina coast (Swift et al., 1972).

Rates of postglacial evolution

If one accepts the concepts involved in the model for the formation and postglacial retreat, then it is not difficult to deduce quantitative estimates of the rates of evolution for the three shoreline entities involved: east side, west side, and the tip of Point Pelee. These rates are summarized in Table 29.1.

Table 29.1. Comparison of long-term and modern rates of shoreline evolution at Point Pelee. the 1918-1973 rates given for the east and west sides are averages of five equi-spaced points located respectively in the northern and southern portions of the shoreline. (The dividing line coincides roughly with the northern boundary of Point Pelee National Park).

Location	Over 3500 years		Recession rate 1918-1973
	Displacement	Recession rates	
	(km)	(m/a)	(m/a)
East side			
north	~6(→west)	~1.7	~2.8
south			-0.4
West side			
north	~1(→east)	~0.3	nil
south	~1(→west)	~ -0.3*	-0.3*
Tip of point	~15(→north)	~4	nil

* denotes accretion. Otherwise, erosion.

Figure 29.2. *Oblique aerial photograph taken April 1976, looking southward along the southern part of the eastern shoreline of Point Pelee. The canal (centre right) marks the northern boundary of Point Pelee National Park. The inlet into the marsh was opened initially in November 1972. Some attempts at shore protection are visible at the bottom of the photograph. The approximate position of the 1969 shoreline is shown by the dotted line.*

East side. Even on casual examination of the present aspect of Point Pelee, it is apparent that the east side of the point originated lakeward of its present position and has receded considerably over the long term. As indicated in Coakley (1976), the main signs of this recession are the nearshore zone peat outcrops and the obvious truncation of marsh ponds and longitudinal ridges.

Because of the regression of the east side over such a long period, there are no credible indicators of previous shoreline positions still preserved in the sedimentation record offshore. The original position of this shoreline therefore had to be deduced from inferred lake level histories and original postglacial surface topography for the central basin of Lake Erie (based mainly on Lewis, 1966), as illustrated in Figure 29.3. As a result, this shoreline position is not as well founded as that for the west side. Taking these limitations into consideration, we obtain a figure of approximately 6 km for the westward regression of the east side, that is, at an average rate of approximately 1.7 m/a[1] (Table 29.1).

West side. More concrete indications of the evolution of the west side of the point are preserved in the morphology of the series of longitudinal ridges still visible on the point. The interpretation by Coakley (1976) of these ridges (some of which reach elevations of more than 5 m above the present lake level) as successive storm beach positions, which served as the base for subsequent dune formation, was confirmed by Trenhaile (1976). Another feature of these dune/beach ridge elements is the tendency toward a more northsouth orientation as one progresses from the innermost to the most recent, that is, the northern ends coincide but as one progresses southward, the ridges gradually become farther apart. At the extreme southern end, where they are truncated by the receding east side beach ridge, the separation is considerable and the (perpendicular) distance between the innermost and the present shoreline in this area is slightly more than 1 km (Canada-Ontario Great Lakes Shore Damage Survey, 1976).

Taking all these features as indicators of the evolution of the west side of Point Pelee, then the conclusion is obvious that in contrast to the east side, most of the west side of the point has apparently advanced lakeward to its present position at rates of up to 0.3 m/a. In the northern portions near the base of the landform, however, the shoreline trend departs noticeably from the northward projection of the innermost beach ridge, indicating a comparable amount of recession over the same period. The apparent clockwise pivoting of the shoreline (as indicated by the changing orientation of successive longitudinal ridges) suggests the adjustment of this shoreline to long-term changes in wave climate, especially wave direction (Coakley, 1976).

Tip of Point Pelee. Because of its low relief and the amplified effects of east side recession[2], it is to be expected that the tip of the Point Pelee feature was the most adversely affected by any steady rise in lake levels. This is borne out by the projected retreat estimate based on an original position of 10 to 20 km to the south of the present tip around 3500 years ago. This would yield a crude recession rate of around 4 m/a, or about twice that of the east side. In addition, borings through the spit sands near the tip of Point Pelee by Terasmae (1970) indicate that the tip of the spit is now migrating westward into deeper water

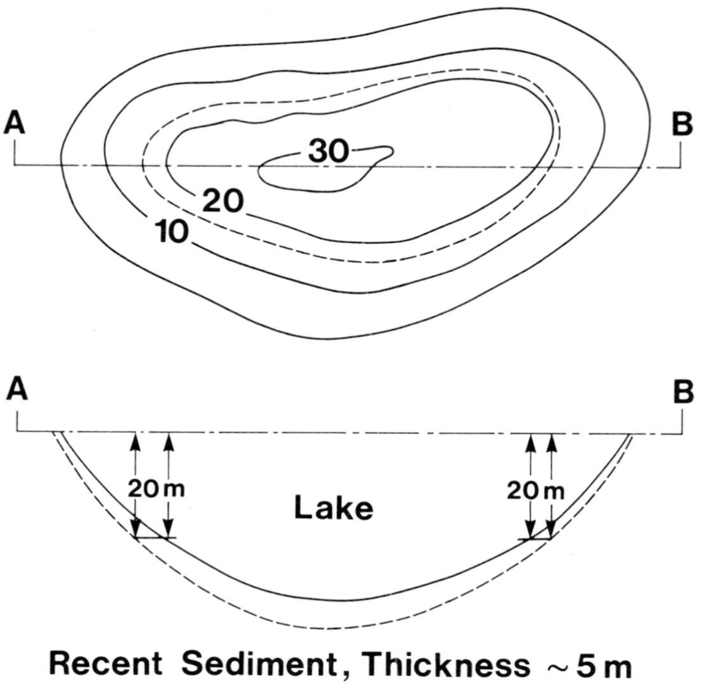

Recent Sediment, Thickness ~5 m

Figure 29.3. *Hypothetical example to illustrate the technique used in inferring the position of a previous shoreline prior to a 20 m rise in lake levels and an interval of sedimentation, using present bathymetric maps. The previous shoreline does not coincide with the 20 m contour, but is offset landward in proportion to the sediment thickness accumulated since the rise, and the slope of the previous bottom surface.*

(sand thicknesses at the tip now reach 10 m), presumably coinciding with the clockwise pivoting mentioned above. Such a trend would also be a factor in decreasing the total length of the spit, as sand would presumably go toward building up the profile rather than toward maintenance of the spit length.

The Pelee Shoal. The present (1974) aspect of the Pelee Shoal is presented in Figure 29.4. The total volume of sandy material comprising the present deposit has been estimated by Coakley (1977) at more than 500 million m[3]. If one accepts the interpretation of the Pelee Shoal as a submerged remnant of the northward-retreating Point Pelee feature (analogous in development to the shoal-retreat massifs described for the eastern U.S. shelf by Swift et al., 1972), then it is clear that the shoal has evolved considerably since its submergence. Although no inference can be made as to whether it has expanded or contracted in a spatial sense, there are two morphological developments that are noteworthy.

First, at its northern extremity, where it joins the submerged spit of Point Pelee, the width of the sandy shoal feature is now only slightly more than 1 km compared with more than 4 km in the central portion. It is difficult to explain this narrowing in any way other than as a result of

---

[1] a is the SI symbol for year.

[2] Because of the small junction angle of the shores of Point Pelee, a 1 m recession of the east side could induce several metres of recession at the tip.

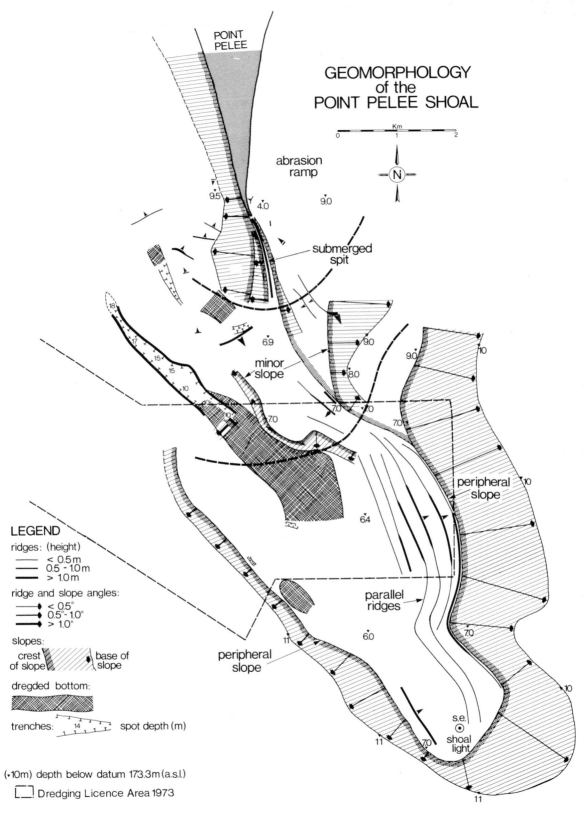

**GEOMORPHOLOGY
of the
POINT PELEE SHOAL**

POINT PELEE

abrasion
ramp

submerged
spit

minor
slope

peripheral
slope

parallel
ridges

peripheral
slope

s.e.
shoal
light

LEGEND

ridges: (height)
— < 0.5 m
— 0.5 - 1.0 m
— > 1.0 m

ridge and slope angles:
→ < 0.5°
⇒ 0.5° - 1.0°
⇒ > 1.0°

slopes:
crest
of slope   base of
           slope

dredged bottom:

trenches: 14   spot depth (m)

(·10m) depth below datum 173.3m (a.s.l.)

⌐⌐⌐ Dredging Licence Area 1973

Figure 29.4. *Geomorphological features mapped on the Pelee Shoal (after Coakley, 1977). Present on the shoal surface are palimpsest features presumed to be related to the natural postglacial evolution of the Point Pelee shoal complex as well as those related to cultural activities such as commercial dredging (1973 licensed area shown by light dashed lines). The positions of two channel features traversing the northern portion of the shoal are shown in heavy dashed lines.*

erosion, probably associated with the above-mentioned migration of the tip of the point westward into deeper water. This interpretation is supported by the series of terraces visible off the northeast portion of the shoal (Fig. 29.4) suggestive of progressive shoreline or spit positions.

The other development is the presence on the surface of the shoal of depressions and trenches apparently caused by dredging activities. Since the early 1900s, some 19 million m³* of sand and gravel have been removed by dredging, which, until recently, was located on the shoal and initially (ca. 1900) extended up to the dry portion of the spit itself. Although suspended in 1973, these activities have apparently left their mark on the surface relief, and have probably contributed to a general lowering of the shoal surface. In addition, the two channels across the narrow northern part of the shoal (Fig. 29.4) might also date back to these early dredging activities, and probably serve to increase the east-to-west transfer of littoral materials deposited in this area.

MODERN TRENDS IN POINT PELEE SHORELINE DYNAMICS

Modern shoreline evolution

The historical record of southwestern Ontario dates from the entry of European explorers and settlers into the area in the mid-nineteenth century. Written observations of Point Pelee began somewhat later when the area was taken over in the late 1800s by the Federal Department of Marine (East, 1976). Although earlier surveys of the point exist (e.g., that of Baird in 1883) the most reliable original survey for defining the shoreline position was that made by the Department of Public Works in 1918. By superimposing a plot of this survey over the most recent high-precision survey conducted in 1973 and shown in the Canada-Ontario Great Lakes Shore Damage Survey (1976), a reasonably accurate picture is obtained of shoreline evolution at this 55-year 'modern' interval.

Table 29.1 shows the results of this comparison, reduced to annual rates of shoreline change over the above 55-year interval. The recession rates over this interval are average rates at approximately equally spaced points on the northern and southern shorelines of both sides of the point (from Coakley, 1977). What is immediately clear from the table is that while the west side is evolving at a relatively slow rate, much of the east side is retreating at what appears to be extremely high rates, especially in the northern portion of this shoreline. Some of this high rate could be due to undetermined errors in fitting the two surveys, but the overall trends are borne out by field observations. Figure 29.2 shows a portion of the east side, where recession rates over the past 55 years have averaged 1.6 m/a and over 1973 and 1974 averaged 7 m/a. North of this area inferred rates reach 4.4 m/a.

In summary, the east side of Point Pelee, especially the northern portion, is receding at what appears to be accelerated rates during modern times. On the other hand, the west side is evolving at much lesser rates and involves relatively low rates of both recession and accretion. In the section which follows, the probable causes of these trends, namely the main physical processes now acting on Point Pelee, will be examined.

Modern coastal processes

A detailed outline of the coastal process regime at Point Pelee (based on field data collected in 1974) is presented in

Coakley (1977), so attention here will be focused mainly on the processes that appear to be the most important along the more actively receding east side of the point:

(a) The combined effect of easterly storm waves and wind setup.
(b) Periods of high lake levels.
(c) Deficiencies and losses in littoral sediment supplies.

Ice plays an undetermined, but apparently lesser, role than the above processes (Dickie and Cape, 1974) and the effects of lake circulation and seiche-related currents are of importance only on the Pelee Shoal to the south. Aeolian processes, especially deflation, also appear to be of some importance in exacerbating the recession of the east side, especially when the above-listed processes have resulted in a loss of surface vegetation. No studies aimed at quantifying this process have been conducted to date.

Wave and wind setup

Deep-water waves measured during 1974 off the east side of Point Pelee reached a maximum significant height of approximately 3.0 m. Such waves are usually associated with high winds (9.3 m/s) from the east or northeast, which occur at an average frequency of 6 per cent of the yearly record, usually in late fall or early spring (Richards and Phillips, 1970).

When one considers that the height of the east-side barrier beach seldom exceeds 2 m, the serious erosive effect of such 3 m waves (even after breaking) when superimposed on wind setup is easily appreciated.

In fact, during one storm in November 1972 (Coakley et al., 1973), wind setup at the east side of Point Pelee, which reached 60 cm above mean levels in the early phases of the storm, combined with waves in excess of 2 m resulted in the beach berm being overtopped along most of its length. Recession of the berm crest reached 10 m in places and, at the northern boundary of Point Pelee National Park, an inlet into the marsh was initiated. This inlet has persisted and has reached widths of several hundred metres (Fig. 29.2).

The main result of storm events, combining high waves with wind setup, is that large amounts of beach and nearshore sand are transferred by overwash or through inlets to the back beach and marsh areas, where they are, for all practical purposes, lost to the littoral drift system.

High lake levels

High lake levels have been identified in the popular media as the major cause of shore erosion in the Great Lakes. This is probably true for those shorelines composed of unconsolidated clay and silt bluffs, which lose much of their strength when acted upon by water. However, for sandy shorelines, which readily adjust their geometry to changes in lake level, lake levels might be of less importance as a cause of the chronic recession noted along the east side of Point Pelee.

Lake Erie average monthly levels recorded at Port Colborne have fluctuated between a low of 173.0 m (IGLD) in 1935 to a high of 174.8 m in 1973, based on records kept since 1860. Nevertheless, no statistically significant upward trends were found in similar records from Cleveland, with the exception of a vaguely defined eight-year cycle (Liu, 1970).

When one examines the respective durations of levels higher and lower than a value midway between the above extremes (173.9 m), the following pattern emerges. During the past 114 years of record, yearly average lake levels were above 173.9 m for 53 years (47%). In other words, the record

---

* Source: Extrapolation of recorded dredging volumes 1965-1972, obtained from the Lands Administration Branch, Ontario Ministry of Natural Resources.

is almost evenly balanced between low and high water periods. The duration of consecutive years of high and low levels was as follows:

1860 - 1890	considerably above median
1891 - 1902	slightly below median
1903 - 1909	slightly above median
1910 - 1942	intermediate
1943 - 1961	considerably above median
1962 - 1967	considerably below median
1968 - 1974	considerably above median

Although high or rising lake levels have undoubtedly been a factor in promoting shoreline retreat since 1968, there is no evidence of the reverse effect during periods of low or falling levels.

Coakley and Cho (1972), using aerial photograph comparison techniques, showed that although overall recession of the west side was coincident with a rise in lake levels between 1931 and 1947 and a slight accession was evident between 1947 and 1970 (years of about equally high lake levels), recession was the rule on the east side for the entire 1931-1970 period, regardless of levels. Also, detailed recession rates (Coakley, 1977) further suggest that at Point Pelee the net rate of shoreline changes (not the type of change) is the most sensitive feature with regard to changes in lake level. In other words, net accession tends to occur on the west side and recession on the east side regardless of whether lake levels compared are similar (1953, 1973) or had risen (1964, 1973). Therefore, no direct and consistent relationship between Point Pelee shoreline change and lake levels could be deduced. What remains untested is the type and rate of shoreline change related to a fall in lake levels, for instance, for the period 1955 to 1964, a period for which neither aerial photographs nor field studies are available.

In summary, there is no long-term upward trend in lake levels to which the continuous recession of the east side of Point Pelee coud be linked. However, periods of high lake levels, such as at present, play a major role in aggravating recession of the low-lying beach barriers along the east side by facilitating overwash during storms. High lake levels could also adversely affect the sand-binding vegetation cover and thus make aeolian removal of beach material more likely.

Modern trends in littoral drift supply

The main source of littoral drift for the east side of Point Pelee is generally believed to be the eroding shore bluffs between Wheatley and Port Alma (Fig. 29.1). According to St. Jacques and Rukavina (1976), the bluffs supply approximately 50 000 m³/a of sand material to the westward-directed littoral drift system. However, maintenance dredging figures for Wheatley at the base of Point Pelee, a crude indicator of littoral drift rates, show an average of only 6000 m³/a between 1950 and 1974.* Net littoral drift rates were calculated by Skafel (1975) and by Kampuis (1972) for the east side of Point Pelee, using empirical wave-energy relationships and nearby bluff recession rates, respectively. They obtained southward-directed rates of 25 000 and 19 000 m³/a, respectively. Furthermore, the incidence of severe shore erosion in the area between Wheatley and Point Pelee National Park indicates that at present only a proportion of the original 50 000 m³/a mentioned above reaches Point Pelee, and the larger portion is either trapped behind the Wheatley jetties, or is diverted offshore. It should be noted that streams in the area contribute only negligible amounts of sand. The severe erosion

in the northern part of Point Pelee west of Wheatley prompted Mersea township in the mid-1950s to undertake a shore-protection program in the form of a 2 km long, 3 m high armour stone seawall. The precise effect of this almost vertical structure on littoral drift patterns has not been determined. However, the nearshore lake bottom in front of it is completely devoid of any sand cover over the pitted glacial clay, indicating that scouring of the nearshore bottom is probably active. It therefore appears likely that part of the littoral drift in this area is actually being diverted offshore. This hypothetical effect could be further aggravated by another seawall of similar design, which was erected later on in the central portion of the reach south of Hillman Creek.

South of this latter seawall, the major sinks for littoral (and beach) material are created through overtopping of the berm by storm waves, causing overwash of sand into the marsh and back beach areas. The result of this transport is dramatically illustrated on Figure 29.2, which shows the extensive overwash fans and an inlet into the Point Pelee National Park marshes and ponds. Such quasi-permanent losses in littoral drift supply serve to intensify erosion of the barrier beach to the south.

Another sink for east side sediments occurs to the south of the tip of Point Pelee, where the southward-directed littoral drift system ends. Profile studies (Dickie and Cape, 1974) and longshore current flow measurements (Coakley, 1977) all indicate that part of the east side littoral drift is transferred across the low submerged spit and enters the northward littoral drift of the west side. The remainder is believed to be deposited near the tip in what Coakley (1977) postulated as a storage area, from which sediments periodically re-enter the littoral drift system of both sides of the point, depending on wave direction.

The above concept of sediment transport patterns at Point Pelee is summarized in Figure 29.5.

SUMMARY AND CONCLUSIONS

Although the reconstruction of the origin and subsequent evolution of the Point Pelee complex remains largely based on hypotheses regarding postglacial developments in western Lake Erie, evidence in its support is growing as more research is carried out. What is reasonably clear is that modern analogues exist that can be used to infer how such an evolution probably occurred. The more prominent of these analogues are the barrier island coasts of eastern Northern America and the relict and palimpsest features preserved on the continental shelf.

Contrary to theories that invoke an accretional origin for modern Point Pelee, there is good evidence to conclude that the present landform originated as a much larger feature and has receded to its present position. The submerged Pelee Shoal immediately to the south is thus seen as a relict feature which was once a part of the original foreland.

Comparison of modern rates of evolution of Point Pelee shores with those estimated for the period since its postulated origin some 3500 years ago indicates that in general these rates have diminished with time. However, in specific areas of the eastern side, rates of retreat for the barrier shoreline have remained high or have increased. Modern day processes, in particular storm waves superimposed on storm surges and resultant loss of littoral material into the marsh through barrier overwash and inlet formation, appear to be reaching critical levels along these areas.

---

* Source: Department of Public Works dredging records, London, Ontario.

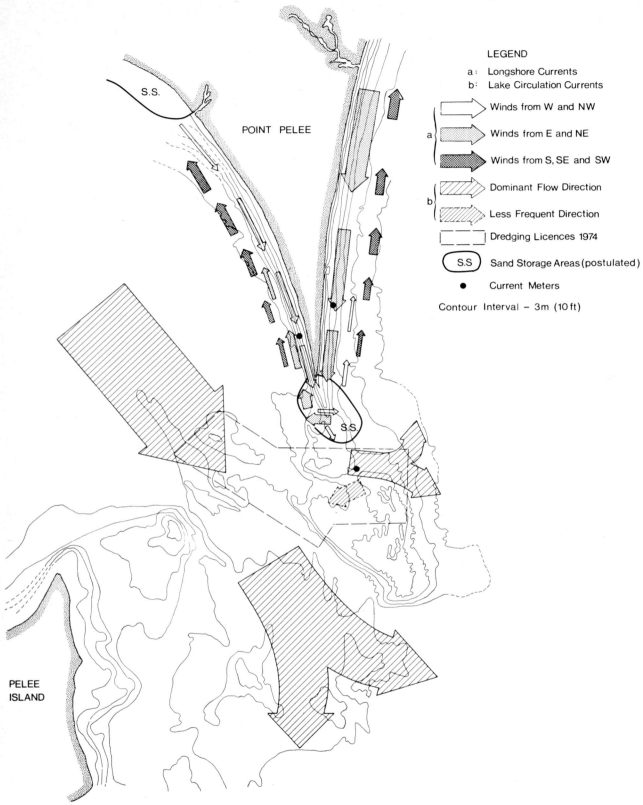

Figure 29.5. *Schematic interpretation of the major patterns of sediment dispersal in the Point Pelee-Pelee Shoal area, based on studies of longshore and mid-shoal current meter data and bottom sediment distributions recorded in 1974 (after Coakley, 1977).*

In conclusion, the accelerated recession noted over the past 55 years along sections of the eastern shore of Point Pelee appears to be caused by a combination of the above processes and deficiencies in littoral drift supplies. Most of the more than 50 000 m³/a of sand material being contributed to the Point Pelee littoral drift system from bluff erosion to the east appears to be lost along the way in various sinks, both natural and manmade. As a result, the southern parts of the point appear to be starved for littoral drift. The potential drift volumes calculated on the basis of the wave energy climate would therefore have to be made up by local sources such as erosion of the unprotected southern parts of this eastern shore. These developments are in marked contrast to the relative stability of the western shore of Point Pelee.

Acknowledgments

R.D. Gillie contributed greatly to this paper by plotting the geomorphic map shown as Figure 29.4 and by helpful criticism and discussion. Thanks are also due to C.F.M. Lewis, T.W. Anderson, Jaan Terasmae, and U.J. Vagners for their co-operation in making research material available to the author, and for offering valuable suggestions on the manuscript. The study was funded in part by Parks Canada.

References

Canada-Ontario Great Lakes Shore Damage Survey
1976: Coastal Zone Atlas; W.S. Haras and K.K. Tsui, eds.; Environment Canada and Ontario Ministry of Natural Resources, March 1976, 637 p.

Coakley, J.P.
1976: The formation and evolution of Point Pelee, western Lake Erie; Canadian Journal of Earth Sciences, v. 13, no. 1, p. 136 - 144.
1977: Processes in sediment deposition and shoreline changes in the Point Pelee area, Ontario; Inland Waters Directorate, Scientific Series 79, 76 p.

Coakley, J.P. and Cho, H.K.
1972: Shore erosion in western Lake Erie; Proceedings, 15th Conference on Great Lakes Research, p. 344 - 360.

Coakley, J.P., Haras, W.S. and Freeman, N.G.
1973: The effect of storm surge on beach erosion, Point Pelee; Proceedings, 16th Conference on Great Lakes Research, p. 377 - 389.

Dickie, G.J. and Cape, D.F.
1974: The effect of winter processes on the shoreline of Point Pelee National Park; Industrial Research Institute, University of Windsor.

East, K.M.
1976: Shoreline erosion, Point Pelee National Park, a history and policy analysis; Parks Canada, National Resources Division Working Paper, Ontario Region, 66 p.

Kampuis, J.W.
1972: Progress report on Point Pelee beach study (1970 and 1971) and Marentette Beach protection programme; Report DLFS-3 to Ontario Ministry of Lands and Forests, 77 p.

Lewis, C.F.M.
1966: Sedimentation studies of unconsolidated deposits in the Lake Erie Basin; unpubl. Ph.D. thesis, Department of Geological Science, University of Troronto, 135 p.

Liu, P.D.
1970: Statistics of Great Lakes levels; Proceedings, 13th Conference on Great Lakes Research, p. 360 - 368.

Richards, T.L. and Phillips, D.W.
1970: Synthesized winds and wave heights for the Great Lakes; Canada Department of Transport, Meteorological Branch, Climatological Studies No. 17, 53 p.

Skafel, M.G.
1975: Longshore sediment transport at Point Pelee; Environment Canada, Canada Centre for Inland Waters unpublished report.

St. Jacques, D. and Rukavina, N.A.
1976: Lake Erie nearshore sediments, Port Burwell to Point Pelee, Ontario; Canada Centre for Inland Waters unpublished report.

Swift, D.J.P., Kofoed, J.W., Saulsbury, F.P. and Sears, Phillip
1972: Holocene evolution of the shelf surface, central and southern Atlantic shelf of North America; in Shelf Sediment Transport, D.J.P. Swift, D.B. Duane, and O.H. Pilkey, eds.; Dowden, Hutchinson, and Ross Inc., p. 499 - 574.

Terasmae, J.
1970: Stratigraphic drilling in Point Pelee National Park, Ontario; unpubl. Report, Contract 68-200, National and Historic Parks Branch, Ottawa, 6 p.

Trenhaile, A.S.
1976: Ridge and trough sediment analysis, Point Pelee National Park; Report Contract No. CR 75-141, Indian and Northern Affairs, Ottawa, 28 p.

AUTHOR INDEX

DUE DATE

MAR 2 7 2002		
~~NOV 2 9~~ 2006		
		Printed in USA